HIGH POLYMERS

Other volumes in preparation

HIGH POLYMERS

A SERIES OF MONOGRAPHS ON THE CHEMISTRY, PHYSICS AND TECHNOLOGY OF HIGH POLYMERIC SUBSTANCES

Volume I

Collected Papers of W. H. Carothers on High Polymeric Substances
Edited by H. MARK and G. S. WHITBY

INTERSCIENCE PUBLISHERS, INC.
New York

Wallace H. Carothers

COLLECTED PAPERS OF
WALLACE HUME ÇAROTHERS
ON HIGH POLYMERIC SUBSTANCES

Edited by

H. MARK

G. STAFFORD WHITBY

Adjunct Professor of Organic Chemistry,
Brooklyn Polytechnic Institute

Director of Chemical Research, Chemical Research
Laboratory, Tedddington, Middx.

With 35 illustrations

1940

INTERSCIENCE PUBLISHERS, INC.
New York

119301

INTERSCIENCE PUBLISHERS, INC.
250 Fifth Avenue   New York 1, N. Y.

For Great Britain and Northern Ireland:
INTERSCIENCE PUBLISHERS LTD.
88/90 Chancery Lane   London W. C. 2

INTRODUCTION TO "HIGH POLYMERS"

While physics is directing its main effort to exploring the structure of matter and the nature of energy in the sub-atomic realm, organic chemistry is becoming increasingly concerned with molecular structures of (*a*) greater and greater complexity, and (*b*) greater and greater size. In both these latter respects, the study of organic chemistry tends, in its most fruitful and significant latter-day developments, to become less the wide-ranging study of "the compounds of carbon" and more the study of the "organic" aspects of carbon compounds, *i. e.*, the study of those aspects bearing on the structure and behavior of living organisms. In both respects, the behavior of the living cell represents the final problem to the understanding of which the whole development trends.

Two conditions are necessary for the development of life, *viz.:*

(*a*) A structural system, acting as a skeleton, which protects the functionally-active living matter from disturbances and at the same time permits the continuation of diffusion and of chemical reactions in the medium contained in the system.

(*b*) Another system of highly reactive and diffusible compounds which serve as reactants and catalysts in the processes necessary to maintain life and direct to a common final result a great number of chemical reactions and colloidal factors.

In the present generation—ever since what was once described as "Chemical Physiology" and later "Physiological Chemistry" acquired full status as "Biochemistry"—much attention has been paid to the latter condition, and much illuminating work has been carried out on the chemistry of metabolism and on catalysis and promoters of vital processes. At the same time, and independently of this, a keen interest has developed in the study of the natural skeletal and storage substances of organisms—in cellulose, keratin, starch, rubber, etc.—and as a result a new field of research has defined itself, namely, *the chemistry of high polymers*.

During the last twenty years the study of this field has been steadily extended and intensified. Important forward steps can already be signalized in the preparation of synthetic high-polymers; in the elucidation of the mechanism and kinetics of polymerization processes; in the determination of the chemical structure of natural and synthetic high-polymers; in the determination and understanding of their colloidal behavior, and in the development of formulas capable of describing quantitatively the properties of high-polymers. Generalized structural principles applicable to all the large molecules in question have become apparent, and, although still

v

far from satisfactory in all details, obviously represent a useful frame of reference within which high-polymers may be classified and described. To refine and improve the structural picture for every significant high-molecular material, in the hope of arriving at a fuller and more satisfying explanation of its chemical, colloidal and physical properties, is one of the tasks to which the further study of high-polymers must be addressed.

New representatives of high-polymers are continually being synthesized, and thus offering for comparative quantitative investigation an increasingly large body of experimental material. And, too, new experimental technics, especially physical technics, are continually being applied to the study of high-polymers with illuminating results. In short, the whole field is expanding rapidly.

In these circumstances it is felt that a useful purpose should be served by an attempt, such as this series of volumes represents, to bring together our present knowledge of the subject in a manner both comprehensive and critical. Such a survey of the subject should serve to throw into clear relief the generalizations which it is already possible to make; it should anchor the new branch of high-polymeric chemistry firmly to the fundamentals of chemical science, and, generally, it should contribute to fostering and facilitating the further study of the subject.

In addition to being of purely scientific interest, high-molecular materials are of great general and economic importance. Much of our daily life depends on their use, and a large proportion of the wealth of all civilized countries is invested in industries which either use natural high-polymers as raw materials or manufacture and fabricate synthetic polymers. It is certainly a conservative estimate if one assumes that more than 30% of all graduate chemists employed in industries are engaged in work connected with high-polymeric materials. In making such an estimate, one must bear in mind the fact that high polymeric substances are closely connected with the various branches of the textile industry dealing with natural and artificial fibers, the production of natural rubber and its synthetic congeners and the fabrication of goods therefrom, many branches of the food industry, the production of molded plastics, of lacquers, of synthetic resins and of varnishes based on synthetic resins, the industries concerned with starch and its conversion products, and so on. All who have had experience in such industries cannot but be aware of the sore need for advancing our fundamental knowledge of high-polymeric materials, and cannot but have noted how, speedily, every forward step in such knowledge is reflected in improvement in the technical processes and in the products of the relevant industries.

It may, further, be noted that a very substantial proportion of the students obtaining university degrees in chemistry in various parts of the world are likely to find themselves called upon to apply their knowledge to industries concerned in some degree or other with high-polymeric materials, and hence should benefit directly by at least some acquaintance with the fundamentals of high-polymeric chemistry.

It should be added that, as notified in the title of the series, it is proposed to include in the series, not only volumes on High Polymers in the strict sense, but also certain volumes on "Allied Subjects." This is done because it is thought undesirable to exclude from the survey certain solid systems, such as, e. g., those represented by bitumen and clay, which, although not strictly high-polymeric, nevertheless behave in many respects, especially rheologically, in a manner closely related to, and in some cases partly dependent on, high-polymers.

It should perhaps be mentioned that, as this series of volumes, although employing the English language, is international in character, it has been considered appropriately catholic that contributors to the volumes which it will comprise should be free to follow in their various contributions either English or American spellings, where these differ.

R. E. BURK,
H. MARK,
G. S. WHITBY,
Editors.

May, 1940

INTRODUCTION TO "COLLECTED PAPERS OF WALLACE HUME CAROTHERS"

It is perhaps fair to say that the progress of organic chemistry in our day is most distinctively characterized by two particularly attractive and promising lines of research, namely by the investigation of biochemical catalysts—ferments, vitamins, hormones and auxins—and by the systematic development of the chemistry of high polymeric substances. Both these lines of research are founded solidly on the experimental methods and theoretical viewpoints of classical organic chemistry. The former reaches far into biology, physiology and medicine, and touches some of the central problems of the functioning of living organisms. The latter cuts deeply into the fundamentals of the structure of matter—especially of those parts of the structure of organisms which are not obviously involved in their metabolism—and, further, is the basis of a field of chemical industry, already wide, and with great possibilities of expansion.

In this series on high polymers, of which the present monograph is the first volume, an attempt will be made to offer a collection of treatises covering the most significant studies made in the field, in order to show where the subject now stands and to facilitate the further development which its study is surely destined to have.

Our present knowledge of high polymers is due to a considerable and now rapidly growing number of workers, who have contributed essential material from various points of view. Some have, with success, employed chiefly the tried and well known methods of organic chemistry. Others have, with illuminating results, applied the methods of modern physics and physical chemistry to the study of high polymers. Again, the work of numerous investigators, whose concern was not primarily or wholly with the study of high polymers and polymerization, has contributed experimental facts and theoretical conceptions which form a not unimportant part of our present body of knowledge of the subject.

No investigator has excelled Wallace Hume Carothers in advancing our knowledge of high polymeric chemistry and at the same time providing a basis for the development of technically useful synthetic polymeric materials. He may rightly be called the outstanding personality in this new branch of organic chemistry. His brilliant experimental technique, the abundance of his ideas, and the constructive manner in which he applied his critical faculty, together with the excellent facilities at his disposal and the competent collaborators who assisted him, enabled

VIII

Carothers to carry out in the short space of twelve years more than most of us accomplish in a lifetime, and to produce an output which is at once very considerable in volume and compact in character. His publications are deservedly to be considered as "classical": they will always remain an essential part of the foundation on which the high polymeric chemistry of the future will be erected. Their study should be undertaken by all who wish to be familiar with the chemistry of high polymers. They are highly inspiring, and at the same time they point out many of the difficulties which work in this field is bound to meet.

With such thoughts in mind, it was felt that there could be no better start for this series than to publish, as the first volume in it, a collection of the papers embodying Carothers' studies of high polymers and closely related matters. The two editors regard it as a privilege to prepare this edition, not only because the issue of Carothers' papers in a convenient, collected form will, it is felt, be an addition to chemical literature which will be generally appreciated, but also because it will serve as an expression of the admiration and esteem which they and other workers in the field of high polymers feel for a great chemist, whose premature death was a severe loss to chemistry and humanity.

* * * * * *

Carothers' work on polymerization and polymers divides itself into two distinct series of studies devoted to (1) "Studies on Polymerization and Ring Formation," (2) "Acetylene Polymers and their Derivatives." The papers in the first of these series are reprinted in Part One of this volume; those in the second, in Part Two. A few other papers, mostly concerned with general discussions of the subject of polymerization, are reprinted in Part Three.

Part One is concerned essentially with condensation polymers produced by the recurring condensation of long, so-called polyfunctional molecules, at both ends of which are reactive groups capable of reacting, with the elimination of water, with the reactive end groups of other molecules of the same of another type to yield long condensed-polymeric chains, the products being, typically, polyamides, polyesters and polyanhydrides. The work, in addition to contributing in the most important way to our knowledge of condensation polymers, forms the basis of an interesting industrial development, namely, the manufacture of a synthetic polyamide product ("Nylon"), which may be considered, chemically, as representing a simplified protein-like material, and which can be drawn into fibers ranging in size from finest textile fibers suitable for making hosiery and having a tensile strength at least as great as that of natural silk to coarser fibers suited to serve as "bristles." Not only is the work the basis of the particular industrial development just mentioned; it also carries possibilities of other practical developments in the future not yet realized industrially.

Part Two is concerned with polymers, in the narrower sense of the term, produced by the self-addition of conjugated systems, especially conjugated butadienoid systems containing chlorine and other substituents. In it, also, a good deal of attention is given to the chemical reactions of vinylacetylene and divinylacetylene, two new polymers of acetylene, which are the source of the butadienoid systems in question and are the first readily-available compounds containing the interesting conjugated enine system, $H_2C{=}CH{-}C{\equiv}C{-}$. This work is the basis on which there has been developed the commercial manufacture of a synthetic rubber, "Neoprene." A survey of the work is given in the Introduction to Part Two.

A few early papers of Carothers, dealing with subjects other than polymerization, are omitted from this volume. A bibliography of Carothers' publications relative to polymerization is given (p. 423 *et seq.*); it includes United States patents.

H. MARK
G. STAFFORD WHITBY

April, 1940

ACKNOWLEDGMENTS

The editors and publishers wish to thank the numerous individuals and organizations for their assistance in the preparation and publication of this book and without whose valuable aid, this volume might not have been possible.

We desire especially to mention the cooperation and encouragement given the editors by du Pont de Nemours and Company, in which laboratories the greater part of Carothers' work was carried out.

We are deeply indebted to:

Dr. E. K. Bolton, Chemical Director of du Pont de Nemours and Company, in Wilmington, Del.

Dr. A. P. Tanberg, Director of the Experimental Station, and

Dr. A. W. Kenney, of the Experimental Station, Wilmington, Del.

We have also had the opportunity to discuss our plans with several former collaborators, friends and pupils of W. H. Carothers and wish to express our gratitude to them. We are particularly grateful to Dr. E. O. Kraemer and Dr. H. Kienle for their valuable assistance.

It is through the cooperation of those societies and publishers who published the original papers, that we were enabled to reprint them.

For this reason, we are very grateful to:

The American Chemical Society, and its Secretary, Mr. Charles W. Parsons, who permitted the reprinting of all the papers from the "Journal of the American Chemical Society," and the use of the illustrations.

The Faraday Society, and its Secretary, Mr. G. S. W. Marlow, who permitted the reprinting of a paper from the "Transactions of the Faraday Society."

Mr. H. E. Howe, for permission for the reprinting of a paper from "Industrial & Engineering Chemistry."

The Williams and Wilkins Company, Baltimore, Md., for permission to reprint a paper from the "Chemical Reviews."

Professor Roger Adams and the National Academy of Sciences, Washington, D. C., for permission to reprint the Biography of W. H. Carothers by Roger Adams, and for the block for the frontispiece.

The index has been carefully prepared by Dr. Dora Stern, New York.

The editors wish finally to express their gratitude for the cooperation and assistance given them by Interscience Publishers, Inc. and especially, by Dr. E. S. Proskauer of this firm.

H. MARK
G. S. WHITBY

July, 1940

CONTENTS

Part Two

Part Three

A BIOGRAPHY

By Roger Adams

Wallace Hume Carothers, who died on April 29, 1937, was born in Burlington, Iowa, on April 27, 1896. His contributions to organic chemistry were recognized as outstanding and, in spite of the relatively short span of time for his productive accomplishments, he became a leader in his field with an enviable international reputation.

His paternal forbears were of Scotch origin and settled in Pennsylvania in prerevolutionary days. His father, Ira Hume Carothers, taught country school at the age of 19. Later he entered the field of commercial education and for forty-five years has been engaged in that type of work as teacher and vice-president.

His maternal ancestors were of Scotch-Irish stock and were also, for the most part, farmers and artisans. They were great lovers of music, and this may account for the intense interest in and appreciation of music which Carothers possessed. His mother, who was Mary Evalina McMullin of Burlington, Iowa, exerted a powerful influence and guidance in the earlier years of his life.

On February 21, 1936, he married Helen Everett Sweetman of Wilmington, Delaware. A daughter, Jane, was born November 27, 1937.

Wallace was the oldest of four children. His education began in the public schools of Des Moines, Iowa. In 1914 he was graduated from the North High School. As a growing boy he had zest for work as well as play. He enjoyed tools and mechanical things and spent much time in experimenting. His school work was characterized by thoroughness and his high school classmates testify that when he was called upon to recite, his answers revealed careful preparation. It was his habit to leave no task unfinished or done in a careless manner. To begin a task was to complete it.

He entered the Capital City Commercial College in the fall of 1914 and was graduated in the accountancy and secretarial curriculum in July, 1915, taking considerably less time than the average. He entered Tarkio College, Tarkio, Missouri, in September, 1915, to pursue a scientific course, and simultaneously accepted a position as assistant in the Commercial Department. He continued in this capacity for two years and then was made an assistant in English, although he had specialized in chemistry from the time he entered college. During the World War the head of the department in chemistry, Dr. Arthur M. Pardee, was called to another institution, and Tarkio College found it impossible to secure a fully equipped teacher of chemistry. Carothers, who previously had taken all of the chemistry courses offered, was appointed to take over the instruction. Since he was rejected as a soldier on account of a slight physical defect, he was free to serve in this capacity during his junior and senior years. It is interesting that during his senior year there were four senior chemistry-major students in his class and every one of them later completed work for the doctorate, studying in the universities of this country and abroad. Today they bear testimony to the fact that as undergraduates they owed much to the inspiration and leadership of Carothers.

Upon entering college his interest in chemistry and physical sciences was immediate and lasting, and he rapidly outdistanced his classmates in accomplishment. As a student he showed mature judgment and was always regarded by his fellow students as an exceptional person. Invariably he was the brightest student in the class regardless of the subject. Financial necessity required that he earn a large portion of his educational expenses. He always found time, however, to associate with the other students, though he showed little interest for the boisterous enthusiasms of the average underclassman. During his last two years in college he was entrusted with a number of student offices to which he gave freely of his time and energy.

Leaving Tarkio College in 1920 with his bachelor of science degree, he enrolled in the chemistry department of the University of Illinois where he completed the requirements for the master of arts degree in the summer of 1921. His former instructor at Tarkio College, then head of the chemistry department at the University of South Dakota, desired a young instructor to handle courses in analytical and physical chemistry and was fortunate in securing Carothers for this position during the school year, 1921–1922. He went to South Dakota only with the intention of securing sufficient funds to enable him to complete his graduate work, but the careful and adequate preparation of his courses, as well as his care of the students under his direction, showed that he could be a very successful teacher of chemistry. He was still the same quiet, methodical worker and scholar, not forceful as a lecturer, but careful and systematic in his contact with the students. He always required adequate preparation of assigned work and was able to get a large volume in student accomplishment.

Simultaneously with his teaching work he started to develop some independent research problems. He was especially interested in the 1916 paper of Irving Langmuir on valence electrons and desired to investigate some of the implications it held in organic chemistry. Pursuing this idea he carried out laboratory studies which were reported in his first independent contribution to the Journal of the American Chemical Society, "The Isosterism of Phenyl Isocyanate and Diazobenzene-Imide." His second independent paper, published while still a student, was that on "The Double Bond." In this he presented the first clear, definite application of the electronic theory to organic chemistry on a workable basis. He described the electronic characteristics of the double bond and in essence included in his discussion everything that has since been written on this particular subject.

He returned to the University of Illinois in 1922 to complete his studies for the degree of doctor of philosophy, which he received in 1924. His major work was in organic chemistry with a thesis under the direction of Dr. Roger Adams, on the catalytic reduction of aldehydes with platinum-oxide platinum-black and on the effect of promoters and poisons on this catalyst in the reduction of various organic compounds. His minors were physical chemistry and mathematics. He exhibited the same brilliance in all of his courses and in research which characterized his earlier accomplishments. Although specializing in organic chemistry, he was considered by the physical chemists to have a more comprehensive knowledge of physical chemistry than any of the students majoring in that field. In 1920–1921 he held an assistantship for one semester in inorganic chemistry and for one semester in organic chemistry. He was a research assistant during 1922–1923, and during 1923–1924 held the Carr Fellowship, the highest award offered at that time by the department of chemistry at Illinois. During these two years his seminar reports demonstrated his wide grasp of chemical subjects. The frequency with which his student colleagues sought his advice and help was indicative of his outstanding ability. At graduation he was considered by the staff as one of the most brilliant students who had ever been awarded the doctor's degree. A vacancy on the staff of the chemistry department of the University of Illinois made it possible to appoint him as an instructor in organic chemistry in the fall of 1924. In this capacity he continued with unusual success for two years, teaching qualitative organic analysis and two organic laboratory courses, one for premedical students and the other for chemists.

Harvard University, in 1926, was in need of an instructor in organic chemistry. After carefully surveying the available candidates from the various universities of the country, Carothers was selected. In this new position he taught during the first year a course in experimental organic chemistry and an advanced course in structural chemistry, and during the second year he gave the lectures and laboratory instruction in elementary organic chemistry.

President James B. Conant, of Harvard University, was professor of organic chemistry at the time that Carothers was instructor. He says of him—

"Dr. Carothers' stay at Harvard was all too short. In the brief space of time during which he was a member of the chemistry department, he greatly impressed both his colleagues and the students. He presented elementary organic chemistry to a large class with distinction. Although he was always loath to speak in public even at scientific meetings, his diffidence seemed to disappear in the classroom. His lectures were well ordered, interesting, and enthusiastically received by a body of students only few of whom planned to make chemistry a career. In his research, Dr. Carothers showed even at this time that high degree of originality which marked his later work. He was never content to follow the beaten track or to accept the usual interpretations of organic reactions. His first thinking about polymerization and the structure of substances of high molecular weight began while he was at Harvard. His resignation from the faculty to accept an important position in the research laboratory of the du Pont Company, was Harvard's loss but chemistry's gain. Under the new conditions at Wilmington, he had facilities for carrying on his research on a scale that would be difficult or impossible to duplicate in most university laboratories. Those of us in academic life, however, always cherished the hope that some day he would return to university work. In his death, academic chemistry, quite as much as industrial chemistry, has suffered a severe loss."

In 1928 the du Pont Company had completed plans to embark on a new program of fundamental research at their central laboratory, the Experimental Station at Wilmington, Delaware. Carothers was selected to head the research in organic chemistry. The decision to leave his academic position was a difficult one. The new place demanded only research and offered the opportunity of trained research men as assistants. This overbalanced the freedom of university life and he accepted. From then on until his death his accomplishments were numerous and significant. He had the rare quality of recognizing the significant points in each problem he undertook and unusual ability for presenting his results in a most explicit and precise way, which led to clarity and understanding. In these nine years he made several major contributions to the theory of organic chemistry and discoveries which led to materials of significant commercial importance. Dr. Elmer K. Bolton, Chemical Director of the du Pont Company, writes concerning Carothers—

"At the time the du Pont Company embarked upon its program of fundamental research in organic chemistry in the Chemical Department, Dr. Carothers was selected to direct this activity, because he had received the highest recommendations from Harvard University and the University of Illinois, and was considered to have unusual potentiality for future development. There was placed under his direction a small group of excellently trained chemists to work on problems of his own selection. The results of his work, extending over a period of nine years, have been of outstanding scientific interest and have been considered of great value to the Company as they have laid the foundation for several basically new developments of commercial importance.

"In our association with Dr. Carothers, we were always impressed by the breadth and depth of his knowledge. He not only provided inspiration and guidance to men under his immediate direction, but gave freely of his knowledge to the chemists of the department engaged in applied research. In addition, he was a brilliant experimentalist. Regarding his personal characteristics, he was modest, unassuming to a fault, most uncomplaining, a tireless worker—deeply absorbed in his work, and was greatly respected by his associates. He suffered, however, from a nervous condition which in his later years was reflected in poor health and which became progressively worse in spite of the best medical advice and care, and the untiring efforts of his friends and associates. His death has been a great loss to chemistry and particularly to the Chemical Department. In my judgment, he was one of the most brilliant organic chemists ever employed by the du Pont Company."

His reputation spread rapidly; his advice was sought continually, not only by his colleagues but also by chemists throughout the world. In 1929 he was elected Associate Editor of the Journal of the American Chemical Society; in 1930 he became an editor of Organic Syntheses. He took an active part in the meetings of the organic division of the American Chemical Society. He was invited frequently to speak before various chemical groups. He addressed the Johns Hopkins summer colloquium in 1935 on "Polymers and the Theory of Polymerization." That year he also spoke on the same subject before the Faraday Society in London, when his paper was considered one of the outstanding presentations on the program. His achievements were recognized by his election to the National Academy of Sciences in 1936—the first organic chemist associated with industry to be elected to that organization. During these years from 1928–1937 several attractive academic positions were offered him but he chose to remain to the end with the Company which had given him his opportunity for accomplishment.

Carothers was deeply emotional, generous and modest. He had a lovable personality. Although generally silent in a group of people, he was a brilliant conversationalist when with a single individual, and quickly displayed his broad education, his wide fund of information on all problems of current life, and his critical analysis of politics, labor problems and business, as well as of music, art, and philosophy. With all his fine physique he had an extremely sensitive nature and suffered from periods of depression which grew more pronounced as he grew older, despite the best efforts of his friends and medical advisers.[*]

* This biography is an abbreviated reprint of Roger Adams, Wallace Hume Carothers, 1896–1937. *National Academy of Sciences of the U. S., Biographical Memoirs.* **20.** 12th Memoirs. 1939.

PART ONE

STUDIES ON POLYMERIZATION AND RING FORMATION

PART ONE

STUDIES ON POLYMERIZATION AND RING FORMATION

INTRODUCTION

This series of articles extends from 1929 to 1936 and comprises twenty-eight papers.

Reactions which produce giant molecules can be divided into polycondensation and polymerization processes; Carothers has called them *C-polymers* and *A-polymers*, respectively. The articles of Part 1 are especially devoted to the study of *C-polymerization*. The following are the outstanding problems which are open for investigation.

(a) If two bifunctional molecules, *e. g.*, one dibasic acid and one glycol, or diamine, react, two possibilities occur. The reaction can result (1) in a chain polymer of lower or higher molecular weight, which still bears either hydroxyl or carbonyl terminal groups or (2) in a smaller or larger ring, which does not contain the reactive group. The following questions arise: Under what conditions does either of these two possibilities take place and what is the molecular weight of the resulting compound. Papers I to XIV are chiefly concerned with this problem. A large number of dibasic acids, glycols, diamines, ω-hydroxy and amino-carbonic acids were included in the investigation and many formerly unknown compounds were synthesized and described.

If 5- or 6-membered rings can be formed during a polycondensation of the type described, the reaction almost invariably leads to ring formation; this may be put forward as a general result. There is still a certain possibility also for the production of 7- and 8-membered rings, while larger rings are not formed during such polycondensation reactions. This rule is associated with the stereochemical points of view of Sachse and Mohr.

(b) The second problem is concerned with the behavior of the high polymeric compounds, which can be produced by polycondensation, and their possible technical utilization. Polyesters and polyamides may be very readily cast into films or drawn. into filaments which display very interesting technical properties. Papers XV, XVIII and XIX deal in part with this question. In general, as soon as the degree of polymerization exceeds a number between 30 and 40, the material begins to exhibit strength and extensibility. Such products can be cast or spun from solution and also from the molten state; they can later undergo a stretching process

3

which increases the strength and pliability of the resulting samples and also causes the material to assume a lustrous appearance. This investigation can certainly be regarded as an outstanding example of successful scientific work, which bears at the same time considerable technical importance. One of the polyamides, which has been prepared and investigated, was selected for technical production, and is now coming into great importance under the trade name of "Nylon."

(c) Another attractive line of investigation was the more thorough study of the second type of compounds which result from polycondensation reactions, namely poly-membered rings. Ruzicka has shown that such compounds exhibit peculiar properties and are of considerable interest from the point of view of their odor. In papers XX, XXI, XXII, XXIII and XXVI, a new method for the preparation of such rings is described; their formation and properties are studied. It turns out that the specific odor is closely connected with the number of bonds and varies with it in a characteristic way.

It is of importance to point out that an experimental method has been developed to deal with such high polymeric chains or multi-membered rings or mixtures of the two. Pure samples suitable for quantitative characterization could hardly be obtained by the normal experimental methods of organic chemistry. Therefore, a new type of molecular still has been developed, which is briefly described in paper XI and which is extensively applied in all these investigations.

In the following, each single paper is reprinted without any change; a short abstract of its contents is given at the beginning in italics; and a few additional references concerning the recent development and literature are added. The purpose of this brief introduction is to emphasize the main general results and to refer briefly to their scientific and technical importance.

I.   An Introduction to the General Theory of Condensation Polymers*

This first paper contains a general introduction to the theory of polymers. With the aid of a comprehensive table Carothers distinguishes between two classes of polymers:

A-polymers, produced by recurring addition of monomers. The molecular formula of the monomer is identical with that of the structural unit. The

*W. H. Carothers; Journ. Am. Chem. Soc., 51, 2548–59 (1929); Contribution No. 10 from the Experimental Station of E. I. du Pont de Nemours and Co. Received April 13, 1929.   Published August 7, 1929.

monomer can be obtained from the polymer by thermal or photochemical decomposition; the polymer is formed by self-addition.

C-polymers, *produced by recurring condensation of monomers. The molecular formula of the monomer differs from that of the structural unit. The monomer can be obtained from the polymer by a hydrolytic process; the polymer is formed by a polyintermolecular condensation.** *

Then the conditions for the formation of C-polymers are explored. The term "functionality" is introduced. A functional group in the monomer is such an arrangement of atoms as might lead to a reaction step. Such groups are, e. g., OH, NH_2, COOH, SO_3H, etc. According as the monomer contains one, two, three, etc., of them it is called mono-functional, bifunctional, etc.

Multifunctional monomers can react intra- or intermolecularly. In the first case they lead to rings, in the second to C-polymers.

If during a bifunctional reaction a 5- or 6-ring can be formed intra-molecuarly, then it almost invariably happens that the reaction leads to ring formation.

Bifunctional reactions which if intramolecular would lead to larger than 6-rings generally proceed intermolecularly and give C-polymers. The formation of 7-rings, however, may possibly occur, while 8-rings are much less probable.

This empirical rule, which has of course also several exceptions is discussed in the paper from the point of view of the stereochemical considerations of Sachse and Mohr.

Polymerization frequently leads to substances of very high molecular weights, and the problem of the structure of high polymers is attracting a great deal of attention, especially because such important materials as rubber, cellulose, proteins and resins either are high polymers or have certain properties which are common to high polymers.

The conditions which Berzelius (1) was concerned to recognize by the term polymer, were the presence of the same atoms in the same proportions in compounds having different molecular weights. These conditions are satisfied by the members of a great many thousand pairs of compounds which are not now regarded as polymers. Thus, of the compounds paracetaldehyde, butyric acids and hydroxycaproic acids, only the first would now be considered a polymer of acetaldehyde, although there is nothing in the conditions of the Berzelius definition to exclude the others. Hence,

* In modern literature A-polymers are frequently called polymerisation products, while C-polymers are termed polycondensation products. The shorter terminology of Carothers would certainly be practical.

whatever the term polymer may mean now, it does not mean precisely what Berzelius intended, and the conditions which he set up are not sufficient to define it.   In current attempts to define this term (2) it is still stated that a polymer and its monomer must have the same atoms in the same proportions.   But this condition is not satisfied by the polyoxy-methylenes (see Table I) which are universally considered to be polymers of formaldehyde.   It seems desirable, therefore, to attempt to formulate a definition which will be in so far as possible in accordance with both the current usage and the essential facts.

The structures of a good many polymers, including some of very high molecular weights, are known either completely or in part and an examina-tion of their formulas shows some interesting relationships (see Table I). They are characterized by a recurring structural unit, so that if this is represented by —R—, the structure of these polymers may be represented in part by the general formula —R—R—R—R—R—R—R—R—, etc., or $(—R—)_n$.   In this formula n may be small as in paracetaldehyde ($n = 3$), or it may be very large as in the polyoxymethylenes.   The end valences may be united as they are in paracetaldehyde to form a ring, or they may be saturated by univalent groups such as H— and —OH to form an open chain of the type $H(—R—)_n OH$ as they are in α-polyoxymethylene. It seems probable that cellulose and silk fibroin are of this type, and in any event it may be observed that no high polymer is certainly known to be cyclic (3).   There are polymers which do not conform to the type $(—R—)_n$ but those which do will be called linear whether the chain is open or closed; and the subsequent discussion is concerned only with these.

The structural units —R— are bivalent radicals which, in general, are not capable of independent existence.   The presence of a recurring struc-tural unit is, of course, characteristic of most organic compounds (e. g., —CH$_2$— in aliphatic compounds), but in the case of polymers there exists a molecule, the monomer, corresponding to the structural unit, and from which the polymer may be formed or to which it may be degraded.

Examination of the formulas of Table I will show that two types of polymers may be distinguished.   In the first type, which includes paracet-aldehyde, rubber, polystyrene and polyoxymethylenes, the molecular formula of the structural unit is identical with that of the monomer, i. e., the formula of the structural unit, —R—, is isomeric with that of the monomer.   In the second type, which includes the polyethylene glycols, cellulose and silk fibroin, the molecular formula of the structural unit differs from that of the monomer by H_2O, i. e., the monomer is H—R—OH. The transformation of polymers of the first type into their monomers is brought about simply by heating, and the reverse transformation (poly-merization) occurs spontaneously or by the action of catalysts. In the second type, degradation to the monomer occurs by hydrolysis, and if the reverse process were to take place it would require the elimination of water among many molecules. This would be polyintermolecular con-densation (4).

These two classes will be distinguished as (1) addition or A polymers. The molecular formula of the monomer is identical with that of the struc-tural unit. The monomer can be obtained from the polymer by ther-molysis or the polymer can be synthesized from the monomer by self-addition. (2) Condensation or C polymers: the molecular formula of the monomer differs from that of the structural unit. The monomer can be obtained from the polymer by hydrolysis or its equivalent or the polymer can be synthesized from the monomer by polyintermolecular condensation. Polymerization then is the chemical union of many similar molecules either (A) without or (C) with the elimination of simpler molecules (H_2O, HCl, NaCl, NH_3, etc.) (5).

Assuming that polyintermolecular condensation exists, the above ex-amples and definitions and their implications provide ample reason for referring to this process as a type of polymerization. These examples, of course, do not provide any proof that this process as distinct from and independent of A polymerization does exist. This proof will appear incidentally in the following discussion, which is concerned with the general principles involved in the formation of condensation polymers.

Polyfunctional Compounds.—Polyintermolecular condensation re-quires as starting materials compounds in which at least two functional groups are present in the same molecule (*e. g.*, hydroxy acids, HORCOOH, might lead to poly-esters, HORCOORCOORCOORCOORCO—, etc.; amino acids, to poly-amides, $NH_2RCONHCONHRCONHR-$ CONHRCONHRCO—, etc.).

Among compounds having more than one functional group, those of the type x—R—y may be called bifunctional, $R''x_3$, trifunctional, etc. In these formulas R stands for a bivalent radical (R'' for a trivalent radical) and x and y for functional groups capable of reacting with each other in a known fashion to form the new functional group z. Thus x—R—y $\longrightarrow$ —R—z—, where —R—z— evidently represents a structural unit which will appear in the product and which may be present 1, 2, 3, ... n times. Reactions of this type will be called bifunctional regardless of the num-ber of molecules involved. Reactions of the type x—R—x + y—R'—y $\longrightarrow$ —z—R—z—R'— may be called bi-bifunctional. All such reactions may, at least by hypothesis, pass through the stage $x—R—x—R'—y''$ which is equivalent to $x—R—y$, and for purposes of discussion they may therefore be classed as simple bifunctional reactions. Reactions of the type $R'x_3 + Ry_2 \longrightarrow product$ will be called tri-bifunctional. Similarly there may be tetra-bifunctional, tri-trifunctional reactions, etc., and all these may be classed together as polyfunctional reactions. The present discussion is concerned only with bifunctional reactions.

Bifunctional Reactions.—These always present two possibilities: they may be intramolecular or intermolecular. If intramolecular they can lead only to the simple monomeric ring I. If intermolecular they may lead either to a polymeric ring II or to a polymeric chain III.

$$x—R—y \longrightarrow R \overset{\displaystyle \diagup\diagdown}{\underset{\displaystyle \diagdown\diagup}{}} z \qquad\qquad \text{I}$$
$$\longrightarrow (—R—z—)_n \qquad\qquad \text{II}$$
$$\longrightarrow x—(—R—z—)_{n-1}—R—y \quad \text{III}$$

These obviously represent three possibly competing reactions.

The question now arises, what factors will determine which of these possible courses a bifunctional reaction will take? It is obvious, for example, that in general dilution would favor intra- over intermolecular reactions (6). Temperature and catalysts might favor either one or the other. It appears, however, that structural and stereochemical factors will usually be more important than any others. That is, though it may be possible in some bifunctional reactions to control the choice between intra- and intermolecular reaction by suitable adjustment of experimental conditions, this choice will, in general, be almost completely determined by the nature of the reacting molecules.

The effects of these factors may be stated as follows. (1) If the product of intramolecular reaction would be a ring which, on stereochemical grounds, is incapable of existence, reaction will be intermolecular. This is apparently the case with p-$NH_2C_6H_4CH_2CH_2Cl$, which reacts with itself intermolecularly (7), and not as had previously been supposed (8) with the formation of the so-called dihydro-p-indole (9). The utility of this very obvious principle is somewhat diminished by the fact that, in the present state of stereochemical knowledge, it is sometimes impossible to predict whether a given ring system will be capable of existence or not.

(2) Bifunctional reactions which can lead to the formation of 5- or 6-rings almost invariably proceed intramolecularly. This well-established

TABLE I
POLYMERS

Polymer		Monomer	Mer or structural unit

Polystyrene

?—CH₂—CH₂—CH₂—CH₂—CH₂—CH₂— . . . —CH₂—CH₂—CH₂—CH₂—CH₂—CH₂—?
 | | | | | |
C₆H₅ C₆H₅ C₆H₅ C₆H₅   C₆H₅ C₆H₅

heat ⇌   Styrene CH=CH₂ | C₆H₅   → —CH—CH₂— | C₆H₅

Rubber

?—CH₂—C=CH—CH₂—CH₂—C=CH—CH₂— . . . —CH₂—CH₂—C=CH—CH₂—?
        | | |
       CH₃   CH₃   CH₃

heat ⇌   Isoprene CH₂=C—CH=CH₂ | CH₃ → —CH₂—C=CH—CH₂— | CH₃

α-Polyoxymethylene

HO—CH₂—O—CH₂—O—CH₂—O— . . . —CH₂—O—CH₂—O—CH₂—O—CH₂—OH

heat ⇌   Formaldehyde H₂C=O → —CH₂—O—

β-Polyoxymethylene

HSO₃—O—CH₂—O—CH₂—O—CH₂—O— . . . —CH₂—O—CH₂—O—H

heat ⇌   H₂C=O → —CH₂—O—

Polyethylene glycols

HO—CH₂—O—CH₂—O—CH₂—O— . . . —CH₂—CH₂—OH

HOH ↑   Ethylene glycol HO·CH₂—CH₂·OH → —CH₂·CH₂·O—

Silk fibroin

NH₂—CH₂—CONH—CH—CONH—CH—CONH—CH—CO— . . . —NH—CH₂—CONH—CH—CO—
                      | | |
                     CH₃   CH₃   CH₃

HOH ↑   Glycyl alanine CH₂—CONH—CH—COOH | NH₂ | CH₃ → CH₂—CONH—CH—CO— | NH— | CH₃

Cellulose

[cellulose structural formula]

HOH ↑   Glucose [glucose structural formula] → [glucose structural unit]

The above formulas for the polyoxymethylenes, polystyrenes and rubber have been well established especially by the work of Staudinger and his students: *Helv. Chim. Acta*, **5**, 785 (1922); **7**, 23, 842 (1924); **8**, 41, 65, 67 (1925); **9**, 529 (1926); **11**, 1047, 1052 (1928); *Ber.*, **53**, 1073 (1920); **57**, 1203 (1924); **59**, 3019 (1926); **60**, 1782 (1927); **61**, 2427 (1928); **62**, 241, 263 (1929); *Ann.*, **447**, 97, 110 (1926); *Z. physik. Chem.*, **126**, 425 (1927); *Kautschuk*, 237 (1927). For the formulas for cellulose, silk fibroin and rubber see Freudenberg and Braun, *Ann.*, **460**, 288 (1928); Meyer and Mark, *Ber.*, **61**, 593, 1932, 1939 (1928); Meyer, *Naturwissenschaften*, **42**, 790 (1928). The formulas for cellulose and silk fibroin are not, of course, regarded as finally established.

fact is responsible for the existence of the majority of the very large number of 5- and 6-rings which is known.

(3) Bifunctional reactions which, if intramolecular, could lead only to larger-than-6-rings, generally proceed intermolecularly and lead to polymeric products. If this rule were free from any exceptions, it would necessarily follow that the polymeric products would always be of the open-chain type, III.

Although a great many bifunctional reactions have been studied in the hope of forming large rings, our information as to the precise nature of the products of these reactions is very meager. That they do not usually proceed intramolecularly follows from the fact that very few large rings are known. It is true that such reactions frequently do not proceed at all under conditions which, in analogous cases, lead to the formation of 5- and 6-rings; but the formation of the latter often proceeds under conditions which do not permit intermolecular reaction even among unifunctional compounds (compare the formation of γ-lactones in the presence of a large excess of water, with the esterification of acetic acid). There are, however, a good many types of reaction which are intermolecular among simple compounds, which are practically free from side reactions, and which by suitable adjustment of experimental conditions may be forced to completion. It should be possible to conduct reactions of these types even when bifunctional, so as to obtain analytically homogeneous products whether they proceed intramolecularly or not. These simple principles have been repeatedly applied to bifunctional reactions in this Laboratory, and they have seldom failed to lead to analytically homogeneous products. Moreover, where the formation of 5- or 6-rings was excluded by the nature of the reacting materials, these reactions have, *without exception*, led to *high polymers*. This fact provides a possible explanation for the meagerness of the information which is available concerning the precise nature of the products of such bifunctional reactions. High polymers frequently have properties which make their investigation very difficult. Moreover, if a chemist is expecting a reaction to lead to materials of simple properties, he is usually inclined to regard the appearance of a resinous or sirupy product which neither can be crystallized nor distilled as signifying only that the experiment has failed. When the products of such reactions have been capable of purification and have shown the expected analytical composition, they have frequently been assumed to be dimeric (and cyclic) for no other reason than that they were obviously not monomeric. In this connection it should be emphasized that substances of very high molecular weights may nevertheless be microcrystalline and very soluble (see the following paper).

Some of the points discussed above are illustrated by the following examples.

Anhydrides of the acids of the series $HOOC(CH_2)_xCOOH$ are known in which x has all values from 1 to 8 inclusive. Of these only succinic and glutaric anhydrides are monomeric. These are, respectively, 5- and 6-rings. The other anhydrides which, if monomeric, would be 4-, 7-, 8-, 9-, 10- and 11-rings, are all highly polymeric (10).

Hydroxy-acids of the series $HO(CH_2)_xCOOH$ may condense with themselves. Only those in which x is 3 or 4 yield monomeric lactones (11). These lactones are 5- and 6-rings, respectively. This series of acids now includes those in which x has all values from 8 to 16 inclusive (12). The lactones corresponding to the acids in which x has the values 12 to 16 are also known (12b), as well as the 17-membered lactone of the unsaturated acid, hexadecene-(7)-ol-(16)-acid-(1) (13). All of these lactones are perfectly stable substances and can be distilled without decomposition (14); and yet none of these lactones has been synthesized by a bifunctional reaction (15). They were synthesized by the oxidation of the corresponding cyclic ketones with persulfuric acid. By heating the acids, products are indeed obtained which have the same analytical composition as the lactones, but (12a) they are "polymeric-like." The properties of the known lactones of this series indicate that lactones cannot be intermediates in the formation of these polymers. The formation of these must, therefore, involve C polymerization.

Amino acids of the series $NH_2(CH_2)_xCOOH$ are known in which x has the values 3, 4, 5 and 6. When x is 3 and 4, intramolecular anhydride formation occurs spontaneously at the melting point of the acids, the products being the 5- and 6-membered rings, pyrrolidone and piperidone (16). When x is 5 the acid is, on heating, converted to the extent of 20 to 30% of the theoretical into the 7-membered lactam. "The rest of the acid is converted into a viscous gelatinous mass which could be obtained in a state of only approximate purity and which, according to the analysis, is isomeric with the 7-membered lactam; that is, it is a polymeric product" (17). Where x is 6 no trace of the corresponding lactam could be obtained by heating the acid, although this lactam (suberone-isoxime) is a known and stable substance (18). By heating the acid a product was obtained having the same composition as this lactam, but it was an undistillable solid, insoluble in most solvents (17).

The compounds $Br(CH_2)_xNH_2$, where x is 4, 5 and 6, react with themselves with the formation of secondary amines containing the structural unit $(-CH_2-)_xNH-$. Where x is 4 and 5 the products are the monomeric 5- and 6-rings, pyrrolidine and piperidine (19). Where x is 6 the amount of the monomeric base (7-ring) formed was too small to permit purification (20). The product was for the most part an oil which solidified to a waxy solid. It could not be distilled in vacuum without decomposition, and though no molecular weight determination is recorded, v. Braun seems inclined to regard it as dimeric. Its properties are obviously more consistent with a more highly polymeric structure.

An interesting example of a bi-bifunctional reaction is found in the reaction between glycols and acetaldehyde (or acetylene). This presents the possibility of forming cyclic acetals, CH$_3$CH $\overset{\diagup O \diagdown}{\underset{\diagdown O \diagup}{}}$ R, or polyacetals,

HO—R—O—CH—O—R—O—CH—O—R—O—CH—O—, etc. This re-
$\quad\quad\quad\underset{CH_3}{|}\quad\quad\quad\quad\quad\underset{CH_3}{|}\quad\quad\quad\quad\quad\underset{CH_3}{|}$

action has been studied by Hill and Hibbert (21). Ethylene and trimethylene glycols gave in excellent yields the cyclic acetals which are 5- and 6-rings. Tetramethylene glycol gave in poor yield a volatile compound which was apparently the monomeric cyclic acetal containing a 7-ring. A considerable part of the product was an undistillable sirup. The products from octamethylene and decamethylene glycols were also undistillable sirups. No molecular weight determinations are recorded. Hill and Hibbert recognized of course that these sirups might have the polymeric linear structure indicated above, but seemed inclined to regard them as simple rings of a peculiar kind.

The only reaction which has led to the formation of large carbon rings from open-chain compounds is the action of heat on certain salts of dibasic acids (22). In no case are these large rings the chief products of this reaction, nor can it be established that they are primary products, since the reaction takes place at high temperature. If polymeric products were formed they would be decomposed thermally. High polymers could not appear in the distillate from which the products are isolated, because high polymers cannot be distilled. These features sharply distinguish this reaction from other truly bifunctional reactions which might, but which do not, so far as our information goes, lead to rings of the same type (23).

Any theory which attempts to explain why 5- and 6-rings are formed very readily and larger rings with very great difficulty must take into account the fact that these larger rings are not less stable than the smaller. A satisfactory theory is already available. The Baeyer strain theory in its original form is made untenable by the existence of the higher cyclo-paraffins, and has been replaced by the Sachse–Mohr theory which permits the existence of non-planar and strainless rings and which has besides a great deal of other evidence in its support (24). The features of this theory essential to the present argument are exceedingly simple. They involve the assumption of the tretrahedral angle in the carbon valences and of free rotation about each carbon–carbon single bond in a chain. No description of stereochemical relations can be as convincing as a demonstration with suitable models (25). Such models show that there is a certain inevitability in the formation of 5- and 6-rings and a large degree of fortuity in the formation of larger rings. This question has been considered in some detail by Mohr (26). Regarding the possibility of the formation of a cyclic ketonic ester by the internal condensation of sebacic ester he says:

The molecule of sebacic ester is a very long chain. The multiplicity of forms which this molecule can assume is extraordinarily great. It is clear that by the random collisions of the molecules, fewer molecules of sebacic ester will in unit time assume the form necessary for ring closure than is the case with adipic ester under the same conditions, since this contains in its molecule only four methylene groups, and four less points of rotation than does sebacic ester. To bring the two ends of the sebacic ester molecule together in the least forced fashion apparently requires a very small amount of energy or none at all. Unfortunately, however, we have not the means arbitrarily and with the least possible expenditure of energy to bring about the desired change in form of the molecules and to hinder the undesired. In this connection we are left entirely to chance, that is, to random collision, which will bring about a given form the more rarely the more forms are possible, *i. e.*, the longer the chain between the two carboxyl groups.

In perhaps two dozen cases it is well established that a bifunctional reaction proceeds fairly smoothly with the formation of a larger-than-6-ring. These cases include more 7-membered than larger rings and more aromatic than aliphatic compounds. The Sachse–Mohr theory would lead one to expect that the formation of 7-rings would not be very much more difficult than the formation of 6-rings. The bifunctional reactions discussed in the examples offered above all involve purely aliphatic compounds, and for the most part the chains are unsubstituted. In most of these examples the formation of a 7-ring occurs to a certain extent, and the formation of the corresponding 8-ring not at all. It appears that in such 7-atom chains the probabilities of intra- and intermolecular reaction are about equal. The addition of one more atom to the chain diminishes the probability of intra- with respect to intermolecular reaction to such an extent that only the latter appears. These relations may be somewhat modified by the presence of substituents on the chains and even by the nature of the reacting groups in ways which it is, at present, impossible to predict. It is evident, however, that if two atoms of such a chain are adjacent atoms of a benzene ring their position with respect to each other is fixed, and the chances of intramolecular reaction are greater than in an analogous simple chain of the same length. (The latter will have one more axis of rotation than the former.) It is therefore not surprising that in $NH_2(CH_2)_6Cl$ intramolecular reaction occurs only to a slight extent, and in o-$NH_2C_6H_4(CH_2)_4Cl$ almost quantitatively (27). Other similar examples might be cited.

There is also some evidence to indicate that even simple substituents such as methyl groups on a chain may increase the tendency toward the formation of larger rings (28). Researches in the diphenyl series have established that substituent groups suitably placed may completely inhibit rotation about a nearby single bond, and a similar effect in aliphatic chains is at least conceivable. Any restriction of the freedom of rotation of the atoms of a chain would, on the basis of the Sachse–Mohr theory, increase the chances of ring formation.

The process of polyintermolecular condensation finds no mention in treatises on polymerization. This may be due to the fact that such a process is not admitted to exist, or that it is not admitted to be polymerization. The examples cited above, and others to be described later, prove that such a process does exist, and that it may result in the formation of very large molecules. Whether it is to be regarded as polymerization or not will depend upon the definition which is adopted for that term. The definitions offered above include it as a special type of polymerization. This classification finds more to justify it than the analogies which are recognized in these definitions.

The process of A polymerization (the only type which appears to have been generally recognized) results in the formation of large molecules from small; and it has come about that any process which has this result is called polymerization. Since, however, A polymerization is by definition a process of self-addition, chemists have often been misled to the assumption that condensation leads directly only to small molecules, and that if large molecules are formed from small as the apparent result of condensation, this is due to the intervention of some unsaturated molecules capable of undergoing A polymerization (29). It is quite certain, however, that in many such cases (*i. e.*, in all cases of true C polymerization) no such intermediate products occur. This is a matter of important practical implications. The reactions involved in the formation of A polymers must, in the nature of the case, be for the most part reactions which are peculiar to the process of polymerization. For this reason the mechanism of A polymerization still remains somewhat obscure. Hence, the mere assumption that unsaturated intermediates intervene in a reaction which leads to high polymers contributes little to one's understanding of the mechanism of the process, or the structure of the product. In those cases in which this assumption is wrong its use leads one to regard as complicated and mysterious a process which may be simple and obvious. C polymerization merely involves the use in a multiple fashion of the typical reactions of common functional groups. Among bifunctional compounds these reactions may proceed in such a way as to guarantee the structure of the structural unit, —R—, in the polymer, $(-R-)_n$, formed. It is one of the immediate objects of the researches to be described in subsequent papers to discover how the physical and chemical properties of high polymers of this type are related to the nature of the structural unit.

Summary

Linear polymers confrom to the type —R—R—R—R—R—, etc., which is characterized by a recurring structural unit. The structural unit —R— is a bivalent radical. Two types of polymers are recognized. (1) Addition of A polymers: the polymeric molecule is converted by heat into a monomer having the same composition as the structural unit, or the polymer is formed by the mutual addition of a number of such monomers. (2) Condensation or C polymers: the polymeric molecule is converted by hydrolysis or its equivalent to a monomer which differs in composition from the structural unit by one H_2O (or HCl, NH_3, etc.), or the polymeric molecule is formed from numbers of the monomers by a process of polyintermolecular condensation. Rubber, polystyrene, polyoxymethylene and paracetaldehyde are A polymers. Cellulose, silk fibroin and hexa-ethylene glycol are probably C polymers.

Substances of the type x—R—x and x—R—y are called bifunctional. In these formulas —R— represents a bivalent radical and x and y functional groups capable of reacting with each other in a known fashion to form the new functional group, z. Reactions of the type x—R—y ⟶ *product* are called bifunctional and those of the type x—R—x + y—R—y ⟶ *product* are called bi-bifunctional. Such reactions will lead to compounds containing the structural units —R—z— and —R—z—R—z—. Bifunctional reactions will be intramolecular and will lead to the monomeric product, R⟨z⟩

when this can be a 5- or 6-ring.   If the monomeric product can only be a larger-than-6-ring, reaction will usually be intermolecular and the product a polymer of the type —R—z—R—z—R—z—R—z—R—z—, etc.

Bibliography and Remarks

(1) Berzelius, *Jahresbericht*, **12**, 63 (1833).

(2) Hess, "Chemie der Zellulose," Leipzig, 1928, p. 577; Meerwein, Houben-Weyl, "Die Methoden der organischen Chemie," Leipzig, 1923, zweite Auflage, dritter Band, p. 1013;   Staudinger, *Ber.*, **58**, 1074 (1920).

(3) However, Staudinger, in his latest papers, favors the view that polystyrene and rubber are very large rings, *Ber.*, **62**, 241 (1929).

(4) The term condensation is used here to name any reaction which occurs with the formation of a new bond between atoms not already joined and which proceeds with the elimination of elements (H_2, N_2, etc.) or of simple compounds (H_2O, C_2H_5OH, NH_3, $NaBr$, etc.).   Examples are the Wurtz reaction, Friedel–Crafts reaction, esterification, etc.

(5) It would not be difficult to suggest examples in which a single polymer might belong to either or to both of these classes depending upon the method by which it was synthesized.   So far as cellulose is concerned there is little to justify its classification as a C rather than as an A polymer other than the criteria which are set forth in the above definitions, and these may at present appear somewhat arbitrary.   Thus even if cellulose were synthesized by the dehydration of glucose, this might occur by the formation of a glucosan which subsequently polymerized by self-addition.   It may be observed, however, that of the two trimethylglucosans which might conceivably polymerize in this way to form trimethylcellulose, one is known and does not polymerize, and the other is probably incapable of existence on stereochemical grounds.   See Freudenberg and Braun, *Ann.*, **460**, 288 (1928).

(6) *Cf.* Ruggli, *Ann.*, **392**, 92 (1912), where the recognition of this principle made possible the synthesis of large rings containing an acetylenic linkage.

(7) Ferber, *Ber.*, **62**, 183 (1929).

(8) v. Braun and Gawrilow, *ibid.*, **45**, 1274 (1912).

(9) For some other examples, see Titley, *J. Chem. Soc.*, 2571 (1928).

(10) For malonic anhydride see Staudinger and Ott, *Ber.*, **41**, 2214 (1908).   For the other anhydrides see Voerman, *Rec. trav. chim.*, **23**, 265 (1904).   The cryoscopic data which Voerman presents on phenol solutions have no bearing on the molecular weights of the anhydrides, since even succinic anhydride reacts rapidly with phenol to form phenyl succinate;   Bischoff and von Hedenström, *Ber.*, **35**, 4076 (1902).   Farmer and Kracovski have recently obtained adipic anhydride in a monomeric form, *J. Chem. Soc.*, 680 (1927).

(11) On this point no data are available for those in which x is 5 and 6 [*J. Am. Chem. Soc.*, **46**, 2838 (1924); *Ber.*, **60**, 605 (1927); *ibid.*, **33**, 864 (1900)].   The analogous acids, $CH_3CHOH(CH_2)_2CH$-$(CH_3)CH_2COOH$ [Baeyer and Seuffert, *ibid.*, **32**, 3619 (1899)] and $C_2H_5CHOH(CH_2)_4COOH$ [Blaise and Kohler, *Compt. rend.*, **148**, 1772 (1909)], have been prepared, and by heating are converted at least partially into the 7-membered lactones.   The acid $C_2H_5CHOH(CH_2)_5COOH$ has also been prepared.   On heating, it also loses water, but the 8-membered lactone is not formed.   The product is a lactide like material which cannot be distilled without decomposition (Blaise and Kohler).

(12) (a) Lycan and Adams, *J. Am. Chem. Soc.*, **51**, 625 (1929); (b) Ruzicka and Stoll, *Helv. Chim. Acta.*, **11**, 1159 (1928).   Since this paper was written a great deal of further information concerning these acids has become available in the paper of Chuit and Hausser, *ibid.*, **12**, 463 (1929).

(13) Kerschbaum, *Ber.*, **60**, 902 (1927).

(14) This indicates that large heterocyclic rings are not less stable than their lower homologs. Their physical properties are such as would be expected from the known properties of their lower homologs.   The mere presence of a large ring does not result in the development of any of those unusual secondary, residual or supermolecular forces which are sometimes supposed to confer "polymeric" properties on relatively simple molecules.

(15) Kerschbaum (ref. 13) records various attempts to prepare ambretollid by the methods commonly used for the preparation of lactones.   By heating the acid he obtained traces of an oil which had the odor of the lactone.   (It is powerfully odorous.)   The product was, however, for the most part, a gelatinous material *soluble in alkali*.   For the usefulness of the method proposed in German Patent Application 150,677, see Ruzicka and Stoll, ref. 12b.

(16) Gabriel, *Ber.*, **22**, 3338 (1889); Schotten, *ibid.*, **21**, 2240 (1888).

(17) v. Braun, *Ber.*, **40**, 1840 (1907).

(18) B. p. 156° at 8 mm. It is, however, not prepared by a bifunctional reaction, but from cycloheptanone oxime by the Beckmann rearrangement. Wallach, *Ann.*, **312**, 305; **309**, 18 (1899).

(19) v. Braun and Beschke, *Ber.*, **39**, 4121 (1906); Blank, *ibid.*, **25**, 3044 (1892); v. Braun and Steindorf, *ibid.*, **38**, 172 (1905).

(20) v. Braun and Steindorf, *ibid.*, **38**, 1083 (1905); v. Braun, *ibid.* **43**, 2853 (1910).

(21) Hill and Hibbert, *J. Am. Chem. Soc.*, **45**, 3108, 3124 (1923). See also Franke and Gigerl, *Monatsh.*, **49**, 8 (1928).

(22) Ruzicka and co-workers, *Helv. Chim. Acta*, **9**, 230, 249, 339, 389, 399, 499, 715, 1008 (1926); **10**, 695 (1927); **11**, 496, 670, 686, 1159 1174 (1928).

(23) For example, the action of metals on a dihalide, $Br(CH_2)_x Br$. Thus decamethylene bromide reacts rapidly and very smoothly with metallic sodium, but no cyclodecane is formed. See Franke and Kienberger, *Monatsh.*, **33**, 1189 (1912). This reaction will be discussed in a later paper.

(24) See Hückel, "Der gegenwärtige Stand der Spannungstheorie," *Fortschritte Chem. Physik und physik. Chem.*, Band 19, Heft 4, **1927**.

(25) Ordinary (preferably quite small) wire tetrahedra may be joined by short pieces of rubber tubing in such a way that the arms which are being connected overlap. This provides free rotation about the union, but prevents bending. This method of union insures that any model which is built up is practically strainless (*i. e.*, the tetrahedral angle is always retained) and at the same time is sufficiently mobile to illustrate the multiplicity of forms which long chains and large rings can assume.

(26) Mohr, *J. prakt. Chem.*, **98**, 348 (1918).

(27) v. Braun and Bartsch, *Ber.*, **32**, 1270 (1899).

(28) See "Annual Reports of the Progress of Chemistry," **1927**, p. 100; Moyer and Adams, *J. Am. Chem. Soc.*, **51**, 630 (1929).

(29) Thus, Drummond, *Inst. Rubber Ind.*, **4**, 43 (1928), states, "Where resins are formed by a preliminary condensation as are the phenol-formaldehyde products, it is logical to assume that in the preliminary reaction, unsaturated atomic linkings are introduced which provide the necessary arrangement for polymerization subsequently to occur." Scheiber, *Chem. Umschau, Fette, Oele, Wachse Harze*, **15**, 181 (1928), is even more explicit: "Für den Aufbau organischer Stoffe kommen bekanntlich nur zwei Prozesse in Betracht, und zwar Kondensationen und Polymerisationen. Vorgänge der ersteren Art führen im allgemeinen zu Molekulverbänden beschränkter Grösse—.. Bei Polymerisationen hingegen kommt es in manchen Fallen zur Ausbildung extrem grosser Moleküle..."

II. Polyesters*

In this paper a bi-bifunctional reaction is studied by condensing dibasic carboxylic acids with dihydric alcohols. The number of carbon atoms in the structural units are 7, 8, 9, 10, 11, 12, 14, 15, 16, 18 and 22. Consequently† only C-polymers and no other products are obtained. Their molecular (or better average molecular) weights were measured by the freezing and boiling point methods. They range between 2500 and 5000. With the exception of the liquid ethylene malonate all polyesters are microcrystalline materials, with a melting point, which is not quite sharp.

* W. H. Carothers and G. A. Arvin; *Journ. Am. Chem. Soc.*, **51**, 2560–70 (1929); Contribution No. 11 from the Experimental Station of E. I. du Pont de Nemours and Co.

Received April 13, 1929. Published August 7, 1929.

† See the thesis developed on pages 10 and 11.

*The following combinations were prepared**

ethylene malonate	hexamethylene succinate
ethylene succinate	hexamethylene adipate
ethylene adipate	hexamethylene sebacate
ethylene sebacate	hexamethylene phthalate
ethylene maleate	
ethylene fumarate	decamethylene succinate
ethylene phthalate	decamethylene adipate
	decamethylene sebacate
trimethylene succinate	decamethylene phthalate
trimethylene adipate	
trimethylene sebacate	
trimethylene phthalate	

An example of a bi-bifunctional reaction is found in the reaction between a dibasic acid and a dihydric alcohol, HOOC—R′—COOH + HO—R″—OH, which, if it is conducted so as to involve both functional groups of each reactant, must lead to an ester having the structural unit, —OC—R′—CO—O—R″—O— = —R—. In accordance with the thesis developed in the previous paper, esters formed in this way will be polymeric unless the number of atoms in the chain of the structural unit is less than seven. In this paper esters are described in which the number of atoms in the chain of the structural unit is 7, 8, 9, 10, 11, 12, 14, 15, 16, 18 and 22 atoms. All these esters are highly polymeric, and, although some of them have been prepared by various methods, no monomeric form of any of them has as yet been isolated.

Preparation of the Esters

The following method was used for the preparation of the solid esters whose properties are listed in the table. The acid together with a 5% excess of the glycol was placed in a Claisen flask provided with a receiver and condenser, and the flask was heated in a metal-bath. At about 160° (bath temperature) reaction set in. Water distilled off freely during the first hour (temp., 175–185°) and very slowly if at all during the succeeding two hours at the same temperature. The receiver was now changed, the flask provided with a very fine capillary and heating continued under a good vacuum (usually less than 0.2 mm.) for about three hours, the temperature of the bath being raised to 200–250°. During this period little or no distillate collected (provided only a 5% excess of glycol was used). The residue, which was a slightly dark and, at 150°, more or less viscous liquid, was poured from the flask. The amount of this residue corresponded with the theoretical (based on the acid used), and the amount of water actually collected approached the calculated more closely the larger the sample used (60–90%). The esters were purified by crystallization.

* Mostly by direct condensation of the acid with the glycol in different proportions, in one case (ethylene succinate) by combining silver succinate with ethylene bromide (comp. p. 25).

Ethylene malonate was prepared by heating ethyl malonate and glycol in the same fashion. There was some decomposition (evolution of gas) when the residue was heated to 240° *in vacuo*. This residue was a thick sirup which could not be induced to crystallize. It was dissolved in acetone, filtered and heated for several hours at 175–190° in high vacuum. Nothing corresponding to a monomeric ethylene malonate was found on redistilling the distillates from this preparation.

The preparation and properties of some esters not included in the table are described in the Experimental Part of this paper.

Structure of the Esters

The conclusion that these compounds are esters and that they contain the structural unit —R— indicated above follows directly from the method of preparation and is supported by the analytical data and chemical behavior. Comparison of Cols. 4 and 5 in Table I shows that the carbon and hydrogen percentages in general agree with those calculated for —R—. So also did saponification numbers where these were determined. The products of saponification of the esters are the acids and glycols from which they were prepared.

That the esters are not monomeric 7-, 8-, 9-, . . ., 22-membered rings is indicated by their physical properties and by their molecular weights. In Col. 7 are given the molecular weights calculated from the observed boiling point elevations or freezing point lowerings, and in Col. 8 the solvents and methods used. The solvents used in the ebullioscopic determinations include chloroform, ethylene chloride, benzene and acetone. Those used in the cryoscopic determinations include benzene, glacial acetic acid and diphenyl ether.

In these determinations it was necessary to use rather large samples to obtain boiling point or freezing point changes of 0.02 to 0.05°. Judged by their self-consistency, the values obtained with the use of freezing benzene have about the same relative accuracy as is ordinarily attained with simple compounds. With other solvents, and especially in the boiling point determinations, observations were much less consistent. This was due in part at least to changes of surface tension, associated no doubt with molecular size, since there was much foaming. The values obtained by this method are recorded, since for some of the esters they are the only ones available, and for others they clearly indicate that the order of magnitude of the apparent molecular weights is quite independent of the character of the solvent used.

The lowest molecular weight observed for any of the solid esters was 2300 and the highest 5000. The mean of all the determinations is 3200, and for purposes of calculation the molecular weight of each ester has

TABLE I
POLYESTERS

Compound	Formula of structural unit —R—	Atoms in chain of str. unit	Found, % C	Found, % H	Calcd. for —R—, % C	Calcd. for —R—, % H	Anal. calcd. for HO—(R),—R"—OH assuming for M. w. the nearest value to 3000: C, %	H, %	n	M. w.	App. mean M. w. obs.	Solvent and method	M. p., °C.
Ethylene malonate	—C(=O)—CH_2—C(=O)—O—$(CH_2)_2$—O—	7	46.42, 46.46	4.85, 4.84	46.15	4.65					2700, 2500; 3500, 2700, 2300	B. p., AcMe; B. p., CHCl₃	Liquid
Ethylene succinate	—C(=O)—$(CH_2)_2$—C(=O)—O—$(CH_2)_2$—O—	8	49.75, 49.82	5.71, 5.61	49.97	5.58	49.75	5.69	20	2943	3400, 3500, 2500; 2900, 2500, 2300	B. p., CHCl₃; B. p., (ClCH₂)₂	108
Trimethylene succinate	—C(=O)—$(CH_2)_2$—C(=O)—O—$(CH_2)_3$—O—	9	52.95, 52.72	6.45, 6.32	53.13	6.38	52.99	6.48	19	3080	4300, 3500	F. p., AcOH	52
Ethylene adipate	—C(=O)—$(CH_2)_4$—C(=O)—O—$(CH_2)_2$—O—	10	55.23, 55.28	7.08, 7.06	55.78	7.03	55.42	7.08	17	2988	3600, 3900; 3400	B. p., C₆H₆; F. p., AcOH	50
Trimethylene adipate	—C(=O)—$(CH_2)_4$—C(=O)—O—$(CH_2)_3$—O—	11	57.42, 57.21	7.62, 7.50	58.03	7.58	57.76	7.66	16	3054	2700, 2900 2700; 3600, 3300, 3200	F. p., C₆H₆; B. p., C₆H₆	45
Hexamethylene succinate	—C(=O)—$(CH_2)_2$—C(=O)—O—$(CH_2)_6$—O—	12	59.41, 59.32	7.95, 7.92	59.97	8.05	60.00	8.22	14	2920	4300, 2400	F. p., AcOH	57
Hexamethylene adipate	—C(=O)—$(CH_2)_4$—C(=O)—O—$(CH_2)_6$—O—	14	62.67, 62.57	8.82, 8.86	63.10	8.85	63.09	8.96	13	3084	3200, 3500	B. p., C₆H₆	56
Ethylene sebacate	—C(=O)—$(CH_2)_8$—C(=O)—O—$(CH_2)_2$—O—	14	62.37, 62.38	8.96, 8.81	63.10	8.85	62.62	8.86	13	3028	3300	F. p., AcOH	79
Trimethylene sebacate	—C(=O)—$(CH_2)_8$—C(=O)—O—$(CH_2)_3$—O—	15	64.20, 64.62	9.09, 9.53	64.41	9.17	63.98	9.20	12	2982	3100, 3100; 4600, 5000; 3100, 3100	F. p., C₆H₆; B. p., (ClCH₂)₂; F. p., C₆H₆	56
Decamethylene succinate	—C(=O)—$(CH_2)_2$—C(=O)—O—$(CH_2)_{10}$—O—	16	64.67	9.28	65.57	9.45	65.78	9.63	11	2992	3500, 3400, 3200	B. p., C₆H₆	68
Hexamethylene sebacate	—C(=O)—$(CH_2)_8$—C(=O)—O—$(CH_2)_6$—O—	18	66.72, 66.97	9.81, 9.94	67.56	9.92	67.30	10.01	10	2960	2700, 2600	F. p., C₆H₆	67
Decamethylene adipate	—C(=O)—$(CH_2)_4$—C(=O)—O—$(CH_2)_{10}$—O—	18	67.23, 67.01, 67.27	9.82, 9.93, 9.94	67.56	9.92	67.64	10.09	10	3016	3300, 3200	F. p., C₆H₆	77
Decamethylene sebacate	—C(=O)—$(CH_2)_8$—C(=O)—O—$(CH_2)_{10}$—O—	22	70.32, 70.76	10.70, 10.73	70.53	10.67	70.44	10.79	8	2896	2000, 3000	F. p., C₆H₆	74

been assumed to be approximately 3000. Such a molecular weight corresponds with a value of 8 to 20 (depending on the length of the chain of the structural unit) for n in the general formula —(—CO—R′—CO—O—R″—O—)—$_n$. It can scarcely be supposed that the molecules present in a given sample are all identical so far as the values of n are concerned, but their crystallinity and a certain homogeneity in such physical behavior as solubility indicate that the varieties of molecular species present in a given sample probably do not include a very wide range.

The disposition of the valences at the ends of the chains in the above formula cannot as yet be definitely decided. A cyclic structure is rendered improbable by the same considerations which led us to expect that these esters would be polymeric and which have been discussed in the previous paper. Esters prepared by the method indicated above are definitely not acidic, and since the detection of a carboxyl group in a molecule having a weight of 3000 to 5000 should present no difficulties, no carboxyl groups can be present at the ends of the chains. Attempts to detect the presence of hydroxyl groups have not as yet succeeded. Ethylene succinate crystallizes unchanged from acetic anhydride, and is not affected by phenyl or naphthyl isocyanate. Nevertheless we are inclined to assume that hydroxyl groups are present at each end of the chain due to the presence of one more molecule of glycol than acid: HO—R″—O—(—CO—R′—CO—O—R″—O—)$_n$—H. The failure of these groups to react with reagents may be ascribed to the operation of the same factors which set a limit to the size of the molecules formed.

In general the analytical values agree more closely for such a formula than for a cyclic formula. In Col. 6 of Table I are given the carbon and hydrogen percentages calculated for this formula assuming a molecular weight as close as possible to 3000. The means of the deviations between the carbon and hydrogen percentages found and those calculated for the —(—R—)—$_n$ formula are -0.48 and -0.01%; while the deviations calculated for the HO—(—R—)$_n$—R′—OH formula are -0.31 and -0.11%.

Assuming a molecular weight of 3000 the chains, H—[—O—(CH$_2$)$_y$—O—CO—(CH$_2$)$_x$—CO—]$_n$—O—(CH$_2$)$_y$—OH, would contain 170–200 atoms and their lengths would lie between 240 and 280 Å. (1). Their lengths are therefore of the same order of magnitude as that assumed by Meyer (1) for the cellulose chains (100 glucose units per chain = 510 Å.). The molecular cohesions calculated from the data presented by Meyer (2) lie between 250,000 and 300,000 cal. or 3.3 to 4 times the heat of separation of a carbon–carbon bond (75,000 cal.). These molecular cohesions are, however, only about 10% of those calculated for a cellulose chain of 500 Å.

The structure of these esters will be discussed in more detail later in the light of experimental work which is not yet completed.

Properties of the Esters

All the esters of the type $—(—CO—(CH_2)_x—CO—O—(CH_2)_y—O—)—$ with the exception of ethylene malonate are crystalline solids. The property of crystallinity is not very highly developed, but it is quite definitely present (3). This fact is of interest because examples of crystalline highly polymeric substances are not very numerous. As with all crystalline substances of this class, it is not possible to develop large crystals. Ethylene succinate when it separates from a melt or from concentrated solutions (in chloroform) crystallizes in doubly refracting spherolites (microscopic) which grow to what appear to be star-like groups of needles. From dilute alcohol solutions it separates in discrete microscopic needles (4).

Crystallized ethylene succinate and decamethylene sebacate are dusty powders which have a great tendency to become electrified. Some of the intervening members are quite soft and even somewhat sticky. Ethylene succinate solidifies from a melt as a hard, brittle, opaque, white mass. Decamethylene sebacate solidifies to a white, brittle, waxy solid.

The non-crystalline members include ethylene malonate, ethylene fumarate and ethylene, trimethylene, hexamethylene and decamethylene phthalates. The phthalates and the fumarate evidently have less symmetry than the saturated straight-chain purely aliphatic type. The lack of crystallinity of the malonate may be associated with the low melting point of the malonic acid; or it may be due to the fact that considerable decomposition occurred during the process of esterification.

The melting points of the solid esters are not very sharp and they depend somewhat upon the rate of heating. This latter effect is noticed especially with ethylene succinate.

When the crude reaction mixture is dissolved in chloroform and precipitated with benzene, the resulting dusty white powder melts in a capillary tube at about 102°. If, however, the tube is placed in a bath which has already been heated to 96° the sample melts at once. The two melting points are called the slow and instantaneous melting points, respectively, and they are best observed on a bloc Maquenne. Samples which are dusted on the bloc when it is below 96° do not melt until it reaches 102°, but as soon as the bloc reaches 96° samples melt the instant they touch it. Both these temperatures may be changed somewhat by repeated crystallization, but a sample whose melting point has been raised by repeated crystallization may suddenly show the original melting point on further crystallization. By long extraction with boiling absolute alcohol in which it is practically insoluble, ethylene succinate is modified so that the instantaneous and slow melting points coincide at about 107–108°, and from the extracts may be isolated a very small amount of lower-melting material. When such a high-melting sample is again crystallized from a mixture of chloroform and benzene or ether, the melting point usually drops, and one observes again the instantaneous melting point of 96° and the slow melting point 102°. The melting point of such samples may also be raised by long heating just below 100°, and both melting points then gradually approach 107°. When a 96, 102° sample is quickly melted, then allowed to solidify in an agate mortar and powdered, the instantaneous melting point is lowered somewhat, and the slow melting point may be either raised or lowered, depending upon the time during which the molten material is heated.

Attempts to define the melting point more clearly by heating or cooling curves on fairly large samples were unsuccessful (5). Apparently the viscosity of the melt is so great as to make the process of crystallization slow even in the presence of previously formed crystals and under a considerable temperature gradient.

The erratic behavior of the melting points may be associated with the fact that all these esters are hygroscopic, but the absorption of water cannot be the sole cause for this behavior, for samples of ethylene succinate having various melting points were stored over 20% sulfuric acid for ten days and all of them gained considerably in weight without changing in physical appearance or melting point.

Anomalies in melting points are not unknown among compounds of definite constitutions and relatively low molecular weights. One may cite, for example, the fact that sucrose separates from methyl alcohol in crystals melting at 169–170° and from other solvents in crystals melting at 179–180°, and these two forms do not show any detectable chemical differences (6). But the case of ethylene succinate appears to be more complicated and confused than this. Its melting point depends upon its history in a fashion which can as yet be defined only to the following extent—it always rises and approaches 107° as it is, while still in the solid state, heated or extracted with boiling absolute alcohol.

Among the other esters these irregularities were less pronounced. Nevertheless, the melting points are not very characteristic and no attempt was made to crystallize them to constant melting points. Instead they were crystallized two to six times depending upon the color and softness of the sample. The melting points recorded are the highest observed for complete melting and are usually within 5° of the lowest observed for any sample of the same material. The melting range was usually less than 2°. The melting point of the decamethylene ester of a given acid was higher than that of the hexamethylene ester. The melting point of the hexamethylene ester was higher than that of the trimethylene ester, which was in turn lower than that of the ethylene ester. With one exception, the adipic ester of each glycol melted lower than either its succinic or sebacic ester.

All of these esters are, when molten, quite viscous. Those which do not crystallize on cooling become more or less hard, tough and glassy. The use as resins of esters formed by the action of polybasic acids on polyhydric alcohols has been covered by numerous patents (7). The impression seems to prevail that all such esters are resins. Of the esters described in this paper the majority are crystalline. The phthalates which we have prepared are, however, all resinous. Ethylene phthalate is quite tough and moderately hard. Neither this ester nor the trimethylene, hexamethylene nor decamethylene esters of the same acid have been described in the scientific literature. As the length of the alcohol chain increases, these phthalates become progressively softer. Decamethylene phthalate has the consistency of a moderately thick sirup.

None of these esters is volatile. Each of them has been heated to 200° *in vacuo* without showing any tendency to distil. Ethylene succinate heated for three hours at 250° under a pressure of 2 mm. is not changed in properties, and its analytical composition (carbon, hydrogen and saponification number) is not changed. It shows no tendency to distil or to evolve any volatile products when heated to 280° at a pressure of 1 *micron*. At 350° ethylene succinate undergoes complete thermal decomposition, the products being ethylene, acetaldehyde, succinic anhydride, carbon, etc. (8).

All of these esters are insoluble, or nearly so in water, alcohol, petroleum ether and ether (9). The least soluble of the saturated aliphatic esters is ethylene succinate. It is more or less soluble in hot ethyl acetate, acetic acid, acetic anhydride, ethyl succinate and acetone, and it crystallizes from these solvents on cooling. It is insoluble in benzene. The other saturated aliphatic esters with the exception of ethylene malonate are readily soluble in cold benzene and at least moderately soluble in acetone, ethyl acetate and glacial acetic acid. The solutions are noticeably viscous only when fairly concentrated (*e. g.*, 10% or stronger). This fact and the rapidity with which solution occurs lead us to believe that the solutions are true molecular dispersions.

Although none of these esters is soluble in water they are all somewhat hygroscopic. This property is especially pronounced in those polyesters which are not crystalline. The drying of these resins was very difficult and, as the analytical results indicate, was not always successful. Drying to constant weight was complicated by the tendency to foam when heated *in vacuo* (10).

Other Methods of Preparation

The only detailed study of polyesters of the type here described which we have found is reported in a paper by Vorländer (11).

Ethylene succinate was first prepared by Lourenço (12) by heating succinic acid and ethylene glycol to 300° (m. p. about 90°). Subsequently Davidoff (13) prepared Lourenço's ester and identified it with one which he obtained by heating silver succinate with ethylene bromide. Vorländer studied this latter compound in detail and showed that its chemical behavior was in all respects what would be expected of an ethylene ester of succinic acid. He also identified it with Lourenço's ester and with one obtained by the action of succinyl chloride on the disodium derivative of ethylene glycol.

Vorländer found that his ethylene succinates prepared from silver succinate and from succinyl chloride had apparent molecular weights ranging from 265 to 321 in freezing phenol and in freezing acetic acid. He supposed them to be dimeric, and in accordance with this view was able to prepare the same compound from silver succinate and di-(β-chloro-ethyl)-succinate. This method of synthesis evidently merely establishes that the compound was probably not monomeric.

The properties which Vorländer records for ethylene succinate agree in general with those which we have observed. We have found that it is possible to prepare ethylene succinates having, within certain limits, various melting points (and molecular weights) by heating succinic acid and glycol in various proportions. The highest melting (102°) is that described above. It was prepared from acid and excess glycol. Vorländer and other writers on this subject ascribe to ethylene succinate a melting point of 88–90°. We have obtained samples showing this melting point by using the acid and glycol in equivalent amounts; and, by using excess acid, have obtained lower-melting samples. These ethylene succinates differ somewhat in solubility, but they are alike in physical appearance in their lack of volatility and in their viscous character when molten. All of these materials are highly polymeric. We have also prepared ethylene succinate from silver succinate and ethylene bromide according to Vorländer's directions. This reaction does not proceed smoothly, and our product was slightly colored and melted at 75° instead of at 90°. Nevertheless, molecular weight determinations in boiling ethylene chloride gave values ranging from 1400 to 2000. We think, therefore, that Vorländer's molecular weight determinations must be in error; and this conclusion is supported by the fact that the properties which he records and which we have observed are not consistent with so low a molecular weight as 288.

We have also prepared ethylene succinate from ethyl succinate and glycol. It is also highly polymeric. Thus the methods which have been used for the preparation of this compound include four separate and distinct methods commonly used in the preparation of esters. They all lead to products of the expected composition but of high molecular weights. There is not the slightest reason for supposing that the monomeric ethylene succinate should be incapable of existence, or even that it should be unstable, but it still remains unknown. These facts find their explanation in the thesis developed in the previous paper.

Vorländer also prepared ethylene maleate and ethylene fumarate by the silver salt method. He could not obtain any consistent values for the molecular weights of these materials. We have prepared the fumarate from ethyl fumarate and the maleate from maleic anhydride. Our preparations differ from those of Vorländer in several respects. Thus, our maleate was crystalline and our fumarate resinous. The reverse was true for Vorländer's compounds. Neither our analytical values nor his agree well with the calculated. These esters appear to be much more complicated in their behavior than ethylene succinate. They both become completely insoluble on heating.

Experimental Part

Ethylene Phthalate No. 1.—Ethylene glycol 62 g. (1 mole) and phthalic anhydride 74 g. (0.5 mole) were heated together for eight hours at 190° under ordinary pressure and for three hours at 300° under 3 mm. The viscous residue was heated with boiling water for twenty minutes, dissolved in chloroform, filtered and precipitated with ether and then dissolved in acetone, filtered and precipitated with water. It was then dried by heating to 160–170°. The resulting glassy resin was fairly hard when cold, and became softer on heating. All attempts to induce it to crystallize failed. It was neutral: 2 g. required 0.03 cc. of 0.23 N NaOH for alkalinity toward phenolphthalein. It was soluble in chloroform, acetone, ethyl acetate and acetic acid; insoluble in petroleum ether, ether, benzene, alcohol and water.

Anal. Substance dried to constant weight in high vacuum at 70°. Calcd. for $C_{10}H_8O_4$: C, 62.48; H, 4.19; molecular weight, 192; saponification number, 96. Calcd. for $H[O(CH_2)_2OOCC_6H_4CO]_{25}O(CH_2)_2OH = C_{252}H_{206}O_{102}$: C, 62.15; H, 4.28; molecular weight, 4864; saponification number, 97.3. Found: C, 61.86, 61.95; H, 4.29, 4.30; molecular weight by micro boiling point method in ethylene chloride, 4830, 5070, 4680, 4690; saponification number, 95.7.

Ethylene Phthalate No. 2.—This was prepared in the same way as No. 1, but with a 20% excess of phthalic anhydride and was purified in a similar fashion. Appearance and solubility were the same as for No. 1.

Anal. After drying to constant weight in high vacuum at 70°. Found: C, 62.11, 62.07; H, 4.29, 4.33; molecular weight, by method of Menzies and Wright in ethylene chloride, 2940, 2700, 3020; by micro boiling point method in ethylene chloride, 3030, 2930; saponification number, 96.2.

Ethylene Phthalate No. 3.—Prepared by heating diethyl phthalate (0.5 mole) with ethylene glycol (1 mole) in the same fashion and purified as before. Appearance and solubility were the same as for No. 1.

Anal. after drying to constant weight in high vacuum at 70°. Found: C, 62.35, 62.14; H, 4.40, 4.37; molecular weight, by freezing point lowering in diphenyl ether, 2070, 2030; by method of Menzies and Wright in ethylene chloride, 1990, 2100, 2050, 1770; by micro boiling point method in ethylene chloride, 2100, 1870.

Ethylene Phthalate No. 4.—This was prepared by stirring vigorously 19 g. of glycol (added slowly) with 60 g. of phthalyl chloride and 51 g. of dry pyridine in 125 cc. of chloroform at 0–5°. The reaction mixture was washed thoroughly with dilute acid and dilute sodium carbonate and water, and decolorized with Darco. After drying the chloroform solution the ester was precipitated with ether. The yield was 53 g. It resembled the other ethylene phthalates, but its solutions in chloroform were less viscous —0.016 poise for a 20% solution at 27° as compared with 0.027–0.031 poise for the other ethylene phthalates. Its apparent molecular weight was also lower.

Anal. after drying to constant weight in high vacuum at 70°. Found: C, 61.64, 61.64; H, 4.28, 4.30; molecular weight, by method of Menzies and Wright in ethylene chloride, 1550, 1610; saponification number, 99.5, 99.6.

Hydrolysis of Ethylene Phthalate.—Twenty grams of ethylene phthalate was refluxed for sixty-four hours with 60 g. of 48% hydrobromic acid. After neutralization with sodium carbonate, the reaction mixture was steam distilled. From the distillate was isolated 16.7 g. or 86.6% of the calculated amount of ethylene bromide, b. p. 131–134°. The residue on acidification gave 16.3 g. or 93.6% of the calculated amount of phthalic acid. This on conversion to the anhydride melted at 130–131°

Trimethylene Phthalate.—Seventy-four grams (0.5 mole) of phthalic anhydride and 38 g. (0.5 mole) of trimethylene glycol were heated at 250° for two hours under ordinary pressure and under diminished pressure for two hours. The residue was dissolved in benzene, treated with Darco, filtered and precipitated with ether. When cold it was a clear, glassy solid, somewhat softer than ethylene phthalate. It was soluble in chloroform, benzene, acetone, ethyl acetate and acetic acid; slightly soluble in alcohol; insoluble in ether, petroleum ether and water.

Anal. Calcd. for $C_{11}H_{10}O_4$: C, 64.08; H, 4.89; molecular weight, 206. Calcd. for $H[OOCC_6H_4COO(CH_2)_3]_{15}O(CH_2)_3OH = C_{168}H_{158}O_{62}$: C, 63.63; H, 5.05; molecular weight, 3168. Found: C, 63.68, 63.51; H, 5.17, 5.12; molecular weight by micro boiling point method in ethylene chloride, 3180, 3030.

Hexamethylene Phthalate.—Twenty-nine and six-tenths g. of phthalic anhydride and 23.6 g. of hexamethylene glycol were heated to 180–190° under atmospheric pressure for two and one-half hours and then for one and one-half hours at 250° under 5 mm. In addition to the water, some phthalic anhydride collected in the receiver. The residual dark gum was purified by dissolving in benzene, decolorizing with Darco, and precipitating with ether. It formed a clear, light brown, sticky gum. Solubility: solvents are the same as for trimethylene phthalate, but hexamethylene phthalate is more soluble.

Anal. after drying to constant weight in high vacuum at 70°. Calcd. for $C_{14}H_{16}O_4$: C, 67.75; H, 6.50; molecular weight, 248. Calcd. for $H[O(CH_2)_6OOCC_6H_4CO]_7O-(CH_2)_6OH = C_{194}H_{126}O_{30}$: C, 67.35; H, 6.85; molecular weight, 1855. Found: C, 66.74, 66.84; H, 6.75, 6.85; molecular weight by freezing point lowering in benzene, 1700, 1830.

Decamethylene Phthalate.—Seven and four-tenths g. of phthalic anhydride and 9 g. of decamethylene glycol were heated at 190–200° for two hours under atmospheric pressure, and at 210–220° for one and one-half hours at 5 mm. The residue was dissolved in benzene, decolorized with Darco and precipitated by petroleum ether. It was a clear, light brown, thick, sticky sirup. Solubility: solvents for decamethylene phthalate are the same as for hexamethylene phthalate, but the former is more soluble.

Anal. after drying to constant weight in high vacuum at 70°. Calcd. for $C_{18}H_{24}O_4$: C, 71.01; H, 7.95; molecular weight, 304. Calcd. for $H[O(CH_2)_{10}OOCC_6H_4CO]_7O$-$(CH_2)_{10}OH = C_{126}H_{190}O_{30}$: C, 70.80; H, 8.39; mol. wt. 2303. Found: C, 70.66, 70.44; H, 8.21, 8.26; molecular weight by freezing point lowering in benzene, 2250, 2060.

Ethylene Fumarate.—Fifty-seven and three-tenths g. of diethyl fumarate (0.33 mole) and 25 g. of ethylene glycol (0.4 mole) were heated for ten hours in a stream of nitrogen, the temperature being gradually raised from 190 to 230° and the pressure being reduced at the end to 4 mm. The residue weighed 35 g. or 75% of the calculated amount. It was accompanied by some insoluble material from which it was freed by solution in chloroform, filtration and precipitation with ether. It was washed several times with dry ether. It formed a transparent, slightly yellow, moderately tough mass. After drying it became insoluble in the common solvents.

Anal. after drying to constant weight in high vacuum at 70°. Calcd. for $C_6H_6O_4$: C, 50.70; H, 4.22. Found: C, 51.95, 51.89. H, 6.06, 6.12. Molecular weight determinations could not be made because of the lack of solubility after drying.

Ethylene Maleate.—Thirty-two and five-tenths g. of maleic anhydride (0.33 mole) and 18.6 g. (0.30 mole) of glycol were heated at 195–200° for four hours, and then for some time at 210–215° under reduced pressure. The residue (40 g.) was separated from some insoluble material by solution in warm ethylene chloride and filtration. It was precipitated by cold ether. The product separated as an oil but solidified on standing at 5–10° for two hours. It was a white powder. Most of it melted between 88 and 95°. After drying *in vacuo* it had become insoluble in the common solvents including ethylene chloride and it did not melt below 250°.

Anal. after drying to constant weight in high vacuum at 70°. Calcd. for $C_6H_6O_4$: C, 50.70; H, 4.22. Found: C, 49.87, 49.70; H, 4.36, 4.28. Molecular weight determinations could not be made because of the lack of solubility after drying.

For his kind assistance in the analytical work we here express our thanks to Mr. Wendell H. Taylor.

Summary

The following esters have been prepared: ethylene malonate, ethylene succinate, trimethylene succinate, ethylene adipate, trimethylene adipate, hexamethylene succinate, hexamethylene adipate, ethylene sebacate, trimethylene sebacate, decamethylene succinate, hexamethylene sebacate, decamethylene adipate, decamethylene sebacate, ethylene maleate, ethylene fumarate, ethylene phthalate, trimethylene phthalate, hexamethylene phthalate and decamethylene phthalate. Their molecular weights have been determined. They are all highly polymeric. Their properties are described and their structures are discussed.

Bibliography and Remarks

(1) The values C = 1.5 Å. and O = 1.1 Å. are taken from Meyer, *Naturwissenschaften*, **42**, 782 (1928).

(2) Ref. 1, p. 21.

(3) So far as they have been examined in this respect, all these esters give sharp x-ray diffraction patterns.

(4) Incidentally these are the forms in which Hess' trimethylcellulose crystallizes, and the photomicrographs (Figs. 78, 80 and 81) which he presents ("Die Chemie der Zellulose," Leipzig, **1928**, p. 432) for this substance would serve almost perfectly as pictures of ethylene succinate. The crystallinity of this trimethylcellulose therefore provides no guarantee either that it contains only a single molecular species, or that the molecules present are not very large.

(5) Some experiments were kindly made for us by Dr. E. L. Skau with the special apparatus which he has devised for the precise determination of the melting points of pure organic compounds.

(6) Pictet and Vogel, *Helv. Chim. Acta*, **11**, 901 (1928).

(7) See for example U. S. Patents Nos. 1,108,332; 1,091,627; 1,091,628; 1,091,732; 1,108,329; 1,108,330; 1,108,331; 1,642,079; 1,678,105; 1,098,776; 1,098,777; 1,424,137; 1,413,144; 1,413,145; 1,667,199; 1,667,200; 1,119,592; 1,141,944; 1,663,183.

(8) Tilitschejew, *J. Russ. Phys. Chem. Soc.*, **57**, 143 (1925).

(9) It is interesting to note that Freudenberg and Braun's trimethylcellulose, like ethylene succinate, is insoluble in ether and carbon tetrachloride, but quite soluble in chloroform [*Ann.*, **460**, 288 (1928)].

(10) It is interesting to observe that inulin, a polymeric substance of a different type, but probably of the same degree of molecular complexity as the esters here described is also quite hygroscopic. *Cf.* Drew and Haworth, *J. Chem. Soc.*, 2690 (1928).

(11) Vorländer, *Ann.*, **280**, 167 (1894). See also Bischoff, *Ber.*, **27**, 2940 (1894); **40**, 2779, 2803 (1907). Glycol esters of adipic acid are referred to in German patent 318,222, *Chem. Zentr.*, II, 536 (1920).

(12) Lourenço, *Ann. chim. phys.*, 293 (1863).

(13) Davidoff, *Ber.*, **19**, 406 (1886).

III. Glycol Esters of Carbonic Acid*

This paper describes different glycol esters of carbonic acid. The aim is to check whether condensations which can lead to 5- and 6-rings remain intramolecular, while such as can give only larger rings lead to C-polymers. In fact it was shown that as long as 5- or 6-rings can be formed (ethylene carbonate and trimethylene carbonate) well crystallized, low molecular compounds, with molecular weights of about 90 and 110, are produced; as soon as only larger rings can be formed C-polymers, with molecular weights up to about 3000, result).[†]

Trimethylene carbonate

$$O=C\diagup_{O-CH_2}^{O-CH_2}\diagdown CH_2$$

* W. H. Carothers and F. J. van Natta; *Journ. Am. Chem. Soc.* 52, 314–26 (1930); Contribution No. 19 from the Experimental Station of E. I. du Pont de Nemours and Co.

Received July 24, 1929.   Published January 8, 1930.

[†] Compare the thesis developed on pages 10 and 12.

which contains a 6-ring can be obtained in both forms: as a monomeric diester with a molecular weight of 104 and as a polymer with a polymerization degree between 38 and 45. This latter is apparently formed by an A-polymerization of the monomeric trimethylene carbonate.

The preparation and the properties of the following substances are described and discussed:

trimethylene carbonate	*decamethylene carbonate*
tetramethylene carbonate	*diethylene carbonate*
pentamethylene carbonate	*p-xylylene carbonate*
hexamethylene carbonate	

The glycol esters of dibasic acids described in a previous paper (1) are all highly polymeric. This was expected from the generalization (2) that bifunctional reactions which, if intramolecular, could lead only to larger-than-6 rings proceed intermolecularly. It seemed desirable to examine an homologous series of similar compounds in which the length of the structural unit might be as short as 5 or 6 atoms, since in these cases reaction should be intramolecular and the products monomeric, and in the longer chains of the same series reaction should be intermolecular and the products polymeric.

Such a series is found in the glycol esters of carbonic acid. The first member of this series, ethylene carbonate, $O=C\overset{O-CH_2}{\underset{O-CH_2}{\big<}}\big|$, has long been known (3). It is a crystalline solid which boils at 238° and it is definitely established to be the monomeric 5-ring by both cryoscopic and vapor density data (4).

We have now prepared the trimethylene, tetramethylene, hexamethylene, decamethylene, diethylene and *p*-xylylene esters of carbonic acid. The properties of these esters, together with the apparent mean molecular weights determined by cryoscopic and ebullioscopic methods, are indicated in Table I. The analytical compositions of all these esters correspond with the formulas of their structural units $-O-(CH_2)_n-CO-$, but where the length of the chain of this unit is 5 or 6, only one such unit is present in a molecule of the ester. On the other hand, where the length of the chain of the structural unit is 7, 8, 9 or 13, eight to twenty-two structural units are present in each molecule. The method of preparation and the analytical compositions of the polymeric esters indicate a structure which may be represented by the general formula $-O-(CH_2)_n-O-CO-O-$ $(CH_2)_n-O-CO-O-(CH_2)_n-O-CO-O-(CH_2)_n-O-CO-$, etc. To

TABLE

GLYCOL ESTERS OF CARBONIC ACID

Names of carbonate	Formula of structural unit	No. of atoms in chain of structural unit	Anal. calcd. for structural unit	Analysis found,[a]	Mol. wt. obs.	Method	Av. no. of structural units per molecule	Physical properties
Ethylene	$-O(CH_2)_2-O-CO-$	5	C 40.91 H 4.54	41.07[b] 4.88	90 93[b] 76	F. p., C₆H₆OH[b] Vapor density	1	M. p. 39%[b] B. p. 238°
Trimethylene (monomeric)	$-O(CH_2)_3-O-CO-$	6	C 47.06 H 5.92	48.97 47.14 5.96 5.98	105 114 112 114	F. p. C₆H₆ B. p. C₆H₆	1	Colorless needles M. p. 47–8° B. p. 135° at 4 mm.
Trimethylene (polymeric)	$-O(CH_2)_3-O-CO-$	6	C 47.06 H 5.92	47.06 47.08 6.01 6.19	4670 3880	B. p. C₆H₆	38–45	Glass gradually changes to powder
Tetramethylene	$-O(CH_2)_4-O-CO-$	7	C 51.71 H 6.94	52.18 52.32 7.05 7.06	1450 1400 1350 1310 1290 1370	B. p. C₆H₆ F. p. C₆H₆	11–12	Powder M. p. 59°
Pentamethylene	$-O(CH_2)_5-O-CO-$	8	C 55.96 H 7.75	55.29 55.47 7.90 7.83	2840 2830 2550	B. p. C₆H₆	20–22	Powder M. p. 44–6°
Hexamethylene	$-O(CH_2)_6-O-CO-$	9	C 58.33 H 8.33	58.58 58.54 8.46 8.21	2740 2970 2610	B. p. C₆H₆	18–21	Horny and elastic M. p. 55–60°
Decamethylene	$-O(CH_2)_{10}-O-CO-$	13	C 65.96 H 10.07	65.80 66.04 10.18 10.10	1880 1800 1810 1640 1770 1830	B. p. C₆H₆ F. p. C₆H₆	8–10	Powder M. p. 55°
Diethylene	$-O(CH_2)_2-O-(CH_2)_2-O-CO-$	8	C 45.44 H 6.11	45.53 45.33 6.30 6.38	1540 1550	B. p. C₆H₆	12	Sirup
p-Xylylene (soluble)	$-O\cdot CH_2C_6H_4CH_2-O-CO-$	9	C 65.84 H 4.91	65.81 66.00 5.60 5.63	840 780 810	B. p. C₂H₄Cl₂	5	Powder M. p. 137–8°
p-Xylylene (insoluble)	$-O\cdot CH_2C_6H_4CH_2-O-CO-$	9	C 65.84 H 4.91	65.02 65.03 5.29 5.19	1010 1030	M. p. camphor	6	Powder M. p. 177–85°

[a] The analyses were carried out by the Pregl micro method.

[b] Vorländer, *Ann.*, **280**, 187 (1894).

complete this formula, it is necessary to discover whether the valences at the ends of the chains are saturated mutually with the formation of a ring, or are saturated by univalent groups to give open chains. The 7-, 8-, 9- and 13-membered rings which might be formed in this reaction are not found, and there is no reason to suppose that much larger rings would be formed more readily. For some polyesters similar to those described here we have direct experimental proof of the open-chain structure. It seems quite certain, therefore, that these polycarbonates are also open chains. From the method of preparation it follows that the ends of the chains must bear hydroxyl groups (from an extra molecule of glycol) or carbethoxy groups (from an extra molecule of ethyl carbonate). In this connection it is interesting to observe that when an excess of ethyl carbonate was used in the preparation of hexamethylene carbonate, pure dicarbethoxyhexane, C_2H_5O—CO—$O(CH_2)_6O$—CO—OC_2H_5, was isolated, and an oil which, judging by its composition, was composed chiefly of C_2H_5-O—CO—$O(CH_2)_6O$—CO—$O(CH_2)_6O$—CO—$O(CH_2)_6O$—CO—OC_2H_5.

Properties of the Polycarbonates.—The physical properties of these polycarbonates again illustrate the fact that neither melting points nor solubilities offer any general criteria of molecular size.

In this connection trimethylene carbonate is of especial interest since it has been obtained in both the monomeric form and a form in which the degree of polymerization is 38–45. The monomeric form is hygroscopic and is soluble in water, benzene and alcohol, but only slightly soluble in ether and ligroin. The polymeric form is not soluble in water and alcohol, but is still soluble in benzene. Solubility here diminishes with considerable increase in molecular size, but it does not disappear. Practically all the polymeric esters described in this and the previous paper are insoluble in water and alcohol, but soluble in chloroform and somewhat soluble in acetone. Those polyesters in which the structural units contain polymethylene chains $(CH_2)_x$, in which x is greater than 3–5, show great solubility in benzene.

Polyesters of high molecular weight may be either liquid (diethylene carbonate, ethylene malonate (1), decamethylene phthalate (1)) or solids. Most of the solid polyesters are *crystalline*. These crystalline polyesters differ from analogously constituted crystalline esters of low molecular weight in that the crystals are always microscopic. In some cases it is not possible to decide even by microscopic examination whether these solid polymers are crystalline, but x-ray examination always shows definite crystallinity. Thus hexamethylene carbonate was an opaque, tough, horny material with considerable elasticity. Nevertheless, it had a fairly definite melting point and it gave a quite sharp x-ray diffraction pattern (Fig. 3).

The following generalizations concerning the influence of the structure of the structural units of polyesters on their physical properties can now be offered. As the lengths of the polymethylene chains, $(CH_2)_x$, which separate the ester groups increase, solubility in organic solvents increases and viscosity of the molten ester diminishes. This would be expected from the fact that carbonyl groups contribute much more heavily to intermolecular association forces than do methylene groups. With one exception (ethylene malonate (1)) all of the linear polyesters in which the ester groups are separated only by polymethylene chains, $(CH_2)_x$, are solids. Less symmetrical linear polyesters such as the alkylene phthalates are resins (transparent glasses or sirups). The solid polyesters when melted and then cooled yield opaque masses. These may be brittle and porcelain-like or soft and waxy. The waxy quality increases with the lengths of the polymethylene chains just as it does in the glycols and the acids from which the polyesters are derived.

The problem of the more precise expression of the relationship between the structure and the properties of high polymers is complicated by the fact that some of the properties of this class of substances which are of the greatest practical importance and which distinguish them most sharply from simple compounds cannot be accurately measured and indeed are not precisely defined. Examples of such properties are toughness and elasticity. We have found these two properties in only one of the polyesters which we have prepared. This polyester is hexamethylene carbonate. Like pentamethylene and decamethylene carbonates, this material is crystalline; it has a fairly definite melting point (55–60°) and it gives a sharp x-ray diffraction pattern (see Fig. 3). But the higher and lower members of this series separate from solution as powders, while hexamethylene carbonate separates in the form of rubbery flakes. It is not yet certain that this peculiar combination of properties is inherently associated with the molecular structure of this particular ester (i. e., with the linear union of a large number of the structural units —CO—O—$(CH_2)_6$—O—) rather than with some accidental features of its formation which may have been absent in the preparation of other members of the series, but the important problem of the relationship between chemical or physical structure and rubber-like properties is so poorly provided with material suitable for inductive argument that the discovery of a new synthetic and analytically homogeneous material exhibiting these properties is of some significance. So far as we are aware there is nothing in current theories which would lead one to expect that polymeric hexamethylene carbonate would be elastic.

As indicated above, high polymers, like materials of low molecular weight, may show great variety in certain physical properties—they may be either liquids or high-melting solids; they may show slight or very great solubility. The following properties, however, are inherently associated with the highly polymeric state.

(1) **Lack of Volatility.**—None of the polyesters which we have prepared can be volatilized as such even at very low pressures and high temperatures. Volatility diminishes continuously with increase in molecular size due to the increase in intermolecular forces. It is probably true in general that compounds whose molecular cohesions lie above 75,000 cal. (the heat of separation of a carbon–carbon bond) cannot be distilled. The calculated molecular cohesion (about 250,000 cal.) (5) of our polyesters lies far above this value.

(2) **Viscosity in Liquid State.**—This would be expected to increase with the intermolecular forces and so with molecular size. All of the polyesters which we have studied are extremely viscous in the molten state.

(3) **Micro-crystallinity in the Solid State.**—This has been referred to above. In this connection it is interesting to observe that considerable difficulty was experienced in preparing and keeping crystals of monomeric trimethylene carbonate sufficiently small to yield a powder diagram in an x-ray diffraction experiment. On the other hand, it has not been possible to prepare macroscopic crystals of any polymeric ester.

Trimethylene Carbonate.—Among all the esters formed from bifunctional reactions which we have studied, trimethylene carbonate and ethylene oxalate (6) present the peculiar property of exhibiting reversible transformation between a monomeric and a polymeric form. These monomeric esters contain 6-membered rings. The polymerization of trimethylene carbonate is brought about by heating and is catalyzed by a trace of potassium carbonate. The polymer is a perfectly colorless, transparent glass, which on long standing becomes opaque (crystallization). X-ray diffraction patterns of the monomeric and polymeric forms are shown in Figs. 1 and 2. The polymer has the same apparent analytical composition as the monomer. Its degree of polymerization as measured by molecular weight determinations in boiling benzene is 38–45. On heating *in vacuo*, it distils and the distillate is found to be the monomeric form. Examination of the literature shows that the property of undergoing reversible polymerization is common to many 6-rings containing ester linkages. Thus, the lactones of δ-hydroxyvaleric acid and of the hydroxyethyl ether of glycolic acid polymerize on heating (7) and so does glycolide (8). The action of heat on lactic acid leads to polylactyl lactic acids, and these on further heating are converted to the 6-ring lactide (9).

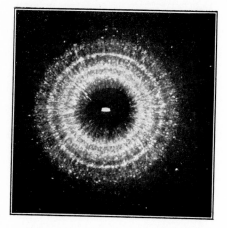

Fig. 1.—Monomeric trimethylene carbonate (Mo radiation). The intensity of the numerous outer rings is weak and these do not appear in the reproductions.

The unique position occupied in this respect by 6-rings containing an ester linkage is indicated by the following facts. No record of the polymerization of a γ-lactone (5-ring) is found. Our own attempts to polymerize ethylene carbonate (5-ring) were unsuccessful. The polyesters which we have prepared and in which the length of the chain of the structural unit is greater than 7 are not depolymerized on heating. The monomeric form of none of these esters is known.

In an attempt to force the depolymerization of tetramethylene carbonate, it was heated above 300° at 0.9 mm. This caused it to decompose with the evolution of considerable gas. From the distillate was isolated a very small amount (about 1% of the calculated) of a crystalline solid having the analytical composition of tetramethylene carbonate. Molecular weight determinations indicated that it

$$\overline{COO(CH_2)_4OCOO(CH_2)_4O}$$

is a dimer: $\overline{COO(CH_2)_4OCOO(CH_2)_4O}$. The absence of a monomer was not definitely established, but it could only have been present in very small amount. Thus, the behavior of polymeric tetramethylene carbonate is very different from that of its next lower homolog.

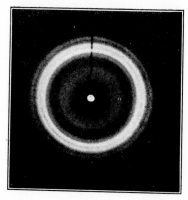

Fig. 2.—Polymeric trimethylene carbonate (Cu radiation).

In the self-esters of some of the higher ω-hydroxy fatty acids, $HO(CH_2)_xCOOH$, both the monomeric lactones and the polyesters are known (10). The polyesters, however, are not depolymerized on heating, and the polyesters, not the lactones, are formed on heating the acids.

These facts, together with others which will be discussed later, indicate clearly that polyesters formed by bifunctional reactions in which the length of the structural unit is greater than 6 atoms are the direct result of intermolecular condensation (C polymerization) (2). The formation of polymeric trimethylene carbonate from its monomer is obviously A polymerization, and the same is true of the polymerization of lactides and of δ-lactones.

A fairly satisfactory explanation of these peculiarities may be found in the Mohr theory (11), which has proved adequate to explain all of the previously observed influences of structural features on the course of bifunctional reactions (2). In accordance with the terms of this theory, 5-rings will be readily formed and very stable since they are free from strain. The formation of seven-membered and larger rings by bifunctional reactions is very improbable, but such rings once they are formed will be quite stable, since they too are practically free from strain. Six-rings will be readily formed, but they present the possibility of strains which are absent or present only to a diminished degree in larger rings. Thus, the Mohr theory predicts the possible existence of two cyclohexanes (*cis* and *trans*) but only one is known. However, where structural features would preclude the possibility of the interconversion of these two forms, as in decalin, both forms are known. It is concluded, therefore, that in simple 6-rings, such as cyclohexane, equilibrium with reversible interconversion of the two forms exists. At every such interconversion the molecule must pass through a position of considerable strain. This picture presents the features necessary to rationalize the peculiar position of 6-membered ester rings. A polyester in which the recurring structural unit is a chain of six atoms would be readily converted into the corresponding monomeric 6-ring by a process of ester interchange, as indicated below:

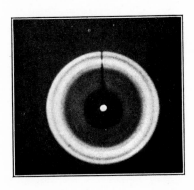

Fig. 3.—Hexamethylene carbonate (Cu radiation).

$$-O-(C)_4-C \overset{O}{\underset{}{\diagup}} ---O---(C)_4-C \overset{O}{\underset{}{\diagup}} ---O---(C)_4-C \overset{O}{\underset{}{\diagup}} ---O---(C_4)---C \overset{O}{\underset{}{\diagup}} ---etc.$$

If the chain of the structural unit were longer than 6 atoms, this reaction would be less probable for the same reason that the higher ω-hydroxy fatty acids do not yield lactones, *i. e.*, the number of points of rotation in the chain between carbonyl and alcoholic oxygen are so numerous that the probability of close intramolecular approach of these groups is very low.

The polymerization of the 6-ring esters seems also to involve ester interchange. This process may involve the coalescence of two such rings, as indicated below

The resulting 12-ring might then coalesce with another six-ring, and so on, with the formation of very large rings. It is possible also that traces of water may intervene at some stage in the process and that the large molecules produced are open rather than closed chains. In any event the peculiar mobility of the 6-ring esters may be ascribed to the fact that these rings are subject to strains, and that the strains may be relieved by an ester interchange resulting in an enlargement of the molecule.

The precise mechanism of the polymerization of the 6-membered ester rings shares to a certain extent the obscurity which is common to most cases of A polymerization, but further attention is being devoted to this problem and the study is being extended to the corresponding amides. In this connection the analogy which exists between lactides and diketopiperazines on the one hand, and polyesters and polypeptides on the other hand, is of especial interest because of its possible relationship to the structure of proteins.

Dimeric Tetramethylene Carbonate.—The dimeric tetramethylene carbonate referred to above deserves special mention. There can be little doubt that it is a 14-membered cyclic ester, and as such it represents a class of compounds of which few members are known. Other dimeric cyclic esters have been obtained and will be described in later papers.

Previous Work on the Carbonates of Dihydric Alcohols.—Reference to ethylene carbonate has already been made. Carbonates of the three dihydroxybenzenes were prepared by Bischoff and v. Hedenström (12).

The carbonate of catechol is apparently monomeric since it can be distilled. The *m*-phenylene carbonate is a non-volatile, brown, glassy material of uncertain melting point (197–202°) and low solubility, and the corresponding para compound shows similar properties. These two compounds are evidently polymeric.

Experimental Part

Preparation of Carbonates.—The carbonates here described were all prepared by ester interchange (alcoholysis) between the glycol and ethyl carbonate. This reaction proceeds very smoothly in the presence of an alkaline catalyst and may be forced to completion; the process need not be modified to take into account the solubility of the resulting ester, as is necessary when phosgene and the glycol are used as starting materials.

Trimethylene Carbonate.—A mixture of 60.8 g. (0.8 mole) of trimethylene glycol, 114 g. (16% excess) of ethyl carbonate and a small cube of sodium was warmed in a Claisen flask until the sodium had completely dissolved. The flask was then immersed in an oil-bath at 130°. During three hours the temperature was allowed to rise to 170°. The evolved alcohol condensed and collected weighed 69.1 g. or 94% of the calculated.

The oily residue was dissolved in benzene, washed twice with 20 cc. portions of water and dried over calcium chloride. After removal of the solvent, the residue was subjected to vacuum distillation. A small initial fraction, b. p. 120–135° at 20 mm., was unchanged glycol. The pure trimethylene carbonate then distilled fairly constantly; b. p. 160–165° at 6 mm.; 135° at 4 mm., 105° at 0.2 mm.; weight 53 g., or 65% of the calculated. It completely crystallized in the receiver; recrystallization from absolute ether produced colorless needles, m. p. 47–48°. This hygroscopic ester is very soluble in benzene, alcohol and water and slightly soluble in ether and ligroin. It decomposes on distillation at ordinary pressure. This ester gave a sharp x-ray powder diagram (Fig. 1) slightly scattered due to the difficulty of obtaining sufficiently small crystals. For analysis, see Table I.

Polymerization of Trimethylene Carbonate.—In the distillation of trimethylene carbonate it was frequently observed that the distilling residue was very thick and viscous while the warm distillate was comparatively thin and mobile. The distillation of 53 g. of trimethylene carbonate was interrupted while still incomplete. The distillate was monomeric trimethylene carbonate, m. p. 48°. The undistilled residue (15.6 g.) was very viscous even when hot and it cooled to a colorless sticky resin. Molecular weight determinations showed it to be polymeric; molecular weight in boiling benzene, found: 2390, 2320.

This residue was distilled at 10 mm. It yielded 13.6 g. of monomeric trimethylene carbonate (observed b. p. 150–190°) which completely crystallized on cooling; mol. wt., calcd. for monomeric trimethylene carbonate: 102. Found: (in boiling benzene) 115, 118.

The tarry residue (1.7 g.) remaining in the flask was insoluble in the common organic solvents.

A trace (0.1% of finely powdered anhydrous potassium carbonate was added to a sample of the pure crystalline monomeric ester and the mixture was heated at 130°.

After shaking and heating for ten minutes the mixture suddenly became very viscous and a slight amount of gas was evolved. After five hours of heating the colorless product formed a clear glassy mass on cooling; mol. wt., found: (in boiling benzene) 4670, 3880. For analysis see Table I. After standing for a week, this glassy polymer became opaque and x-ray examination showed it to be crystalline (Fig. 2).

Under similar conditions (temp. 130°; time of reaction, four hours) ethylene carbonate did not polymerize.

When polymeric trimethylene carbonate was heated to 210° at ordinary pressure, it was decomposed. Allyl alcohol was identified as one of the products of this reaction by its boiling point and by the melting point of its phenylurethan. This fact indicated decomposition according to the scheme

$$-O-CH_2-CH_2-CH_2-O-\overset{\overset{\displaystyle O}{\|}}{C}- \longrightarrow CH_2{=}CH-CH_2OH + CO_2$$

The allyl alcohol isolated accounted for only about 25% of the ester decomposed. Higher boiling unsaturated materials present in the products of this reaction were not identified.

Tetramethylene Carbonate.—This was prepared from 9.0 g. of tetramethylene glycol, to which a small piece (2 mm.[3]) of sodium had been added and 11.8 g. of ethyl carbonate. The mixture was heated to 120° and then the temperature was allowed gradually to rise to 160° during seven hours. The distillate was poured back several times to insure complete reaction of the ethyl carbonate. From the distillate was isolated 5.7 g. or 62% of the calculated amount of ethyl alcohol.

The non-volatile reaction product was dissolved in benzene and the solution washed with water, dilute hydrochloric acid and water. It was dried with calcium chloride and the solvent was removed by distillation. On heating the residue *in vacuo* there was obtained a very small amount of distillate boiling at 100–110° at 1 mm. This was chiefly unchanged tetramethylene glycol since it gave a di-*p*-nitrobenzoate, m. p. 175°. No further distillation could be effected when the bath was heated to 250° and the pressure reduced to 0.2 mm.

The residue was purified by dissolving it in chloroform and precipitating it with absolute alcohol while cold. The oily precipitate soon crystallized to a cream-colored powder; weight 6.3 g. or 54% of the calculated; m. p. 55–59°; very soluble in cold benzene, chloroform, acetone and acetic acid; insoluble in ether, alcohol and petroleum ether. It gave a sharp x-ray diffraction pattern. Before analysis it was dried for four days at 80° in high vacuum. For analytical data see Table I.

Di-*p*-nitrobenzoate of Tetramethylene Glycol.—Prepared from the glycol and the acid chloride in pyridine; crystallized from boiling acetic acid; m. p. 175°.

Anal. Calcd. for $C_{18}H_{16}O_nN_2$: C, 55.67; H, 4.12. Found: C, 56.19, 56.00; H, 4.31, 4.14.

Thermal Decomposition of Tetramethylene Carbonate.—An attempt was made to bring about the depolymerization of tetramethylene carbonate by heating it to a high temperature *in vacuo*. The tetramethylene carbonate was prepared from 9.0 g. of glycol and 11.8 g. of ethyl carbonate in the same manner as described above. It was heated at 0.9 mm. in a small Claisen flask by means of a metal bath. Very slight distillation occurred as the temperature of the bath was raised from 270 to 300°. Between 300 and 325° evolution of gas occurred and the pressure increased. From the distillate were isolated 0.1 g. of crystalline solid and 2.8 g. of oil.   The residue remaining in the distilling flask weighed 3 g. and was apparently identical with the polymeric tetramethylene carbonate described above; it melted at 55° and had the same physical appearance and solubility behavior.

The crystalline distillate separated from alcohol in minute prisms melting at 175–176°.   Analysis and molecular weight determinations showed it to be dimeric tetra-

methylene carbonate, $\overline{CO—O(CH_2)_4O—CO—O(CH_2)_4O}$.

Anal.   Calcd. for $(C_5H_8O_3)_2$: C, 51.71; H, 6.94; mol. wt., 232.   Found: C, 51.77; 51.80; H, 6.95; 7.02; mol. wt., in boiling ethylene chloride, 194, 231; mol. wt., in freezing benzene, 204.

The liquid distillate had a pungent mint-like odor and readily absorbed bromine in acetic acid solution.   It is a mixture and no chemical individuals have as yet been isolated from it.

Pentamethylene Carbonate.—This was prepared from 5.9 g. of ethyl carbonate and 5.2 g. of pentamethylene glycol to which a small amount of sodium had been added. The mixture was heated for twelve hours at 120–160°; 76% of the calculated amount of alcohol was found in the distillate.   The residue after it had been freed from sodium was heated at 250° under 0.15 mm.   The distillate (1.1 g.) boiled at 110–130° and consisted chiefly of unchanged glycol; di-*p*-nitrobenzoate, m. p., 104–105°.   The non-volatile sirupy residue crystallized on standing to a hard waxy material; weight, 4.1 g. or 63% of the theoretical.   It was purified by precipitation with absolute alcohol from a cold chloroform solution as a granular and slightly colored powder; m. p., 44–46°; very soluble in benzene, chloroform, acetone and acetic acid; insoluble in ether, alcohol and petroleum ether.   Before analysis it was dried to constant weight in high *vacuo*.   For analysis see Table I.

Di-*p*-nitrobenzoate of Pentamethylene Glycol.—From the glycol and the acid chloride in pyridine; crystallized from a mixture of benzene and alcohol; m. p., 104–105°.

Anal.   Calcd. for $C_{19}H_{18}O_8N_2$: C, 56.71; H, 4.51.   Found: C, 56.95, 57.02; H, 4.59, 4.69.

Hexamethylene Carbonate.—This was prepared from 12 g. of ethyl carbonate and 12 g. of hexamethylene glycol to which a small piece of sodium had been added.   The mixture was heated from 130 to 170° during two hours; 86% of the calculated amount of alcohol was found in the distillate.   The residue after the removal of the sodium was subjected to distillation in high vacuum.   A very small amount of distillate was found to consist of unchanged glycol.   The residue, which amounted to 10 g. or 67% of the calculated, solidified on cooling to a light colored, horny, tough mass.   It was soluble in benzene, acetone and chloroform; insoluble in ether and alcohol; m. p. 55–60°.   A sharply defined x-ray diffraction pattern (Fig. 3) showed it to be crystalline.   For analysis see Table I.

Dicarbethoxyhexane.—In an experiment similar to the above, ethyl carbonate and glycol were used in the ratio of 2 moles to 1 (24 g. of ester and 12 g. of glycol).   The calculated amount (9.2 g.) of alcohol was collected.   The residue after removal of sodium was subjected to vacuum distillation.   It yielded 5.5 g. of distillate, b. p. 130–140° at 0.8 mm.   The residue could not be distilled, and neither the distillate nor the residue could be induced to crystallize.   No ethyl carbonate was found in the distillate.   The distillate was dicarbethoxyhexane; n_D^{20} 1.4310; d_{20}^{20} 1.065; d_{20}^{25} 1.056.

Anal. Calcd. for $C_{12}H_{22}O_6$: C, 54.94; H, 8.41; mol. wt., 262. Found: C, 55.00; H, 8.41; mol. wt. in boiling benzene, 236, 240, 245.

The oily residue was very soluble in alcohol and ether. Its analytical composition corresponded with the formula C_2H_5O—CO—$O(CH_2)_6O$—CO—$O(CH_2)_6O$—CO—O-$(CH_2)_6O$—CO—OC_2H_5.

Anal. Calcd. for $C_{26}H_{46}O_{12}$: C, 56.73; H, 8.36; CO_2 on hydrolysis, 33.1%; mol. wt., 532. Found: C, 56.77, 57.00; H, 8.41, 8.53; CO_2, 34.15; mol. wt. in boiling benzene, 573, 549, 528. The CO_2 was determined by saponifying with alcoholic sodium hydroxide and weighing the sodium carbonate formed.

Carbonate of Diethylene Glycol.—This was prepared in 43% yield by the method used in the preparation of the other carbonates. It was a light colored sirup which could not be induced to crystallize; insoluble in alcohol and ether, quite soluble in acetone and benzene, very soluble in chloroform and hot ethyl acetate. On standing it appeared to decompose to some extent into acetaldehyde and carbon dioxide and for this reason it could not be dried to constant weight. For analysis see Table I.

Decamethylene Carbonate.—This was prepared in 75% yield by the method used for the preparation of the other carbonates. It was soluble in benzene and chloroform but insoluble in alcohol. It was purified by precipitation from chloroform with alcohol in the cold. The oily product gradually solidified to a cream-colored powder; m. p. 55°; very soluble in chloroform, slightly soluble in ether, benzene, acetone and acetic acid; insoluble in alcohol and petroleum ether. This powder gave a sharply defined x-ray diffraction pattern. Before analysis it was dried to constant weight in high vacuum at 90°. For analysis see Table I.

p-**Xylylene Carbonate.**—This was prepared from *p*-xylylene glycol and ethyl carbonate as in the preparation of the other carbonates. The residue after completion of the ester interchange was insoluble in hot benzene, absolute alcohol, chloroform and carbon tetrachloride; slightly soluble in acetic acid. It dissolved more or less completely in ethylene chloride, anisole and dioxane. It was thoroughly triturated with water and with cold alcohol to remove sodium and excess glycol and ethyl carbonate. The amount of the white solid remaining corresponded to 82% of the calculated. It was separated into two fractions by extraction with ethylene chloride.

(a) **Soluble Fraction.**—This was precipitated with ether from ethylene chloride in the form of white flocks; m. p. 137–138°. For analysis see Table I.

(b) **Fraction Insoluble in Ethylene Chloride.**—This was insoluble in the common organic solvents; m. p. 177–185° (rather indefinite). For analysis see Table I.

Attempted Preparation of Methylene Carbonate.—Silver carbonate (81 g.) was heated with methylene bromide (51 g.) in dry toluene solution. Formaldehyde and carbon dioxide were formed and free silver was produced. From the reaction mixture there was isolated only a small amount of oil with a sweet odor—probably methylene carbonate. This liberated formaldehyde on heating: $CH_2CO_3 \rightarrow H_2CO + CO_2$.

We are indebted to Dr. A. W. Kenney and Mr. Henry Aughey for the x-ray diffraction pictures, to Mr. W. H. Taylor for many molecular-weight determinations and to Mr. G. A. Jones for determinations of carbon and hydrogen.

Summary

The following compounds have been prepared by the action of the appropriate glycols on ethyl carbonate: trimethylene carbonate, tetramethylene carbonate, pentamethylene carbonate, hexamethylene carbonate, decamethylene carbonate, diethylene carbonate and p-xylylene carbonate. Their properties are described. In accordance with a generalization already set forth, ethylene carbonate and trimethylene carbonate are monomeric and the other carbonates are polymeric. Trimethylene carbonate undergoes reversible A polymerization. A stable dimeric form of tetramethylene carbonate has been prepared by thermal decomposition of its usual polymeric form. Hexamethylene carbonate is tough and elastic.

Bibliography and Remarks

(1) Carothers and Arvin, *Journ. Am. Chem. Soc.*, **51**, 2560 (1929).

(2) Carothers, *ibid.*, **51**, 2548 (1929).

(3) Nemirowski, *J. prakt. Chem.*, [2] **28**, 439 (1883); *Chem. Zentr.*, 23 (1884).

(4) Vorländer, *Ann.*, **280**, 186 (1894).

(5) Meyer and Mark, *Z. angew. Chem.*, **41**, 943 (1928).

(6) See Bischoff, *Ber.*, **40**, 2803 (1907). Our own studies of alkylene oxalates will be described later.

(7) Hollo, *Ber.*, **61**, 895 (1928).

(8) Bischoff and Walden, *Ann.*, **279**, 45 (1894).

(9) Dietzel and Krug, *Ber.*, **58**, 1307 (1925).

(10) Ruzicka and Stoll, *Helv. Chim. Acta*, 11, 1159 (1928); Lycan and Adams, *Journ. Am. Chem. Soc.*, **51**, 625 (1929); Chuit and Hausser, *Helv. Chim. Acta*, **12**, 463 (1929); Lycan and Adams, *Journ. Am. Chem. Soc.*, **51**, 3450 (1929).

(11) Mohr, *J. prakt. Chem.*, **98**, 348 (1918).

(12) Bischoff and v. Hedenström, *Ber.*, **35**, 3431 (1902).

IV.   Ethylene Succinates*

This contribution contains a more thorough investigation of ethylene succinate, its formation, structure and bearing on the association theory of high polymers.

Neutral ethylene succinates are prepared by heating succinic acid with excess glycol at 180° until the distillation of water stops: they are chains of about 3000 m. w.

Acidic ethylene succinates are obtained if an excess of succinic acid is applied. The reactants are heated to 180° until no more water is evolved and then the temperature is raised to 200–240° for one to five hours to make

* W. H. Carothers and G. L. Dorough; *Journ. Am. Chem. Soc.*, 52, 711–21 (1930); Contribution No. 20 from the Experimental Station of E. I. du Pont de Nemours and Co.

Received August 7, 1929.   Published February 6, 1930.

reaction as complete as possible. The products are always acidic. The polymerization degree varied from 6 to 23. Molecular weights were determined by the boiling point method and by titration of the end-standing acid group. Excellent agreement was obtained between the two methods* and the theoretical values for the above mentioned polymerization degrees. The mechanism of the formation of chain polymers is investigated and the possibility of an association of a number of 8-rings through exceptionally strong van der Waals forces discussed.

Carothers expresses himself in favor of the main valence chain theory.

Ethylene succinate as a typical example of a condensation polymer (1) has been submitted to further study with the view of gaining more information in regard to its structure. The presence of the structural unit, (1) I, in this ester has been established by the methods used in its synthesis (2, 3), by its chemical behavior and by its analytical composition (2, 3).

$$-O-CH_2-CH_2-O-OC-CH_2-CH_2-CO- \qquad (I)$$

Of the various polymeric forms described in this paper, the apparent molecular weights indicate average values of 6 and 23, respectively, for the number of structural units contained in each molecule of the lowest and highest polymers. It is assumed that these units are joined together in a linear fashion by real primary valences, as in II. Since it is very improbable that there are free valences at the ends of the resulting chains, the problem of the structure of these polymers resolves itself into finding whether the end valences are mutually saturated with the formation of very large rings or are saturated by univalent groups of some kind.

$$-O-(CH_2)_2-O-OC-(CH_2)_2-CO-O-(CH_2)_2-O-OC-(CH_2)_2-CO-O-$$
$$(CH_2)_2-O-OC-(CH_2)_2-CO-, \text{ etc.} \quad (II)$$

Any of the reactions by which this ester is prepared offers the formal possibility of establishing either rings (closed chains) of 8, 16, 24, ... $(8)n$ members or of open chains corresponding to each of these rings. The observed molecular weights indicate the presence of 50 to 180 atoms in each chain. This fact and the physical properties of the ethylene succinates indicate the absence of more than traces of rings of less than 32 members. Since the same theoretical considerations (1, 4) which predict the improbability of the formation in bifunctional reactions of rings of 8 to 32 members apply *a fortiori* to still larger rings, an open chain seemed much more probable than a cyclic structure, and our efforts were directed toward the detection of the univalent groups which would constitute the ends

* Titration values were 1016, 1344, 1795 and 3417; boiling point values 1070, 1380, 1582 and 3110; theoretical values 982, 1414, 1847 and 3432, respectively.

of the open chains. We have proved the presence of such groups, and the open-chain structure for the polymeric ethylene succinates is clearly established.

Neutral Ethylene Succinate.—This ester is prepared by heating succinic acid with excess glycol at 180° until the distillation of water ceases and then removing the excess glycol by heating in high vacuum at 200–250°. The ester is purified by crystallization and melts at 102° (5).

Its apparent molecular weight is about 3000.

If this ester is an open chain, its method of formation and its observed molecular weight would lead one to assign to it the structure III, and it

$$\text{H—[O—(CH}_2)_2\text{—O—OC—(CH}_2)_2\text{—CO—]}_{22}\text{—O—(CH}_2)_2\text{—OH} \qquad \text{(III)}$$

should therefore show the reactions of a dihydric alcohol. The possibility of applying to it many of the typical reactions for the detection of primary alcohol groups was excluded for one reason or another. Thus the presence of ester linkages excluded any reactions which might result to hydrolysis. The fact that the compound is hygroscopic and insoluble in ether made it useless to attempt to apply any such methods as the Zerewitinoff. The compound crystallizes from acetic anhydride and is apparently unchanged even on long boiling in this solvent in the presence of catalysts, but in so large a molecule acetylation might occur without any apparent change in physical properties, and the amount of acetic acid which would be liberated on hydrolysis of even a completely acetylated product would be so small as to make its estimation difficult. The ester reacts very slowly and incompletely with phosphorus tribromide.

Six grams of the ester heated for five hours in 30 cc. of boiling chloroform with 6 cc. of phosphorus tribromide after thorough washing and repeated crystallization was found to contain 0.58% Br.

The ester was also recovered apparently unchanged after treatment with phenyl and naphthyl isocyanates under various conditions. These failures appear to be due to a reluctance of the hydroxyl groups to react, and they are not altogether surprising in view of the diminished reactivity which is frequently associated with increased molecular size.

Reaction occurred completely in the expected sense with succinic and with p-bromobenzoic anhydrides at elevated temperatures. These reactions led to the dibasic acid which agreed in properties and composition with Formula IV, and to a p-bromobenzoyl ester which agreed in composition with Formula V.

$$\text{HO—OC—(CH}_2)_2\text{—CO—[—O—(CH}_2)_2\text{—O—OC—(CH}_2)_2\text{—CO—]}_{23}\text{—OH} \qquad \text{(IV)}$$
$$p\text{-BrC}_6\text{H}_4\text{—CO—[—O—(CH}_2)_2\text{—O—OC—(CH}_2)_2\text{—CO—]}_{22}\text{—O—(CH}_2)_2\text{—O—OC—}$$
$$\text{C}_6\text{H}_4\text{Br-}p \qquad \text{(V)}$$

Preparation of IV.—Twelve grams of neutral ethylene succinate was heated with 3 g. of succinic anhydride at 175–180° for three hours. The reaction mixture was washed three times with hot water, dried, precipitated from chloroform with ether and crystallized 6 times from acetone. Its properties identified it as the dibasic acid IV, which would be formed by the reaction of each hydroxyl group of III with one molecule of succinic anhydride.

The ester III melted at 102°, had an apparent molecular weight of about 3000, was neutral and did not form a sodium salt. IV prepared from III melted at 98° and had an apparent molecular weight of 3110 (method of Menzies and Wright in ethylene chloride, observed values 3170, 3040) and a neutral equivalent of 1708. The action of sodium bicarbonate on IV led to a sodium salt which melted at 104° and contained 1.23% of sodium. The analytical data are given in Table I.

TABLE I
ACIDIC ETHYLENE SUCCINATES

Sample	M. p., °C.	Neut. equiv.	Mol. wt. calcd. from neut. equiv.	Mol. wt. found in boiling ethylene chloride	X = structural units per molecule	Mol. wt. calcd. from formula
VIa	73	508	1016	1070	6	982
VIb	82	672	1344	1380	9	1414
VIc	90	898	1795	1582	12	1847
IV	98	1708	3417	3110	23	3432

Anal. calcd., %		Anal. found, %			Sodium salt		
C	H	C		H	M. p., °C.	Anal., sodium Calcd.	Found
48.86	5.44	48.42	48.58	5.57	5.29	91	4.48	4.26
49.22	5.56	48.84	48.88	5.74	5.62	97	3.16	3.13
49.38	5.57	49.34	49.37	5.86	5.81	100	2.43	2.29
49.66	5.58	49.41	49.44	5.70	5.69	104	1.32	1.23

Preparation of Di-p-bromobenzoyl Derivative of III.—Two and one-half grams of III was heated for five hours with 0.75 g. of p-bromobenzoic anhydride at 175–185°. The reaction mixture was dissolved in chloroform and precipitated by ether, washed with hot water, dried and precipitated from acetone by ether. It melted at 93°. Analysis showed it to be the expected di-p-bromobenzoyl derivative, V, of III.

Anal. Calcd. for V as $C_{176}H_{172}O_{84}Br_2$: C, 49.30; H, 5.20; Br, 4.84. Found: C, 49.47, 49.39; H, 5.59, 5.60; Br, 4.84, 5.01, 4.88, 4.91.

Acidic Ethylene Succinates.—If glycol and succinic acid would react completely in the proportions in which they are brought together, it would be possible to prepare chains of various lengths by using the glycol and acid in various ratios. In a number of experiments various excess amounts of succinic acid were allowed to react with glycol. The reactants were heated together at 180° until no more water was evolved and the temperature of the bath was then raised to 200–240° for one to five hours to make the reaction as complete as possible. Only traces of acid and glycol appeared in the distillates. The residues were always acidic and, when the excess of acid was large, always contained some unchanged succinic acid. Moreover, products of high molecular weight could be isolated from these residues even when the ratio of acid was as high as 2:1. This showed that under the conditions of these experiments complete control of the length of the chain produced was not possible by adjustment of the ratios of the reactants. On the other hand, this factor had some influence in controlling the lengths of these chains, and by making use of such control as it offered, together with fractional crystallization, it was possible to isolate samples of material representing chains of various lengths, each of which was quite homogeneous in its physical behavior. A comparison of the analytical data and molecular weights for these acidic ethylene succinates clearly indicates that their structure may be represented by VI, in which x has various average values for different fractions.

$$HO—OC—(CH_2)_2—CO—[—O—(CH_2)_2—O—OC—(CH_2)_2—CO—]_x—OH \quad (VI)$$

VIa, $x = 6$ VIb, $x = 9$ VIc, $x = 12$

Preparation of VI, a, b and c.—Ethylene glycol, 41 g., and succinic acid, 93.5 g. (20% excess), were heated at 200–210° for four hours, and the residual water was then removed as completely as possible by heating *in vacuo*. The residue was dissolved in chloroform and precipitated with ether. The powder which resulted from the drying of this precipitate weighed 92.2 g. and melted at 87.5–90°. It was extracted several times with boiling water. The residue (59 g.) was dissolved in chloroform and precipitated by ether. It melted at 90°. This constituted fraction VIc. The hot aqueous extracts on cooling deposited 11 g. of solid which after drying melted at 73–74°.

In another similar experiment the acid and glycol were heated for two hours at 190–210° under ordinary pressure, and then immediately extracted several times with boiling water (3 × 300 cc.). The residue amounted to 10.5 g. After solution in chloroform and precipitation by ether, it melted at 82–83°. This constituted fraction VIb. On cooling, the aqueous extract deposited considerable white solid. This after precipitation from chloroform by ether melted at 73°. This material together with the fraction from the previous experiment melting at the same temperature constituted fraction VIa. By evaporation of the aqueous extracts from this experiment there was obtained another fraction melting at 86°. The analytical data for this fraction indicated that it lay between the 73° and the 82° fractions.

Fraction IV was prepared from III in the manner already indicated.

The analytical data for these fractions (see Table I) indicate that we are here dealing with a polymeric series in which the average values for the degree of polymerization vary from 6 up to 23. These fractions closely resemble each other in physical properties: they have the same appearance under the microscope, and they show similar solubility relations. All the fractions are soluble in cold chloroform and in hot 50% alcohol. The lowest fraction is quite soluble in hot water and the higher fractions only very slightly soluble. The melting points rise with increasing degree of polymerization.

All these fractions form sodium salts on treatment with sodium bicarbonate, and these resemble very closely in properties the acids from which they are derived. Thus they are readily soluble in cold chloroform and in warm acetone. They are only slightly soluble in cold water. All of them, however, are readily soluble in warm water, and in this respect the higher members are sharply differentiated from the corresponding acids. The magnitude of the change in properties which is produced by the transformation of the slightly polar carboxyl group into the completely polar sodium salt will be expected to vary with the size of the chains to which these groups are attached, but we found it somewhat surprising, nevertheless, that these sodium salts should melt only a few degrees above the melting points of the corresponding acids. This difference diminishes continuously with the increase in length of the chain and in the highest polymer, IV, amounts to only 6°.

The general plan of the structure of these acid esters is clearly established by the formation of the sodium salts. Attempts to prepare other derivatives from acids met with little success. Treatment with thionyl chloride and with phosphorus pentachloride under various conditions furnished products which contained chlorine, but it could not be established that these materials were really acid chlorides. Attempts to prepare amides by heating the sodium salts of the acids with p-toluidine hydrochloride led to the formation of N-p-tolyl succinimide. Heating the sodium salts with p-bromophenacyl bromide led to the formation of derivatives, but these contained less than the calculated amount of bromine. Thus the sodium salt of VIa led to a derivative, m. p. 73°, containing 8.66% of bromine, while the calculated value for a di-(p-bromophenacyl) ester of VIa is 11.61% Br. Similarly, the sodium salt of VIc led to a p-bromophenacyl derivative containing 4.12 instead of the calculated 7.13% of bromine.

Mechanism of the Formation of Ethylene Succinate.—The formation of an open-chain polyester of the type exemplified by II might occur in either one of two ways. (1) The cyclic monomeric ester VII might first be formed, and this might then undergo A polymerization (self-addition) with the formation of II. (2) II might be formed directly from the acid and the glycol (C polymerization) by a series of successive reactions. That polyesters of this general type may be formed by the first mecha-

nism is clearly indicated by the fact (6) that the monomeric form of trimethylene carbonate can be isolated by the distillation of its polymer,
and, by heating the monomer can be changed to the polymeric form.   This is also true of other polyesters, but, so
far as our information extends now, only of those in which
the monomer is a 6-membered ring.   The 5-ring esters
do not polymerize; the polyesters whose monomers would
be larger-than-6-rings are not depolymerized; and, although monomers of this type are known (7) and are
stable, none of them has ever been prepared by a bifunctional reaction.
The general theory underlying these facts has already been discussed (1, 6).

VII

The evidence that ethylene succinate is formed by Mechanism 2 (C
polymerization) rather than 1 is fairly conclusive.   Experimental evidence
in support of Mechanism 2 may be found in the fact that the molecules
of ethylene succinate are open chains with functional groups at the ends.
The supposition that the monomeric ring VII is first formed involves the
tacit assumption that 8-rings are readily formed, but are unstable, whereas
fact and theory alike indicate that such rings are formed only with great
difficulty, but are stable when they have been formed.   We have made a
good many attempts to isolate the monomeric 8-ring, VII.   All of these
attempts have failed, and all of the observations which we have made are
best interpreted on the assumption that the long chains are built up by a
series of successive reactions and that rings are not formed at any stage of
the process.   Some light is thrown at one or two points on the details of the
mechanism of the reaction by the following observations.

When glycol was allowed to react with succinic acid in the proportions
of 1 to 2 moles, the product was found to be a mixture composed chiefly
of unchanged succinic acid and polyester of fairly high molecular weight.
The compound, $HO-OC-(CH_2)_2-CO-O-(CH_2)_2-O-OC-(CH_2)_2-$
$CO-OH$, which might be expected to form under these stoichiometrical
conditions was not found.

Neutral ethylene succinate was prepared by heating the acid with excess
glycol and, after some time, distilling off the excess glycol as completely
as possible at high temperature and under greatly reduced pressure.   Under
these conditions the formation of some di-β-hydroxyethyl succinate, VIII,
might be expected.   This ester was in fact formed, and it distilled

$$HO-(CH_2)_2-O-OC-(CH_2)_2-CO-O-(CH_2)_2-OH \qquad (VIII)$$

out of the reaction mixture when this was heated *in vacuo*.   It was obtained in a state of approximate purity by redistillation in a carefully cleaned all-glass apparatus under high vacuum.

Di-(β-hydroxyethyl)-succinate.—Sixty-two grams of ethylene glycol (1 mole) and 39.3 g. of succinic acid ($^1/_3$ mole) in a pyrex Claisen flask fitted with ground-glass stoppers and provided with a receiver were heated for six hours by means of an oil-bath at 174–180°; 8.8 g. of water, b. p. 100–102°, n_D^{28} 1.3323, collected in the receiver. The residue was heated *in vacuo* finally to a temperature of 250° at 0.015 mm., until distillation ceased. The residue was a pale yellow viscous liquid which readily solidified on cooling. It was dissolved in 100 cc. of warm chloroform and precipitated as a powder by the addition of 250 cc. of benzene. After drying, this powder weighed 36 g. (0.25 g. equivalent). Its instantaneous melting point was 98° and its slow melting point 105.5°. The distillates were redistilled and yielded 9.97 g. or 0.648 mole of water, 33.9 g. or 0.548 mole of glycol and 14.5 g. or 0.07 mole of di-(β-hydroxyethyl) succinate. The total esters (0.7 mole + 0.25 g. equivalent) accounted for 0.32 mole of the 0.333 mole of succinic acid used, and these esters plus the glycol recovered accounted for 94.6% of the glycol used, while the water isolated was 87.5% of the calculated amount.

The di-β-hydroxyethyl succinate was never isolated in a state of purity. When distilled in a carefully cleaned all-glass (pyrex) Claisen flask, it boiled at 176–180° at 0.001 mm. as a colorless viscous liquid, leaving only a trace of residue.

Anal. Calcd. for $C_{10}H_{14}O_6$: C, 46.58; H, 6.88. Found: C, 45.76, 45.70; H, 6.86, 6.95.

Treatment with *p*-nitrobenzoyl chloride in pyridine yielded a di-(*p*-nitrobenzoate) as white needles from alcohol; m. p. 90–91°.

Anal. Calcd. for $C_{22}H_{20}O_{12}N_2$: C, 52.35; H, 3.97. Found: C, 52.36, 52.36; H, 4.19, 4.14.

The di-phenylurethan formed by the action of phenyl isocyanate on di-(β-hydroxyethyl) succinate and crystallized from a mixture of benzene and petroleum ether melted at 113°.

Anal. Calcd. for $C_{22}H_{24}O_8N_2$: C, 59.45; H, 5.41. Found: C, 59.40, 59.56; H, 5.53, 5.52.

When heated slowly *in vacuo* di-β-hydroxyethyl succinate was completely converted into neutral (polymeric) ethylene succinate and ethylene glycol, the former appearing in the distillate and the latter remaining in the distilling flask. This process evidently involves an ester interchange: glycol is eliminated between two molecules of the dihydroxy ester with the formation of a new dihydroxy ester containing two of the structural units of ethylene succinate. Repetition of this process finally results in such a molecule as III. It is evident that so long as one of the products of a possible ester interchange can be eliminated in this way, no merely stoichiometrical factors can set up a limit to the length of the molecules which might be produced. Nevertheless a fairly definite limit exists: polyintermolecular esterification has never led us to molecules of greater average length than about 200 atoms. No doubt various factors are involved in this point.   There can be no question that the reactivity of functional groups diminishes with the size of the molecules which contain them. It is apparently this factor which accounts for the failure of the ester III to react with many of the typical reagents for hydroxyl groups.   Moreover, as Staudinger has frequently emphasized (8), the thermal stability of molecules must diminish with increase in their size.   These two factors act in opposition.   To force the completion of the reaction between succinic acid and glycol we have used high temperature (250°) to increase reaction velocity and high vacuum to remove the water as completely as possible. The ester produced under these conditions has a molecular weight of about 3000.   It is interesting to observe that in the thermal polymerization of styrene the product formed at 250° also has an apparent molecular weight of about 3000, while the polystyrenes formed at lower temperatures have much higher molecular weights.   And so also the A polymerization of trimethylene carbonate described in the previous paper (6), although it also involves an ester interchange, leads to a polyester with a molecular weight considerably above 3000, since the reaction consists merely in self-addition and proceeds rapidly at 100°.

Dimeric Ethylene Succinate.—Tilitschejew (9) has reported the isolation of a new ethylene succinate from the volatile materials formed by heating the product of the action of succinic acid on glycol (m. p. 88–89°) to 340–390° under 3–4 mm. pressure.   The new product was distinguished from the usual form not only by its different melting point (129–130°), but by its definite macrocrystallinity.   Cryoscopic data on acetic acid solutions of the new ethylene succinate indicated a double formula and, since Vorländer had already reported (10) that the old form was dimeric, Tilitschejew regarded his new ester as an isomer of the old.   It has now been established that the usual form of ethylene succinate is not dimeric, but much more highly polymeric; the new compound cannot, therefore, be simply an isomer of the old.   Aside from this, however, repetition of Tilitschejew's experiments has completely verified the correctness of his claims as to the nature of the new compound.   It crystallizes in thin plates melting sharply at 130°.   The analytical data clearly indicate that it is dimeric ethylene succinate.

Anal. Calcd. for $(C_6H_8O_4)_2$: C, 50.00; H, 5.50; mol. wt., 288; saponification equivalent, 72. Found: C, 49.85, 50.00; H, 5.60, 5.57; mol. wt., in boiling ethylene chloride, 302, 299; in freezing benzene 279; saponification equivalent, 71.97, 71.95, 71.66.

Attempts to partially saponify this ester were unsuccessful—a part of the ester was recovered unchanged and the remainder was degraded to sodium succinate and glycol. Nevertheless, it seems fairly certain that this compound is the 16-membered ring, IX. No alternative formula seems

$$\left\langle\begin{array}{l}O-(CH_2)_2-O-OC-(CH_2)_2-CO-O-(CH_2)_2-O-OC-(CH_2)_2-CO\\ OC-(CH_2)_2-CO-O-(CH_2)_2-O-OC-(CH_2)_2-CO-O-(CH_2)_2-O\end{array}\right\rangle \quad (IX)$$

plausible. It is very improbable that this compound is present as such in the polymeric ester from which it is prepared. The dimer is quite soluble in hot absolute alcohol; the neutral polymer is quite insoluble. Continuous extraction of the polymer with hot absolute alcohol resulted in the solution of only a very small amount of material and this had the properties of the polymer not of the dimer. The dimer must therefore be formed during the process of thermal decomposition. The transformation of polymeric trimethylene carbonate into monomeric ethylene carbonate described in the previous paper (6) proceeds smoothly and practically quantitatively at about 200°. The formation of the dimeric tetramethylene carbonate, described in the same paper, and of dimeric ethylene succinate occurs only at a much higher temperature. Large amounts of gaseous and liquid products are formed as well as considerable carbonaceous residue. The yields of the dimers are quite small, e. g., 3–4% of the theoretical under the best conditions (Tilitschejew, however, reports 5.5%). In these respects the reaction resembles that used by Ruzicka for the preparation of the large cyclic ketones (11). As yet we have not succeeded in isolating any monomeric ethylene succinate from the products of this reaction.

Ethylene Succinate and the Association Theory of High Polymers.— The discussion in this and the previous papers will, it is hoped, have amply demonstrated the adequacy of the ordinary structural theory of organic chemistry to deal with the polyesters, a fairly complicated class of high polymers.

A possible explanation of the structure of the polyesters which has not yet been considered is the following. The chemical unit or molecule of ethylene succinate is the monomeric 8-ring, VII. Because of the great strains in this structure, or for some other reason, it exhibits exceptionally strong residual or lattice forces, so that the osmotic unit becomes an aggregate of a great many of these ultimate chemical units. There is such a complete lack of any general theoretical justification for this view that there would be no need to consider it in connection with the polyesters were it not that in the field of natural polymers such as cellulose, rubber, etc., in various slightly differing forms it has been defended at great length by so many investigators (12).

Among the many facts which are quite incompatible with any association theory of the structure of polyesters, the following deserve special mention.

(1) All of the known cyclic esters containing larger-than-6-rings are stable substances with definite properties corresponding with their simple formulas. They do not show any tendency to associate in solution.

(2) The polymeric esters corresponding to these monomers show no tendency to dissociate.

(3) In the polymeric ethylene succinates the chemical and osmotic units have been shown to be identical within the limits of experimental error, i. e., *ebullioscopic data give the same values for the molecular weights that are given by the determination of hydroxyl or carboxyl.*

The association theory is not clearly enough defined to permit any more crucial tests than these, but the following experiment at any rate agrees with these in the conclusions to which it leads.

If two different association polymers (A)n and (B)m are mixed in solution or in the liquid state so that they constitute a single phase, then since (A)n $\rightleftarrows$ nA and (B)m $\rightleftarrows$ mB, the resulting mixture should be composed at least in part of (AB)$_p$.

Ethylene sebacate (m. p. 78°) and ethylene succinate (m. p. 103°) were melted together and thoroughly mixed. After cooling, the mass was extracted with benzene, which is a solvent for the sebacate but not for the succinate. The residue melted at 103° (unchanged succinate). To the benzene solution petroleum ether was added; the precipitated solid melted at 78–79° (unchanged sebacate). An ester was prepared by the action of glycol on equivalent amounts of succinic and sebacic acids. This was quite different in its properties from either the succinate or sebacate and it was homogeneous in its solubility behavior (m. p. 38–40°; mol. wt. 1540). This demonstrates the existence of a mixed polymer and the absence of any reversible relationship of association between it and the two corresponding simple polymers.

In the 6-ring esters a reversible relationship exists between the monomeric and polymeric forms, and some of the statements made above do not apply to these polymers. But it is possible, nevertheless, to account satisfactorily for the behavior of these esters without the assumption of any special or peculiar kinds of valence (6).

The view that the ordinary structural theory of organic chemistry is adequate to deal with high polymers has been now for several years ably defended by Staudinger and his collaborators (13), and recently the same view has been applied in a brilliant fashion to such natural polymers as cellulose, rubber, silk fibroin, etc., by Meyer and Mark (14). So far as the minor differences (15) in the views of these two groups of investigators are concerned, our own experiments on polyesters incline us to favor those of Staudinger.   That is, we can find no real objection to referring to primary valence chains as molecules, and among the polyesters these molecules are experimentally identical with the osmotic units of their solutions.

The writers are indebted to Mr. W. H. Taylor for the molecular weight determinations and to Mr. G. A. Jones for the determinations of carbon and hydrogen.

Summary

The polymeric ethylene succinate previously described is shown to be a long chain made up of the recurring unit —O—$(CH_2)_2$—O—CO— $(CH_2)_2$—CO— and bearing hydroxyl groups at its ends.   Acidic ethylene succinates made up of similar chains of various lengths and bearing carboxyl groups at their ends have been prepared.   Molecular weight determinations of these esters based on ebullioscopic measurements agree with those based on chemical evidence (estimation of hydroxyl or carboxyl).

A study of the ethylene succinate prepared by Tilitschejew verifies his claim that it is dimeric, and this ester is undoubtedly a 16-membered ring.

Bibliography and Remarks

(1) Carothers, *Journ. Am. Chem. Soc.*, **51**, 2548 (1929).

(2) Vorländer, *Ann.*, **280**, 167 (1894).

(3) Carothers and Arvin, *Journ. Am. Chem. Soc.*, **51**, 2560 (1929).

(4) Mohr, *J. prakt. Chem.*, **98**, 348 (1918).

(5) Capillary tube melting point.   See Carothers and Arvin, *Journ. Am. Chem. Soc.*, **51**, 2560 (1929), for a description of the peculiar melting point behavior of this compound.

(6) Carothers and van Natta, *J. Am. Chem. Soc.*, **52**, 314 (1930).

(7) Ruzicka and Stoll, *Helv. Chim. Acta*, **11**, 1159 (1928).

(8) See Staudinger, *Ber.*, **59**, 3019 (1926).

(9) Tilitschejew, *J. Russ. Phys.-Chem. Soc.*, **57**, 143–150 (1925); *Chem. Zentr.*, I, 2667 (1926).

(10) Vorländer, *Ann.*, **280**, 167 (1894).

(11) Ruzicka and co-workers, *Helv. Chim. Acta*, **9**, 230, 249, 339, 389, 399, 499, 715, 1008 (1926); **10**, 695 (1927); **11**, 496, 670, 686, 1159, 1174 (1928).

(12) See for example Bergman, Knehe and Lippmann, *Ann.*, **458**, 93 (1927); Hess, Trogus and Friese, *ibid.*, **466**, 80 (1928); Schlubach and Elsner, *Ber.*, **61**, 2358 (1928); Pummerer, Nielsen and Gündel, *ibid.*, **60**, 2167 (1927).

(13) Staudinger and co-workers, *Helv. Chim. Acta*, **5**, 785 (1922); **7**, 23, 842 (1924); **8**, 41, 65, 67 (1925); **9**, 529 (1926); **11**, 1047, 1052 (1928); *Ber.*, **53**, 1073 (1920); **57**, 1203 (1924); **60**, 1782 (1927); **59**, 3019 (1926); **61**, 2427 (1928); **62**, 241, 263, 442 (1929); *Ann.*, **447**, 97, 110 (1926); **467**, 73 (1928); *Z. physik. Chem.*, **126**, 425 (1927); *Kautschuk*, 237 (1927); *Z. angew. Chem.*, **42**, 37, 67 (1929); *Z. Krist.*, **70**, 193 (1929).

(14) Meyer and Mark, *Ber.*, **61**, 593, 1932, 1939 (1928); Meyer, *Naturwissenschaften*, **16**, 790 (1928); *Z. angew. Chem.*, **41**, 935 (1928).

(15) Meyer, *Naturwissenschaften*, **17**, 255 (1929).

V. Glycol Esters of Oxalic Acid*

This is a study of the glycol esters of oxalic acid.

Monomeric ethylene oxalate is a macrocrystalline substance with a melting point of 144°; it undergoes polymerization under various conditions and yields microcrystalline, white, dusty polymers with melting points up to 172°. This material is insoluble and no molecular weight determination was possible. An intermediate polymer showed a melting point at 158–159°; it was called B-polymer, is soluble and gave in boiling acetonitrile a molecular weight around 2400. The polymers can be depolymerized and fractionated by extraction with acetonitrile.

Propylene oxalate was obtained as monomeric crystalline material with a melting point of 142° and as polymeric resinous substance with an apparent molecular weight of 700.†

Trimethylene oxalate is obtained as dimeric and polymeric material with molecular weights of 270 and about 2000, respectively.

Hexamethylene oxalate is a white powder with a m. p. of 79° and a molecular weight around 1150.

Melting points ranging from 110 to 172° have been ascribed to ethylene oxalate (1). Bischoff (2), by distillation, prepared a form melting at 142 to 143°, which he showed to be monomeric. He observed that the melting points of this and higher-melting forms change spontaneously on standing, and he ascribed this change to reversible polymerization but without the support of any comparative molecular weight data. In connection with a study of glycol esters of dibasic acids (3) we have made some further observations on ethylene oxalate and have also prepared some other alkylene oxalates.

Preparation of Ethylene Oxalate.—The ester was prepared by heating ethylene glycol and ethyl oxalate in a Claisen flask provided with a receiver. Alcohol distilled off fairly rapidly when the heating bath was kept at 180–190°. The residue was heated in a vacuum for a time to remove unchanged reactants. The distillate was found to contain some ethyl (β-hydroxyethyl) oxalate.

Ethyl (β-Hydroxyethyl) Oxalate.—Colorless liquid; b. p. (0.2 mm.), 108–110°; d_4^{20} 1.2241; n_D^{20} 1.4405.

Anal. Calcd. for $C_6H_{10}O_5$: C, 44.42; H, 6.22. Found: C, 44.01; H, 6.02.

* W. H. Carothers, J. A. Arvin and G. L. Dorough; *Journ. Am. Chem. Soc.*, **52**, 3292–3300 (1930); Contribution No. 35 from the Experimental Station of E. I. du Pont de Nemours and Co.

Received April 23, 1930. Published August 5, 1930.

† Corresponding to a polymerization degree of about 7 to 8.

The residue after crystallization from glacial acetic acid or from ethyl oxalate was a dusty white powder that usually melted at about 153°. This material was polymeric.

Anal. Calcd. for $C_4H_4O_4$: C, 41.38; H, 3.45; mol. wt., 116; saponification equivalent, 58. Calcd. for $C_{54}H_{58}O_{53} = C_2H_5O—(CO—CO—O—(CH_2)_2—O)_{13}H$: C, 41.70; H, 3.73; mol. wt., 1554; saponification equivalent, 59.4. Found: C, 41.66, 41 97; H, 3.76, 4.05; mol. wt. (in boiling acetonitrile), 1510, 1580, 1610; saponification equivalent, 59.0, 60.8, 61.0.

When this polymer was heated in a vacuum, distillation occurred and from the distillate Bischoff's 143° ester was obtained (observed m. p., 143–144°). Molecular weight determinations in boiling acetonitrile agreed with those in freezing acetic acid reported by Bischoff, indicating that this material is monomeric.

Anal. Calcd. for $C_4H_4O_4$: C, 41.38; H, 3.45; mol. wt., 116. Found: C, 41.42, 41.44; H, 3.56, 3.45; mol. wt. (in boiling acetonitrile), 118, 120, 123, 126.

Small samples of polymer, if distilled rapidly, gave better than 50% yields of the monomer. Under other conditions the yield was smaller owing to thermolysis (1d) to ethylene, carbon dioxide, ethylene carbonate, carbon monoxide and other gaseous, liquid and tarry products.

Fig. 1.—Crystals of monomeric ethylene oxalate. × 94. (These crystals were placed for observation in a microscopic culture plate and sealed against the access of air and moisture by means of a cover glass. Mechanical disturbances were avoided, and subsequent observations, except the last, were made from exactly the same position as the first.)

Properties of Ethylene Oxalate and its Polymers.—Monomeric ethylene oxalate is definitely macrocrystalline and shows a relatively high solubility (Table II). It is so readily hydrolyzed that it may be titrated directly with warm tenth normal alkali. On standing at room temperature, the sharply defined crystals of the monomer rapidly disintegrate

(Figs. 1–3) with the appearance of having been violently disrupted, and finally are transformed into very minute crystals, which, if undisturbed, may become spontaneously oriented on a glass surface to thread-like aggregates (Fig. 4).

This transformation is due to polymerization. It is accelerated by moderate heat and catalyzed by acids or alkalies. The polymerization is accompanied by changes in melting point and solubility. In the first stages of the polymerization the melting point drops (*e. g.*, to 106–110°); higher-melting polymers are formed by heating the monomer in the presence or absence of solvents or catalysts, and the final product is an insoluble material melting at 172–173°.

A sample of monomeric ethylene oxalate was heated at 135–140° for seven hours, and then extracted repeatedly with cold acetone. The material that separated on evaporation of the acetone was identified as unchanged monomer. The acetone-insoluble material was a dusty white powder which after drying melted at 171–172°. It was insoluble in all common organic solvents, so no molecular weight determinations could be made.

Fig. 2.—The crystals of Fig. 1 after five days at room temperature. × 94.

Anal. Calcd. for $(C_4H_4O_4)_x$: C, 41.38; H, 3.45; saponification equivalent, 58.0. Found: C, 41.48, 41.59; H, 3.71, 3.96; saponification equivalent, 58.45.

By fractional crystallization of polymerized monomer and of the 153° polymer formed directly from glycol and oxalic ester, a great variety of samples was obtained showing such melting points as 106–108°, 122–125°, 140–142°, 148–150°, 153°, 155–157°, 157–159°, 160–163°, 163–164°, 172–173°, as well as others having much wider melting ranges. Attempts to segregate homogeneous samples from these fractions met with difficulties due to the rapidity with which spontaneous transformations occurred even in the absence of solvents and at room temperature. Portions of three sharply melting samples were stored in glass-stoppered bottles, and melting point determinations were made at intervals with the following results.

TABLE I

MELTING POINTS

Nature and m. p. of sample	M. p. after standing at room temperature		
	2 months	4 months	5½ months
144° (monomer)	105–140°	105–135°	105–122° (A)
153° (polymer)	149–155°	149–155°	149–155° (B)
172° (polymer)	160–170°	160–170°	160–170° (C)

To avoid these changes during the process of fractionation, it was necessary to work rapidly and to use cold solvents as far as possible. Solubility data established the homogeneity of the monomer (144°) and the apparent homogeneity of the highest (172°) polymer. Intermediate fractions, unlike the 172° polymer, were completely soluble in warm acetonitrile, and since the solubility of the latter was not affected by the presence of monomer, intermediate polymers must have been present in these fractions. This led to the hope that it might be possible to isolate polymers sufficiently low for a study of structure.

The fractions A, B and C of Table I were recrystallized with the following results: extrac-

Fig. 3.—The crystals of Fig. 1 after seven days at room temperature. × 113.

tion of A with cold acetone removed a small amount of monomer. The residue was treated with warm acetonitrile, which dissolved all but a small amount of material that melted at 170–172° (high polymer). The material that separated from the acetonitrile solution, after recrystallization, melted at 157–159°. Similarly from B, fractions were isolated corresponding with monomer, high (172°) polymer, and 157–159° polymer. C yielded a small amount of material melting at 155–157°. The rest was unchanged 172° polymer. Extractions of various other samples were made, and in one case a small fraction melting at 106–108° and having an apparent molecular weight of about 900 was isolated.   There is still considerable doubt, however, concerning the homogeneity of this fraction.

The 153° material, which was the usual (recrystallized) product of the action of ethylene glycol on ethyl oxalate, was not homogeneous in spite of its fairly sharp melting point, for its apparent solubility changed with changing ratio of solute to solvent as shown below.

Sample, g.	Acetonitrile, cc.	Apparent soly. in g. per 100 g. at 25°
0.025	15	0.0821
.100	15	.2633
.500	15	.8644

A four-gram sample of the 153° material was then extracted repeatedly with 25 cc. portions of acetonitrile.   With each extraction the apparent solubility decreased until a constant value was reached.

Extraction number	Apparent soly. in g. per 100 g. at 25°	M. p. of residue, °C.
1	1.4321	152–153
2	0.8111	152–155
3	.3240	155–159
4	.2390	155–160
5	.1729	157–160
6	.1315	157–159
7	.0894	157–159
8	.0891	158–159
9	.0890	158–159

The apparent solubility of the residue did not change on increasing the ratio of solute to solvent five-fold, so this material must be regarded as essentially homogeneous.   Its apparent molecular weight in boiling aceto-nitrile was about 2380 (observed values, 2070, 2480, 2670, 2370, 2275, 2520).

One may conclude that at least two polymers of ethylene oxalate exist: a soluble form melting at 158–159° of molecular weight about 2400, and an

TABLE II

SOLUBILITIES OF ALKYLENE OXALATES

Nature of oxalate sample	M. p., °C.	Observed mol. wt.	Acetonitrile	Solvent Acetone	Chloroform
Monomeric ethylene	144	118–126	11.29	4.13	0.35
Polymeric ethylene	159	2070–2670	0.0891	.....	.....
Polymeric ethylene	172	....	<0.01	<0.01	<0.01
Monomeric propylene	142	·131–147	12.31	3.47	0.06
Monomeric ethylene heated at 90° for two weeks	148–150	1620–1640	0.1823[a]·	0.1630[a]	0.0390[a]

[a] These values have no quantitative significance since the sample was not homogeneous.

insoluble form melting at 172° of unknown but probably much higher molecular weight. Either of these forms may arise spontaneously from the other, and both of them may be formed from the monomer. Definite evidence for the existence of other polymers of ethylene oxalate is lacking.

Chemical Properties of the Polymeric Ethylene Oxalates.—Monomeric ethylene oxalate is hydrolyzed with extraordinary rapidity. To a certain extent this property is shared by its polymers. Hence, although the polymers show acid reactions toward litmus in contact with water, this fact cannot be used to argue for the presence of long primary valence chains bearing carboxyl groups at the end. Attempts to prepare sodium salts from the polymers by the action of cold sodium bicarbonate solution led to the isolation of sodium oxalate and unchanged polymer. This ease of hydrolysis is associated with great sensitivity toward other reagents. The attempt to detect hydroxyl groups or carboxyl groups by heating polymeric ethylene oxalate with *m*-bromobenzoic anhydride and with phenylhydrazine led to the isolation of ethylene-*bis*-*m*-bromobenzoate and to the phenylhydrazide of oxalic acid. The latter reaction is what would be expected from an ester having the structure —CO—CO—O—(CH₂)₂—O—CO—CO— O—(CH₂)₂—O—, etc., whether the chain is open or closed, but the first reaction requires the elimination of —CO—CO—O— residues. These fragments of the molecules appeared as carbon monoxide and carbon dioxide, which were observed to be evolved from the reaction mixture.

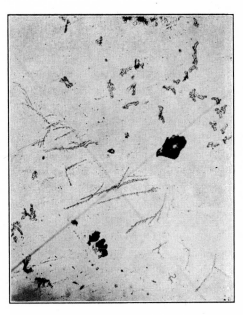

Fig. 4.—The crystals of Fig. 1 after two weeks at room temperature. × 185.

Ethylene *bis*-*m*-**Bromobenzoate.**—Prepared by the action of *m*-bromobenzoic anhydride on ethylene glycol or on ethylene oxalate; crystallized from a mixture of chloroform and alcohol; m. p. 78–79°

Anal.   Calcd. for C₁₆H₁₂O₄Br₂: C, 44.86; H, 2.80; Br, 37.38; mol. wt., 428. Found.

C, 44.85, 45.06; H, 2.92, 2.98; Br, 37.26, 37.03; mol. wt. (in boiling benzene), 430.

Propylene Oxalate.—By heating propylene glycol and ethyl oxalate together and removing unchanged reactants in a vacuum, a colored viscous resin was obtained. In boiling acetonitrile this showed an apparent molecular weight of about 700 (observed, 670, 660). No crystalline material could be isolated from it. When this resin was strongly heated at a pressure of 5 mm., distillation occurred. A crystalline solid that separated from the liquid distillate melted at 142° after recrystallization from hot alcohol. This was identified as monomeric propylene oxalate.

> *Anal.* Calcd. for $C_5H_6O_4$: oxalic acid, 69.24; saponification equivalent, 65; mol. wt., 130. Found: oxalic acid, 69.82; saponification equivalent, 64.5, 65.1; mol. wt. (in boiling acetonitrile), 131, 147.
>
> Carbon and hydrogen values (Pregl method) were consistently low, perhaps owing to the loss of methane.

The monomeric methyl ethylene oxalate showed no tendency to polymerize spontaneously at room temperature, but on being heated to 140–150° for eight hours it was converted to a white powder that melted at 176–178° and was insoluble in all common organic solvents.

Trimethylene Oxalate.—This ester has been prepared by Tilitcheev (4) as a solid melting at 82–84° by heating methyl oxalate with trimethylene glycol first at atmospheric and then under diminished pressure, dissolving the residue in chloroform, and precipitating it with methyl alcohol. On distillation at 3–4 mm. pressure it was converted into an "isomeric" form melting at 186–187°.

Since the length of the chain of the structural unit of trimethylene oxalate is seven atoms, the reaction between oxalic ester and trimethylene glycol should be intermolecular and the product polymeric, in accordance with the generalization based on the study of other similar reactions (3, 5).

We prepared trimethylene oxalate by heating ethyl oxalate with trimethylene glycol. After three crystallizations from a mixture of chloroform and ethyl alcohol it melted at 87–88°. Its apparent molecular weight in boiling acetonitrile was about 2000 (observed value, 2040, 1980).

> *Anal.* Calcd. for $C_5H_6O_4$: C, 46.15; H, 4.65. Found: C, 46.03, 46.34; H, 4.90, 4.95.

When this polymeric material was heated at 250° at 3–4 mm., thermolysis and distillation occurred. Gaseous, liquid and carbonaceous products were formed. The liquid distillate from 52 g. of polymer weighed 23.6 g., and on being cooled and treated with alcohol it yielded a small amount of crystalline solid, which after repeated crystallization melted at 186–187°. This was Tilitcheev's "isomeric" trimethylene oxalate.

Anal. Calcd. for $(C_5H_6O_4)_2$: C, 4.165; H, 4.65; mol. wt., 260. Found: C, 45.75, 46.12; H, 4.61, 4.69; mol. wt. in boiling acetonitrile, 282, 278; in freezing phenol, 272, 265.

The molecular weight determinations prove this material to be dimeric. The liquid distillate from which the dimeric trimethylene oxalate was isolated was redistilled. It boiled from 70° at 20 mm. to 185° at 0.25 mm. From the higher-boiling fractions a considerable amount of trimethylene carbonate was isolated. This is a product that Tilitcheev assumed to be intermediate in the thermolysis of trimethylene oxalate, but he was unable to isolate it. Saponification of the remaining liquid led to the isolation (as calcium oxalate) of about 1.5 g. of oxalic acid. Hence it is possible that some monomeric trimethylene oxalate may have been present in the mixture.

These results lead to the following conclusions. The action of trimethylene glycol on ethyl oxalate proceeds intermolecularly and leads to an ester of the type —CO—CO—O—$(CH_2)_3$—O—CO—CO—O—$(CH_2)_3$—O—CO—CO—O—$(CH_2)_3$—O—, etc. This on being heated to a high temperature undergoes thermal decomposition and yields a complicated mixture of products containing a small amount of the 14-membered cyclic ester

$$\overline{\text{—CO—CO—O—}(CH_2)_3\text{—O—CO—CO—O—}(CH_2)_3\text{—O—}}$$

These reactions are analogous to those observed in the formation and decomposition of ethylene succinate (6) and tetramethylene carbonate (7). No truly reversible relationship between a monomeric and polymeric form of trimethylene oxalate exists, as it does in ethylene oxalate and in trimethylene carbonate (7). The dimeric trimethylene oxalate shows no tendency to polymerize spontaneously.

Hexamethylene Oxalate and Decamethylene Oxalate.—From considerations which have already been set forth it is to be expected that these esters, by whatever method they are prepared, will be linear condensation polymers. They are readily prepared by heating ethyl oxalate with the corresponding glycols at first under atmospheric pressure and finally in high vacuum.

Hexamethylene Oxalate.—White powder purified by precipitation from chloroform by methyl alcohol, m. p. 66°.

Anal. Calcd. for $C_8H_{12}O_4$: C, 55.79; H, 7.03; mol. wt., 172. Found: C, 55.77, 55.58; H, 7.17, 7.08; mol. wt. (in boiling benzene), 1050, 1160, 1120.

Decamethylene Oxalate.—White powder purified by precipitation from chloro-fc .n by methyl alcohol, m. p. 79°.

Anal. Calcd. for $C_{12}H_{24}O_4$: C, 62.57; H, 9.63; mol. wt., 232. Found: C, 62.89, 62.73; H, 8.97, 8.90; mol. wt. (in boiling benzene), 1160, 1190.

Summary

Ethylene oxalate exists in three mutually interconvertible forms: a monomer (m. p. 144°), a soluble polymer (m. p. 159°) and an insoluble polymer (m. p. 172°). Ethylene oxalates showing other melting points are probably mixtures of these three forms, since evidence for the existence of any other individual forms is lacking. None of these forms are stable at ordinary temperature. The monomer polymerizes spontaneously, and the purified polymers are partially depolymerized.

Propylene oxalate exists in at least two mutually interconvertible forms: a monomer and a polymer. Monomeric propylene oxalate polymerizes much less rapidly than ethylene oxalate.

Trimethylene oxalate (m. p. 86°) prepared from ethyl oxalate and tri-methylene glycol is a linear condensation polymer. It shows no tendency to depolymerize spontaneously. At high temperature it undergoes ther-mal decomposition, and one of the products of this reaction is the dimeric 14-membered heterocycle, m. p. 187°. This is stable and shows no tend-ency to polymerize further.

Hexamethylene oxalate and decamethylene oxalate prepared by the action of the glycols on ethyl oxalate are linear condensation polymers.

Ethyl(*p*-hydroxyethyl)-oxalate and ethylene-*bis*-*m*-bromobenzoate are described.

Bibliography and Remarks

(1) (a) Bischoff, *Ber.*, **27**, 2939 (1894); (b) **40**, 2803 (1907); (c) Adams and Weeks, *Journ. Am. Chem. Soc.*, **38**, 2518 (1916); (d) Tilitcheev, *Ber.*, **56**, 2218 (1923).

(2) Bischoff, *ibid.*, **40**, 2803 (1907).

(3) Carothers and Arvin, *Journ. Am. Chem. Soc.*, **51**, 2560 (1929); Carothers and van Natta, *ibid.*, **52**, 314 (1930); Carothers and Dorough, *ibid.*, **52**, 711 (1930).

(4) Tilitcheev, *J. Russ. Phys.-Chem. Soc.*, **58**, 447 (1926); *C. A.* **21**, 3358 (1927); *Chem. Zentr.*, II, 440 (1927).

(5) Carothers, *Journ. Am. Chem. Soc.*, **51**, 2548 (1929).

(6) Carothers and Dorough, *Journ. Am. Chem. Soc.*, **52**, 718 (1930).

(7) Carothers and van Natta, *ibid.*, **52**, 314 (1930).

VI. Adipic Anhydride*

J. W. Hill describes the preparation of adipic anhydride. In accordance with the general rule put forward by Carothers, the anhydride of adipic acid should be capable of existing as a 7-ring and as a long chain polymer. The author has succeeded in preparing both forms and also in converting the monomer (m. w. 128) into the polymer of a molecular weight around 800 (polymerization degree 6-7). The reaction of the monomer with aniline and of the polymer with aniline and phenol was studied.

The anhydrides of succinic and glutaric acids are known and are monomeric rings of five and six atoms, respectively. The monomeric anhydride of the next member of the series, adipic acid, is a seven-atom ring, and therefore the direct preparation of this anhydride by the removal of water from the acid should give a polymolecular product, in accordance with the generalizations formulated in the previous papers in this series (1). This has been found to be the case. We have also been successful in preparing monomeric adipic anhydride for the first time.

Adipic anhydride has been prepared by Voerman (2) and by Farmer and Kracovski (3), both of whom describe it as a solid. Voerman prepared the compound by treating adipic acid with acetyl chloride, removing volatile compounds *in vacuo*, and finally crystallizing from benzene He gives a melting point of 98°. On the basis of a molecular weight determination in phenol, with which, however, we have found it to react, he seemed to regard the compound as a monomeric ring. The abnormally high molecular weight obtained in boiling acetone, the lack of definite crystallinity and the relatively low solubility of the compound, however, led him to consider that it might be polymeric. He does not make his viewpoint altogether clear, but apparently he regarded the anomalous properties of the compound as due to some sort of association of simple rings and did not consider the probability of the existence of a long chain or large ring.

Farmer and Kracovski state that adipic anhydride is definitely unimolecular and ascribe to it a melting point of 97° This is certainly not correct since we have found the monomer to melt at a very much lower temperature.

* J. W. Hill; *Journ. Am. Chem. Soc.*, **52**, 4110–14 (1930); Communication No. 40 from the Experimental Station of E. I. du Pont de Nemours and Co.
Received July 26, 1930. Published October 6, 1930.
This paper does not bear the name of W. H. Carothers, but it is appropriate to include it in this volume and give a short abstract. This will maintain the full continuity of this interesting and important series of contributions to high polymeric chemistry. Compare also paper No. XVII on page 192.

We have prepared adipic anhydride by both of these methods and have found that the product before subjection to distillation is polymeric, as we had anticipated and Voerman suspected. Polymeric adipic anhydride separates from hot benzene as a microcrystalline powder. Samples prepared in various experiments showed melting points ranging from 70 to 85°. This variation and the difference between the melting points of our products and those of previous investigators may be due to differences in molecular size. A molecular weight determination in boiling benzene gave a value about six times the normal value. This value is probably low as the substance is very sensitive to moisture, and only the ordinary precautions were taken to exclude it. The compound hydrolyzes in boiling water to yield the acid and reacts rapidly with aniline and phenol. It is hygroscopic and on standing unprotected gradually reverts to the acid. It is not distillable as such, but when heated *in vacuo* to somewhat above 200°, it breaks down and yields the true monomeric adipic anhydride, which distils out.

Monomeric adipic anhydride is a liquid freezing at about 20° and boiling at about 100° at 0.1 mm. It reacts with cold water quickly with the evolution of much heat to yield the acid. It reacts almost instantly with aniline to give a very high yield of pure monoanilide. On being heated at 100° for a few hours, it changes to a polymer melting at 80–85°. On standing at room temperature for ten days or more, it gradually solidifies. It is probable that traces of water bring about the polymerization. When a sample of liquid anhydride is transferred to a vessel which has not been very carefully dried, an amorphous skin soon coats the glass.

The reactions of the monomeric and polymeric adipic anhydrides with aniline establish the structures of these compounds, the former as a seven-membered ring and the latter as a long chain, which may be a large ring or an open chain with terminal carboxyl groups. Monomeric anhydride (I), which has a symmetrical structure, can react with aniline to give but one product, adipic acid monoanilide (II). This has been verified experi-

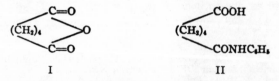

I   II

mentally. Polymeric adipic anhydride, to which we may assign formula III, on the other hand, is no longer symmetrical as soon as one anhydride group reacts with aniline. The product formed, therefore, depends on which side of the oxygen atom the next anhydride group along the chain breaks. It will be seen from the scheme above that the reaction of polymeric adipic anhydride with aniline may lead to three products: adipic

$$
\underset{\substack{\text{monoanilide}}}{\text{HO}-\overset{\overset{\displaystyle O}{\|}}{\underset{\underset{\displaystyle C_6H_5NH}{|}}{C}}(CH_2)_4\overset{\overset{\displaystyle O}{\|}}{C}} \cdots
$$

HO—C(CH₂)₄C— —O—C(CH₂)₄C—O— —C(CH₂)₄C— —O— C(CH₂)₄C—O— H
     C₆H₅NH   H   H   NHC₆H₅   H
                                              C₆H₅NH

monoanilide   adipic acid   dianilide, etc.

III

acid, adipic acid monoanilide and adipic acid dianilide. All of these compounds have been isolated from the reaction of the polymer with aniline. On the assumption that a random reaction takes place and that the carboxyl groups which are probably at the ends of the chain may be neglected, these products should be formed in the proportion of one mole of acid to one mole of dianilide to two moles of monoanilide. In a quantitative experiment a 25% yield of dianilide was obtained. The adipic acid and monoanilide formed were not estimated quantitatively. Similarly the solid anhydride yields diphenyl adipate on warming with phenol.

The experiments with aniline show definitely that the solid adipic anhydride is a true condensation polymer in which the structural units are held together by primary valence forces. It is presumed that the polymers are open chains with carboxyl groups at the ends as has been demonstrated in the case of some of the polymeric ethylene succinates (4). This view is further supported by the presence of adipic acid in the distillate when the polymeric anhydride is cracked to form the monomer.

The writer wishes to thank Dr. W. H. Carothers for his interest and advice, and Mr. S. B. Kuykendall for determinations of carbon and hydrogen.

Experimental Part

Preparation of Polymeric Adipic Anhydride.—One hundred grams of recrystallized adipic acid and 300 cc. of redistilled acetic anhydride were refluxed together for four to six hours, and the volatile constituents were removed in a vacuum at 100°. The residue melted at about 70°. It was repeatedly recrystallized from dry benzene, from which it separated as a micro-crystalline powder. Various samples prepared in this same way melted at temperatures varying from 70 to 85°. At temperatures above the melting point, all these samples were viscous liquids, which solidified on cooling to waxy masses. In all experiments moisture was carefully excluded. In the most careful preparation carried out, moisture was excluded by phosphorus pentoxide tubes, the residue was heated overnight in an exhausted system which contained caustic potash in an adjacent vessel and then recrystallized four times with one filtration in a closed system. After each recrystallization the mother liquor was removed by careful decantation. The product melted at 73–75°. The polymeric anhydride melted under boiling water and gradually went into solution. On cooling adipic acid crystallized out.

Anal. Calcd. for $(C_6H_8O_3)_n$: saponification equivalent, 64.0. Found: saponification equivalent, 63.2, 63.4.

Reaction of Polymeric Adipic Anhydride with Aniline.—A sample of polymer prepared directly from adipic acid and acetic anhydride (m. p. 75°) was added to a slight excess of aniline and triturated in a mortar. Reaction took place spontaneously with the evolution of heat. The mixture was treated with dilute hydrochloric acid and the solid precipitate was filtered off. The filtrate was evaporated to dryness and the residue was then taken up in a volume of water not quite sufficient for complete solution, filtered and washed. The residue after crystallization from water was identified as adipic acid by a mixed melting point determination. The residue from the hydrochloric acid treatment was boiled with water and filtered. The filtrate deposited needles on cooling, which after recrystallization from water, were identified as adipic acid monoanilide by a mixed melting point with an authentic sample. The residue insoluble in boiling water, consisting of adipic acid dianilide, was recrystallized from alcohol; needles, m. p. 240–241°. (5). This experiment was carried out with various samples of polymeric anhydride: crude polymer prepared directly from adipic acid and acetic anhydride, recrystallized polymer, polymer formed by heating the monomer and still-residue from distillation of the monomer. In every case dianilide was isolated and identified. The experiment with the heat polymer was carried out quantitatively and gave a 25% yield of dianilide.

Anal. Calcd. for $C_{18}H_{20}O_2N_2$: C, 72.96; H, 6.81. Found: C, 73.31, 73.24; H, 6.95, 7.12.

Reaction of Polymeric Adipic Anhydride with Phenol.—Polymeric adipic anhydride was warmed with phenol to fusion and poured into cold water. On agitation a white solid separated out. This, after two recrystallizations from a mixture of alcohol and water (1:1), separated as lustrous plates of m. p. 105.5–106°. The method of preparation and the ultimate analysis showed this compound to be diphenyl adipate.

Anal. Calcd. for $C_{18}H_{18}O_4$: C, 72.45; H, 6.08. Found: C, 72.63, 72.19; H, 6.07, 6.29.

Preparation of Monomeric Adipic Anhydride.—One hundred grams of adipic acid and 300 cc. of acetic anhydride were refluxed together for four hours. The acetic acid formed in the reaction and the excess acetic anhydride were removed by distillation in a vacuum. The residue was transferred to a Claisen flask and heated under vacuum. After the removal of the residual acetic anhydride at 0.1 mm. no further distillation took place up to 210° bath temperature. At this temperature the pressure rose, and in different experiments from 50 to 60 g. distilled between 105 and 125° under pressure from 3 to 8 mm., the bath temperature ranging from 210 to 235°. The residue was viscous when hot and solidified to a dark colored mass on cooling. The distillate consisted of a light pink liquid containing a small amount of crystalline material. The liquid and solid phases were separated by centrifuging. The crystalline material was washed with benzene, recrystallized from ethyl acetate, and identified as adipic acid by a mixed melting point determination. The liquid was redistilled in an all-glass apparatus. The boiling point was 98 to 100° at 0.1 mm. at a bath temperature of 117 to 120°. Only about half of the material could be recovered by distillation since the residue gradually polymerized.

Samples of the colorless distillate were sealed in small, carefully dried glass tubes for freezing point determinations. The compound froze at 19° to large translucent plates and remelted at 22°.

Anal. Calcd. for $C_6H_8O_3$: C, 56.25; H, 6.30; mol. wt., 128; saponification equiv., 64.0. Found: C, 55.89, 55.98; H, 6.51, 6.52; mol. wt. (in boiling benzene), 134, 131; saponification equiv., 63.7, 63.6.

Polymerization of Monomeric Adipic Anhydride.—When monomeric adipic anhydride was transferred to a vessel which had not been carefully dried, a translucent coating appeared on the surface of the glass. The coating was amorphous and in places skin-like. It melted at 60–65°. When the liquid was heated in a sealed tube at 100°, it polymerized completely and a maximum melting point of 80–84° was reached in about seven hours. On being heated at 138°, a maximum melting point of 81–85° was reached in about two hours. In neither experiment did further heating affect the melting point.

Anal. Calcd. for $(C_6H_8O_3)_n$: saponification equiv., 64.0. Found: saponification equiv., 63.5, 63.3; mol. wt. (in boiling benzene), 860, 710.

Reaction of Monomeric Adipic Anhydride with Aniline.—One cubic centimeter of anhydride was added to about eight cubic centimeters of aniline with stirring. Reaction was immediate and much heat was evolved. The excess aniline was dissolved in dilute hydrochloric acid. The solution was diluted to 200 cc. and filtered. The crude product was dried and weighed; m. p. 152–153°; yield 80%. The monoanilide of adipic acid has previously been prepared by heating $C_6H_5NHCOCH(COOH)(CH_2)_3COOH$ (6).

Recrystallization from water did not raise the melting point. The crude compound was completely soluble in hot water (absence of dianilide). A similar experiment was carried out and worked up in smaller volume; m. p. (crude), 151–153°; yield, 87%.

Anal. Calcd. for $C_{12}H_{15}O_3N$: C, 65.12; H, 6.80; neutralization equiv., 221. Found: C, 64.76, 64.86; H, 6.81, 7.01; neutralization equiv., 222, 223.

Summary

The monomeric and polymeric forms of adipic anhydride have been prepared, the former for the first time, and they have been shown to be mutually interconvertible. The reactions of the compounds with aniline have shown the monomer to be a seven-atom ring and the polymer a long chain or large ring. Diphenyl adipate is described.

Bibliography and Remarks

(1) Carothers, *Journ. Am. Chem. Soc.*, **51**, 2548 (1929); Carothers and Arvin, *ibid.*, **51**, 2560 (1929); Carothers and van Natta, *ibid.*, **52**, 314 (1930); Carothers and Dorough, *ibid.*, **52**, 711 (1930).

(2) Voerman, *Rec. trav. chim.*, **23**, 265 (1904).

(3) Farmer and Kracovski, *J. Chem. Soc.*, 680 (1927).

(4) Carothers and Dorough, *Journ. Am. Chem. Soc.*, **52**, 711 (1930).

(5) Bödtker [*Ber.*, **39**, 2765, 4003 (1906)] gives 240°; Balbiano [*Gazz. chim. ital.*, **32**, I, 446 (1902)] gives 240–241°; Bouveault and Titry [*Bull. soc. chim.*, [3] **25**, 444 (1901)] gives 235°.

(6) Dieckmann, *Ann.*, **317**, 62 (1901). The melting point given is 152–153°.

VII. Normal Paraffin Hydrocarbons of High Molecular Weight Prepared by the Action of Sodium on Decamethylene-bromide*

Long chain paraffins can be obtained by treating decamethylenebromide with metallic sodium in ethereal solution.

After an enumeration and discussion of the different reactions, which are feasible in this system, the preparation of the hydrocarbon mixture and its separation are described. The latter is carried out in a molecular still at a pressure of about 10^{-5} mm. Hg. Between the melting points of $35°$ and $106°$ eighteen fractions were separated. The distillates were grouped together into eight fractions and redistilled; they crystallized with constant melting points and proved to be hydrocarbons up to $C_{70}H_{142}$. A curve showing the melting points as a function of chain length is given and thoroughly discussed.

Finally a detailed description of the preparation of decamethylene bromide is given.

No rationally synthetic and practical methods for the preparation of giant individuals of the simpler homologous series are available, and one of the objects of the experiments here reported was to explore the possibilities of bifunctional Wurtz reactions as a means of access to this realm.

The first step in simple Wurtz reactions is the formation of the corresponding sodium alkyl, RNa (1). This normally couples with the halide, forming the hydrocarbon R-R, but it may react in other ways and yield by-products. Sodium ethide reacts with diethyl ether

$$C_2H_5Na + (C_2H_5)_2O = C_2H_6 + C_2H_5ONa + C_2H_4 \quad (2)$$

and one may expect the formation of considerable amounts of the hydrocarbon RH when the Wurtz reaction is carried out in that solvent.

The experiments presently described are concerned with the action of sodium on decamethylene bromide in ethereal solution, and the normal course of this reaction including that due to the participation of the solvent (but ignoring for the moment the possibility of intramolecular reaction) may be formulated as follows

$$Br(CH_2)_{10}Br + 2Na = Br(CH_2)_{10}Na + NaBr$$
$$Br(CH_2)_{10}Na + (C_2H_5)_2O = H(CH_2)_{10}Br + C_2H_5ONa + C_2H_4$$
$$Br(CH_2)_{10}Na + Br(CH_2)_{10}Br = Br(CH_2)_{20}Br + NaBr$$

* W. H. Carothers, J. W. Hill, G. E. Kirby and R. A. Jacobson; *Journ. Am. Chem. Soc.*, **52**, 5279–88 (1930); Contribution No. 46 from the Experimental Station of E. I. du Pont de Nemours and Co.
      Received October 9, 1930. Published December 18, 1930.

$$H(CH_2)_{10}Br + 2Na = H(CH_2)_{10}Na + NaBr$$
$$H(CH_2)_{10}Na + (C_2H_5)_2O = H(CH_2)_{10}H + C_2H_5ONa + C_2H_4$$
$$H(CH_2)_{10}Na + H(CH_2)_{10}Br = H(CH_2)_{20}H + NaBr$$
$$H(CH_2)_{10}Na + Br(CH_2)_{10}Br = H(CH_2)_{20}Br + NaBr$$
$$H(CH_2)_{10}Na + H(CH_2)_{20}Br = H(CH_2)_{30}H + NaBr$$
$$H(CH_2)_{10}Na + Br(CH_2)_{20}Br = H(CH_2)_{30}Br + NaBr$$
$$H(CH_2)_{30}Br + 2Na = H(CH_2)_{30}Na + NaBr$$
$$H(CH_2)_{30}Na + Br(CH_2)_{20}Br = H(CH_2)_{50}Br + NaBr, etc.$$

The product will be composed of individuals of the general formula $H[(CH_2)_{10}]_xH$ and possibly of similar chains terminated at one or both ends by bromine atoms. The length of these chains will be determined by the relative rates of reaction of the sodium compounds with the solvent and with the halides. Solubility effects may also come into play.

The suitability of this reaction as a source of straight chain hydrocarbons will depend upon the extent to which it is possible to avoid undesirable side reactions, and some indications on this point may be had from the known behavior of simple halides. Sodium and n-heptyl bromide at the boiling temperature give tetradecane, 67%; heptane, 9%; heptene, 3%; heneicosane, 3%; hydrocarbons of higher molecular weight, some (3). Sodium and butyl bromide in ether under specified conditions give n-octane, 68%; butane ?, ?%; butene, ca. 1.5%; dodecane, ca. 0.15%; hexadecane, ca. 0.05% (4). In both these typical cases the principal by-product is probably the hydrocarbon RH. In the reaction of the dihalide, this type of by-product would be identical with one of the normal reaction products. The higher hydrocarbons from butyl bromide and from heptyl bromide are probably not straight chains, and the formation of analogous products from the dihalide would be definitely pernicious because of the difficulty of separating isomeric individuals of high molecular weight. The quoted data on butyl bromide indicate however that in simple Wurtz reactions in ether not more than traces of these higher by-products need be formed.

The action of sodium wire on decamethylene bromide in absolute ether has been studied by Franke and Kienberger (5). The reaction proceeded smoothly to completion, and the products isolated were: n-decane, 34%; C_{20} hydrocarbon, 30%; a small amount of C_{40} hydrocarbon; and a considerable amount of solid hydrocarbon of higher molecular weight. All of these products were free of halogen. The melting point of the C_{20} hydrocarbon identifies it as n-eicosane. The formation of large amounts of n-decane apparently puzzled Franke and Kienberger, and they repeated their experiments with elaborate precautions to exclude water and alcohol from the solvent and the halide. The results were the same. n-Decane and n-eicosane are, however, strictly normal products of the reaction as it has been formulated above. The fact that Franke and Kienberger could find neither decene nor cyclodecane in the products is worthy of note, for any side reaction would almost certainly be accompanied by the formation of some decene, and any intramolecular reaction by the formation of some cyclodecane. These data indicate that the course of this reaction is, at least for the most part, strictly normal and exclusively intermolecular. The major part of the product is composed of relatively short chains, but this is a matter which may be expected to be susceptible of some control by changes in the experimental conditions, and, as it appears to be in fact, especially by increase in the surface of the sodium.

We had already treated decamethylene bromide in ether with finely divided sodium with stirring before Franke and Kienberger's paper had come to our attention. The product, obtained in good yield, was an ether-insoluble solid, and no material boiling as low as n-decane was present. This product, by extraction and crystallization, was separated into $C_{20}H_{42}$, $C_{30}H_{62}$ and $C_{40}H_{82}$, each fairly pure, representing together about 25% of the total, and a higher fraction, m. p. 108–112°, representing about 75% of the total. This contained 1.39% organic halogen, from which it was freed by heating and stirring it with a small amount of molten sodium in boiling butyl ether. The apparent molecular weight of the resulting hydrocarbon was about 1000. No individuals could be isolated from it by repeated fractional crystallization, and it could not be distilled at 0.1 mm. pressure. It was finally separated into a series of individuals by distillation in the molecular still and by crystallization of the distillates.

Preparation of the Hydrocarbon Mixture.—In a 500-cc. flask provided with a reflux condenser and a mercury-sealed mechanical stirrer, 95 g. (1.52 atoms) of sodium was pulverized under hot xylene. The xylene was removed and replaced by absolute ether, and then 75 g. (0.25 mole) of decamethylene bromide was added. The reaction mixture was stirred continuously. It soon developed a deep blue color. It was gently heated for one hour and then allowed to boil without external heating for two and one-half hours. Finally it was heated for two and one-half hours more and then allowed to stand overnight. The excess sodium in the thick mass was decomposed by alcohol, a large volume of water was added and the mixture was filtered with suction. The only material found in the ethereal layer of the filtrate was 0.5 cc. of an oil boiling at 240–330°. The soft white residue on the funnel liquefied almost completely on being stirred with boiling water and solidified to a crystalline mass on cooling. It weighed 30.5 g. (87.1% calculated as CH_2). It melted from 85 to 100° and contained bromine (found, 2.17, 2.27%). This solid was heated and vigorously stirred for five hours with 7 g. of molten sodium in boiling butyl ether. The excess sodium was decomposed by alcohol, a large volume of water was added and the mixture was filtered. The solid residue on the funnel was washed with boiling water and dried. It weighed 21 g. It was free of halogen and melted from 87 to 105°. This is the material which was sub-

mitted to fractionation in the molecular still.   After the butyl ether had been removed
from the non-aqueous layer of the distillate, there remained 6 g. of a soft waxy solid
.melting at 48–54°.

Separation of the Hydrocarbon Mixture.—Eight grams of the solid
hydrocarbon, m. p. 87–105°, described above was heated in a small molecular still (6) provided with a water-cooled condenser and a trap cooled
with liquid air.   The pressure in the system was continually maintained
below 10^{-5} mm.   Fractions were collected as follows.

Temp. of bath, °C.	Wt. of distillate, g.	M. p. of distillate, °C.
130	0.7	35 – 55
150–160	.27	60 – 75
150–160	.15	60 – 78
150–160	.20	77 – 79
160	.12	78 – 81
180	.20	79 – 84
190	.19	87 – 89
195	.08	87 – 91
195	.10	90 – 90.5
200–220	.52	90.5– 92
250	.31	94.5– 97
250	.11	96 – 98
250	.20	97 – 99.5
250	.10	98 –100.5
250	.05	99 –101
250	.08	99 –102
300	.47	103 –105
300	.17	103 –106.5

Total   4.02
Residue 3.16
Loss   0.82

TABLE I
INDIVIDUAL HYDROCARBONS

Hydro-carbon	M. p. found, °C.	Solvent used for crys-tallization	Distn. temp., °C.	Anal. calcd. C	H	Anal. found C	H
$C_{20}H_{42}$	35 – 35.6	Abs. EtOH	60	85.00	15.00	85.45	15.03
$C_{30}H_{62}$	65 – 66	Abs. EtOH + Et_2O	100	85.21	14.79	85.28	14.45
$C_{40}H_{82}$	80.5– 81	Ethylene chloride	150	85.31	14.49	85.59	14.74
$C_{50}H_{102}$	91.9– 92.3	Ligroin + petroleum ether	200	85.37	14.63	85.34	14.53
$C_{60}H_{122}$	98.5– 99.3	Butyl acetate	250	85.41	14.59	85.66	14.34
$C_{70}H_{142}$	105 –105.5	Butyl acetate	300	85.44	14.56	85.50	14.58
Soluble residue	110 –114	Butyl acetate	Not distillable				

The loss is due to the impossibility of quantitatively removing the distillate from the condenser.   In this distillation the average area of the evaporating surface was about 18 sq. cm.   About twenty hours was required for the collection of each of the above listed fractions. When the temperature of the heating bath was raised above 300° with the view of distilling the residue, the pressure rose and no distillation could be effected.

The distillates were grouped together into eight fractions and redistilled.   The rate of distillation from these partially purified materials was very much higher than from the initial mixture.   The distillates were crystallized to constant melting points.   The properties of all the fractions thus obtained are indicated in Table I.

Identity and Properties of the Hydrocarbons.—The melting points 36.7° (7) and 65.6–66° (8), respectively, have been assigned to n-eicosane and n-triacontane, and these values are in good agreement with our observations.   The other four hydrocarbons listed in Table I are all new, and the last one stands six atoms above any paraffin previously described. Several [intermediate members of this same series have been described, however, and from the available data it is possible to construct a smooth curve of melting points covering the range C_{18}–C_{70}.   The usefulness of such a curve in estimating the most probable values for individual hydrocarbons has already been emphasized (9), and in the curve presented in Fig. 1 the

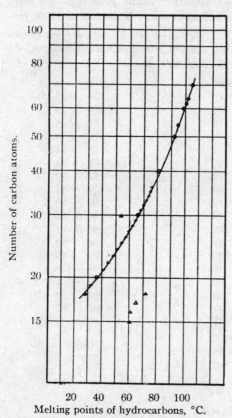

Melting points of hydrocarbons, °C.

Fig. 1.—Normal paraffins: ●, Gascard, *Ann. Chim.*, [9] **15**, 332 (1921); +, Hildebrand and Wachter, *Journ. Am. Chem. Soc.*, **51**, 2487 (1929); ○, new data.   Cyclopolymethylenes: △, Ruzicka and co-workers, *Helv. Chim. Acta*, **9**, 499 (1926); **11**, 496 (1928).

crosses are Hildebrand and Wachter's estimates of the best values for hydrocarbons in the range C_{19}–C_{36}. We have used a method of plotting similar to that suggested by Austin (10) and have included the values for the three previously known hydrocarbons above $C_{36}H_{74}$. These are $C_{54}H_{110}$, $C_{62}H_{126}$ and $C_{64}H_{130}$, all described by Gascard (8). Our data and those of Gascard fall very close to the same smooth curve which fits the best data for the lower hydrocarbons, and this fact incidentally affords confirmation of Hildebrand and Wachter's contention that the melting points accepted by the "International Critical Tables" for some of the hydrocarbons in the range C_{24} to C_{32} are much too high. Hell and Haegele described dimyricyl in 1889 (11) and ascribed to it the formula $C_{60}H_{122}$. This ascription acquired the sanction of recognition by Beilstein (third and fourth editions) and remained unquestioned until evidence that the myricyl radical contains 31 carbon atoms appeared. In 1921 Gascard (8) concluded that Hell and Haegele's hydrocarbon was $C_{62}H_{124}$ and that hexacontane had never been prepared. Our data confirm this conclusion. Hexacontane melts at 98.5 to 99.3°, while the observed melting points ascribed to dimyricyl have ranged from 100.5–102°.

Independent proof of the identity of the six hydrocarbons is furnished by x-ray diffraction patterns which have been obtained by Dr. A. W. Kenney and will be described in a separate publication.

Melting point data are available for only five cyclic polymethylenes above C_{10}. These fragmentary data do not fall on any smooth curve (see Fig. 1), but they are all widely enough separated from the data for the normal paraffins to provide additional assurance that none of our paraffin compounds are cyclic.

Under the heading distillation temperature in Table I are listed the minimum bath temperatures required to effect evaporation at a moderate rate in the molecular still. These temperatures are quite characteristic since they are, in each case, only a few degrees above the temperatures at which no distillation occurs. Using the Langmuir formula (6) it is possible to make a rough calculation of the order of magnitude of the vapor pressures of these hydrocarbons from the minimum distillation temperatures. Such calculations indicate a value less than 0.01 mm. for heptacontane at 300° and a value less than 1 mm. for triacontane at 100°. Heptacontane has a molecular weight of 983, and it is probable that no organic compound of much higher molecular weight than this can ever be distilled under any experimental conditions however favorable. The residue remaining from the removal of the heptacontane undoubtedly contained some octacontane, but none of this distilled out at a bath temperature of 300° and when the temperature was raised higher than this, decomposition set in. This experimental result agrees remarkably well with the inferences to be drawn from the data presented by Meyer and Dunkel (12). From these data one can calculate that the molecular cohesion of heptacontane will be about 71,000 calories and that of octacontane about 81,000 calories. Since the heat of separation of the carbon–carbon bond is about 75,000 calories, it should be possible to distil the first of these compounds, but not the second. Saturated paraffins have, in general, a lower molecular cohesion for a given molecular weight than any other types of compounds, and hence the limit of distillability will be found at a lower molecular weight for other compounds than hydrocarbons. These results are also in agreement with data of a different kind presented by Burch (13) who, by distilling a Pennsylvania petroleum in a molecular still, obtained as the highest distillable fraction a material having an apparent average molecular weight of 801 and a residue of apparent molecular weight of 1550.

The physical properties of n-heptacontane are similar to those ascribed to dohexacontane and tetrahexacontane. It is very slightly soluble in boiling alcohol, ether or petroleum ether, but crystallizes well in the form of minute needles from hot butyl acetate or benzene. It dries to a starch-like powder which has a great tendency to become electrified.

It was hoped that it might be possible to isolate hydrocarbons much higher than heptacontane, since information concerning simple individuals of very high molecular weight would be of great importance to the study of macromolecular materials generally, but there seems little probability of achieving this result without some change in method or advance in technique. The residue from which the n-heptacontane was distilled is a mixture which undoubtedly contains n-octacontane, n-nonacontane, n-decacontane and still higher hydrocarbons. It is readily soluble in hot butyl acetate (except for a trace of insoluble and infusible material), and it separates as a powder melting at 110–114°. Its apparent average molecular weight in boiling benzene is about 1300. (Calcd. for $C_{90}H_{182}$, 1263.) By extraction with hot ethylene chloride, it was separated into fractions melting at 100–107°, 106–111° and 110–114°. In a sense this mixture is a polymeric homologous series, but its solubility is much lower than that of such supposedly analogous series of higher molecular weight as polystyrene and hydro-rubber. It resembles a probably similar but more complex mixture of hydrocarbons obtained by Fischer and Tropsch by the catalytic hydrogenation of carbon monoxide (14).

There is one point bearing on the behavior of highly polymeric materials which is capable of a rough preliminary test with the series of hydrocarbons described above. It has been suggested (15) that the apparent decrease of molecular weight (decrease of viscosity, etc.), which is observed when rubber and other very high polymers are gently heated or treated with certain mild chemical agents or subjected to mechanical stresses, is real and is due to the fact that the thermal stability of molecules decreases continuously with increasing size, and in these materials has reached so low a value that cracking occurs at slightly above room temperature. Samples of each of the hydrocarbons from C_{30} to C_{70} were sealed off in small bulbs under nitrogen and heated side by side in a metal-bath. After five minutes at 400° all the melting points were unchanged. After five minutes at 410° the melting point of C_{70} was lowered from 106–107° to 104–105°. The melt, moreover, was not clear as before but turbid. The turbidity disappeared rather sharply at 110°—like a liquid crystal. The melting points of the other hydrocarbons were substantially unchanged, but, except for C_{30}, they all gave hazy melts which cleared up only at temperatures somewhat above their true melting points. After five minutes more at 420° all the melting points had become lower (that of C_{70} most) and there was some coloration. The C_{30} was white, the C_{40} was cream-colored and the higher hydrocarbons in regular order were increasingly darker. When the tubes were finally opened after five minutes more at each of the temperatures 430, 450 and 470°, they were found to contain considerable gas—most above the C_{70} and least above the C_{30}. Thus, the decrease in thermal stability with increasing molecular weight which is so marked in passing from methane (ca. 700°) (16) to ethane (ca. 550°) (17), and from ethane to hexadecane (ca. 470°) (18) is still detectable in going from triacontane to heptacontane, but it has already fallen to such a small value that it would be somewhat unsafe to infer that a paraffin hydrocarbon of molecular weight 200,000 or even greater might not persist at room temperature.

Mechanism of the Action of Sodium on Decamethylene Bromide.—It has already been pointed out that all the observed products of this reaction are accounted for by assuming replacement of the bromine atoms of the halide by sodium, and the subsequent coupling of this with other molecules of the halide, or its reaction with the solvent. The absence of cyclic hydrocarbons is not surprising since, although the higher cycloparaffins are no less stable than cyclohexane (19), the formation of large rings in bifunctional reactions occurs only under very exceptional conditions (20). In the formation of esters from ω-hydroxy acids, amides from amino acids and anhydrides from dibasic acids, intramolecular reaction occurs exclusively only if there is a possibility of forming a 5- or a 6-membered ring. The behavior of alkylene halides toward metals however is peculiar in that there seems to be little tendency toward intramolecular reaction even when a 5- or a 6-membered ring might be formed. Thus the action of magnesium on alkylene halides leads to considerable coupling, but even from pentamethylene halides no cyclic hydrocarbon is formed (21). This suggests that the coupling perhaps occurs largely at the metal surface where the atoms at the ends of the chains may be fixed by forces of adsorption and their freedom of intramolecular approach hindered.

Our main objective in the experiments described above was to prepare normal paraffins of very high molecular weight, and we made a number of attempts to adjust the experimental conditions so as to increase the length of the reaction chains. We treated decamethylene bromide with molten sodium in boiling butyl ether, with liquid sodium–potassium alloy in ethyl ether, with molten sodium in boiling octane and with finely divided sodium in the absence of a solvent. There was no evidence of the formation of considerable amounts of paraffins higher than C_{100} in any of these experiments. We also prepared decamethylene dimagnesium bromide and treated it with cupric chloride in the expectation that products of the formula $BrMg[(CH_2)_{10}]_x MgBr$ would be formed. The chief product (71%), however, after the addition of water, was a volatile liquid apparently chiefly composed of decane and decene. The amount of higher boiling material (20%) did not exceed that which would arise from the coupling products usually produced in the formation of such reagents as decamethylene dimagnesium bromide (21).

Preparation of Decamethylene Bromide.—The preparation, in good yields, of a whole series of polymethylene bromides from the glycols *via* the esters of the corresponding dibasic acids has been described by Chuit (22) but without great experimental detail. We first attempted to reduce ethyl sebacate by Levene and Allen's modification (23) of the original Bouveault procedure (24). In this modification, which has given good results in the reduction of esters of monobasic acids, the sodium is first granulated by stirring in hot toluene, and the reaction mixture is vigorously stirred during the addition of the alcohol–ester mixture. This procedure gave very poor yields of decamethylene glycol; the yields were increased by diminishing the speed of stirring and became quite good when the stirring was omitted altogether. The procedure finally adopted was almost identical with that of Bouveault, and the details are given below.

A condenser having a length of 2 meters and an inside diameter of about 2.5 cm. is connected with the side neck of a 5-liter two-necked round-bottomed flask, and the central neck of the flask is provided with a 1-liter dropping funnel. One hundred and fifteen grams (5 atoms) of sodium in a single piece or in two or three large pieces is placed in the flask. One hundred and twenty-nine grams (0.5 mole) of ethyl sebacate is dissolved in one liter of thoroughly dried absolute ethyl alcohol and poured into the dropping funnel. One hundred and fifty to two hundred cubic centimeters of the alcohol–ester mixture is allowed to fall onto the sodium at once. After two or three minutes the reaction becomes vigorous and the sodium melts. As soon as the sodium has melted another portion (about 100 cc.) of the alcohol–ester mixture is suddenly added. This causes the molten sodium to break up into fine particles, and the reaction becomes much more vigorous. The rest of the alcohol–ester mixture is then added as rapidly as possible (five to six minutes). As soon as the vigor of the reaction has somewhat subsided, the flask is heated by an oil-bath to 110–115° until most of the sodium has dissolved. The ethyl alcohol is then removed from the reaction mixture by steam distillation, and the glycol is removed from the residue by extended (about seventy-two hours) continuous extraction with ether. The glycol is purified by distillation. The combined yield from nine such runs was 593 g. or 75% of the theoretical.

Continuous ether extraction as a means of isolating glycols produced by the reduction of esters has been successfully used by C. S. Marvel (25); otherwise the above procedure is similar to that which has also been used by Müller for preparing a series of glycols (26).

Using the method described by Chuit (22), we obtained from decamethylene glycol only a 70% yield of bromide and this was contaminated with bromohydrin. The following modification of this method gave a purer product and a better yield.

Dry hydrogen bromide was led into a well-stirred melt of 255 g. (1.47 moles) of decamethylene glycol in an open flask until the mass was saturated. The temperature of a metal-bath surrounding the flask was kept at 90–95°. After saturation was complete the bath temperature was raised to 135–140° and a slow stream of hydrogen bromide was led in for six hours. The reaction mass was then cooled, diluted with benzene and decanted from a small amount of water remaining in the flask. The benzene was then removed by distillation, and the product distilled under diminished pressure; yield, 376 g. (85.5%); b. p., 168–172° (10 mm.).

Anal. Calcd. for $C_{10}H_{20}Br_2$: Br, 53.33. Found: Br, 53.16, 53.16.

We are indebted to Mr. W. L. McEwen for the preparation of decamethylene glycol.

Summary

By the action of sodium on decamethylene bromide in ether a mixture of paraffins of the general formula $H—[(CH_2)_{10}]_x—H$ has been prepared. By fractional distillation in the molecular still and by crystallization, the following individuals have been isolated from this mixture: *n*-eicosane, *n*-triacontane, *n*-tetracontane, *n*-pentacontane, *n*-hexacontane, *n*-heptacontane. The last four of these are new, and the last one has a higher molecular weight than any pure paraffin hydrocarbon hitherto described. The residue remaining from the separation of the hydrocarbons named amounts to about 25% of the total and is composed of still higher members of the same series which it has not yet been possible to separate. The mechanism of the reaction and the properties of the products are discussed.

Bibliography and Remarks

(1) Schorigin, *Ber.*, **40**, 3111 (1907); **43**, 1931 (1910); Schlubach and Goes, *ibid.*, **55**, 2889 (1922); Ziegler and Colonius, *Ann.*, **479**, 135 (1930).

(2) Schorigin, Ref. 1; *Ber.*, **41**, 2723 (1908).

(3) Bachmann and Clarke, *Journ. Am. Chem. Soc.*, **49**, 2089 (1927).

(4) Lewis, Hendricks and Yohe, *ibid.*, **50**, 1993 (1928).

(5) Franke and Kienberger, *Monatsh.*, **33**, 1189 (1912).

(6) Washburn, *Bur. Standards J. Research*, **2**, 476 (1929).

(7) Krafft, *Ber.*, **19**, 2220 (1886). The C$_{20}$ hydrocarbon of Franke and Kienberger (Ref. 5) which melted at 36° was unquestionably *n*-eicosane; and their C$_{40}$ hydrocarbon, which melted at 72°, was probably a mixture of *n*-triacontane and *n*-tetracontane.

(8) Gascard, *Ann. chim.*, [9] **15**, 332 (1921); Peterson, *Ber.*, **12**, 741 (1879).

(9) Hildebrand and Wachter, *Journ. Am. Chem. Soc.*, [9] **51**, 2487 (1929).

(10) Austin, *ibid.*, **52**, 1049 (1930).

(11) Hell and Haegele, *Ber.*, **22**, 502 (1889).

(12) Meyer, *Naturw.*, **16**, 781 (1928); Dunkel, *Z. physik. Chem.*, **138** 42 (1928).

(13) Burch, *Proc. Roy. Soc.* (London), **123**, 271 (1929).

(14) Fischer and Tropsch, *Brennstoff-Chemie*, **8**, 165 (1927).

(15) Staudinger, *Ber.*, **59**, 3037 (1926).

(16) Bone and Wheeler, *J. Chem. Soc.*, **81**, 542 (1902).

(17) Williams-Gardner, *Fuel Science Practice*, **4**, 430 (1925).

(18) Gault and Hessel, *Ann. chim.*, [10] **2**, 319 (1924).

(19) Ruzicka and co-workers, *Helv. Chim. Acta*, **9**, 499 (1926); **11**, 496 (1928).

(20) Carothers, *Journ. Am. Chem. Soc.*, **51**, 2548 (1929); and subsequent papers of this series.

(21) Zappi, *Bull. soc. chim.*, [4] **19**, 249 (1916); v. Braun and Sobecki, *Ber.*, **44**, 1918 (1911).

(22) Chuit, *Helv. Chim. Acta*, **9**, 264 (1926); Chuit and Hauser, *ibid.*, **12**, 850 (1929).

(23) Levene and Allen, *J. Biol. Chem.*, **27**, 443 (1916); cf. Adams and Marvel, *Univ. Illinois Bull.*, **20**, 50 (1922).

(24) Bouveault and Blanc, *Bull. soc. chim.*, [3] **31**, 666 (1904).

(25) Private communication.

(26) Müller, *Monatsh.*, **49**, 27 (1928).

VIII.   Amides from ε-Aminocaproic Acid*

ε-Aminocaproic acid when heated reacts intra- and intermolecularly, and there are formed 20–30% of the seven-membered lactam ring and 80–70% of a C-polymer, containing probably at least ten molecules of the amino acid. No information can be given as to the end group of the chain molecule, but it is improbable that the molecule is a multi-membered ring.

ε-Aminocaproic acid on being heated reacts with itself and yields two products—the corresponding 7-membered lactam, 20–30%, and an undistillable material of approximately the same composition, 80–70% (1).

* W. H. Carothers and G. J. Berchet; *Journ. Am. Chem. Soc.*, 52, 5289–91 (1930); Contribution No. 42 from the Experimental Station of E. I. du Pont de Nemours and Co.
Received October 9, 1930.   Published December 18, 1930.

The following related facts are of interest. δ-Aminobutyric acid and ε-aminovaleric acid readily lose water and yield the corresponding 5- and 6-membered lactams (2). No corresponding polymers are formed or known. The reaction of ζ-aminoheptoic acid with itself is apparently exclusively intermolecular, for it leads to an undistillable product quite different in its properties from the known 8-membered lactam (3). Similar relationships are found among the hydroxy acids: γ- and δ-hydroxy acids yield lactones; ε-hydroxy acids yield both lactones and polyesters (4) and the higher ω-hydroxy acids yield only the polyesters (5), although many of the higher lactones are known (6). Polyesters have now been studied in some detail (7), but (except for polypeptides) little attention has been devoted to the polyamides. In this paper we record some observations concerning the polyamide derived from ε-aminocaproic acid.

Water is rapidly evolved when ε-aminocaproic acid is heated above its melting point (e. g., to 210–220°). The polymer and the lactam which result are readily separated by allowing the latter to distil under diminished pressure, or by extracting it with boiling alcohol. In different experiments the yield of lactam was 20–30% and the polymer 80–70%. The same products were obtained by gradually heating the ethyl ester of the acid from 160 to 200° during six hours, and the yield of lactam was about 38%.

The polymer is a hard gray wax, insoluble in most organic solvents, but soluble in hot formamide, from which it separates as a microcrystalline powder melting at 212–214°. Its analytical composition agrees very closely with that required for the structural unit —NH—$(CH_2)_5$CO—.

Anal. Calcd. for $C_6H_{11}ON$: C, 63.71; H, 9.73. Found: C, 63.35, 63.62; H, 9.93, 10.07. A product from another preparation gave: C, 63.35, 63.45; H, 9.56, 9.43.

It is quantitatively hydrolyzed in six hours by boiling concentrated hydrochloric acid to ε-aminocaproic acid (identified by conversion to the *p*-toluenesulfonyl derivative, melting point and mixed melting point, 105–106°).

By partial hydrolysis, polyaminocaproylaminocaproic acids are formed. Thus, a sample of the polyamide was heated to boiling for one hour in concentrated hydrochloric acid solution, and the solution was diluted with water to precipitate the unchanged polymer (about 50%). The material, remaining in solution, on being treated with alkali and *p*-toluenesulfonyl chloride, gave a solid product which, after repeated crystallization, showed a neutral equivalent corresponding with the formula C_7H_7-SO_2-$[NH(CH_2)_5CO]_3$-$NH(CH_2)_5COOH$ (calcd., 607; found, 601). The structure of the polymer may, therefore, be represented by the formula

?—NH(CH₂)₅CO—[NH(CH₂)₅CO]ₓ—NH(CH₂)₅CO—?

It is a true condensation polymer and is formed directly from the amino acid by intermolecular reaction. This is proved by the fact that the lactam does not polymerize under the conditions of formation of the polyamide either in the presence or absence of catalysts. Moreover, no lactam can be obtained from the polyamide by heating it to high temperature in high vacuum. Thus there is no such reversible relationship between lactam and polyamide as is found (7c, e) to exist between six-membered cyclic esters and corresponding polyesters. Lactam and polyamide result from the amino acid by two independent and simultaneous processes. The lactam incidentally is really the 7-ring ⌐NH(CH₂)₅CO⌐ (8). This was proved by identifying its hydrolytic product with ε-aminocaproic acid through its p-toluenesulfonyl derivative by means of a mixed melting point.

The polyamide is sufficiently soluble in phenol to permit a determination of molecular weight by cryoscopy. Values obtained ranged from 800 to 1200, and since the errors of this method are such as to lead to low results it may be assumed that at least 10 molecules of the amino acid must have participated in the formation of a single molecule of the polyamide.

The question of the nature of the groups at the ends of the polyamide chains cannot yet be answered. The formation of large rings is very improbable on theoretical grounds (9), and in the formation of polyesters ring formation is known not to occur—the hydroxyl or carboxyl groups still persist at the ends of the polyester chain (7b, c, d, 5c). However, no certain evidence of the presence of terminal amino or carboxyl group in the molecule of the polyamide could be obtained. The polyamide dissolves readily in cold concentrated hydrochloric acid, but when the solution is diluted with water it separates unchanged and free from more than traces of halogen. It is not soluble in hot or cold aqueous sodium hydroxide nor does it form any sodium salt. It reacts with molten m-bromobenzoic anhydride and, in hot pyridine, with p-bromobenzene-sulfonyl chloride. The products contain bromine in amounts which correspond with derivatives of minimum molecular weights about 1100 and 1500, respectively, but in view of the failure of other reactions these cannot be accepted as evidence of the presence of free amino groups in the polyamide. At present we are inclined to assume that the amino and carboxyl groups which would normally be present at the ends of the polyamide chains are lost by pyrolysis. (The evolution of carbon dioxide during the formation of the polyamide could not be detected, but the vapors evolved had a strong amine odor.)

Summary

ε-Aminocaproic acid (or its ethyl ester) on being heated reacts with itself both intra- and intermolecularly and yields the 7-ring lactam (*ca.* 30%) and a polyamide (*ca.* 70%). The formation of a molecule of the latter probably involves at least ten molecules of the amino acid.

Bibliography and Remarks

(1) v. Braun, *Ber.*, **40**, 1840 (1907); Gabriel and Maas, *ibid.*, **32**, 1266 (1899).

(2) Gabriel, *ibid.*, **22**, 3338 (1889); Schotten, *ibid.*, **21**, 2240 (1888).

(3) v. Braun, *ibid.*, **40**, 1834 (1907); Wallach, *Ann.*, **312**, 205; **309**, 18 (1899); Manasse, *Ber.*, **35**, 1367 (1902).

(4) Baeyer and Seuffert, *ibid.*, **32**, 3619 (1899); Blaise and Koehler, *Compt. rend.*, **148**, 1772 (1909); Marvel and co-workers, *Journ. Am. Chem. Soc.*, **46**, 2838 (1924).

(5) (a) Blaise and Koehler, Ref. 4; (b) Chuit and Hauser, *Helv. Chim. Acta*, **12**, 4634 (1929); (c) Lycan and Adams, *Journ. Am. Chem. Soc.*, **51**, 625, 3450 (1929); (d) Blaise and Marcilly, *Bull. soc. chim.*, **31**, 308 (1904).

(6) Ruzicka and Stoll, *Helv. Chim. Acta*, **11**, 1159 (1928).

(7) (a) Lycan and Adams, *Journ. Am. Chem. Soc.*, Ref. 5c; (b) Carothers and Arvin, *ibid.*, **51**, 2560 (1929); (c) Carothers and Van Natta, *ibid.*, **52**, 314 (1930); (d) Carothers and Dorough, *ibid.*, **52**, 711 (1930); (e) Carothers, Dorough and Arvin, *ibid.*, **52**, 3292 (1930); (f) Chuit and Hauser, Ref. 5b; (g) Blaise and Marcilly, Ref. 5d; (h) Bougault and Bourdier, *J. pharm. chim.*, [6] **29**, 561 (1909); [6] **30**, 10 (1909).

(8) The shifting of a functional group down a chain in attempts to prepare large rings by bifunctional reactions has been reported by various investigators. See, for example Blaise and Koehler, Ref. 4.

(9) Carothers, *Journ. Am. Chem. Soc.*, **51**, 2556 (1929).

IX. Polymerization*

TABLE OF CONTENTS

* Wallace H. Carothers; *Chemical Reviews* **8**, 353–426 (1931); Communication No. 55 from the Experimental Station of the E. I. du Pont de Nemours and Company. Received March 21, 1931. Published June 1931.

This review is concerned with reactions that result in the combination of simple molecules to form materials of high molecular weight, and especially with the nature of such reactions and the structure and properties of the products. For the sake of comparison, the structures of certain natural polymers concerning which it is possible to make definite statements are briefly considered also. The literature on the subject of high polymers is most profuse, and from the theoretical side it has until very recently been contradictory and confused. For these reasons the present discussion is of necessity rather selective and critical. (For other general discussions of certain aspects of this field the reader may consult references 1 to 7 and 18.) It is necessary also to define especially the sense in which certain terms are to be used.

I. Definitions

1. **Current Definitions.**—It is generally agreed by organic chemists (9) that polymerization is chemical combination involving the operation of primary valence forces, and that the term polymer should not be used

(as it frequently is by physical and inorganic chemists) to name loose or vaguely defined molecular aggregates. Beyond this, however, there is not much agreement. The word polymer was introduced by Berzelius (12) nearly a century ago to recognize the fact that two compounds may have the same composition but different molecular weights, and he classified polymerism as a special type of isomerism. The accepted meaning of these terms has subsequently undergone considerable change, but current textbook definitions always state that a monomer and its polymer have the same composition, and it is usually either stated or implied that the process of polymerization is peculiar to unsaturated compounds and consists in self-addition. But recently discovered facts show that these conditions really are not satisfied in many instances to which the terms polymer and polymerization are applied. The formula of α-polyoxymethylene, for example, is not $(CH_2O)_x$, but $(CH_2O)_xH_2O$ (110).

It is true also that many compounds which are not unsaturated are capable of reacting with themselves to form products of high molecular weight, and that such reactions are quite commonly called polymerization. For example, benzyl chloride in the presence of aluminum chloride:

$$xC_6H_5CH_2Cl \rightarrow (C_7H_6)_x + xHCl$$

One can assume that the first step in this reaction is the elimination of HCl to yield the radical $C_6H_5CH=$, which, being unsaturated, is capable of reacting with itself by addition. On the other hand, it may be that this is simply a polymolecular Friedel Crafts reaction, the first step being the formation of $C_6H_5CH_2C_6H_4CH_2Cl$, which is capable of reacting with itself by the same mechanism and finally yielding a very long chain in which the chlorine content is negligible. If the usual definitions are adopted, this reaction can properly be called polymerization only if it proceeds by the first mechanism. Curiously enough, one actually finds in the literature cases in which the fact that a reaction is called polymerization is used to prove that the first step must be the formation of an unsaturated intermediate capable of reaction with itself by addition. It is perhaps unnecessary to say that the questions of the composition of high polymers and the mechanism of their formation are frequently rather intricate and cannot be solved in advance by definition.

2. **Proposed Definitions.**—It is more practical and useful (and also more consistent with actual usage) to define polymerization as any chemical combination of a number of similar molecules to form a single molecule. A polymer then will be any compound that can be formed by this process or degraded by the reverse process: formaldehyde can be regenerated

from polyoxymethylene by the action of heat; ethylene glycol can be obtained from polyethylene glycol by hydrolysis; cellulose can be hydrolyzed to glucose; and rubber can be formed by the reaction of isoprene with itself.

3. Linear and Non-linear Polymers.—The simplest and perhaps the most numerous and important high polymers are characterized structurally by the fact that their molecules are long chains built up from a repeating radical or unit. This type of structure may be represented by the general formula,

$$\ldots\ldots \text{—A—A—A—A—A—A—A—A—A—} \ldots\ldots$$

The repeating radical —A— is called the *structural unit*. The number and nature of these units determine the nature of the molecule. To complete this formula it is necessary to specify the disposition of the terminal valences; they may conceivably be mutually joined to form a cyclic structure or saturated by univalent groups. Whether the chain is open or closed, polymers of this class will be called *linear polymers*. It should be added that linear high polymers are usually mixtures containing chains of different lengths.

If the polymer is derived from a single compound the structural units of the chain will in general be identical, but the mutual reaction of two or more compounds that are chemically similar but not identical may lead to chains made up from two or more different units. Such products will be called linear mixed polymers.* Many polypeptides and proteins belong to this class. Non-linear polymers also exist; they can be formed, for example, by the cross linking of long chains into two- or three-dimensional structures.

4. Types of Compounds Capable of Polymerizing.—The step-by-step synthesis of long molecular chains containing a repeating unit is illustrated by Fischer's famous synthesis of polypeptides. Reactions of polymerization, however, lead to the formation of polymeric chains in a single operation. The capacity for self-combination of this kind is found among simple molecules of three different types: (*a*) unsaturated compounds; (*b*) cyclic compounds; (*c*) polyfunctional compounds. These are illustrated by the following examples.

(*a*) $nCH_2 \!=\! O + H_2O \rightarrow HO—CH_2O—CH_2O—\ldots—CH_2O—CH_2O—CH_2O—H$
  Formaldehyde α-Polyoxymethylene

(*b*) $n[CH_2CH_2O] + H_2O \rightarrow HO—CH_2CH_2O—CH_2CH_2O—\ldots—CH_2CH_2O—H$
  Ethylene oxide   Polyethylene glycol

* The term heteropolymer has also been suggested (23).

(c) n[HO—CH$_2$CH$_2$—OH] − (n − 1)H$_2$O →
    Ethylene glycol

$$HO—CH_2CH_2O—CH_2CH_2O—\ldots—CH_2CH_2O—H*$$
Polyethylene glycol

In each of these examples the product molecule is made up of a repeating series of identical units. Each unit corresponds with one molecule of the starting material. The latter, therefore, is called the monomer (*mer* = part). Ethylene glycol and ethylene oxide are both monomers since, although they differ in structure and composition, their molecules contain one —CH$_2$CH$_2$O— unit each. Similarly diethylene glycol, HO—CH$_2$CH$_2$O—CH$_2$CH$_2$O—H, is a dimer.

5. Types of Polymerization.—Molecules can combine to form larger molecules either by addition or by condensation,† and two corresponding types of polymerization may be recognized. The formation of polyoxymethylene from formaldehyde is addition or A polymerization. The formation of polyethylene glycol directly from ethylene glycol is condensation or C polymerization.** This second type of polymerization, although its existence as a general phenomenon has only recently been recognized (18), is especially simple both practically and theoretically since it involves the known behavior of typical functional groups.

6. Condensation Polymerizations and Bifunctional Reactions.—A general class of condensation polymerizations is represented by the equation

$$x—R—y + x—R—y + x—R—y + \ldots \rightarrow x—R—z—R—z—R—\ldots$$

In the formula x—R—y, R is a bivalent radical and x and y are functional groups capable of reacting with each other to form the known functional group z.   Thus if x is HO and y is COOH, z will be CO—O. The compounds x—R—y are called bifunctional compounds and their reactions, bifunctional reactions.   Reactions of the type, x—R—x + y—R′—y → *product*, may be included in this class.

* The direct polyintermolecular dehydration of ethylene glycol to polyethylene glycol not involving the intermediate formation of ethylene oxide is perhaps somewhat hypothetical.   It is used here merely as a formal illustration.

† The term condensation is used here to name any reaction that occurs with the formation of a new bond between atoms not already joined and proceeds with the elimination of elements (hydrogen, nitrogen, etc.) or of simple compounds (water, ethyl alcohol, ammonia, sodium bromide, etc.).   Examples are the Wurtz reaction, Friedel–Crafts reaction, esterification, etc.   See Kempf in *Houben-Weyl*, ref. 6, Volume II, p. 717.

** The term condensation polymerization was at one time applied by Staudinger (38) to addition polymerizations that involve the migration or displacement of a group or an atom, but its use in this sense has never become general.   In view of its obvious propriety for the purpose, it was adopted by the writer (18) as a name for polyintermolecular condensation.

Bifunctional reactions present the possibility of following various courses. (*a*) They may be intramolecular at the first stage. The product will then be the cyclic monomer

$$[R—z].$$

(*b*) Reaction may be intermolecular at the first stage and intramolecular at some subsequent stage. The product will then be a cyclic polymer

$$[(—R—z—)_n].$$

(*c*) Reaction may be exclusively intermolecular. In this case the product will be an open chain of the type x—R—z—R—z . . . . —R—z—R—y. These possibilities may be illustrated by the hydroxy acids of the series H—O—(CH₂)ₙ—CO—OH. The self-esterification of these might lead to the simple lactones

$$[O—(CH_2)_n—CO],$$

or to cyclic polyesters

$$[[O—(CH_2)_n—CO]_p]$$

or to open chain polyesters

$$H[O—(CH_2)_n—CO]_pOH.$$

All three of these possibilities can be realized.

II. Condensation Polymerization

1. **Polyesters.**—Bifunctional esterifications are especially suitable for the study of condensation polymerization, because esterification is a reversible reaction, and it is entirely free from side reactions under conditions that are easy to realize.

a. The self-esterification of hydroxy acids. It is well known that hydroxy acids react with themselves to form cyclic esters when there is the possibility of forming a 5- or a 6-membered ring: γ- and δ-hydroxy acids lead to the corresponding lactones, and α-hydroxy acids yield the cyclic dimers. Thus glycolic acid reacts with itself to form glycolide:*

$$2HO—CH_2—COOH → [O—CH_2—CO—O—CH_2—CO] + 2H_2O$$

The γ-lactones are stable substances, but the δ-lactones and glycolide and its analogs on being heated are rapidly transformed into polyesters of

---

* But it is by no means certain that the glycolide is ever formed through the steps glycolic acid → glycolylglycolic acid → glycolide. Dietzel and Krug (19) have shown that in the self-esterification of lactic acid the primary steps are: lactic acid → lactyllactic acid → polylactyllactic acids. Lactide when it is formed results from the depolymerization of these polylactyllactic acids.

high molecular weight. This peculiar behavior of the 6-membered cyclic esters is considered in more detail in a later paragraph.

No information is available concerning the behavior of the simplest ε-hydroxy acid, hydroxycaproic acid, but the corresponding bromo acid when treated with sodium ethylate in alcohol solution gives a poor yield of the seven-membered lactone (37). The chief product is an undistillable material, undoubtedly polyester. ε-Hydroxycaprylic acid, C_2H_5—CH-OH—$(CH_2)_4$—COOH is partly converted into the corresponding seven-membered lactone on being heated, but the next member of this series, C_2H_5—CHOH—$(CH_2)_5$—COOH, under the same conditions gives only an undistillable residue (24).

Larger lactones containing rings of fourteen to eighteen atoms are known (25), and also β-lactones (4-membered rings) (26, 27). All of these are fairly stable compounds, but none of them has ever been prepared directly from the corresponding acid.*

The attempt to prepare self-esters from simple β-hydroxy acids results merely in dehydration to the unsaturated acid, but in hydroxypivalic acid, HO—CH_2—$C(CH_3)_2$—COOH, this usual behavior is impossible because of the absence of any α-hydrogen. The self-esterification of this acid has been studied by Blaise and Marcilly (28). It occurs at 200°C. or at lower temperatures in the presence of certain catalysts. The product is a microcrystalline powder insoluble in most organic solvents. It forms sodium salts insoluble in cold water, and it is readily hydrolyzed to hydroxypivalic acid. These facts clearly indicate a structure of the type

$$HO—CH_2—C(CH_3)_2—COO—[—CH_2—C(CH_3)_2—COO—]_n—CH_2—C(CH_3)_2—COOH$$

and on the basis of molecular weight and analytical data Blaise and Marcilly assign to n the value 4.

In regard to the higher ω-hydroxy acids, Chuit and Hausser (29) have recently synthesized the entire series from HO—$(CH_2)_7$—COOH to HO—$(CH_2)_{20}$—COOH. All these acids readily undergo self-esterification on being heated. The products are not the corresponding lactones (which in several cases are known), but solid acidic materials whose properties are

* Kerschbaum (36) records various attempts to prepare the lactone of ambrettolic acid (hexadecene-7-ol-16-acid-1) from the acid obtained by hydrolyzing the naturally occurring lactone. By heating the acid he obtained a small amount of oil which, from its odor, was inferred to contain lactone. The chief product, however, was a non-volatile material soluble in alkali. Neither Chuit and Hausser (29) nor Lycan and Adams (30) report any evidence for the presence of lactone in the self-esters prepared from higher ω-hydroxy acids. Unpublished experiments made in this laboratory have failed to reveal the presence of any lactone among the products of the dehydration of ω-hydroxypentadecanoic acid.

TABLE I

POLYESTERS FROM GLYCOLS AND DIBASIC ACIDS

Compound	Formula of structural unit	Atoms in chain of structural unit	Average observed molecular weight	Average number of structural units per molecule	Physical properties
Tetramethylene carbonate..	—O—$(CH_2)_4$—O—CO—	7	1400	11–12	Microcrystalline powder, m. p. 59°
Pentamethylene carbonate..	—O—$(CH_2)_5$—O—CO—	8	2700	20–22	Microcrystalline powder, m. p. 44–46°
Hexamethylene carbonate...	—O—$(CH_2)_6$—O—CO—	9	2800	18–21	Microcrystalline powder, m. p. 55–60°
Decamethylene carbonate...	—O—$(CH_2)_{10}$—O—CO—	13	1800	8–10	Microcrystalline powder, m. p. 55°
Ethylene succinate.........	—O—$(CH_2)_2$—O—CO—$(CH_2)_2$—CO—	8	3000	20	Microcrystalline powder, m. p. 108°
Ethylene adipate...........	—O—$(CH_2)_2$—O—CO—$(CH_2)_4$—CO—	10	2900	17	Microcrystalline powder, m. p. 50°
Hexamethylene succinate...	—O—$(CH_2)_6$—O—CO—$(CH_2)_2$—CO—	12	3400	14	Microcrystalline powder, m. p. 57°
Ethylene sebacate..........	—O—$(CH_2)_2$—O—CO—$(CH_2)_8$—CO—	14	4000	13	Microcrystalline powder, m. p. 79°
Trimethylene sebacate......	—O—$(CH_2)_3$—O—CO—$(CH_2)_8$—CO—	15	3100	12	Microcrystalline powder, m. p. 56°

TABLE I—(Continued)

POLYESTERS FROM GLYCOLS AND DIBASIC ACIDS

Compound	Formula of structural unit	Atoms in chain of structural unit	Average observed molecular weight	Average number of structural units per molecule	Physical properties
Decamethylene adipate	—O—(CH$_2$)$_{10}$—O—CO—(CH$_2$)$_4$—CO—	18	3000	10	Microcrystalline powder, m. p. 77°
Decamethylene sebacate	—O—(CH$_2$)$_{10}$—O—CO—(CH$_2$)$_8$—CO—	22	3000	8	Microcrystalline powder, m. p. 74°
Ethylene phthalate	—O—(CH$_2$)$_2$—O—CO—C$_6$H$_4$—CO—	8	4800	25	Hard, transparent resin
Trimethylene phthalate	—O—(CH$_2$)$_3$—O—CO—C$_6$H$_4$—CO—	9	3100	14	Soft, transparent resin
Hexamethylene phthalate	—O(CH$_2$)$_6$—O—CO—C$_6$H$_4$—CO—	12	1800	7	Soft, transparent gum
Decamethylene phthalate	—O—(CH$_2$)$_{10}$—O—CO—C$_6$H$_4$—CO—	16	2100	7	Very viscous, transparent sirup
Trimethylene oxalate	—O—(CH$_2$)$_3$—O—CO—CO—	7	2000	15	Microcrystalline powder, m. p. 88°
Hexamethylene oxalate	—O—(CH$_2$)$_6$—O—CO—CO—	10	1100	7	Microcrystalline powder, m. p. 66°
Decamethylene oxalate	—O—(CH$_2$)$_{10}$—O—CO—CO—	14	1200	6	Microcrystalline powder, m. p. 79°
Polyester from hydroxydecanoic acid	—O—(CH$_2$)$_9$—CO—	11	5000	20	Microcrystalline powder, m. p. 76° (30)

consistent with the general formula HO—R—CO—O—R—CO—. . . .—O—R—COOH. Similar products obtained by the self-esterification of higher hydroxy acids have also been investigated by Bougalt and Bourdier (31) and by Lycan and Adams (30).

The presence of a terminal carboxyl group in each of these products proves that the ester formation is exclusively intermolecular. It should be possible, therefore, by regulating the degree of completeness of the esterification to obtain molecules of various lengths and, in particular, to obtain exceedingly long molecules. Such molecules are of especial interest in connection with the study of high polymers, since the nature of the acid used absolutely determines the structural unit of the polyester.

b. Polyesters from dibasic acids and glycols. The study of bifunctional esterifications from this standpoint was first undertaken by the writer and his collaborators (32 to 35). Dibasic acids and glycols were used as starting materials since these are more readily accessible than hydroxy acids, and they also permit more numerous structural variations in the ester product.

Esters derived from dibasic acids and glycols can be prepared by any of the typical reactions ordinarily used in the preparation of simple esters, *e. g.*:

(a)   HO—R—OH + HOOC—R'—COOH → —O—R—O—CO—R'—CO— + H_2O

(b)   HO—R—OH + EtOOC—R'—COOEt → —O—R—O—CO—R'—CO— + EtOH

(c)   HO—R—OH + C_6H_5OOC—R'—COOC$_6$H$_5$ → —O—R—O—CO—R'—CO— + C_6H_5OH

(d)   HO—R—OH + ClCO—R'—COCl → —O—R—O—CO—R'—CO— + HCl

(e)   Br—R—Br + AgOCO—R'—COOAg → —O—R—O—CO—R'—CO— + AgBr

In these equations —O—R—O—CO—R'—CO— represents the structural unit of the product. The studies have proved that the nature of the ester is completely determined by the number of atoms in the chain of the unit: if this number is five, the product is monomeric and cyclic (*i. e.*, it contains only one unit); if the number is six, the product can be obtained in both monomeric and polymeric forms and these are interconvertible; if the number is more than six, the product is exclusively polymeric.

The preparation of an ester of this last class may be illustrated by the action of succinic acid on ethylene glycol.* Succinic acid mixed with a

---

* The preparation of ethylene succinate by reaction between the acid and glycol was first carried out by Lourenco (17). Later Davidoff (40) and Vorländer (41) prepared it by various methods, and the latter investigator assigned to it the formula of a 16-membered cyclic dimer. His molecular weight determinations were apparently in error. The dimeric ester is now known (42, 34) and its properties are quite different from those of Vorländer's ester, which closely resembles the polymeric ester prepared from the acid and the glycol.

slight excess of glycol is heated in a distilling flask. At about 160–175°C. rapid esterification sets in, accompanied by the liberation of water. When no more water is evolved the temperature is raised to 220–250°C. and the pressure is reduced below 1 mm., whereupon most of the excess glycol distils. The ester product is completely non-volatile and remains in the distilling flask in the form of an exceedingly viscous liquid. When this is cooled it solidifies to a hard, brittle, opaque, white mass. This can be dissolved in cold chloroform and precipitated as a granular powder by the addition of ether or benzene. It can be recrystallized from hot ethyl acetate or a large volume of hot acetone. The recrystallized ester melts at about 102°C. A product having the same physical properties can be prepared in the same way by the action of diethyl succinate or diphenyl succinate on ethylene glycol. The reaction then consists in ester interchange and the volatile product liberated is alcohol or phenol.

By the method of direct esterification or by ester interchange the esters listed in Table I have been prepared. They are without exception highly polymeric, the molecular weights being on the average in the neighborhood of 3000. Molecular weights of several of the esters have been determined in a variety of solvents and by both freezing and boiling point methods, and within the limits of experimental error the same values have been found.

These esters show considerable similarity in their physical properties. They are completely non-volatile and all of them dissolve quite readily in cold chloroform. Those derived from the higher glycols or acids also dissolve in cold benzene, and in the solid state they are less hard and more wax-like than ethylene succinate. In spite of their high molecular weight and lack of complete homogeneity all these esters except the phthalates are crystalline. The melting points vary slightly from one preparation to another of a given ester and usually cover a range of about 2°.

The ethylene succinate described above is neutral, and its composition and molecular weight indicate the average formula*

$$HO—[(CH_2)_2—O—CO—(CH_2)_2—CO—O]_{22}—(CH_2)_2—OH,$$

* The molecules of this product certainly do not all have the same length, but on the other hand it appears to be much more nearly homogeneous than any products ever obtained by addition polymerization (polystyrene, etc.). In its qualitative solubility behavior it resembles a chemical individual, and fairly elaborate fractional crystallizations have failed to separate it into portions showing any considerable difference in their properties. The reason for its relatively great homogeneity lies in the conditions of its formation, which are such as to force much smaller molecules to react with themselves, but are not sufficiently drastic to cause the formation of much larger molecules. Under other conditions, polymeric mixtures having a wide range of molecular weights can be obtained.

i. e., it is an open chain derived from twenty-two molecules of acid and twenty-three molecules of glycol.

The hydroxyls at the end of this chain do not readily react with the usual reagents for alcohol groups; their sluggish behavior in this respect is characteristic of many high molecular weight materials. However, on being heated to a fairly high temperature with p-bromobenzoic anhydride the ester yields a di-p-bromobenzoyl derivative identified as such by its bromine content. The ester also reacts with molten succinic anhydride and yields an acidic ester whose neutral equivalent and observed molecular weight agree with the formula I d.

(I) $HO—CO—(CH_2)_2—CO—[—O—(CH_2)_2—O—CO—(CH_2)_2—CO]_x—OH$

I a, $x = 6$; I b, $x = 9$; I c, $x = 12$; I d, $x = 23$.

Similar acidic esters of lower molecular weight have also been obtained by partial esterification of glycol with an excess of succinic acid and fractional crystallization of the product. The observed molecular weights and neutral equivalents of the fractions corresponding to various values of x in formula I are indicated in Table II.

TABLE II

ACIDIC ETHYLENE SUCCINATES

Formula	Melting point °C.	Molecular weight Calculated from neutralization equivalent	Found by ebullioscopy	Sodium salt Melting point °C.	Molecular weight Calculated from sodium content
I a	73	1020	1070	91	1030
I b	82	1340	1380	97	1460
I c	90	1800	1580	100	2010
I d	98	3400	3110	109	3740

The presence of these terminal groups proves that the esterification of succinic acid by ethylene glycol is intermolecular at every stage.* The reaction evidently involves a series of condensations resulting in the production of ester molecules of progressively greater length. The first product might be

$HO(CH_2)_2OCO(CH_2)_2COOH$,

and the second

$HO(CH_2)_2OCO(CH_2)_2COO(CH_2)_2OCO(CH_2)_2COOH$.

* Lycan and Adams (30) also present convincing evidence of the open chain structures of polyesters derived from ω-hydroxydecanoic acid. They isolated fractions whose molecular weights estimated by titration with alkali ranged from 1000 to nearly 9000. All of these fractions formed potassium salts which were completely soluble in warm water.

Moreover, since both glycols and dibasic acids have a tendency to esterify at both ends simultaneously, it is reasonable to suppose that similar chains will be present, some of which are terminated at both ends by carboxyl and others by hydroxyl.   It is evident that an exceedingly large number of species may be involved in the ester equilibrium.*   But as the amount of water participating in the equilibrium is diminished by its constant removal, the smaller molecules are forced to couple with each other until finally practically none of them remains.   A further simplification of the kinds of molecular species present in the product is effected by using an excess of glycol, since this makes all the terminal groups alike.   For this purpose, it makes no difference how large an excess of glycol is used, provided the reaction mixture is finally heated for some time in a high vacuum, since under these conditions the reaction can be propagated by ester interchange. Thus it is possible to isolate the monomeric ester, bis-β-hydroxyethyl-succinate,

$$HO—(CH_2)_2—O—CO—(CH_2)_2—CO—O—(CH_2)_2—OH,$$

and this on being heated to 200°C. in a vacuum loses glycol and is converted into the neutral polyethylene succinate of molecular weight 3000 already described.   In view of this fact it is obvious that the accidental mutilation of the terminal groups ($e.$ $g.$, the loss of OH or CO_2) cannot in itself prohibit the progress of the coupling; the reaction can progress by ester interchange involving the last ester linkage.

Apparently the ultimate factors that set the attainable limit on the length of polyester molecules are purely physical.   As the molecular weight becomes greater, the reaction product becomes more viscous and the rate of diffusion of the volatile product (water or alcohol) to the surface becomes slower and slower.†   Moreover as the reaction progresses, the mobility of the reacting molecules diminishes and the relative concentration of the reactive groups becomes smaller.   All of these factors affect the rate and some of them affect the position of equilibrium, but the molecular weight at which a practical limit is reached will depend upon the temperature and pressure, the area and thickness of the reacting mass, etc., and by a suitable adjustment of these factors it is possible to obtain polyesters having very much higher molecular weights than those listed in Table I (51).

2. **Bifunctional Wurtz Reactions and Friedel Crafts Reactions.**—The action of sodium on polymethylene bromides, $Br(CH_2)_xBr$, leads in certain

---

* The kinetics of the reaction between phthalic anhydride and ethylene glycol have been studied by Kienle and Hovey (43).

† At least in the crystalline state polyesters adsorb water and hold it very tenaciously.

cases to the formation of cyclic hydrocarbons. Cyclopropane, cyclopentane, and cyclohexane have been prepared in this way. On the other hand, the action of sodium on decamethylene bromide does not yield any cyclic hydrocarbons.

In the presence of absolute ether this reaction proceeds very smoothly (44, 45). The product, which is for the most part insoluble in ether, consists of a complex mixture formed by the coupling of various numbers of molecules of the halide with each other, e. g.,

$$Br(CH_2)_{10}Br + 2Na + Br(CH_2)_{10}Br + 2Na + Br(CH_2)_{10}Br \rightarrow$$
$$Br(CH_2)_{30}Br + 4NaBr.$$

At the same time, owing to the participation of the ether in the reaction, most of the terminal bromine atoms are replaced by hydrogen.* This reduction of the terminal groups can finally be carried to completion by the action of sodium in boiling butyl ether, and the product then consists of a mixture having the general formula

$$H—[(CH_2)_{10}]_x—H$$

in which the values of x range from 1 to at least 10. The various members of this mixture up to and including $n\text{-}C_{70}H_{142}$ can be separated and isolated in a state of purity by fractional evaporation in a molecular still followed by crystallization. The identity of these fractions is established by their melting points and their x-ray diffraction patterns. There is no evidence of the presence of any materials in the mixture not belonging to the series

$$H—[(CH_2)_{10}]_x—H$$

About 25 per cent. of the total product consists of members standing above $C_{70}H_{142}$. These are not capable of being distilled, and they cannot be separated from each other by fractional crystallization. The average molecular weight of this material indicates that it must contain hydrocarbons at least as high as $C_{100}H_{202}$.

The following results of unpublished studies made by Dr. R. A. Jacobson in this laboratory are more or less closely related to those described above. The action of metallic sodium on p-dibromobenzene in absolute ether leads to a product corresponding in composition to the formula $Br—C_6H_4—(C_6H_4)_6—C_6H_4Br$. When the reaction is carried out in boiling toluene the product formed corresponds approximately in composition and

---

* In its mechanism the Wurtz reaction undoubtedly involves as its first step the formation of the sodium compound RNa (46). This normally couples with another molecule of the halide, but if ether is present it may be destroyed by the reaction
$$RNa + (C_2H_5)_2O \rightarrow RH + C_2H_4 + C_2H_5ONa \quad (47).$$

molecular weight to the formula Br—C_6H_4—$(C_6H_4)_{12}$—C_6H_4Br. Both of
these products are readily soluble in benzene. p-Xylylene bromide,
$BrCH_2$—C_6H_4—CH_2Br, when treated with sodium in hot toluene, yields a
very insoluble hydrocarbon which does not melt below 350°C. Apparently
a very large number of p-xylylene units participate in this coupling.

Benzyl chloride in the presence of aluminum chloride or ferric chloride
(see 10) reacts with itself to form resins of high molecular weight. This is
evidently a bifunctional Friedel Crafts reaction involving the progressive
coupling of successively longer chains with the elimination of hydrogen
chloride. Depending upon the conditions of their formation these resins
are fusible and soluble, or infusible and insoluble. Molecular weight values
indicate that the fusible resins are formed from 14 to 25 molecules of benzyl
chloride. The infusible resins are no doubt much more highly polymeric.
Benzyl fluoride in the presence of a trace of acid reacts very vigorously
with itself in a similar manner (11).

3. Other Bifunctional Reactions.—The number of possible types of
condensation polymers is practically unlimited. Although very few of
these possibilities have received any considerable study, the following examples at least indicate that the formation of such polymers is the usual
result of bifunctional reactions when structural features preclude the
formation of a 5- or a 6-membered ring.

a. Polyamides. The acids $NH_2(CH_2)_3COOH$ and $NH_2(CH_2)_4COOH$
are readily dehydrated to the corresponding monomeric lactams (48).
There is no record of either of these being caused to polymerize. The
next higher member yields two products (49, 50a). One of these (20–30
per cent.) is the lactam (7-membered ring), a distillable crystalline material; the other is a polyamide, an undistillable hard, waxy material insoluble in most solvents except concentrated hydrochloric acid, phenol, and
hot formamide. It can be hydrolyzed quantitatively to the amino acid.
Molecular weight determinations indicate the presence of at least ten
structural units in its molecule. The formation of this polymer is due
to direct intermolecular condensation and the formation of the lactam is
an independent reaction, for the latter cannot be polymerized under the
conditions that lead to the production of the former. The acid $NH_2(CH_2)_6$-
COOH on being dehydrated yields exclusively a product that is polymeric
(50), although the corresponding monomeric lactam has been prepared by
another method and is a stable substance (164). The acid $NH_2(CH_2)_{10}$-
COOH also yields only polyamide (51).

A number of polyamides have been prepared by Dr. J. E. Kirby in this
laboratory by the action of dibasic acids on aliphatic diamines. These

materials are all much less soluble, and when crystalline have much higher melting points than the analogous polyesters (51).

b. Polyamines. v. Braun observed (52) that the compound NH_2-$(CH_2)_6Cl$, unlike its immediate lower homologs, when it reacts with itself yields only a very small amount of the volatile cyclic base. The chief product is an undistillable, waxy solid, but this has never been studied in detail.

The formation of quaternary ammonium salts from various compounds of the series $(CH_3)_2N(CH_2)_nBr$ has been studied (53). The products have been assumed to be cyclic monomers or dimers, but it still remains to be demonstrated that none of them are linear polymers.

c. Polyacetals. The reaction between glycols and acetaldehyde (or acetylene) presents the possibility of forming cyclic acetals,

$$CH_3CH \overset{\displaystyle O}{\underset{\displaystyle O}{\diamond}} R$$

or polyacetals

$$HO—R—O—\underset{\displaystyle CH_3}{\overset{\displaystyle |}{CH}}—O—R—O—\underset{\displaystyle CH_3}{\overset{\displaystyle |}{CH}}—O—R—O—\underset{\displaystyle CH_3}{\overset{\displaystyle |}{CH}}—O—\ldots$$

This reaction has been studied by Hill and Hibbert (8). Ethylene and trimethylene glycols gave in excellent yields the cyclic acetals which are 5- and 6-atom rings. Tetramethylene glycol gave in poor yield a volatile compound which was apparently the monomeric cyclic acetal containing a 7-atom ring. A considerable part of the product was an undistillable sirup. The products from octamethylene and decamethylene glycols were also undistillable sirups. No molecular weight determinations are recorded, but it may be assumed that the undistillable products are polymeric. An analogous compound prepared in this laboratory (51) from benzaldehyde and diethylene glycol had an apparent molecular weight of about 1370.

d. Polyanhydrides. Dibasic acids of the series $HOOC(CH_2)_xCOOH$ are readily converted into the corresponding anhydrides. Malonic anhydride, the first member of the series, is polymeric (54). The next two members, succinic and·glutaric anhydrides, are known only as the monomeric 5- and 6-membered rings. The anhydrides of all the higher acids are polymeric.* The monomeric anhydrides are macrocrystalline, readily

* The known examples are anhydrides of adipic, pimelic, suberic, azelaic, sebacic (55) and hexadecamethylene dicarboxylic (51) acids. These if monomeric would be respectively, 7-, 8-, 9-, 10-, 11-, and 19-membered rings. Adipic anhydride can be obtained in both a monomeric and a polymeric form (56).

distillable solids; the polymeric anhydrides are non-volatile microcrystalline powders or waxes, and they are less soluble than the monomeric anhydrides. Both types are very reactive, but qualitatively their chemical behavior is not the same. The monomers react with aniline to give pure monoanilide; the polymers give a mixture of acid, monoanilide, and dianilide in the ratio 1:2:1. This is precisely in accordance with the calculated behavior of a very long chain having the general structure.

$$CO—R—CO—O—CO—R—CO—O—CO—R—CO—O—, \text{ etc.}$$

e. Grignard reactions. Bifunctional Grignard reagents such as BrMg-$(CH_2)_5$MgBr are capable of reacting with bifunctional reactants (dialdehydes, diketones, simple esters, etc.). The products may be rings or long chains. Several 5- and 6-atom rings have been prepared in this way, and in poor yield one 7-atom ring (57). In this laboratory it has been found (51) that decamethylene dimagnesium bromide reacts readily with methyl formate:

$$...—(CH_2)_{10}MgBr + O{=}D—OCH_3 + BrMg—... \rightarrow$$
$$\overset{|}{H}$$
$$...—[—(CH_2)_{10}—CH(OMgBr)—]_x—...$$

The final product is a microcrystalline solid readily soluble in various organic solvents and melting at about 120°C. Its chemical and analytical behavior shows that it is the expected linear polyalcohol containing about eight of the structural units $—(CH_2)_{10}—CHOH—$.

In the formation of bifunctional Grignard reagents some coupling always occurs: dibromides of the formula $Br(CH_2)_n Br$ yield considerable amounts of $BrMg(CH_2)_{2n}MgBr$ and progressively smaller amounts of higher coupling products. It is a curious fact that this reaction does not occur intramolecularly even in the case of pentamethylene bromide where it would lead to the formation of a 5-membered ring (154).

The coupling of simple Grignard reagents can be effected by the action of iodine, and this method has been applied by Grignard and Tcheoufaki to acetylene dimagnesium bromide (155). Products having the following formulas were isolated:

$$HC{\equiv}C—C{\equiv}CI; \quad HC{\equiv}C—C{\equiv}C—C{\equiv}C—I;$$

and also a form of carbon, which probably resulted from a continuation of the initial reaction in the same sense.

The attempt to prepare a Grignard reagent from *p*-xylylene bromide, $BrCH_2C_6H_4CH_2Br$, leads (51) to an insoluble hydrocarbon having the composition

$$(-CH_2C_6H_4CH_2-)_x.$$

The value of x is probably very large.

f. Sulfur and selenium compounds. The action of sodium sulfide on alkylene halides of the formula $X(CH_2)_nX$ leads to considerable yields of the expected cyclic products $(CH_2)_n > S$ only when these are 5- or 6-membered rings (162). Ethylene bromide gives white amorphous insoluble products (161); when prepared under certain conditions these are capable of being depolymerized by heat to yield the cyclic dimer, diethylene disulfide. Monomeric ethylene sulfide has been prepared by Delepine (86) by treating ethylene thiocyanate with sodium sulfide. It polymerizes spontaneously on standing. The chief product of the action of sodium sulfide on trimethylene halides is an amorphous polymer, although a small amount of the cyclic trimethylene sulfide can be obtained under certain conditions (87). Hexamethylene iodide also yields an amorphous polymer as the chief product (163, 87). v. Braun suggests that its formula is probably

$$I(CH_2)_6 \cdot S \cdot (CH_2)_6 \ldots S(CH_2)_6I,$$

but no estimates of its molecular weight have been presented.

The amorphous material formed from ethylene chloride and sodium sulfide is capable of being molded into a product which is very resistant to solvents and somewhat resembles rubber in its properties. One may infer that its molecular weight is very high. In recent patents (159) it is claimed that similar products can be obtained from alkylene halides generally.

Morgan and Burstall (160) state that the interaction of sodium selenide and the requisite alkylene dibromide leads readily to the production in good yields of cyclic seleno hydrocarbons containing 5- or 6-membered rings, but trimethylene bromide and sodium selenide give little cycloselenopropane. The main product is a sixfold polymer melting at 38–40°C.

g. Miscellaneous. A curious spontaneous progressive coupling is found in the action of water on methyl orthosilicate. The reaction may be formulated as follows:

$$CH_3O-\underset{\underset{OCH_3}{|}}{\overset{\overset{OCH_3}{|}}{Si}}-OCH_3 + H_2O \rightarrow CH_3O-\underset{\underset{OCH_3}{|}}{\overset{\overset{OCH_3}{|}}{Si}}-OH$$

$$2CH_3O-\underset{\underset{OCH_3}{|}}{\overset{\overset{OCH_3}{|}}{Si}}-OH \rightarrow CH_3O-\underset{\underset{OCH_3}{|}}{\overset{\overset{OCH_3}{|}}{Si}}-O-\underset{\underset{OCH_3}{|}}{\overset{\overset{OCH_3}{|}}{Si}}-OCH_3 + H_2O$$

Partial hydrolysis and coupling of this dimeric product lead to a tetramer, and so on. By suitably adjusting the initial ratio of water to ester it is possible to obtain samples representing various degrees of polymerization. The lower members have been isolated as chemical individuals by fractional distillation (156). The intermediate members are viscous undistillable liquids soluble in organic solvents. Solutions of these polymers are used in the preparation of paints having unusual properties (60). Films prepared from these paints harden by a continuation of the initial progressive hydrolysis and coupling, which yields as the final product pure silica. This synthesis incidentally furnishes an elegant proof of the three-dimensional polymeric structure of silica. The OCH_3 groups are responsible for the coupling, which results in the formation of long chains from the monomeric ester.

$$\cdots -\underset{\underset{OCH_3}{|}}{\overset{\overset{OCH_3}{|}}{Si}} -O- \underset{\underset{OCH_3}{|}}{\overset{\overset{OCH_3}{|}}{Si}} -O- \underset{\underset{OCH_3}{|}}{\overset{\overset{OCH_3}{|}}{Si}} -O- \underset{\underset{OCH_3}{|}}{\overset{\overset{OCH_3}{|}}{Si}} -O- \underset{\underset{OCH_3}{|}}{\overset{\overset{OCH_3}{|}}{Si}} -O- \cdots$$

Since each silicon atom in these chains still bears two OCH_3 groups, the coupling can continue in the other dimensions, yielding finally a 3-dimensional lattice in which each silicon atom is joined (through oxygen) to four others.

Metallic sodium acts on compounds of the type R_2SiCl_2 yielding chain structures composed of $-SiR_2-SiR_2-$ groups (157). These products are for the most part amorphous and glue-like.

The specially pronounced tendency toward the formation of 5- and 6-membered rings is frequently manifested in complex coördination compounds (148) and complex formation frequently fails when it would involve the formation of larger rings. Ethylene and trimethylene diamine yield crystalline nickelotriene succinimide compounds of the formula $[Nien_3]$-Suc_2 and $[Nitr_3]Suc_2$, but the compounds from tetra- and penta-methylene diamines are amorphous and, according to Tschugaeff (114), they must be represented as chains of unknown length:

$$H_2N(CH_2)_nNH_2\ldots \underset{\underset{Suc}{|}}{\overset{\overset{Suc}{|}}{Ni}}\ldots H_2N(CH_2)_nNH_2\ldots \underset{\underset{Suc}{|}}{\overset{\overset{Suc}{|}}{Ni}}\ldots$$

Bifunctional couplings probably occur in many reactions of oxidation and reduction. Busch and Schmidt have shown (22) that the catalytic reduction of aryl halides under some conditions proceeds to a considerable extent as follows:

$$2C_6H_5Br + 2H \rightarrow C_6H_5-C_6H_5 + 2HBr$$

When the same reaction is applied to p-diiodobenzene, terphenyl, $C_6H_5\cdot C_6H_4\cdot C_6H_5$, and p,p'-diphenyldiphenyl are obtained.

A preliminary stage in the oxidation of aniline to aniline black is the formation of long chains of the following type (20),

$$C_6H_5\cdot NH\cdot C_6H_4\cdot NH\cdot C_6H_4\cdot NH\cdot C_6H_4\cdot NH\cdot C_6H_4\cdot NH\cdot C_6H_4\cdot NH\cdot C_6H_4\cdot NH\cdot C_6H_4\cdot NH_2.$$

In a similar way the oxidation of phenols may lead to the formation of polyphenylene ethers (21). Substituted polyphenylene ethers of high molecular weight are obtained by the condensation polymerization of silver salts of halogenated phenols (173).

4. Stereochemical Factors Involved in Condensation Polymerization.—Bifunctional reactions always present the possibility of following two courses—they may lead to ring closure, or to progressive coupling—but the very numerous studies of such reactions have been concerned almost exclusively with ring closure. The possibility of progressive coupling has frequently been ignored or rejected as unlikely, and highly improbable cyclic structures have occasionally been assigned to products on the ground merely that they were the result of bifunctional reactions. In other cases the actual products have been discarded simply because they were obviously not the expected cyclic products. This attitude has certainly been partly responsible for the comparative meagerness of the literature on condensation polymers. The examples cited in the previous paragraphs show, however, that bifunctional reactions may proceed in a strictly normal fashion by progressive coupling and result in the formation of large molecules, and that, considering any particular homologous series, this type of reaction is the rule and ring closure is the exception.

This is not an especially astonishing conclusion. Intermolecular reaction is a perfectly general phenomenon; intramolecular reaction is a peculiar and special kind of happening. This is immediately evident from the consideration that if two groups are to react they must meet, *i. e.*, they must approach each other very closely. If the groups are not present in the same molecules, such approach is always possible as long as the molecules are free to move about. But two groups, x and y, that are present at opposite ends of a single molecule are capable of approaching each other only if the architecture of the molecule permits, and even if such approach is permissible it does not necessarily follow that it will occur, or if it occurs that it will be effective. Meanwhile the x groups of this molecule are continually colliding with y groups of other similar molecules. From this standpoint progressive coupling in bifunctional reactions is inherently more probable, generally speaking, than ring closure, and the latter, if it occurs to the exclusion of the former, must be peculiarly favored by some special factors.

The reasons for the great difference in the relative ease with which different types of rings are formed has been the subject of much speculation, and two factors that have frequently been assumed to be of self-evident importance are the relative energy content of the rings and their stability or degree of strain. There is, however, no theoretical justification for this assumption (58), and the facts show that neither of these factors can possibly be decisive. Thus, the action of sodium on propylene bromide yields cyclopropane, not cyclohexane, although the latter has a much lower energy content per unit and is less highly strained than the former.

On the other hand spatial relations in the reacting compound must of necessity have a great influence on the possibility of ring formation. The atoms of the benzene ring, for example, and all the atoms joined directly to it lie in the same plane (59), and to link the two *para* positions of the ring together through a chain of less than four or five accessory atoms would require a very improbable degree of distortion. Many attempts have been made to bring about such linkings, but the supposedly successful examples have proved on reëxamination to be fictitious (62). The same thing is true (61) of alleged examples of ring closure through the *p* and *p'* positions of diphenyl.

The stereochemistry of simple aliphatic chains is a rather complicated matter. Ruzicka's discovery that large aliphatic rings are no less stable than small ones is impossible to reconcile with the Baeyer strain theory, and the latter has been superseded by the Sachse-Mohr theory (66) which permits the existence of large rings in non-planar and strainless forms and is supported by a great deal of other evidence besides. The essential assumption in the Sachse-Mohr theory is simply the usual one that the four valences of the carbon atom are directed toward the corners of a tetrahedron and that there is free rotation about each single bond in a chain. Space models embodying these features can easily be made by joining small wire tetrahedra with rubber tubing in such a way that the arms that are being connected overlap. Rings constructed with such models show graphically that a 5-atom ring is uniplanar and free from strain; a 6-atom ring is highly strained unless two of the atoms are allowed to lie in a different plane from the other four; larger rings if they are to exist must be multiplanar and strainless, and they possess a mobility which makes it possible for them to assume a great multiplicity of shapes.*

The variety of possible configurations of an open chain is much greater than in a ring and it increases rapidly with the length of the chain. In the crystals of fatty acids and paraffins the chains probably are rigidly extended into a zigzag structure (13); but a model of such a chain is exceedingly flexible and mobile, and it seems very improbable that in the liquid condition or in solution the molecules retain their rigidly extended form. No doubt certain possible configurations are more probable than others, but there is at present no means of knowing just what these are.† It is clear, however, that the relative probability of close approach of the ends of a chain diminishes very rapidly as the length of the chain increases. Owing to the fewness of their separate points of rotation, 5- and 6-atom chains can assume relatively few configurations. In fact, if a space model of such a chain is supported at one of the bonds the entire structure can be rotated in such a way that the freely moving and unsupported ends collide at each rotation. This shows that there is a certain inevitability in the closure of such chains. Longer chains on the other hand can assume an extraordinary multiplicity of shapes without any close approach of the ends. The ends of the model can be brought together arbitrarily without any resistance, but as Mohr has pointed out (66) in the molecule itself one is dependent upon random collision,** "which will bring about a given form the more rarely the more forms are possible, i. e., the longer the chain."

One obvious and important implication of this theory is that a cyclic structure for linear high polymers is very improbable. The formation of such polymers usually depends upon the absence of any tendency toward ring closure in the early stages of the coupling, and the probability of ring closure will diminish as the length of the chain increases. This implica-

---

* Apparently the shape that they actually tend to assume involves the close approach of opposite sides of the ring; the ring consists essentially of two parallel chains joined at the end (67, 144, 145).

† Attempts to decide this question by studies of x-ray diffraction (88), electric moment (63), ionization constant (65), and numerous other properties (143) have led to the following rather contradictory conclusions: (a) the chains are straight zigzags; (b) they are straight zigzags except for the 5-atom chain which is coiled; (c) they have a helicoidal configuration which brings the first and fifth atoms very close together and introduces an anomaly in properties when the length of the chain is 5, 10 or 15 atoms. None of these configurations provides any mechanism for the close intramolecular approach of the ends of chains longer than 6 atoms.

** It seems quite possible that this dependence upon random collision is not inherently necessary. It may be that some selective control over molecular form is possible by the use of the orienting effects at surfaces, and such factors may perhaps come into play in the synthesis of large rings in nature. This suggests the possibility of some very interesting studies of a novel kind in surface chemistry.

tion is also in accord with the facts.   It is true that cyclic formulas have been assigned to various high polymers by Staudinger and by other investigators, but none of these formulas has been established.*   On the other hand, in a variety of instances open chain structures have been experimentally proved.

The presence of substituents and the nature of the terminal groups may be expected to modify the stereochemical behavior of chains.   Thus, if two atoms of a chain are adjacent atoms of a benzene ring their position with respect to each other is fixed, and the chances of intramolecular reaction are greater than in an analogous simple chain of the same length. (The latter will have one more axis of rotation than the former.)   It is not surprising therefore that the majority of the known 7- and 8-membered rings have at least two of their atoms members of a benzene ring.   The compound $NH_2(CH_2)_6Cl$ reacts with itself intramolecularly only to a slight extent, while with o-$NH_2C_6H_4(CH_2)_4Cl$ ring closure is almost quantitative (68).   Other similar examples might be cited (50, 163).

There is also some evidence to indicate that even simple substituents such as methyl groups on a chain may increase the tendency toward the formation of larger rings.   Researches in the diphenyl series (69) have established that substituent groups suitably placed may completely inhibit rotation about a nearby single bond, and a similar effect in aliphatic chains is at least conceivable.   Almost any restriction of the freedom of rotation of the atoms of a chain would, on the basis of the Sachse-Mohr theory, increase the chances of ring formation.

The influence of the nature of the terminal groups is seen in the fact that ω-hydroxy acids on dehydration give both lactone and polyester, while attempts to prepare 7-atom cyclic esters from dibasic acids and dihydric alcohols yield only polyesters.   Dilution also may be expected to

---

* In this connection merely negative evidence, e. g., the failure to detect terminal groups, is worthless.   Terminal groups may become lost or mutilated, or they may be present and yet fail to react.   High polymers are frequently very sluggish in their chemical behavior.

The tendency to resort to cyclic formulas does not aid in clarifying the problems of high polymers.   One can assume that the rubber molecule is an enormously large ring, but rubber is very susceptible to degradation by oxygen, heat, mechanical action, etc., and the first step in such degradation must cause the ring to be ruptured.   This product then presents all those problems which the assumption of a cyclic structure was designed to evade.

It seems evident that all polymerizations, whatever their mechanisms, must be progressive stepwise reactions.   The simultaneous combination of 100 molecules presents insuperable kinetic difficulties.   If this view is correct, ring closure can occur only as the last step in the reaction chain.   But at this stage the ends of the chain must be more remote from each other than at any earlier stage, and the opportunities for ring closure must be at a minimum.

favor ring formation as compared with progressive coupling (70), but all these effects are comparatively small.

a. Large rings. The question arises whether large rings are ever formed as the normal primary products of bifunctional reactions. Meyer and Jacobson in their textbook (147) devote over fifteen hundred pages to 5- and 6-membered heterocyclic compounds and only 17 pages to all larger rings. Most of the examples of this class of compounds that they accept as authentic fall into one or more of the following types: the ring contains only 7 or 8 atoms; two or more atoms of the ring are members of a benzene nucleus; the yields are very poor; the compound is formed by ring widening. There remain a few examples (*e. g.*, the cyclic duplomercaptal derived from acetone and pentamethylene dimercaptan) in which the evidence for a very large cyclic structure is good; but this evidence is no better than that on which the 16-membered cyclic formula for ethylene succinate was based (41), and ethylene succinate when reëxamined (32, 34) proved to be a linear polymer of high molecular weight.

Concerning the identity of large rings described by Ruzicka, it is not possible to entertain any doubt at all, but the methods required for the preparation of these materials present some illuminating peculiarities. His lactones were obtained from the corresponding cyclic ketones by oxidation (25),

$$(\overline{CH_2})_x\overline{CO} \rightarrow (\overline{CH_2})_x\overline{CO}^{-O}$$

i. e., the ring was already established in the starting material. All attempts to prepare the lactones by a bifunctional reaction, *e. g.*, from the hydroxy acids or from the silver salts of the bromo acids were unsuccessful. The ketones themselves (71) were obtained by heating the thorium salts of the dibasic acids to a very high temperature (400–500°C.). These conditions of violence lead to thermal rupture, and, whatever the primary products may be, the ultimate products must, for the most part, be volatile materials of fairly low molecular weight. The cyclic ketones are found mixed with a great variety of other materials among these volatile products. It is at least conceivable that the primary products in this reaction are linear polyketones and that the cyclic ketones are thermolysis products of the polymer.

In this connection it is interesting that large heterocyclic rings can also be obtained by thermolysis of the polyesters. Thus when polyethylene

TABLE III

LARGE CYCLIC ESTERS AND ANHYDRIDES

Compound	Formula	Atoms in ring	Melting point °C.	References
Ethylene succinate	$[O(CH_2)_2OCO(CH_2)_2CO—O(CH_2)_2OCO(CH_2)_2CO]$	16	130	42, 34
Tetramethylene carbonate	$[O(CH_2)_4OCO—O(CH_2)_4OCO]$	14	173	33
Trimethylene oxalate	$[O(CH_2)_3OCOCO—O(CH_2)_3OCOCO]$	14	176	64, 35
Dimeric lactone of ω-hydroxydecanoic acid	$[O(CH_2)_9CO—O(CH_2)_9CO]$	22	95.5	30
Dimeric sebacic anhydride	$[OCO(CH_2)_8CO—OCO(CH_2)_8CO]$	22	68	51

succinate is heated to 300°C. in a vacuum, it decomposes and yields a carbonaceous residue and a gaseous and liquid distillate.   From the latter a small amount of the sixteen-membered cyclic dimer can be obtained. Similar cyclic products have been obtained from tetramethylene carbonate, from trimethylene oxalate and from the potassium salt of the acetyl derivative of hydroxydecanoic acid.   The anhydride of sebacic acid can also be depolymerized under certain conditions to a cyclic dimer.   The properties of these compounds are listed in Table III.   Their identity is established by analytical data and repeated molecular weight determinations. They are distinguished from the corresponding polymers by their definite macrocrystallinity and relatively great solubility.   The attempts to obtain corresponding monomers which would be 7-, 8-, and 11-membered rings have been unsuccessful.   It seems possible that this failure may be due to purely practical difficulties, but so far as the data go they are in agreement with the fact that Ruzicka found the yields of the cyclic ketones of 8 to 12 atoms to be much less than the yields of the larger rings.   This fact is not easy to explain on the basis of the simple Sachse-Mohr theory presented above.   A possible explanation has recently been offered by Stoll and Stoll (67).

III.   Polymerization Involving Cyclic Compounds

1.   **Six-Membered Cyclic Esters.**—Among cyclic esters the property of undergoing reversible polymerization is characteristic of and peculiar to the 6-membered rings. γ-Butyrolactone cannot be polymerized, and no corresponding polyester is known.   Higher lactones, e. g.,

$$[O—(CH_2)_{15}—CO],$$

are stable substances which show no tendency to polymerize spontaneously, although polymers are the only products of the self-esterification of the corresponding hydroxy acids.   On the other hand, δ-valerolactone, a mobile liquid, gradually changes on standing to an opaque solid polymer, and from this the lactone can be regenerated by heating.

Various isolated examples of the polymerization of the 6-membered esters have been reported, but only a few of them have been described in any detail.   In this laboratory some study (mostly unpublished) has been made of the mechanism of this phenomenon.

The esters now known to exhibit this behavior are listed in Table IV. (In most cases neither the molecular weights nor the melting points of the polymers can be regarded as very significant, since both are dependent upon the conditions under which the polyester is formed.)

TABLE IV

6-MEMBERED CYCLIC ESTERS AND THEIR POLYMERS

Monomer	Formula	Monomer		Polymer		References
		Melting point °C.	Molecular weight	Melting point °C.	Molecular weight	
δ-Valerolactone	[O(CH₂)₄CO]	Liquid	114	52–53	2180	72, 51
α-Propyl-δ-valerolactone	[O—(CH₂)₃CH(C₃H₇)CO]	Liquid	142	Sirup	1000	51
Lactone of hydroxyethylglycolic acid	[O(CH₂)₂OCH₂CO]	31	102	62–64 87–89	460, 1700	73, 51
2,3,4-Trimethyl-arabonolactone	[OCH₂[CH(OCH₃)]₃CO]	45	170	135–138	2000	74
Ethylene oxalate	[O(CH₂)₂OCOCO]	143	116	159, 172	2300, insoluble	35
Propylene oxalate	[OCH₂CH(CH₃)OCOCO]	142	130	176–180	Insoluble	35
Trimethylene carbonate	[O(CH₂)₃OCO]	47	102	Glassy	4000	33
Glycolide	[OCH₂CO—OCH₂CO]	86	116	223	Insoluble	75, 76
Lactide	[OCH(CH₃)CO—OCH(CH₃)CO]	125	144	Resin	3000	77, 51

Some of these examples present special features worthy of mention. Monomeric trimethylene carbonate is a very soluble, crystalline solid. If it is heated with a trace of potassium carbonate to 130°C. for a few minutes, the mobile melt suddenly becomes very viscous and evolves a small amount of gas. The colorless sirup on being cooled solidifies to a stiff mass which shows an apparent molecular weight of about 4000. When heated in a vacuum this mass distils almost quantitatively, and the distillate consists of pure monomer.

Ethylene oxalate is a solid crystallizing in transparent, flat diamonds, melting at 143°C. These on standing for a few days in a stoppered container disintegrate to a powder, which consists of a mixture of polymers By extraction with cold solvents it can be separated into two definite fractions, one melting at 159°C. and having an apparent molecular weight of about 3000, and one melting at 173°C. and having an unknown but probably much higher molecular weight. These fractions on standing for a few days lose their identity; they are partly converted into each other and into monomer. It is interesting to note in connection with the rapidity of these transformations that monomeric ethylene oxalate is exceedingly sensitive to hydrolysis.

Drew and Haworth (74) have obtained the lactone of 2,3,4-trimethyl-*l*-arabonic acid in crystalline form (m. p. 45°C.) and have observed that in the presence of traces of hydrogen chloride it is converted into a crystalline polymeric powder. This has a considerably higher melting point, a lower solubility, and a lower specific rotation than the lactone. Its molecular weight (about 2000) indicates that it is derived from about 10 molecules of the latter. At 175°C. it distils completely *in vacuo*, and the distillate consists of pure lactone. Drew and Haworth ascribed a linear polyester structure to this polymer and were inclined to accept its crystallinity as evidence of its absolute homogeneity, but it seems much more probable that it is a polymeric mixture.

The ease of polymerization of the 6-membered cyclic esters appears to be related to their susceptibility to hydrolysis. In general, substitution increases the resistance to hydrolysis and diminishes the tendency to polymerize. Thus glycolide polymerizes spontaneously at the ordinary temperature, but lactide only on being heated or exposed to the action of catalysts. Attempts (51) to bring about the polymerization of analogs of glycolide derived from some of the higher α-hydroxy fatty acids have been unsuccessful.

These polyesters are formed from the monomers by a process of ester interchange

O—R—C=O + O—R—C=O + O—R—C=O + O—R—C=O + etc.

⇌ ... —O—R—CO—O—R—CO—O—R—CO—O—R—CO— ...

and the reverse transformation proceeds by a similar mechanism, as indicated by the arrows.   Both transformations are catalyzed by acids and bases—typical interchange catalysts.

Direct evidence for this interchange mechanism is found by polymerizing δ-valerolactone in the presence of various amounts of chloroacetic acid (51).   This acid actually participates in the reaction, and according to the amount present it regulates the length of the chains produced.   The effect of the acid may be compared with that which water might produce.   One molecule of water with one molecule of the lactone would simply yield the hydroxy acid.   A smaller amount of water would yield some hydroxy acid and this might react with the lactone to form a dimeric ester:

HO—R—COOH + O—R—CO → HO—R—CO—O—R—COOH.

If the amount of water were quite small the polyester molecule would have to be quite large.   Apparently chloroacetic acid functions in precisely the same way, and a comparison of the halogen content and neutral equivalent of the polyesters produced under various conditions not only establishes the open chain structure of the polymer, but also clearly indicates the mechanism of the reaction.

It remains to explain why only the 6-membered esters are capable of undergoing reversible transformation of this kind.   The presence of some strain in such esters is indicated by the great instability of δ-lactones as compared with γ-lactones (78, 79).   The Sachse-Mohr theory permits the existence of 6-atom rings in two isomeric strainless forms; but in simple rings these two isomeric forms have never been realized, and one is forced to conclude either that such rings are uniplanar and hence highly strained, or that the two isomeric forms are in dynamic equilibrium.   Practically this amounts to the same thing, since at each conversion the molecule must pass through the uniplanar position of strain.   These strains can be relieved by an ester interchange resulting in the formation of the polyester. The easy depolymerization of the resulting polyester is readily explained by the high degree of probability of the close approach of points 6 atoms apart in a chain.   Polyesters whose structural units are longer than 6 atoms are not readily depolymerized because of the improbability of close approach of the requisite atoms of the chain.   Cyclic esters of 5 atoms or of more than 6 atoms are not polymerized because their cyclic systems are free from strain.

In the formation of 6-membered cyclic esters from open chain compounds, either the monomer or the polymer may first be isolated according to the experimental conditions, but in either event it is not easy to prove that the form isolated is the primary product and not a polymerization or depolymerization product of the primary product. It seems fairly certain that simple δ-lactones may be formed directly from the corresponding hydroxy acids. On the other hand there is evidence (19) that the self-esterification of lactic acid yields only polylactyllactic acids and that lactide, when it is formed, is produced from these by depolymerization. Since lactide can itself be polymerized to a polylactyllactic acid, the latter furnishes an example of a polymer that can be formed either by addition or by condensation polymerization. In most cases, no doubt, either the cyclic ester or the polymer can be formed first depending upon the conditions.

2. Adipic Anhydride.—The behavior of adipic anhydride (56) illustrates the fact that the property of undergoing reversible polymerization of this type is not peculiar to the polyesters. In this case it is the 7-atom ring that is unstable. Succinic and glutaric anhydrides, the 5- and 6-atom rings, cannot be induced to polymerize. Sebacic anhydride is polymeric and cannot be depolymerized to a monomer. Adipic anhydride, when it is prepared from the acid, is also polymeric. It is a waxy solid which separates from solvents as a microcrystalline powder. On being heated *in vacuo* it is depolymerized to a considerable extent, and distillation occurs. The distillate is the monomeric adipic anhydride, a liquid freezing at about 21°C. In the presence of traces of moisture this very rapidly reverts to the waxy polymeric form.

A direct chemical proof of the actual structural difference between the two forms of adipic anhydride is possible (56). Both forms react very rapidly with aniline. The monomer, since it contains in its molecule only a single anhydride linkage, can yield only the monoanilide and this is in fact the only product formed.

$$[CO(CH_2)_4CO—O] + C_6H_5NH_2 \rightarrow HO—CO(CH_2)_4CO—NHC_6H_5.$$

But with the polyanhydride the nature of the final monomeric products will depend upon which side of the anhydride linkage is involved at successive steps:

$$...—CORCO—O—CORCO—O—CORCO—O—CORCO—O—CORCO—O—...$$
$$\quad RNH \quad H \quad RNH \quad H \quad H \quad NHR \quad RNH \quad H \quad RNH \quad H$$

If the molecule is infinitely long, *i. e.*, if it is so long that the terminal groups can be ignored, considerations of probability indicate that the product will be 50 per cent. monoanilide, 25 per cent. dianilide and 25 per cent. acid. Within the experimental error these are the yields actually obtained. This indicates that the molecule must be made up of at least 10 or 15 structural units.   A cyclic polymer would of course give the same result, but a low molecular weight is excluded by the properties of the material, and a cyclic structure of any kind is made improbable by considerations already discussed.

3.   Diketopiperazines and Polypeptides.—The curious behavior of the α-hydroxy acids is especially interesting in connection with the structure and formation of proteins, since these are for the most part derived from α-amino acids.   If glycine were to behave like glycolic acid, the following transformations could be realized.

$$NH_2-CH_2-COOH \quad \underset{+ H_2O}{\overset{- H_2O}{\rightleftarrows}} \quad \begin{array}{c} NH \\ \diagup \quad \diagdown \\ CO \qquad CH_2 \\ | \qquad\quad | \\ CH_2 \qquad CO \\ \diagdown \quad \diagup \\ NH \end{array} \quad \underset{\longleftarrow}{\overset{heat}{\longrightarrow}}$$

$$\downarrow{\scriptstyle - H_2O} \quad \uparrow{\scriptstyle + H_2O}$$

$$\ldots\ -NH-CH_2-CO-NH-CH_2-CO-NH-CH_2-CO-NH-CH_2-CO-\ \ldots$$

It appears that diketopiperazine can be polymerized, though with some difficulty (83), and polypeptides are readily obtained by the self-condensation of glycine and its esters.

Balbiano (80) in 1900 showed that when glycine is heated in glycerol solution it loses water and yields as the principal product a horn-like mass, together with a small amount of diketopiperazine.   The horn-like material is practically insoluble in all solvents except hot concentrated hydrochloric acid, and by hydrolysis it is converted to glycine.   Later this reaction was studied in more detail by Maillard (81), who showed that according to the conditions and time of heating more or less of the dimeric anhydride or the horn-like polymer can be obtained.   He also isolated an intermediate individual, triglycylglycine,

$$NH_2-CH_2-CO-NH-CH_2-CO-NH-CH_2-CO-NH-CH_2-COOH$$

This polypeptide is soluble in water, and Maillard made the curious observation that if its aqueous solutions contain diketopiperazine they deposit on standing an insoluble material.   Analytical evidence indicated that this material is a hexapeptide. Except for the solubility effect in aqueous solutions there is no obvious reason why this coupling of the diketopiperazine with the polypeptide should stop at the hexapeptide stage. In glycerol solution one may suppose that it continues progressively and results in the building up of a very long chain. The final horn-like product would then be a polypeptide containing a very large number of structural units— perhaps forty or more. Maillard assigns to this horn-like polymer the structure of a cyclopolyglycylglycine, but no convincing proof of the cyclic formula is presented, and on general grounds an open chain formula seems more probable.

The production of glycine anhydrides in glycerol solution probably involves the formation of glyceryl esters as transitory intermediates, but diketopiperazines and polypeptides can also be obtained by heating amino acids in the absence of a solvent. Curtius and Benrath (82) state that at high temperature the chief product from glycine is a pentapeptide.

The esters of glycine couple with themselves much more readily than the free acid. Curtius (84) showed that glycine ethyl ester loses alcohol even at the ordinary temperature. When water is present the chief product is diketopiperazine, but some polypeptide ester is formed at the same time. Under anhydrous conditions the latter is the chief product. When glycine ethyl ester is dissolved in a little dry ether and allowed to stand at the ordinary temperature, a crystalline precipitate gradually accumulates. This consists almost exclusively of the ethyl ester of triglycylglycine. The esters of such polypeptides are of course capable of coupling with themselves to form still longer molecules. Fischer (85) observed that when the methyl ester of alanylglycylglycine is heated to 100°C. it yields some hexapeptide ester and some less soluble amorphous material. Curtius (84) found that when his triglycylglycine ester was heated to 100°C. *in vacuo* it was converted into an insoluble infusible material having the composition —NHCH₂CO—. He assigned to this material the structure of a cyclic octapeptide, but a much more highly polymeric open chain structure seems more probable.

In connection with the polypeptides the behavior of the anhydrides of the N-carboxy amino acids may be mentioned (89). The compound

$$\begin{array}{c} CH_2—CO \\ | \qquad \diagdown O \\ NH—CO \end{array}$$

dissolves readily in water at 0°C. At 15°C. carbon dioxide is evolved and an aqueous solution of glycine results. If, however, the compound is rubbed with a little water at room temperature or is heated, carbon dioxide is lost immediately and an insoluble infusible material is the only other product. This has the composition —NHCH$_2$CO— and on hydrolysis it yields glycine. It appears to be similar to the horn-like product obtained by Balbiano (80). It is quite probably a polypeptide of very high molecular weight. The anhydrides of other N-carboxy α-amino acids behave in a similar fashion (90).

4. Ethylene Oxide (14, 15).—Ethylene oxide provides another example of the polymerization of a cyclic compound not involving double bond unsaturation. The polymerization is induced by various catalysts such as alkali metals, tertiary amines, and stannic chloride. Ultraviolet light or Florida earth is not effective. The product is a solid readily soluble in water and in most organic solvents except ether. Its properties vary somewhat according to the method of preparation. By fractional precipitation it can be separated into fractions ranging in apparent molecular weight from about 400 to nearly 5000. The lowest member of this series is liquid and the highest one a solid melting at about 59°C. The polyethylene oxides are not depolymerized by heat; but above 300°C. they decompose and yield a complicated mixture of products containing some acetaldehyde and acrolein. Roithner (15) assigns to polyethylene oxide the following formula,

$$[O\text{—}CH_2\text{—}CH_2\text{—}O\text{—}CH_2\text{—}CH_2\text{—}....\text{—}O\text{—}CH_2\text{—}CH_2]$$

but the evidence for this structure is largely negative. Unpublished work in this laboratory has led to the detection of terminal hydroxyl groups, indicating that the molecule is an open chain.

Ethylene oxide also polymerizes under certain conditions to yield dioxane (16). Apparently this shows no tendency to polymerize further as the 6-membered cyclic esters do.

IV. Addition Polymerization of Unsaturated Compounds

This is the only type of polymerization that is recognized by the usual definitions. Thus Cohen states (91) that "the property of undergoing polymerization is peculiar to unsaturated compounds, from a natural tendency to saturate themselves." So far as the formation of materials of high molecular weight is concerned, such reactions are much less clear-cut than bifunctional condensations, for the latter involve only the application of the known reactions of typical functional groups, and the general structural plan of the product may be inferred directly from the structure of the starting materials.   On the other hand, no clue to the intimate details of the mechanism of self-addition can be found in the reactions of the compound concerned with any compounds other than itself.   Ethylene oxide and certain cyclic esters and anhydrides already discussed polymerize by self-addition, but these reactions in some respects are radically different from the polymerization of compounds containing multiple linkages.

Under sufficiently drastic conditions almost any compound can be converted into a material of high molecular weight.   Thus methane when subjected to the action of alpha particles or to the silent electrical discharge is partly transformed with loss of hydrogen into higher hydrocarbons (165), and benzene in the electrodeless discharge is converted into insoluble, amorphous products (166).   The reaction of acetylene with itself illustrates how complicated the polymerization of an unsaturated compound may be. Polymerization at elevated temperature in the presence of active charcoal leads to a complicated mixture of hydrocarbons containing considerable amounts of benzene and naphthalene (167); the use of copper- or magnesium-containing catalysts yields (168) a completely insoluble amorphous powder (cuprene) of unknown structure, and similar products are obtained by the action of ultraviolet light (169), cathode rays (170), or alpha particles (171) on acetylene.   On the other hand, the action of the silent electrical discharge (172) at low temperature leads to the formation of considerable amounts of liquid products which contain highly unsaturated open chain compounds.

The brief discussion of addition polymerization contained in the following paragraphs is confined to a few of the simplest and most thoroughly studied cases.

1.   **Ethylene and Other Olefines.**—The rather extensive literature on the polymerization of ethylene has recently been reviewed by Stanley (92). Ethylene polymerizes less readily than most of its homologs and derivatives. The polymerization is accelerated by heat, pressure, ultraviolet light, the silent electric discharge, and by certain catalysts such as sulfuric acid (especially in the presence of salts of copper and mercury), zinc chloride, boron trifluoride, and aluminum fluoride.   The products are usually oils having a wide boiling range.   In general, they are not exclusively of the C_nH_{2n} type; hydrogenation, dehydrogenation, and cyclization may occur at the same time.   These products are commercially valuable, but too complicated to furnish any clue as to the mechanism of their formation.

Mignonac and Saint-Aunay (93), however, have succeeded in isolating the first products formed in the action of the silent electrical discharge on ethylene. These products are butene-1 and hexene-1. Pease (94) has found evidence of the presence of butene-1 in the products of the thermal polymerization, and from a study of the kinetics has concluded that this is a chain reaction. In effect at least this reaction involves at the first step the addition of ethylene, as $H + CH\!=\!CH_2$, to the double bond of another molecule of ethylene, and then a similar addition to butylene.

Lebedev and his collaborators (95) have presented interesting data on the early stages of the polymerization of isobutylene. They used especially Florida earth as a catalyst and obtained mixtures from which a whole series of polymers up through the heptamers was isolated. They found that the trimer was not polymerized under the conditions that lead to higher polymers from either the monomer or the dimer. Hence the higher polymers must be built up by the successive addition of monomer or dimer. As to the precise structure of these polymers very little is known.

2. **Vinyl Compounds.**—Substituted ethylenes of the type $CH_2\!=\!CH\!-\!R$, in which R is a negative group, polymerize much more readily than does ethylene itself. Examples are:

$CH_2\!=\!CH\!-\!C_6H_5$	Styrene (96)
$CH_2\!=\!CH\!-\!Cl(Br)$	Vinyl chloride (bromide) (97)
$CH_2\!=\!CH\!-\!O\!-\!COCH_3$	Vinyl acetate (98, 142)
$CH_2\!=\!CH\!-\!COOH$	Acrylic acid (99)
$CH_2\!=\!CH\!-\!CHO$	Acrolein (100)

Indene (101, 105)

The most extensive and important studies of the polymerization of vinyl compounds are those carried out by Staudinger and his co-workers. The behavior of styrene may be taken as typical. On standing or on being heated, this mobile, volatile liquid first becomes more viscous, then changes to a more or less tough elastic jelly, and finally it may become converted into an exceedingly hard brittle mass. This change is powerfully catalyzed by light and by atmospheric oxygen, and it is inhibited by certain antioxidants such as hydroquinone. Other catalysts that are effective in accelerating the change are organic peroxides and certain metallic halides such as stannic chloride and antimony chloride. If a little stannic chloride is added to an alcohol solution of styrene, the solution becomes warm and the polystyrene quickly separates as an amorphous mass.

Polystyrene is not a definite material having a constant set of properties. By whatever method it is prepared it can be separated by fractional extraction or precipitation into fractions having the same composition but different properties and molecular weights. The lower members are readily soluble in ether and the highest members are quite insoluble. The apparent molecular weights range from 1000 up to 25,000 or more (perhaps as high as 200,000). All these fractions are soluble in benzene, and the viscosity of the solutions increases progressively with increasing molecular weight. The average molecular weight of the crude polymer depends upon the conditions of its formation. Those formed very rapidly, *e. g.*, by the action of heat at high temperature or by the action of stannic chloride at ordinary temperature, have relatively low molecular weights. Those formed more slowly, *e. g.*, by spontaneous polymerization at room temperature, have much higher molecular weights.

The polystyrenes having molecular weights above 10,000 show colloidal behavior; they swell before dissolving, and the viscosity of their solutions is very high. Nevertheless, there is considerable evidence to show that these solutions are true molecular dispersions (102), and that the molecule and the colloidal particle are identical.

Chemically the polystyrols are completely saturated. They do not decolorize permanganate or absorb bromine. Under sufficiently drastic conditions they can be completely hydrogenated (in the benzene nucleus) without any significant change in molecular weight (103). On being heated to about 320°C. they revert to the monomer, styrene. It is doubtful if this reversion is ever quantitative.

The polymerization of styrene evidently involves the disappearance of the double bond and the formation of very large molecules. The simplest and most probable structure of these large molecules is that suggested by Staudinger.

$$\ldots-CH-CH_2-CH-CH_2-CH-CH_2-CH-CH_2-\ldots$$
$$\quad\;\; | \qquad\qquad | \qquad\qquad | \qquad\qquad |$$
$$\quad\; C_6H_5 \qquad\; C_6H_5 \qquad\; C_6H_5 \qquad\; C_6H_5$$

The polymerization of vinyl acetate is similar to that of styrene. In both cases the polymer first formed remains dissolved in the monomer, and the mixture of monomer and polymers can be obtained in the form of more or less tough, transparent, elastic masses. The chemical behavior of the polyvinyl acetate indicates that it is a mixture of molecules of various lengths built up according to the plan indicated in the formula

$$\ldots-CH_2-CH-CH_2-CH-CH_2-CH-CH_2-CH-CH_2-CH-\ldots$$
$$\qquad\qquad | \qquad\qquad | \qquad\qquad | \qquad\qquad | \qquad\qquad |$$
$$\qquad\quad OAc \qquad\; OAc \qquad\; OAc \qquad\; OAc \qquad\; OAc$$

The number of molecules of monomer involved probably ranges between forty and one hundred. By fractional precipitation, samples of different average molecular weights can be obtained, and these naturally differ somewhat in their physical properties. In general the polyvinyl acetates are soluble in organic solvents but not in water. As esters they are readily hydrolyzed. The products are acetic acid and polyvinyl alcohol:

$$\ldots\ldots-CH_2-CH-CH_2-CH-CH_2-CH-CH_2-CH-\ldots\ldots$$
$$\qquad\qquad\;\; | \qquad\quad | \qquad\quad | \qquad\quad |$$
$$\qquad\qquad OH \qquad\;\; OH \qquad\;\; OH \qquad\;\; OH$$

The latter as a polyhydroxy compound dissolves in water to form rather highly viscous solutions, but does not dissolve in organic solvents.

Acrylic acid also polymerizes very readily, yielding a product to which the following formula may be assigned.

$$\ldots-CH_2-CH-CH_2-CH-CH_2-CH-CH_2-CH-\ldots$$
$$\qquad\quad\; | \qquad\qquad | \qquad\qquad | \qquad\qquad |$$
$$\qquad\quad COOH \qquad COOH \qquad COOH \qquad COOH$$

As a highly polybasic acid it forms a sodium salt which dissolves in water to yield very viscous solutions. The acid itself also dissolves in water (the most highly polymeric varieties swell very strongly and dissolve with difficulty), but does not dissolve in the typical organic solvents. On the other hand, polyacrylic esters prepared by polymerizing acrylic esters are insoluble in water, but soluble in organic solvents.

The methyl ester of polyacrylic acid on being treated with methyl magnesium iodide yields a product corresponding approximately in composition to the expected polytertiary alcohol, and this on reduction yields a hydrocarbon. Although the composition of this hydrocarbon does not exactly correspond to that required by the expected structure

$$\ldots-CH_2-CH-CH_2-CH-\ldots$$
$$\qquad\qquad | \qquad\qquad\quad |$$
$$\qquad (CH_3)_2HC \qquad\quad CH(CH_3)_2$$

its high molecular weight proves that the ester from which it was derived is also really a material of high molecular weight, and that the units must be joined by carbon-carbon linkages.

The problem of arriving at a definite mechanism for the polymerization of vinyl compounds is complicated by the fact that neither the formation of the polymers nor their chemical behavior furnishes any certain clue to their structure. The general formula

$$\ldots-CH_2-CH-CH_2-CH-CH_2-CH-CH_2-CH-\ldots$$
$$\qquad\qquad | \qquad\qquad | \qquad\qquad | \qquad\qquad |$$
$$\qquad\qquad R \qquad\quad\; R \qquad\quad\; R \qquad\quad\; R$$

is perhaps more plausible than any other, since, as Staudinger has pointed out, it best accounts for the fact that some polyvinyl compounds (*e. g.*, polystyrene) are smoothly depolymerized by the action of heat: the recurring substituent would weaken the linkages of the chain at the points indicated by the dotted lines. But depolymerization is never quantitative, and it is at least conceivable that a fraction of the units of each chain are arranged in the reverse fashion:

$$...-CH-CH_2-CH_2-CH-CH-CH_2-CH_2-CH-...$$
$$\quad\ \ |\qquad\qquad\quad\ \ |\quad\ |\qquad\qquad\quad\ |$$
$$\quad\ \ R\qquad\qquad\quad\ \ R\quad\ R\qquad\qquad\quad\ R$$

It has already been mentioned that the first step in the polymerization of ethylene is the formation of butene-1 and the second step is the formation of hexene-1. Similar terminal unsaturations have been found by Whitby and Katz in a still longer series of polyindenes, and this suggests that the most plausible mechanism for the polymerization of vinyl compounds is "best represented as proceeding stepwise by the addition regularly of successive molecules of monomer to the double bond present at each stage of the polymerization immediately preceding" (105). This mechanism may be formulated as follows:

$$RCH{=}CH_2 + RCH{=}CH_2 \rightarrow RCH_2CH_2C(R){=}CH_2$$

$$RCH_2CH_2C(R){=}CH_2 + RCH{=}CH_2 \rightarrow RCH_2CH_2CH(R)CH_2C(R){=}CH_2, \text{ etc.}$$

Staudinger disagrees with this view. He claims that the polyindenes do not have any terminal unsaturations, and from analogies based on the behavior of α-methylstyrene (104) he assigns a cyclic formula to polyindene and polystyrene. α-Methylstyrene, $CH_2{=}C(CH_3)C_6H_5$, polymerizes much less readily than styrene, but the reaction may be caused to occur quite rapidly by certain catalysts, *e. g.*, stannic chloride (104). The principal product is the saturated dimer, a substituted cyclobutane. A smaller amount of a saturated trimer is formed at the same time, and in progressively smaller amounts saturated tetramer, pentamer, decamer, hexamer, heptamer, and octamer. On the basis of their physical and chemical properties Staudinger assumes that these higher polymers are respectively 6-, 8-, 10-, 12-, 14-, and 16-membered rings.

It should be observed however that these products are quite different from those obtained from styrene under similar conditions; moreover, the absence of the α-hydrogen makes it impossible for α-methylstyrene to polymerize by the mechanism suggested above for vinyl compounds generally. It is therefore scarcely permissible to conclude that the high polymers from styrene must be cyclic because the low polymers from α-

methylstyrene are cyclic. Other more general grounds for rejecting cyclic formulas for linear high ploymers have been presented in previous paragraphs.

The polymerization of vinyl compounds is enormously susceptible to catalytic and anticatalytic effects. Heat also accelerates the polymerization, and in general the more rapidly the polymer is formed, the lower is the average molecular weight of the product. Oxygen and peroxides are catalysts, and antioxidants act as inhibitors. Light, especially the shorter wave lengths of the visible spectrum, accelerates the polymerization. In certain cases the presence of oxygen inhibits this photochemical effect. With the aid of certain specific catalysts, it is possible to convert styrene and certain other vinyl compounds into dimers, but these are stable substances that show no tendency to polymerize further, and they differ structurally from the dimers that have been hypothecated as intermediates in the formation of the high polymers. Under conditions that result in the formation of the latter, no polymers of very low molecular weight can be detected. All these facts indicate that the formation of the high polymer is a chain reaction. The collision of an activated molecule of monomer with another molecule of monomer yields an active dimer capable of coupling with another molecule of monomer, and the activating energy persists in the polymeric chain until it has been built up to a considerable length. Kinetic studies of the polymerization of vinyl acetate (106) and styrene (107) support the idea of a chain mechanism.

3. Dienes.—Butadiene and isoprene are of especial interest in connection with rubber. Nobody knows whether in nature rubber is actually formed from isoprene or not; but it is true that rubber yields some isoprene on thermal decomposition, and that isoprene can be polymerized to a product which more or less resembles natural rubber. Similar products can also be produced from butadiene and from some of its derivatives. Efforts to produce synthetic rubber have led to hundreds of patents and various other publications. This subject is reviewed in a book by Schotz (108). There is space here to mention only two or three points.

Butadiene and isoprene polymerize much less readily than styrene, vinyl acetate, etc., but apparently they are subject to the same kind of accelerating influences. Among the catalysts that have been used are oxygen, peroxides, ozonides, alkali metals, alkali alkyls. When emulsified, especially in the presence of oxygen, they polymerize more rapidly than otherwise. It is claimed in many patents that the presence of proteins, gums, etc., in such emulsions has a favorable effect on the course of the reaction and results in products more nearly resembling natural rubber, but it seems probable that the advantages of such additions are largely imaginary. It is possible to prepare from isoprene and butadiene high polymers that have very little resemblance to natural rubber, and the problem of preparing a synthetic rubber of good quality is enormously complicated and difficult.

The structural unit in the polymeric chain from isoprene appears to be

$$-CH_2-\underset{\underset{CH_3}{|}}{C}=CH-CH_2-$$

In effect, the polymerization involves the union of a large number of these radicals derived from isoprene by the rearrangement of its bonds. Two such radicals might unite in three ways: 1,1; 1,4; 4,4. Midgley and Henne (109) have captured the first step in the reaction by carrying out the polymerization in the presence of sodium and alcohol so that the terminal valences of the dimer are hydrogenated. The structures of the three products, whose formulas are shown below, prove that all three types of combination occur.

$$CH_3-CH=\underset{\underset{CH_3}{|}}{C}-CH_2-CH_2-\underset{\underset{CH_3}{|}}{C}=CH-CH_3$$

$$CH_3-\underset{\underset{CH_3}{|}}{C}=CH-CH_2-CH_2-\underset{\underset{CH_3}{|}}{C}=CH-CH_3$$

$$CH_3-\underset{\underset{CH_3}{|}}{C}=CH-CH_2-CH_2-CH=\underset{\underset{CH_3}{|}}{C}-CH_3$$

This result indicates that the arrangement of the units in synthetic rubber formed under these conditions is less regular than in natural rubber, but it by no means proves that the actual mechanism of the reaction consists in the direct union of radicals corresponding in formula with the structural unit. The 1,4 addition of $H-$ + $-CH=C(CH_3)CH=CH_2$ to isoprene, for example, would lead to the same result.

4. Aldehydes.—The polymerization of formaldehyde under various conditions leads to polyoxymethylenes. These are microcrystalline powders, which in general cannot be melted or dissolved in organic solvents without decomposition. They have been very elaborately studied by Staudinger and his co-workers (110). These studies have proved that the molecules of the polyoxymethylenes are long chains of the type

$$....-O-CH_2-O-CH_2-O-CH_2-O-CH_2-O-CH_2-....$$

The chains contain from forty to at least one hundred structural units. The different varieties of polyoxymethylenes are distinguished by the nature of the terminal groups: in the α-variety the terminal groups are OH; in the β-variety they are OCH_3, and this variety is more inert chemically than the α-variety. By the action of acetic anhydride, the polyoxymethylenes are simultaneously degraded and acetylated. The product consists of a mixture of compounds of the series CH_3CO—$(O$—$CH_2)_x$—O—$COCH_3$. By distillation and crystallization, each individual of this series from $x = 1$ to $x = 20$ has been isolated in a fairly pure state. The melting points and boiling points of these individuals increase continuously with increasing molecular weight and their solubilities diminish. The successive members above $x = 20$ resemble each other so closely and their solubilities are so low, that they cannot be separated into pure fractions.

Formaldehyde also polymerizes to yield the cyclic trimer, trioxymethylene, and analogous trimers are the most common forms of the polymers of other aldehydes. It seems possible, however, that some of the metaldehydes are linear polymers of high molecular weight analogous to the polyoxymethylenes. Conant (111) has obtained from butyraldehyde by the action of very high pressure a solid polymer for which he suggests such a structure. This polymer is apparently stable only under pressure. Under the ordinary conditions it rapidly reverts to the monomer.

The thio aldehydes and ketones show more tendency to polymerize than their oxygen analogs (158). Organic silicon compounds of the types R_2Si=O, RSi(=O)OH, etc., are frequently incapable of being isolated in the monomeric condition, and they invariably polymerize very readily. It is interesting in this connection to compare carbon dioxide and silicon dioxide. The latter is probably a three-dimensional polymer.

V. Polyfunctional Reactions and Non-linear Polymers

The polymers discussed thus far, whether formed by condensation or by self-addition, are of a type that may be symbolized by the formula . . . . —A—A—A—A—A—A—A—. . . . . Reactions of condensation are not limited to bifunctional compounds, however. If one of two reactants contains two functional groups and the other contains more than two, the product will be not a simple chain but a more complicated structure. Such reactions may be called bi-trifunctional, bi-tetrafunctional, tri-trifunctional, etc. (18). Reactions of this class are especially important technically in connection with the formation of synthetic resins. Two examples may be considered.

The glyptal resins are formed by the action of phthalic acid on glycerol. The reaction first leads to the formation of a fairly soft, soluble, thermoplastic resin, and this on being heated further yields a hard, insoluble resin which is completely lacking in thermoplasticity. The only reaction involved in the process is esterification (112), and the resin can be saponified completely to yield phthalic acid and glycerol (51). Analysis of the resin just before the infusible stage is reached shows that the glycerol and the phthalic acid are far from having reacted completely with each other, that is, free carboxyl and presumably free hydroxyl groups are still present. The behavior of a dihydric alcohol such as ethylene glycol in this reaction presents quite a different picture from glycerol. With the glycol it is possible to obtain complete esterification, but however far the reaction is carried the product does not become infusible or insoluble. The reason for this difference is obvious. The polyester formed from the dibasic acid and the glycol is linear; as the reaction progresses the molecules grow, but the growth takes place only in one dimension. Similar chains formed in the reaction of glycerol with phthalic acid would bear hydroxyl groups

$$HO \cdots \overset{|}{\underset{OH}{\rule{0pt}{1em}}} \cdots \overset{|}{\underset{OH}{\rule{0pt}{1em}}} \cdots \overset{|}{\underset{OH}{\rule{0pt}{1em}}} \cdots \overset{|}{\underset{OH}{\rule{0pt}{1em}}} \cdots COOH$$

By reaction of these groups with phthalic acid the chains would be linked together, and thus a very complicated 3-dimensional molecule would be built up. After a certain degree of complexity is reached, the possibility of molecular mobility no longer exists. It is conceivable that this cross-linking of the chains finally results in a mass that is essentially a single molecule. In any event it is easy to see how the possibility of further reaction disappears long before all the carboxyl and hydroxyl groups have a chance to participate. It is easy to see also why the action of any dibasic acid on glycerol always yields an amorphous resin, whereas the polyesters from dibasic acids and dihydric alcohols are frequently crystalline.

The formation of Bakelite from phenol and formaldehyde may also be classified as a tri-bifunctional reaction. The formaldehyde behaves as though it were $HO-CH_2-OH$, and it reacts no doubt largely at the o- and p-hydrogens of the benzene nucleus. With phenol itself the number of possible products even of quite low molecular weight is so great that no intermediate polymeric individuals can be isolated. On the other hand p-cresol has only two readily reactive positions. Thus it is possible as Koebner has shown (113) to isolate the compounds indicated below as crystalline individuals, by causing formaldehyde and p-cresol to react in the appropriate ratios, and these can be used to build up still longer chains of the same series. The progressive hydrolysis of silicic esters to silicon dioxide, already discussed in a previous paragraph, furnishes another example of the formation of a 3-dimensional polymer.

Addition polymerization may also lead to the formation of 3-dimensional structures. Thus acetylene reacts with itself under the influence of certain catalysts (not necessarily copper) with the formation of cuprene, an infusible and insoluble powder, and Staudinger suggests (2) that in this reaction the first step is the formation of unsaturated chains . . . . —CH= CH—CH=CH—CH=CH— . . . . which subsequently combine with one another. The vulcanization of rubber probably also involves the cross-linking of the long chains through the agency of the unsaturated linkages present (39).

VI. Natural Polymers

1. The Association Theory Versus the Structural Theory.—The peculiar and difficult physical and chemical behavior of polymers has occasionally led to the suggestion that forces of a peculiar kind are involved in their formation. Thus Thiele in 1899 (132) suggested that perhaps in such materials as polystyrene the molecules of monomer are bound together merely by partial valences. Röhm in 1901 (115) concluded that the transformation of monomeric acrylic esters into the highly polymeric form is not chemical reaction but a kind of allotropic change. Later Schroeter (116, 117) suggested that the formation of dimeric ketene and of tetra-salicylide is due to the manifestation of an excess of peripheral external force about the monomeric molecules, and that the actual chemical structures of the monomeric molecules are not changed in the process. These particular suggestions are not tenable in the light of chemical evidence now available, but the association theory of polymeric structure reappeared about 1924 and was widely accepted as an explanation of the peculiarities of natural high polymers (118). According to one form of this theory, cellulose, for example, might be an anhydroglucose having the molecular formula $C_6H_{10}O_5$. This molecule, because of the unusual strain of its cyclic structure or for some other reason, is supposed to exhibit enormously exaggerated forces of association or residual valence, and hence to behave physically as though it were a material of very high molecular weight. In the same way proteins might be built up by the mutual association of various small units, $e. g.$, diketopiperazines.

In support of this theory various investigators showed that it was possible by freezing and boiling point methods to obtain small and rapidly shifting values for the molecular weights of polysaccharides, proteins, and rubber. Repetition of these determinations by other investigators proved, however, that the low results were due in most cases to errors in technique. Other support came from x-ray studies, which indicated that the unit cell of the crystal lattice of some high polymers is too small to contain a very large molecule. It was assumed at the time that a unit cell could not contain less than 1 molecule, but studies of known substances of high molecular weight proved that this assumption was incorrect. Meanwhile Staudinger's studies of synthetic materials repeatedly demonstrated that polymerization may lead to the formation of very long chains built up by real chemical forces in a regular fashion, and that such synthetic materials often resemble natural high polymers in many significant physical and chemical properties. Studies made in this laboratory on high polymers formed by condensation reactions led to the same conclusion. The idea that natural high polymers involve some principles of molecular structure peculiar to themselves and not capable of being simulated by synthetic materials is too strongly suggestive of the vital hypothesis, which preceded the dawn of organic chemistry, to be seriously considered.

It should be emphasized in this connection that polymerization is not peculiar to unsaturated compounds, and that a very high degree of mobility in the relation between a monomer and its polymer does not preclude the intervention of real primary valence forces in the process or the presence of a definite macromolecular structure in the polymer. This fact is illustrated especially by adipic anhydride and the 6-membered cyclic esters discussed in previous sections of this paper. These materials appear to exhibit all the supposedly diagnostic features of association polymerization; nevertheless their transformation into polymers is a real chemical process, and the polymers are actually made up of large molecules. No example is yet known in which a small molecule of known structure simulates a material of high molecular weight without undergoing any change in structure.

A return to the simple structural theory of organic chemistry and the application of modern tools have been responsible, during the past five years, for very rapid progress in the interpretation of the structure and properties of some of the simpler, naturally occurring high polymers. It appears that many naturally occurring macromolecular materials have a linear polymeric structure. The present status of this subject has been reviewed by Meyer and Mark (3), and in the following paragraphs only cellulose and rubber are briefly discussed.

2. **Cellulose.**—Chemical evidence for a linear polymeric structure in

the cellulose molecule has long been available (125). More recently, Haworth's proof of the structure of cellobiose (120) and certain studies of the relation of glucose and cellobiose to cellulose (122) furnished the basis for tentative efforts to determine the nature of the units in the molecular chain (121). Sponsler and Dore (123) on the basis of x-ray evidence first put the linear polymeric structure in explicit form. This formula was further developed by Meyer and Mark (119), and it can now be said that the structure of cellulose, at least in its essential outlines, is definitely known. In its simplest chemical form the structural unit of cellulose may be represented by the bivalent radical derived by the removal of water from glucose (glucopyranose).

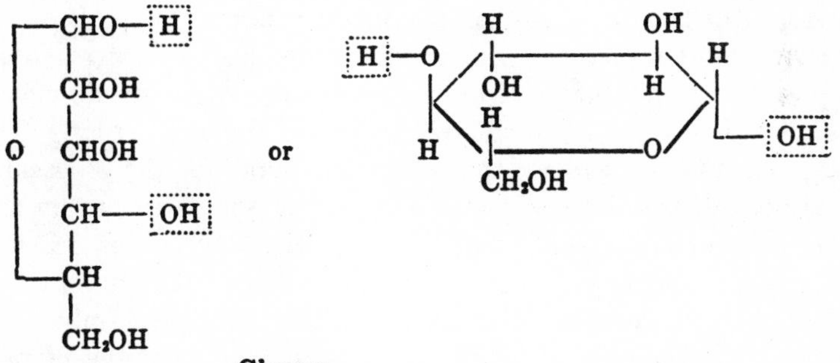

Glucose

A large number of these units are united chemically to form a long chain which constitutes the cellulose molecule.

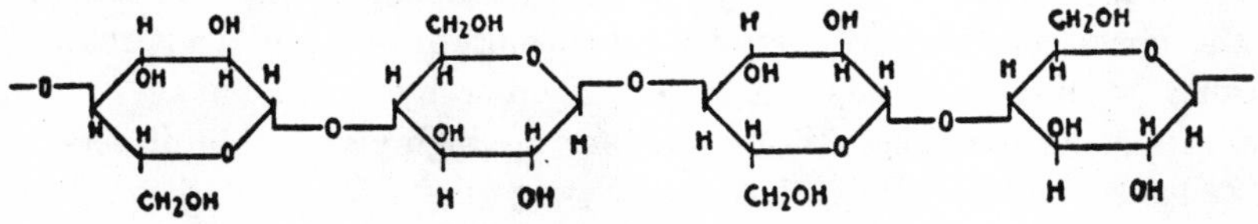

Cellulose

(For a more detailed picture of the spatial arrangements in this chain, including the atomic distances, see reference 3.) In the cellulose fiber (cotton, ramie, etc.) these long molecules are lined up parallel with each other along the fiber axis.

To complete this formula it is necessary to specify the nature of the terminal groups and the length of the chain. The most reasonable assumption is that the chains are open and terminated by hydroxyl groups (alcoholic at one end and semi-acetal at the other), but no very definite experimental evidence on this point is available. Meyer and Mark estimate that the molecular chains are made up of from sixty to one hundred glucose units (molecular weight, 10,000 to 16,000), and they assume that the molecules are segregated into compact bundles (crystallites or micelles) from which the gross structure of the cellulose fiber is built up. Staudinger, however, has presented evidence (124) that the crystallites do not persist in dispersions of cellulose and its derivatives, and that the molecules have a weight much higher than 16,000. Stamm (126) has made direct measurements of particle size in ammoniacal copper dispersions of cellulose by the Svedberg ultracentrifugal method and obtained a value (on the copper-free basis) of 40,000 ± 5 per cent. The molecules in a given sample of cellulose are probably not all of the same length, but Stamm's data indicate a much higher degree of homogeneity than one might expect.

According to this picture cellulose, like other high polymers, is not a chemical individual in the sense of being composed of identical molecules, and its structure cannot be completely specified by a single exactly defined formula. On the other hand, this picture accounts for the physical and chemical behavior of cellulose just as completely and satisfactorily as the formulas of simple compounds account for their properties. Cellulose fibers are very strong because of the parallel arrangement of the long molecular chains along the fiber axis. These chains adhere firmly to one another because of the cumulative force of association of the numerous hydroxyl groups. Strong aqueous alkali is able to penetrate this structure, and the resulting spreading apart of the chains causes lateral swelling. Other reagents (e. g., nitric acid) can penetrate the structure and esterify the hydroxyls without completely changing the apparent physical structure of the fiber. Cellulose is degraded much more rapidly by acids than by alkalies because the units are joined together by acetal linkages. The great length of the molecules accounts for the high viscosity of dispersions of cellulose and its derivatives. The very first stages of degradation greatly reduce the viscosity (124) because, for example, the hydrolytic absorption of 1 part of water in 2000 is capable of reducing by half the average size of the molecules. Undegraded cellulose has little or no reducing power (130) because it contains only one reducing group in an exceedingly large molecule, but reducing power is manifested and increases progressively with hydrolysis (124, 127). Complete hydrolysis finally gives a quantitative yield of glucose (125); cellobiose, a triose, a tetrose (128) and higher polysaccharides are formed as intermediate products. The hydrolysis agrees in its kinetics with the theoretical requirements for the chain structure (129). This structure also accounts for the presence of three esterifiable hydroxyl groups for each C_6 unit, and for the fact that completely methylated cellulose yields 2,3,6-trimethylglucose on hydrolysis (121).

3. Rubber.—It is well known that rubber hydrocarbon has the same empirical composition as isoprene (C_5H_8); that isoprene can be polymerized to yield a material resembling natural rubber; and that the behavior of rubber toward halogens, hydrobromic acid, and hydrogen indicates the presence of one double bond for each five atoms of carbon. Harries many years ago (131) showed that the degradation of rubber by ozone yields chiefly levulinic acid and aldehyde, and this fact indicates that the rubber molecules must be largely built up by the repetition of the unit

$$-CH_2-C=CH-CH_2-$$
$$|$$
$$CH_3$$

in a regular manner as indicated below.

(II) $\ldots-CH_2CMe=CHCH_2-CH_2CMe=CHCH_2-CH_2CMe=CHCH_2-\ldots$

$\ldots-CMe=CHCH_2CH_2CMe=CH-\ldots \xrightarrow{\text{ozonization}} CHOCH_2CH_2COMe$

Rubber   Levulinic aldehyde

Harries first assumed that the rubber molecule is an 8-membered ring. Later the discovery of larger fragments in the products of degradation by ozone led him to suggest a larger cyclic structure. The physical properties of rubber clearly indicate however that it is macromolecular. Pickles (133) suggested the more plausible linear polymeric structure indicated above, and Staudinger (134) has brought forward a large mass of evidence in favor of this structure. The best evidence available indicates that the average weight of the rubber molecule is exceedingly large—perhaps in the neighborhood of 70,000 (135). It appears, moreover, that molecules having widely different sizes must be present in a given sample of rubber. Raw rubber is not homogeneous in its behavior toward solvents. When placed in contact with ether it swells and part of it diffuses into solution fairly rapidly. The action of fresh ether on the residue is much slower, and it is possible to carry the process of extraction so far as to obtain ultimately a residue that shows scarcely any tendency to dissolve. On the basis of such experiments it has been assumed that rubber is made up of two phases, sol and gel, and that the properties of rubber are due to the colloidal relationships of these two phases. In support of this idea there is the fact that colloidal dispersions of the jelly type frequently exhibit striking elasticity. This is true, for example, of polystyrene when it is swollen with unpolymerized styrene or with other hydrocarbon solvents.

Whitby (137), however, has shown that sol-rubber (diffused) alone shows all the characteristic physical properties of raw rubber and differs from the latter only in degree. Moreover, it appears that sol- and gel-rubber are not distinct species and that neither of them is homogeneous. Rubber probably consists of a long continuous series of molecules of differing lengths. The smallest molecules dissolve quite readily and the largest ones only with difficulty.

If the rubber molecule is built up uniformly according to the regular plan indicated in formula II it should yield levulinic acid and aldehyde as the exclusive products of degradation by ozone. The yields of these products obtained by Harries accounted for only about 70 per cent. of the rubber. Pummerer (136) has recently undertaken a reëxamination of the Harries method, using carefully purified rubber, and has been able to account for 90 per cent. of the rubber. He finds significant amounts of succinic acid, acetic acid, and acetone among the products. If the rubber molecule is an open chain, it might have an extra double bond at one end, and according to the disposition of this bond any of the above named by-products might be produced by ozonization. These products might also result from occasional irregularities in the arrangement of the units along the chain. The various possibilities have been outlined by Whitby (137).

Although the examination of unstretched rubber by x-rays gives only an amorphous ring, stretched rubber gives a sharp fiber diffraction pattern (138). When unstretched rubber is cooled in liquid air and then fractured by impact, it breaks up into irregular fragments; stretched rubber treated in the same way breaks up into thin fibers along the axis of stretch (139). These facts show that stretched rubber is much more highly oriented than unstretched rubber.

The structural unit of rubber contains a double bond and this brings about the possibility of stereoisomerism. The units may be in the *cis* or the *trans* form (or both).

$$
\begin{array}{ccc}
\underset{\diagup}{CH_2} \quad H & \qquad & H \quad \underset{\diagdown}{CH_2} \\
\diagdown\diagup & & \diagdown\diagup \\
C & & C \\
\| & & \| \\
C & & C \\
\diagup\diagdown & & \diagup\diagdown \\
CH_2 \quad CH_3 & & CH_2 \quad CH_2 \\
\diagdown & & \diagdown \\
\textit{cis} \text{ form} & & \textit{trans} \text{ form}
\end{array}
$$

The x-ray data are said to favor the *cis* orientation (140). A spatial model of a long chain of such *cis* units is capable of being coiled up into a cylindrical spiral, and this spiral can be stretched out into a long chain. Various writers have suggested that the spiral model is capable of explaining the reversible stretching of rubber. This model has recently been discussed in detail by Fikentscher and Mark (140). It is assumed that the residual valence forces at the double bonds are responsible for holding the spiral in its compressed form. When the rubber is stretched, work is done against these forces, and the molecules assume the chain-like form, where they are much more highly oriented with respect to one another. Vulcanization is assumed to involve the chemical linking of these spiral chains at occasional points through sulfur atoms. A very small amount of combined sulfur does not interfere with the stretching of the spirals, but it prevents the chains from slipping past one another or being torn apart; consequently vulcanized rubber is not plastic, and it is not dissolved but only swelled by rubber solvents. As the amount of combined sulfur increases, the entire structure becomes more rigidly linked together, the plastic properties are completely suppressed, and the ability to imbibe solvent is lost. This picture is useful but it can hardly be said to account completely for the remarkable properties of rubber.

VII. The Physical Properties of High Polymers

Perhaps the most important result of the study of synthetic high polymers has been to establish the fact that such materials are actually made up of exceedingly large molecules in the sense of the ordinary structural theory of organic chemistry. This is a point on which considerable scepticism has prevailed in the past, and the attempt to evade or ignore the idea of the molecules in dealing with high polymers has led to much speculative confusion.

It is true that synthetic linear high polymers are invariably mixtures whose molecules are chains of slightly differing lengths, and it is difficult to obtain reliable estimates of the average size of these molecules. Nevertheless it must be admitted that a molecule does not lose any of its definiteness as an entity either through the fact that it is exceedingly large or through the fact that it cannot be completely separated from other similar but slightly different molecules, and the properties of high polymers must ultimately be conditioned by the kinds of molecules which they contain.

It would be beyond the intended scope of this paper to attempt a detailed discussion of the relation between the molecular structure and the physical properties of high polymers, but there are two or three points that deserve some mention.

It is evident that in some respects the physical behavior of a molecule whose length is 100 times as great as its other dimensions must be profoundly different from that of a small compact molecule. Enormously long, flexible, and clumsy molecules must be very sluggish in their kinetic behavior, and it is not surprising that high polymers cannot be distilled or that they are never obtained in the form of thin mobile liquids.

The cohesive forces which resist the separation of molecules from one another (as measured, for example, by the heat of vaporization) increase continuously with increasing molecular weight in a given series, and in high polymers they reach values greatly in excess of the energy required to rupture a primary valence linkage in a chain (141). For this reason high polymers cannot be distilled without decomposition; indeed it appears that the upper limit of distillability may lie at as low a molecular weight as 1200 to 1500 (44).

1. **Solubility and Colloidal Properties.**—High polymers are subject to the same rough qualitative solubility rules that apply to simple compounds: like dissolves like; polar compounds dissolve in polar solvents and non-polar compounds in non-polar solvents; solubility in a given series diminishes with increasing molecular weight. Thus, rubber and polystyrenes are soluble in benzene, but not in acetone; polyamides are not dissolved by the usual organic solvents, but are dissolved by hot formamide; polyacrylic acid is soluble in water, while its esters dissolve in organic solvents but not in water; polystyrenes of low molecular weight (about 1000) are soluble in ether while polystyrenes of high molecular weight (about 20,000) are only slightly soluble in ether but are still dissolved by benzene.

The solubility of high polymers is sometimes surprisingly great compared with that of analogous simple compounds of much lower molecular weight. The higher normal paraffin hydrocarbons (*e. g.*, heptacontane) are practically insoluble in any solvents at the ordinary temperature, while polystyrene and hydrorubber, which are essentially very long paraffin chains substituted at intervals by phenyl and methyl groups, dissolve readily in benzene. One reason for this no doubt lies in the fact that most high polymers are mixtures of molecules of different lengths, and these are capable to a certain extent of behaving independently in their solubility behavior. Moreover, the crystal lattices of high polymers are not so well ordered and rigidly constructed as those of low molecular weight materials and they may, for this reason, be more susceptible to attack by solvents.

The fact that the cohesive forces operating between large molecules are exceedingly high does not mean that polymers are incapable of forming molecular dispersions. Solubility depends upon specific affinities. Soluble linear polymers of relatively low molecular weight (e. g., 1000 to 5000) dissolve spontaneously and very rapidly in appropriate solvents and yield solutions which are not highly viscous. The osmotic unit in these solutions is the molecule, not an aggregate of molecules. For various polyesters this has been proved (32, 34) by the fact that the same molecular weight values are obtained in a variety of solvents and by both freezing point and boiling point methods. Moreover, as the data of Table II show, direct chemical determinations of molecular weight give the same values as the osmotic methods. Polyesters having molecular weights considerably above 5000 dissolve in the same solvents as the lower polyesters, but the process of solution is slower and the solutions are more viscous (51). The same behavior is observed in other polymeric series. Polystyrenes having molecular weights of about 1000 dissolve instantly in benzene, and the viscosity of the solutions is low; polystyrenes having molecular weights above 10,000 swell before dissolving, and the solutions are highly viscous (102). These evidences of colloidal behavior are due simply to the fact that the molecules are exceedingly long. The probable mechanism of solution of certain polymers is best illustrated by a specific example.

Rubber is made up of enormously long hydrocarbon chains ranging perhaps from 1000 to 10,000 Å. in length. These chains have a high specific affinity for certain non-polar solvents such as benzene. In a mass of rubber, adjacent chains are firmly bound to one another by cohesive forces. The structure is not an entirely regular one and there is no doubt a considerable amount of purely mechanical entanglement. Benzene, by virtue of its specific affinity for the chains, is capable of penetrating into the mass, solvating the chains, and spreading them apart. The structure thus becomes swollen and more tenuous, and finally individual fragments are carried away into solution. The fragments may be single molecules or only incompletely disrupted aggregates, but finally, if sufficient solvent is present, the latter are broken down and what amounts to an actual molecular dispersion results. This dispersion has a very high viscosity even when quite dilute, for the molecules are not only very large, but, owing to the fact that they are solvated and extended in only one dimension, they have an effective radius of action quite out of proportion to their size.

The view that lyophilic dispersions of linear high polymers are usually true molecular dispersions, although it has not yet been generally accepted by colloid chemists (see 174), has been supported by Staudinger with a large mass of evidence (146, 102, 124, 135), which in its cumulative force seems to the writer fairly conclusive. Reference may be made also to Stamm's determination with Svedberg's ultracentrifuge of the particle size of cellulose dispersions in copper-ammonia solutions (126). He obtained the value 40,000 ± 5 per cent. It is quite certain on various grounds that the average molecular weight of cellulose cannot be less than about 16,000, so that if Stamm's particle is an aggregate it cannot contain more than two or three molecules. It seems highly arbitrary to assume that the solvent action of the dispersing agent, which depends upon a specific affinity for the cellulose molecules, should be capable of carrying off the molecules only as pairs or triplets and never as single molecules.

It is of course not contended that association never occurs in lyophilic solutions of high polymers, but merely that association occurs only as the result of some appropriate peculiarity in the molecular structure of the polymer, e. g., through the presence of recurring amide or carboxyl groups.

2. **Crystallinity.**—Linear polymers, in spite of their lack of complete homogeneity and their high molecular weight, are by no means always amorphous. As indicated in Table I, all the polyesters derived from glycols of the series $HO(CH_2)_xOH$ and acids of the series carbonic, oxalic, succinic, etc., separate from solvents in the form of powders which show quite definite melting points. On the other hand, similar esters derived from phthalic acid are invariably transparent, amorphous resins. The ability to crystallize appears to require a high degree of linear symmetry in the structural unit. The presence of side chains such as methyl or phenyl groups on the units, and the random mixing of structural units, which occurs, for example, when polymers are prepared from a single glycol and two different acids, diminish the tendency toward crystallinity. Thus, polyesters and polyamides derived from unsubstituted aliphatic compounds are crystalline, and so also are the polyoxymethylenes and polyethylene oxide, while polymers derived from vinyl compounds of the type $XCH=CH_2$ are usually amorphous. In these vinyl polymers the X group diminishes the linear symmetry of the chain; moreover in the formation of such polymers occasional inversions of the order of the units probably occur.

The behavior of ethylene succinate (molecular weight, 3000) on crystallization appears to be typical of many high molecular weight materials. It separates from a melt or from concentrated solutions in chloroform as doubly refracting microscopic spherulites which grow to what appear to be star-like clusters of needles. Further growth leads to frost-like patterns. The melt finally solidifies to an opaque porcelain-like mass. From dilute alcohol solutions ethylene succinate separates in very thin, discrete needles, but these lose their identity as soon as the solvent has evaporated. This behavior is highly characteristic of very long chains. It is reproduced in all its details by such diverse materials as triacetylinulin (150), *n*-heptacontane (51) and trimethylcellulose. The photomicrographs of crystalline trimethylcellulose presented by Hess (149) would serve equally well to represent ethylene succinate. Linear polymers in the form of microcrystalline powders have a pronounced tendency to become electrified, and they strongly adsorb considerable amounts of water vapor even when they show scarcely any tendency to dissolve in water.

The crystallization of linear polymers probably involves the parallel arrangement of the long chains into compact bundles, since this arrangement enables the molecules to exert their maximum cohesive force (151). Loose parallel swarms of molecules may also exist in melts or solutions of the polymers. Molecules of identical length might be arranged in bundles as shown in Fig. 1(*a*), but especially with very long molecules, a less regular type of structure such as that shown in (*b*) might be produced. The arrangement shown in (*b*) has no sharp boundaries and this defect

FIG. 1*a*   FIG. 1*b*

would be exaggerated if the molecules were not all of the same length. Since the molecules of a specimen of high polymer are very long and have not all the same length the lattice bundles first formed must more nearly resemble (*b*) than (*a*). In the presence of solvent, such crystals might persist as discrete particles, but in the absence of a solvent they would tend to coalesce and lose their identity, owing to the absence of sharp boundaries and the incomplete neutralization of the residual forces of the projecting molecules. Thus, it is never possible to isolate large discrete (unsolvated) crystals of high polymers. Moreover, though solid masses of crystalline high polymers may be either hard and brittle or very tough, or soft and wax-like, they never show any definite planes of cleavage. The coalescence of the initial crystallites, which occurs as a molten mass of polyester finally solidifies, must occur in a random and rather disordered fashion, and it is probable also that the crystallites are cemented together by molecules that have not succeeded in completely identifying themselves with any particular crystallite.

The melting points of crystalline linear polymers show certain regularities. For a given molecular weight the melting points increase with the cohesive force (polarity) of the structural units.   Polyamides have much higher melting points than analogous polyesters.   Polyesters derived from short chain dibasic acids melt higher than those derived from the longer chain acids;   mixed polyesters melt lower than simple ones.   For a given polyester the melting point usually increases with increasing molecular weight up to a certain point, and after that it remains unchanged even though the molecular weight be increased many fold.   Melting points are sometimes rather vague, but more frequently they are surprisingly sharp even when the molecular weight is so high that the molten polymer shows no sign of flowing and the only indication of melting is the disappearance of opacity.

The question of the meaning of the term crystallinity in connection with high polymers is rather confused.   Linear polyesters whose molecular weights lie below 5000 are definitely crystalline;   they have sharp melting points and the crystals can actually be seen under the microscope.   The evidences of crystallinity in polyesters whose molecular weights lie above 10,000 are somewhat more vague, but even these materials furnish sharp x-ray powder diffraction patterns.   Similar though less sharply defined patterns are obtained from a transparent sheet of regenerated cellulose. These patterns indicate that part at least of the molecules of such materials must be definitely ordered with respect to one another.   On the other hand, certain linear polymers, e. g., polystyrene, can be obtained in the form of white powders which show no microscopic or x-ray evidence of crystallinity.   In these cases apparently the molecules tend to collect into discrete aggregates of some kind, but not in a sufficiently orderly fashion to exhibit any of the usual properties associated with crystals.

3.   Mechanical Properties.—High polymers are very extensively used as structural materials in the construction of artifacts.   One has only to mention cellulose, silk, and rubber to indicate the great economic importance of these non-chemical uses of organic materials.   These uses depend upon such properties as mechanical strength, toughness, pliability, and elasticity.   Such properties are found to a useful degree only among polymers of very high molecular weight.   The synthetic materials of this class that have been most successfully used are 3-dimensional polymers such as Bakelite and the glyptals.   These materials have considerable strength, rigidity and toughness, but they are completely amorphous, and they are greatly inferior to natural fibers in breaking strength and pliability.   The breaking strength of a flax fiber (100 kg. per sq. mm.) is of the same order as that of a good grade of steel (152).   The qualities necessary for a useful fiber appear to be associated with a very high molecular weight linear-polymeric structure and a certain degree of crystallinity or definite order in the arrangement of the molecules. The relation between molecular structure and arrangement and the physical properties of fibers has been most clearly recognized and discussed by Meyer and Mark (3). In a natural cellulose or silk fiber the long molecular chains are arranged in an ordered fashion parallel with the fiber axis. This state of affairs is symbolized in Fig. 2. This arrangement provides the maximum

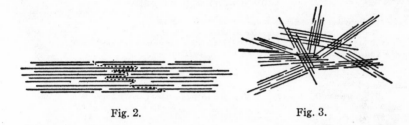

Fig. 2.   Fig. 3.

possible strength in the direction of the fiber axis since the mutual cohesive force of the long chains is fully utilized. To rupture the fiber it is necessary to cause the chains to slip past one another against this cohesive force as indicated in the dotted line. A transparent sheet of regenerated cellulose shows (by x-ray patterns) a certain degree of order in the arrangement of its molecules, but there is no general orientation. This state of affairs is symbolized in Fig. 3. This more or less random arrangement of ordered molecular aggregates can be brought into the more highly ordered state symbolized in Fig. 2 merely by the action of mechanical stress. Thus the strength of a sheet of Cellophane that initially has approximately the same strength in all directions can be so changed, merely by careful stretching, that its strength along the axis of stretch is increased several fold (153). At the same time its strength along the axis normal to its stretch is considerably diminished. The strength of a rayon filament can be increased several fold by the action of stress while it is in the spinning bath, and a comparison of the x-ray patterns shows a much higher degree of orientation along the fiber axis in the filament formed under stress. For a rough mechanical analogy of the mechanism of this process one may picture a disordered mass of long straws (molecules) coated with a semifluid adhesive (cohesive force). The gradual application of stress to such a mass would finally bring the straws into parallel alignment where they would more strongly cohere and resist the further action of stress.

The peculiarities of high polymers are nowhere more strikingly exemplified than in this curious ability to accept permanent orientations through the action of mechanical stress. The properties of simple organic compounds are, generally speaking, independent of their physical history; they are completely determined by the nature of the molecules. Very large molecules, however, are not capable of adjusting themselves instantly to any changes in physical environment, and the properties of a very high molecular weight material may vary over a wide range depending upon the physical treatment it has received.

Bibliography and Remarks

(1) Staudinger, H., *Helv. Chim. Acta*, **12**, 1183 (1929).

(2) Staudinger, H., *Z. angew. Chem.*, **42**, 37, 67 (1929).

(3) Meyer, K., and H. Mark, *Der Aufbau der hochpolymeren organischen Naturstoffe.* Akademische Verlagsgesellschaft, Leipzig (1930).

(4) Staudinger, H., *Ber.*, **59**, 3019 (1926).

(5) Scheiber, J., and K. Sandig, *Die künstlichen Harze.* Wissenschaftliche Verlagsgesellschaft, Stuttgard (1929).

(6) Meerwein, H., *Houben's Die Methoden der organischen Chemie*, 3rd edition, Volume II, p. 593. Georg Thieme, Leipzig (1925).

(7) Meyer, K., *Naturwissenschaften*, **16**, 781 (1928); *Z. angew. Chem.*, **41**, 935 (1928).

(8a) Hill, H. S., and H. Hibbert, *Journ. Am. Chem. Soc.*, **45**, 3124 (1923).

(8b) Franke, A., and E. Gigerl, *Monatsh.*, **49**, 8 (1928).

(9) Hess, K., *Die Chemie der Cellulose*, p. 574. Akademische Verlagsgesellschaft, Leipzig (1928).

(10) Ushakov, S. N., and A. V. Kon, *C. A.*, **24**, 3796 (1930).

(11) Ingold, C. K., and E. H. Ingold, *Journ. Am. Chem. Soc.*, **1928**, 2249.

(12) Berzelius, J. J., *Jahresbericht*, **12**, 63 (1833).

(13) Reference 3, p. 47.

(14) Staudinger, H., and O. Schweitzer, *Ber.*, **62**, 2395 (1929).

(15) Roithner, E., *Monatsh.*, **15**, 665 (1894).

(16) Faworski, A., *Chem. Zentr.*, **1907**, I, 16.

(17) Lourenço, *Ann. chim. phys.*, **67**, 293 (1863).

(18) Carothers, W. H., *Journ. Am. Chem. Soc.*, **51**, 2548 (1929).

(19) Dietzel, R., and R. Krug, *Ber.*, **58**, 1307 (1925)⁸

(20) Willstätter, R., and C. Cramer, *Ber.*, **43**, 2976 (1910).

(21) Goldschmidt, S., E. Schulz and H. Bernard, *Ann.*, **478**, 1 (1930).

(22) Busch, M., and W. Schmidt, *Ber.*, **62**, 2612 (1929).

(23) Wagner-Jauregg, T., *Ber.*, **63**, 3213 (1930).

(24) Blaise, E., and A. Koehler, *Compt. rend.*, **148**, 1773 (1909).

(25) Ruzicka, L., and M. Stoll, *Helv. Chim. Acta*, **11**, 1159 (1928).

(26) Johansson, H., *Lunds Universitets Arsskrift*, II (2), **12**, 3 (1916).

(27) Johansson, H., *Ber.*, **48**, 1262 (1915).

(28) Blaise, E. E., and L. Marcilly, *Bull. soc. chim.*, [3] **31**, 308 (1904).

(29) Chuit, P., and J. Hausser, *Helv. Chim. Acta*, **12**, 463 (1929).

(30) Lycan, W. H., and Roger Adams, *Journ. Am. Chem. Soc.*, **51**, 625, 3450 (1929).

(31) Bougalt, J., and L. Bourdier, *Compt. rend.*, **147**, 1311 (1908).

(32) Carothers, W. H., and J. A. Arvin, *Journ. Am. Chem. Soc.*, **51**, 2560 (1929).

(33) Carothers, W. H., and F. J. van Natta, *Journ. Am. Chem. Soc.*, **52**, 314 (1930).

(34) Carothers, W. H., and G. L. Dorough, *Journ. Am. Chem. Soc.*, **52**, 711 (1930).

(35) Carothers, W. H., J. A. Arvin and G. L. Dorough, *Journ. Am. Chem. Soc.*, **52**, 3292 (1930).

(36) Kerschbaum, M., *Ber.*, **60**, 902 (1927).

(37) Marvel, C. S., and E. R. Birkhimer, *Journ. Am. Chem. Soc.*, **51**, 260 (1929).

(38) Staudinger, H., *Ber.*, **53**, 1073 (1920).

(39) Meyer, K., and H. Mark, *Ber.*, **61**, 1948 (1928).

(40) Davidoff, *Ber.*, **19**, 406 (1886).

(41) Vorländer, D., *Ann.*, **280**, 167 (1894).

(42) Tilitschejew, M., *Journ. Russ. Phys. Chem. Soc.*, **57**, 143 (1925); *Chem. Zentr.*, **1926**, I, 2667.

(43) Kienle, R. H., and G. Hovey, *Journ. Am. Chem. Soc.*, **52**, 3636 (1930).
(44) Carothers, W. H., J. W. Hill, J. E. Kirby and R. A. Jacobson, *Journ. Am. Chem. Soc.*, **52**, 5279 (1930).
(45) Franke, A., and O. Kienberger, *Monatsh.*, **33**, 1189 (1912).
(46) (a) Schlubach, H. H., and E. C. Goes, *Ber.*, **55**, 2889 (1922).
(46) (b) Ziegler, K., and H. Colonius, *Ann.*, **135**, 474 (1930).
(47) Schorigen, P., *Ber.*, **43**, 1931 (1910).
(48) (a) Gabriel, S., *Ber.*, **22**, 3338 (1889).
(48) (b) Schotten, C., *Ber.*, **21**, 2240 (1888).
(49) (a) Carothers, W. H., and G. J. Berchet, *Journ. Am. Chem. Soc.*, **52**, 5289 (1930).
(49) (b) Gabriel, S., and T. A. Maass, *Ber.*, **32**, 1266 (1899).
(50) (a) v. Braun, J., *Ber.*, **40**, 1835 (1907).
(50) (b) Manasse, A., *Ber.*, **35**, 1367 (1902).
(50) (c) Diehl, L., and A. Einhorn, *Ber.*, **20**, 377 (1887).
(51) Unpublished results.
(52) (a) v. Braun, J., and A. Steindorff, *Ber.*, **38**, 3083 (1905).
(52) (b) v. Braun, J., *Ber.*, **43**, 2853 (1910).
(52) (c) v. Braun, J., and C. Müller, *Ber.*, **39**, 4110 (1906).
(53) (a) Littmann, E. R., and C. S. Marvel, *Journ. Am. Chem. Soc.*, **52**, 288 (1930).
(53) (b) Knorr, L., and P. Roth, *Ber.*, **39**, 1420 (1906).
(54) Staudinger, H., and E. Ott, *Ber.*, **41**, 2214 (1908).
(55) Voerman, G. L., *Rec. trav. chim.*, **23**, 265 (1904).
(56) Hill, J. W., *Journ. Am. Chem. Soc.*, **52**, 4110 (1930).
(57) Grignard, V., and G. Vignon, *Compt. rend.*, **144**, 1358 (1907).
(58) Hückel, W., *Fortschritte Chem., Physik. physik. Chem.*, **19**, No. 4, 7 (1927).
(59) Lonsdale, K., *Proc. Roy. Soc.* (London), **123**, 494 (1929).
(60) King, G., *J. Oil Colour Chem. Assocn.*, **13**, 28 (1930).
(61) Le Fevre, J. W., *Journ. Chem. Soc.*, **1929**, 733.
(62) Ferber, E., *Ber.*, **62**, 183 (1929).
(63) Smyth, C. P., and W. S. Walls, *Journ. Am. Chem. Soc.*, **53**, 527 (1931).
(64) Tilitschejew, M., *J. Russ. Phys. Chem. Soc.*, **58**, 447 (1926); *C. A.* **21**, 3358 (1927).
(65) (a) Gane, R., and C. K. Ingold, *Journ. Chem. Soc.*, **1928**, 1594.
(65) (b) Gane, R., and C. K. Ingold, *Journ. Chem. Soc.*, **1928**, 2267.
(66) Mohr, E., *J. prakt. Chem.*, **98**, 315 (1918).
(67) Stoll, M., and G. Stoll-Comte, *Helv. Chim. Acta*, **13**, 1185 (1930).
(68) v. Braun, J., and B. Bartsch, *Ber.*, **45**, 3376 (1912).
(69) Stanley, W. M., and R. Adams, *Journ. Am. Chem. Soc.*, **52**, 1200 (1930).
(70) Ruggli, P., *Ann.*, **392**, 92 (1912).
(71) (a) Ruzicka, L., M. Stoll, H. W. Huyser and H. A. Boekenoogen, *Helv. Chim. Acta*, **13**, 1153 (1930).
(71) (b) Ruzicka and co-workers, *Helv. Chim. Acta*, **9**, 230, 249, 339, 389, 399, 499, 715, 1008 (1926); **10**, 695 (1927); **11**, 496, 670, 686, 1174 (1928).
(72) Fichter, F., and A. Beisswenger, *Ber.*, **36**, 1200 (1903).
(73) Hollo, E., *Ber.*, **61**, 895 (1928).
(74) Drew, H. D. K., and W. N. Haworth, *Journ. Chem. Soc.*, **1927**, 775.
(75) Bischoff, C. A., and P. Walden, *Ann.*, **279**, 45 (1893).
(76) Bischoff, C. A., and P. Walden, *Ber.*, **26**, 262 (1893).
(77) Bischoff, C. A., and P. Walden, *Ann.*, **279**, 71 (1893).
(78) Carter, S. R., W. N. Haworth and R. A. Robinson, *Journ. Chem. Soc.*, **1930**, 2125.
(79) Johannson, H., and H. Sibelius, *Ber.*, **52**, 745 (1919).
(80) (a) Balbiano, L., *Ber.*, **34**, 1501 (1901).
(80) (b) Balbiano, L., and D. Trasciatti, *Ber.*, **33**, 2323 (1900).
(81) (a) Maillard, L. C., *Ann. chim.*, **1**, 519 (1914).
(81) (b) Maillard, L. C., *Ann. chim.*, **2**, 210 (1914).
(82) Curtius, T., and A. Benrath, *Ber.*, **37**, 1279 (1904).
(83) Shibata, K., *Acta. Phytochim.*, **2**, 39 (1925); **2**, 194 (1926).
(84) (a) Curtius, T., *Ber.*, **37**, 1284 (1904).
(84) (b) Curtius, T., *Ber.*, **16**, 753 (1883).
(85) Fischer, E., *Ber.*, **39**, 2924 (1906).
(86) Delepine, M., *Bull. soc. chim.*, [4] **27**, 740 (1920).

(87) Grichkevitch-Trokhimovsky, E., *Bull. soc. chim.*, [4] **24,** 541, 543, 546, 548, 549, 551 (1918).
(88) Katz, J. R., *Z. angew. Chem.*, **41,** 329 (1928).
(89) (a) Leuchs, H., and W. Geiger, *Ber.*, **41,** 1721 (1908).
(89) (b) Leuchs, H., *Ber.*, **39,** 857 (1906).
(90) Curtius, T., and W. Sieber, *Ber.*, **55,** 1543 (1922).
(91) Cohen, J. B., *Organic Chemistry*, Part I, p. 193. Edward Arnold and Company, London (1928).
(92) Stanley, H. M., *Journ. Soc. Chem. Ind.*, **49,** 349T (1930).
(93) Mignonac, G., and R. V. de Saint-Aunay, *Bull. soc. chim.*, **47,** 522 (1930).
(94) Pease, R. H., *Journ. Am. Chem. Soc.*, **52,** 1158 (1930).
(95) Lebedev, S. V., and G. G. Koblyanskii, *Ber.*, **63,** 1432 (1930).
(96) (a) Staudinger, H., M. Brunner, K. Frey, P. Garbsch, R. Signer and S. Wehrli, *Ber.*, **62,** 241 (1929).
(96) (b) Staudinger, H., K. Frey, P. Garbsch and S. Wehrli, *Ber.*, **62,** 2912 (1929).
(96) (c) Staudinger, H., and M. Brunner, *Helv. Chim. Acta*, **12,** 972 (1929).
(96) (d) Milas, N. A., *Proc. Natl. Acad. Sci.*, **14,** 844 (1928).
(97) (a) Staudinger, H., M. Brunner and W. Feist, *Helv. Chim. Acta*, **13,** 805 (1930).
(97) (b) Flumiani, G., *Z. Elektrochem.*, **32,** 221 (1926).
(98) (a) Staudinger, H., K. Frey and W. Starck, *Ber.*, **60,** 1782 (1927).
(98) (b) Whitby, G. S., J. C. McNally and W. Gallay, *Trans. Roy. Soc. Can.*, **22,** 27 (1928).
(98) (c) Hermann, W. O., and W. Haehnel, *Ber.*, **60,** 1658 (1927).
(99) Staudinger, H., and E. Urech, *Helv. Chim. Acta*, **12,** 1107 (1929).
(100) Moureu, C., and C. Dufraisse, *Ann. chim.*, **15,** 158 (1921).
(101) (a) Staudinger, H., A. A. Ashdown, M. Brunner, H. A. Bruson and S. Wehrli, *Helv. Chim. Acta*, **12,** 934 (1929).
(101) (b) Staudinger, H., H. Johner and V. Wiedersheim, *Helv. Chim. Acta*, **12,** 958 (1929).
(101) (c) Staudinger, H., H. Johner, G. Schiemann and V. Wiedersheim, *Helv. Chim. Acta*, **12,** 962 (1929).
(102) (a) Staudinger, H., and W. Heuer, *Ber.*, **63,** 222 (1930).
(102) (b) Staudinger, H., and K. Frey, *Ber.*, **62,** 2909 (1929).
(102) (c) Staudinger, H., and R. Machemer, *Ber.*, **62,** 2921 (1929).
(102) (d) Staudinger, H., *Kolloid-Z.*, **51,** 71 (1930).
(103) (a) Staudinger, H., E. Geiger and E. Huber, *Ber.*, **62,** 263 (1929).
(103) (b) Staudinger, H., and V. Wiedersheim, *Ber.*, **62,** 2406 (1929).
(104) Staudinger, H., and F. Breusch, *Ber.*, **62,** 442 (1929).
(105) Whitby, G. S., and M. Katz, *Journ. Am. Chem. Soc.*, **50,** 1160 (1928).
(106) Starkweather, H. W., and G. B. Taylor, *Journ. Am. Chem. Soc.*, **52,** 4708 (1930).
(107) Taylor, H. S., private communication.
(108) (a) Schotz, S. P., *Synthetic Rubber*. E. Benn, London (1926).
(108) (b) Pankow, M., *Kunststoffe*, **20,** 219, 248 (1930).
(109) Midgley, T., Jr., and A. L. Henne, *Journ. Am. Chem. Soc.*, **52,** 2077 (1930).
(110) (a) Staudinger, H., R. Signer, H. Johner, M. Lüthy, W. Kern, D. Russidis and O. Schweitzer, *Ann.*, **474,** 145 (1929).
(110) (b) Staudinger, H., and M. Lüthy, *Helv. Chim. Acta*, **8,** 41, 65, 67 (1925).
(110) (c) Staudinger, H., H. Johner, R. Signer, G. Mie and G. Hengstenberg, *Z. physik. Chem.*, **126,** 425 (1927).
(110) (d) Staudinger, H., and R. Signer, *Helv. Chim. Acta*, **11,** 1047 (1928).
(110) (e) Mie, G., and J. Hengstenberg, *Helv. Chim. Acta*, **11,** 1052 (1928).
(110) (f) Staudinger, H., and R. Signer, *Z. Krist.*, **70,** 193 (1929).
(110) (g) Kohlschütter, H. W., *Ann.*, **482,** 75 (1930).
(110) (h) Ott, E., *Z. physik. Chem.*, *Abt. B*, **9,** 378 (1930).
(111) (a) Conant, J. B., and C. C. Tongberg, *Journ. Am. Chem. Soc.*, **52,** 1659 (1930).
(111) (b) Bridgman, P. W., and J. B. Conant, *Proc. Natl. Acad. Sci.*, **15,** 680 (1929).
(112) Kienle, R. H., and A. G. Hovey, *Journ. Am. Chem. Soc.*, **51,** 509 (1929).
(113) (a) Koebner, M., *Chem.-Ztg.*, **54,** 619 (1930).
(113) (b) Pollak, F., and F. Riesenfeld, *Z. angew. Chem.*, **43,** 1129 (1930).
(114) Tschugaeff, L., *Ber.*, **39,** 3199 (1906).
(115) Röhm, *Dissertation*, Tübingen, 1901. Cited in reference 99.
(116) Schroeter, G., *Ber.*, **49,** 2697 (1916).
(117) Schroeter, G., *Ber.*, **52,** 2224 (1919).

(118) (a) Abderhalden, E., *Naturwissenschaften*, **12**, 716 (1924).
(118) (b) Bergmann, M., *Naturwissenschaften*, **13**, 1045 (1925).
(118) (c) Pringsheim, H., *Naturwissenschaften*, **13**, 1084 (1925).
(118) (d) Bergmann, M., *Ber.*, **59**, 2973 (1926).
(118) (e) Hess, K., *Ann.*, **435**, 1 (1924).
(119) (a) Meyer, K. H., and H. Mark, *Ber.*, **61**, 593 (1928).
(119) (b) Mark, H., and K. H. Meyer, *Z. physik. Chem., Abt. B*, **2**, 115 (1929).
(119) (c) Mark, H., and G. v. Susich, *Z. physik. Chem., Abt. B*, **4**, 431 (1929).
(120) Haworth, W. N., C. W. Long and J. H. G. Plant, *Journ. Chem. Soc.*, **1927**, 2809.
(121) (a) Freudenberg, K., and E. Braun, *Ann.*, **460**, 288 (1928).
(121) (b) Freudenberg, K., *Ann.*, **461**, 130 (1928).
(122) (a) Irvine, J. C., *Chem. Reviews*, **1**, 41 (1924).
(122) (b) Freudenberg, K., *Ber.*, **54**, 767 (1921).
(123) (a) Sponsler, O. L., and W. H. Dore, *Colloid Symposium Monograph*, **4**, 174 (1926). Chemical Catalog Company, New York.
(123) (b) Sponsler, O. L., *Nature*, **125**, 633 (1930).
(124) (a) Staudinger, H., and O. Schweitzer, *Ber.*, **63**, 3122 (1930).
(124) (b) Staudinger, H., and O. Schweitzer, *Ber.*, **63**, 2317 (1930).
(124) (c) Staudinger, H., and H. Freudenberger, *Ber.*, **63**, 2331 (1930).
(125) Willstätter, R., and L. Zechmeister, *Ber.*, **46**, 2401 (1913).
(126) Stamm, A. J., *Journ. Am. Chem. Soc.*, **52**, 3047 (1930).
(127) Bergmann, M., and H. Machemer, *Ber.*, **63**, 316 (1930).
(128) Willstätter, R., and L. Zechmeister, *Ber.*, **62**, 722 (1929).
(129) (a) Kuhn, W., *Ber.*, **63**, 1503 (1930).
(129) (b) Freudenberg, K., W. Kuhn, W. Dürr, F. Bolz and G. Steinbrunn, *Ber.*, **63**, 1528 (1930).
(130) Bergmann, M., and H. Machemer, *Ber.*, **63**, 2304 (1930).
(131) Harries, C., *Ber.*, **37**, 2708 (1904); **38**, 3985 (1905).
(132) Thiele, J., *Ann.*, **306**, 92 (1899).
(133) Pickles, S. S., *Journ. Chem. Soc.*, **98**, 1085 (1910).
(134) (a) Staudinger, H., and J. Fritschi, *Helv. Chim. Acta*, **5**, 785 (1922).
(134) (b) Staudinger, H., *Ber.*, **57**, 1203 (1924).
(134) (c) Staudinger, H., and W. Widmer, *Helv. Chim. Acta*, **7**, 842 (1924).
(134) (d) Staudinger, H., *Z. angew. Chem.*, **38**, 226 (1925).
(134) (e) Staudinger, H., and E. Geiger, *Helv. Chim. Acta*, **9**, 549 (1926).
(134) (f) Staudinger, H., *Kautschuk*, **1925**, 5.
(134) (g) Staudinger, H., *Kautschuk*, **1927**, 63.
(134) (h) Staudinger, H., M. Asano, H. F. Bondy and R. Signer, *Ber.*, **61**, 2575 (1928).
(134) (i) Staudinger, H., H. F. Bondy and E. Geiger, *Ann.*, **468**, 1 (1929).
(134) (j) Staudinger, H., and H. F. Bondy, *Ann.*, **468**, 1 (1929).
(134) (k) Staudinger, H., *Kautschuk*, **5**, 94, 126 (1929).
(134) (l) Staudinger, H., and H. F. Bondy, *Ber.*, **62**, 2411 (1929).
(134) (m) Staudinger, H., and H. F. Bondy, *Ber.*, **63**, 724 (1930).
(134) (n) Staudinger, H., and E. O. Leupold, *Ber.*, **63**, 730 (1930).
(135) (a) Staudinger, H., and H. F. Bondy, *Ber.*, **63**, 734 (1930).
(135) (b) Staudinger, H., *Ber.*, **63**, 921 (1930).
(135) (c) Staudinger, H., and H. Joseph, *Ber.*, **63**, 2888 (1930).
(135) (d) Staudinger, H., *Kautschuk*, **6**, 153 (1930).
(135) (e) Staudinger, H., and H. F. Bondy, *Ber.*, **63**, 2900 (1930).
(136) Pummerer, R., *Z. angew. Chem.*, **43**, 757 (1930); Pummerer, R., G. Ebermayer and K. Gerlack, *Ber.*, **64**, 809 (1931).
(137) Whitby, G. S., *Trans. Inst. Rubber Ind.*, **5**, 184 (1929); **6**, 40 (1930).
(138) (a) Katz, J. R., *Chem.-Ztg.*, **49**, 353 (1925).
(138) (b) Meyer, K. H., and H. Mark, *Ber.*, **61**, 1939 (1928).
(139) Hock, L., *Gummi-Ztg.*, **39**, 1740 (1925).
(140) Fikentscher, H., and H. Mark, *Kautschuk*, **6**, 2 (1930); *Rubber Chemistry and Technology*, **3**, 201 (1930).
(141) Dunkel, M., *Z. physik. Chem., Abt. A*, **138**, 42 (1928).
(142) Whitby, G. S., J. C. McNally and W. Gallay, *Trans. Roy. Soc. Can.*, **22**, 27 (1928).
(143) Lee, W. B., and P. J. Van Rysselberge, *Journ. Phys. Chem.*, **33**, 1543 (1929).
(144) Katz, J. R., *Z. angew. Chem.*, **42**, 828 (1929).

(145) Ruzicka, L., M. Stoll, H. W. Huyser and H. A. Boekenoogen, *Helv. Chem. Acta*, **13**, 1152 (1930).

(146) (a) Staudinger, H., *Kolloid-Z.*, **53**, 19 (1930).

(146) (b) Signer, R., Z. *physik. Chem.*, *Abt. A*, **150**, 257 (1930).

(147) Meyer, V., and P. Jacobson, *Lehrbuch der organischen Chemie, zweiter Band, dritter Teil*. Walther de Gruyter and Company, Berlin and Leipzig (1920).

(148) Wittig, G., *Stereochemie*, p. 277.   Akademische Verlagsgesellschaft, Leipzig (1930).

(149) Reference 9, p. 432.

(150) Pringsheim, H., and W. G. Hensel, *Ber.*, **63**, 1096 (1930).

(151) Reference 3, p. 50.

(152) Reference 3, p. 153.

(153) Mark, H., *Melliands' Textilber.*, **10**, 695 (1929).

(154) (a) Zappi, E. V., *Bull. soc. chim.*, **19**, 249 (1916).

(154) (b) v. Braun, J., and W. Sobecki, *Ber.*, **44**, 1918 (1911).

(155) Grignard, V., and Tcheoufaki, *Compt. rend.*, **188**, 357 (1929).

(156) Konrad, E., O. Bächle, and R. Signer, *Ann.*, **474**, 276 (1929).

(157) Kipping, F. S., A. G. Murray and J. G. Maltby, *Journ. Chem. Soc.*, **1929**, 1180.

(158) Schönberg, A., *Ber.*, **62**, 195 (1929).

(159) Brit. patents, 279,406 and 314,524.

(160) Morgan, G. T., and F. H. Burstall, *Journ. Chem. Soc.*, **1930**, 1497.

(161) Mansfield, W., *Ber.*, **19**, 696 (1886).

(162) v. Braun, J., and A. Trümpler, *Ber.*, **43**, 547 (1910).

(163) v. Braun, J., *Ber.*, **43**, 3220 (1910).

(164) Wallach, O., *Ann.*, **312**, 205 (1900).

(165) Lind, S. C., and G. Glockler, *Journ. Am. Chem. Soc.*, **51**, 2811 (1929).

(166) (a) Harkins, W. D., and D. M. Gans, *Journ. Am. Chem. Soc.*, **52**, 5165 (1930).

(166) (b) Austin, J. B., and I. A. Black, *Journ. Am. Chem. Soc.*, **52**, 4552 (1930).

(167) (a) Zelinsky, N., *Ber.*, **57**, 264 (1924).

(167) (b) Fischer, F., F. Baugert and H. Pichler, *Brennstoff-Chem.*, **10**, 279 (1929).

(167) (c) Pease, R. N., *Journ. Am. Chem. Soc.*, **51**, 3470 (1929).

(167) (d) Schläpfer, P., and M. Brunner, *Helv. Chim. Acta*, **13**, 1125 (1930).

(168) (a) Sabatier, P., and J. B. Senderens, *Bull. soc. chim.* **25**, 683 (1901).

(168) (b) Brit. patent, 303,797.

(168) (c) Schläpfer, P., and O. Stadler, *Helv. Chim. Acta*, **9**, 185 (1926).

(169) (a) Lind, S. C., and R. S. Livingston, *Journ. Am. Chem. Soc.*, **52**, 4613 (1930).

(169) (b) Bates, J. R., and H. S. Taylor, *Journ. Am. Chem. Soc.*, **49**, 2438 (1927).

(170) (a) McLennon, J. C., M. A. Perrin and J. C. Ireton, *Proc. Roy. Soc.* (London), **125A**, 246 (1929).

(170) (b) Coolidge, W. D., *Science*, **62**, 441 (1925).

(171) Lind, S. C., D. C. Bardwell and J. H. Perry, *Journ. Am. Chem. Soc.*, **48**, 1556 (1926).

(172) Mignonac, G., and R. V. de Saint-Aunay, *Compt. rend.*, **188**, 959 (1929); *Bull. soc. chim.*, **47**, 14 (1930).

(173) Hunter, W. H., and G. H. Woolett, *Journ. Am. Chem. Soc.*, **43**, 135 (1921).

(174) (a) Reference 3, p. 173.

(174) (b) Kraemer, E. O., and G. R. Sears, *Journ. Rheology*, in press.

(174) (c) Loewen, H., *Kautschuk*, **7**, 12 (1931).

(174) (d) Mark, H., *Kolloid-Z.*, **53**, 32 (1930).

X. The Reversible Polymerization of Six-Membered Cyclic Esters*

This publication describes the reversible polymerization of six-membered cyclic esters, which has already been observed in a previous paper of this series.†

Such behavior has been found in several cases by different authors and seems to be fairly common with six-membered cyclic esters or δ-lactones; it does not occur however with ε-lactones nor with rings of a higher number of members.

Different linear polymers of δ-valerolactone were prepared up to molecular weights of 2240, at temperatures between 20 and 150°, with and without catalysts. Their melting points ranged between 35 and 55°. Polymerization took place in 3 to 29 days. The samples represent crystalline powders; they are all acidic. Titration gave molecular weights which closely agreed with the boiling point values.

Depolymerization takes place if the samples are heated and presumably consists of an ester interchange. The behavior of the six-membered rings is in accordance with the stereochemical theory of Sachse and Mohr.

Reactions leading to the formation of high polymers have received considerable attention during the past few years both because of their inherent interest as representatives of a realm that has been relatively little explored, and because of their bearing on the formulation of naturally occurring macromolecular materials. In this connection the behavior of six-membered cyclic esters is of peculiar interest: they combine with themselves, in many cases spontaneously at the ordinary conditions, to form polymers of high molecular weight, and this transformation is reversible. Since these esters are generally free from unsaturation, their self-combination must have its origin in some peculiarity of the heterocyclic system. Six-membered heterocycles are quite common among naturally occurring materials and are closely associated with natural polymers (sugars and polysaccharides, diketopiperazines and polypeptides); it is therefore reasonable to assume that the behavior of the cyclic esters lies closer to the natural processes that result in the formation of macromolecular substances

* W. H. Carothers, G. L. Dorough and F. J. van Natta; *Journ. Am. Chem. Soc.*, 54, 761–72 (1932); Contribution No. 72 from the Experimental Station of E. I. du Pont de Nemours and Co.

Received September 24, 1931. Published February 5, 1932.

† W. H. Carothers and F. J. van Natta; *Journ. Am. Chem. Soc.*, 52, 314 (1930); pages 29 to 42 of this volume and W. H. Carothers, J. A. Arvin and G. L. Dorough; *Journ. Am. Chem. Soc.*, 52, 3292 (1930); this volume pages 54 to 62.

than does the polymerization of unsaturated compounds, such as styrene, which have been more extensively studied.

Several isolated examples of the reversible polymerization of six-membered cyclic esters have been recorded in the literature but the question of the mechanism of this phenomenon has received very little attention. In the present paper, we report some observations bearing on this point.

Previous Work.—Fichter and Beisswenger (1) first reported that "δ-valerolactone (I) is characterized by a remarkable and surprising phenomenon: it polymerizes after a short time; the initially mobile oil becomes gradually thicker and finally solidifies to a crystalline mass." The polymer after recrystallization melted at 47–48°. Attempts to determine its molecular weight gave values ranging from a five- to a seven-fold polymer. Later the same transformation was observed by Hollo (2), who also records the spontaneous polymerization of the lactone (II) of hydroxyethylglycolic acid.

Bischoff and Walden (3) in 1893 described the transformation of glycolide (III) under the influence of heat or a trace of zinc chloride into a polymeric solid melting at 220°. On being distilled in a vacuum it was reconverted to the monomer, melting at 86–87°.

Drew and Haworth (4) have obtained the lactone (IV) of 2,3,4-trimethyl-*l*-arabonic acid in crystalline form (m. p. 45°) and observed that, in the presence of traces of hydrogen chloride, it is converted into a crystalline polymeric powder which has a considerably higher melting point, a lower solubility and a lower specific rotation than the monomer. Its molecular weight (about 2000) indicates that it is derived from about ten molecules of the monomer. At 175° it distils completely *in vacuo*, and the distillate consists of pure lactone. Drew and Haworth (5) favored a linear polyester structure for this polymer.

Trimethylene carbonate (V) was first described by Carothers and van Natta (6). The monomer is a very soluble crystalline solid melting at 47°. If it is heated to 130° for a few minutes with a trace of potassium carbonate, the mobile melt suddenly becomes very viscous and evolves a small amount of gas. The colorless, viscous sirup on cooling solidifies to a stiff mass which shows an apparent molecular weight of about 4000. When this mass is heated in a vacuum it distils almost quantitatively, and the distillate consists of pure monomer.

Monomeric ethylene oxalate (VI) was first described by Bischoff and Walden (7), who obtained it as a crystalline solid melting at 143° by distilling the product of the action of ethylene glycol on monoethyl oxalate. Later Bischoff (8) obtained less soluble, higher melting forms of ethylene

oxalate, and showed that these on distillation were converted into the 143°
form. Bischoff also observed that the melting points of the ethylene
oxalates change on standing, and suspected that these changes might be
due to a reversible polymerization, but he reported no comparative molecular weight data. The relation of the various forms of ethylene oxalate
to one another has lately been studied by Carothers, Arvin and Dorough
(9). It was found that the flat, diamond-shaped crystals of the monomer

completely disintegrate during the course of a few days, yielding a microcrystalline powder which consists of a mixture of polymers. From this
mixture by careful extraction with cold solvents two definite fractions
can be isolated. One of these melts at 159° and has an apparent molecular
weight of about 3000; the other fraction, which is probably much more
highly polymeric, melts at 173° and is too insoluble for molecular weight
determinations. These isolated fractions on standing lose their identity;

they revert spontaneously within a few days to more complicated mixtures which usually contain appreciable amounts of monomer. The polymeric ethylene oxalates can be converted into the monomer (with considerable loss) by vacuum distillation. Propylene oxalate (VIa) (m. p. 142°) is converted by the action of heat into an insoluble, microcrystalline polymer melting at 178° (9).

Generality of the Phenomenon.—The examples cited above show that the capacity to undergo reversible polymerization is quite common among six-membered cyclic esters. The presence of substituent groups, however, has a considerable effect and, in general, a depressing effect, on this tendency. The unsubstituted esters I, II and VI polymerize spontaneously at ordinary temperature in the complete absence of any added catalyst; substituted esters on the other hand, such as Ia, IIa, IV and VIa, require the action of heat, or catalysts, or both, and in some cases polymerization fails altogether.

A number of substituted δ-valerolactones (I) have been described in the literature, but without any record of their polymerization. We have therefore prepared α-n-propyl-δ-valerolactone (Ia) as described in the experimental part. Although δ-valerolactone was found to be completely polymerized to a waxy solid after twenty-nine days at room temperature, the new α-n-propyl-δ-valerolactone was still unchanged after twelve months, nor did it show any signs of polymerization after being heated to 80° for one month. However, when heated to 80° for one month in the presence of a trace of potassium carbonate or zinc chloride, it became more viscous, and its apparent molecular weight rose to 1100–1200.

Hollo (2) records the spontaneous polymerization of the lactone (II) of hydroxyethylglycolic acid, but makes no mention of the polymerization of its α-alkyl derivatives (II, R = C_2H_5, n-C_3H_7 and iso-C_3H_7) which he prepared at the same time. We have made attempts to polymerize the lactone (IIa) of hydroxyethyl-α-hydroxybutyric acid. Sixteen hours of heating at 140–160° failed to produce any change in the viscosity or the color of the pure lactone. Under the same conditions in the presence of a trace of potassium carbonate, only a slight increase in viscosity occurred.

Bischoff and Walden (10) state that lactide (IIIa) does not polymerize under the conditions that result in the polymerization of glycolide (III). We find, however, that at 250–275° the polymerization of lactide is quite rapid: in two hours a sample was transformed into a resinous mass which showed an apparent molecular weight of about 3000. A similar effect can be obtained at much lower temperatures, e. g., 140–150°, if potassium carbonate is present.

We have also examined some of the higher homologs of lactide. The cyclic esters derived from α-hydroxycaprylic and from α-hydroxypalmitic acids were prepared and heated for various periods both in the presence and absence of catalysts. Evidences of polymerization could be found only at temperatures sufficiently high to produce considerable decomposition.

Finally, it may be mentioned that although ethylene oxalate polymerizes spontaneously at the ordinary temperature, propylene oxalate undergoes a similar transformation only at considerably elevated temperatures (9).

Peculiarity of the Phenomenon.—Among cyclic esters the capacity to undergo reversible polymerization in the manner illustrated by the examples cited above is peculiar to six-membered rings. The γ-lactones and other five-membered cyclic esters show no tendency to polymerize, and no corresponding polymers are known. Thus, we have heated samples of pure γ-butyrolactone both with and without catalysts (zinc chloride, potassium carbonate) at 80° for twelve months; none of the samples showed any detectable increase in viscosity. We have also made various attempts to polymerize ethylene carbonate, but these attempts were all unsuccessful, although the corresponding six-membered ring, trimethylene carbonate (V), is readily polymerized (11).

It appears also that cyclic esters of more than six members show no tendency to polymerize spontaneously. Information on this point is somewhat incomplete. No aliphatic cyclic esters of nine to thirteen atoms have been described. In fact no practical means for the preparation of such esters are yet known. In general, the attempt to prepare cyclic esters of more than six atoms from open chain compounds leads to linear polymers.

Thus the six-atom ring trimethylene carbonate (V) is readily obtained by heating diethyl carbonate with trimethylene glycol, and subsequently distilling the product *in vacuo*, but when diethyl carbonate is similarly treated with tetramethylene glycol, the product is a polymeric material that is not capable of being distilled *in vacuo*, *i. e.*, it cannot be depolymerized; only at temperatures above 300°, it undergoes complete thermal decomposition and yields a complicated mixture of products among which are found very small amounts of the dimeric fourteen-membered ring VIII (6). Attempts to detect the presence of the monomer VII have been unsuccessful. Similar behavior is observed with trimethylene oxalate (9) and ethylene succinate (12). The preparation of these esters leads to linear polymeric products of high molecular weight. No smooth depolymerization of these polymers can be effected by the action of heat; but at high temperatures they undergo complete thermal decomposition, yielding a complicated mixture of gaseous, liquid and tarry products containing very small amounts of the cyclic dimers which are, respectively, fourteen and sixteen-membered rings (XI and IX)   The corresponding monomers have never been obtained.

The following observations indicate the relatively great stability of the large cyclic esters. Specimens of dimeric trimethylene oxalate (XI), dimeric ethylene succinate (IX), and exaltolide (X) have been preserved in the laboratory for two years without showing any signs of change. The last two of these compounds have been heated in sealed tubes at 170° for a considerable period of time. After twelve hours they were quite unchanged; after forty-three hours they had become slightly colored and their melting points slightly lowered, but signs of appreciable polymerization were absent (13).

The peculiar position of the six-membered esters is shown in the following outline, in which, for simplicity, the starting material in each case is represented as an hydroxy acid.

(A) The structural unit is five atoms long

$$\text{HO—R—COOH} \underset{+H_2O}{\overset{-H_2O}{\rightleftharpoons}} \ulcorner\text{O—R—CO}\urcorner$$

(B) The structural unit is six atoms long

$$\text{HO—R—COOH} \underset{+H_2O}{\overset{-H_2O}{\rightleftharpoons}} \ulcorner\text{O—R—CO}\urcorner$$

$$+H_2O \Big\updownarrow -H_2O \qquad\qquad \Big\Updownarrow$$

$$\cdots\text{—O—R—CO—O—R—CO—O—R—CO—O—R—CO—}\cdots$$

(C) The structural unit is more than six atoms long

$$\text{HO—R—COOH}$$

$$+H_2O \Big\updownarrow -H_2O$$

$$\cdots\text{—O—R—CO—O—R—CO—O—R—CO—O—R—CO—}\cdots$$

Under B it should be mentioned that the reversible relation between the monomer and the polymer complicates the problem of deciding in a given case which of these is the real primary product of the dehydration of the hydroxy acid. In any event the conditions of the dehydration usually favor the polymerization of the monomer, so that the latter is isolated only by vacuum distillation of the actual reaction product. Dietzel and Krug (14) have presented evidence to show that the self-esterification of lactic acid leads directly only to polylactyl lactic acids and that lactide, when it is produced, results from the depolymerization of these polyesters. On the other hand, it is established, at least in certain instances (4), that δ-lactones may be formed as such directly from the corresponding hydroxy acid. No doubt in most cases, depending upon the conditions, either the monomer or the polymer may be formed as the primary product.

Under C it should be mentioned that although attempts to prepare seven-membered cyclic esters from dibasic acids and dihydric alcohols lead only to polyesters, ε-hydroxy acids appear to be dehydrated with the simultaneous formation of polymer and monomer (15). There is, however, no record of the interconversion of these two forms, and the higher ω-hydroxy acids yield linear polymers exclusively (16).

Mechanism of the Phenomenon.—The smooth reversibility of the polymerization of the six-membered cyclic esters and the absence of double-bond unsaturation at first suggested that here, if anywhere, might be found the missing models of that hypothetical phenomenon, association polymerization, to which for a time the peculiarities of natural polymers were widely attributed (17). This thought was considerably weakened, however, when Dr. J. W. Hill presented in the closely analogous case of adipic anhydride, a direct and decisive proof of the structural difference between monomer and polymer (18). No similar proof is possible in the esters under consideration; nevertheless, all the evidence together conclusively favors the mechanism suggested by Carothers and van Natta (6), namely, that the polymers are linear polyesters and that both the polymerization and its reversal proceed by a process of ester interchange. This is indicated in the equation

$$O-R-CO + O-R-CO + O-R-CO + O-R-CO + \text{etc.} \longrightarrow$$

$$\cdots -O-R-CO-O-R-CO-O-R-CO-O-R-CO-O-R-CO- \cdots$$

The peculiar position occupied by the six-membered cyclic esters may be explained, as we have already suggested (6), by stereochemical factors: rings of six atoms are strained (or may pass through positions of strain); rings of five atoms or more than ten atoms are strainless. In the cyclic esters the strain can be relieved by the process of ester interchange, which results in polymerization. The resulting polymers (from the six-membered esters) are easily depolymerized owing to the high probability of the close approach of atoms six atoms apart in a chain. Polyesters whose de-polymerization would result in larger monomeric rings are not depoly-merized; the probability of the close approach of the requisite atoms is too slight.

The interchange mechanism for the polymerization of the six-membered esters is supported by the following facts: (1) The polymers have the same apparent analytical compositions (19), and saponification equivalents as the corresponding monomers, and they yield the same products on hydrolysis.

(2) The products of the polymerization of the six-membered cyclic esters closely resemble in their physical properties the polymers formed by the action of dibasic acids on glycols, or by the self-esterification of the higher ω-hydroxy acids. It has been definitely established that these polymers are linear polyesters; the chains are open and are terminated by hydroxyl and/or carboxyl groups (12, 20).

(3) Both the forward and the reverse transformations are catalyzed by acids and bases, typical ester-interchange catalysts.

(4) The speed of the polymerization runs parallel with the susceptibility to hydrolysis. The much greater susceptibility of δ-lactones to hydrolysis as compared with analogous γ-lactones is well known. The hydrolysis constant for δ-valerolactone (I) is more than twice that of its α-methyl derivative (2), and the former polymerizes spontaneously while the latter does not. Similar relations hold for the lactone of hydroxyethylglycolic acid (II) and its α-alkyl derivatives (2). The hydrolytic constants for glycolide in its two stages are, respectively, 0.0179 and 0.119, while the corresponding values for lactide are 0.00313 and 0.0611 (21). The former polymerizes much more readily than the latter. Ethylene oxalate, which polymerizes with extraordinary facility, is so sensitive to hydrolysis that, like an acid, it can be titrated directly with moderately warm dilute alkali.

Further Observations.—Data on some polymers of δ-valerolactone are presented in Table I.

TABLE I

POLYMERS OF δ-VALEROLACTONE

No.	Catalyst	Temp. during polym., °C.	Time	M. p. of polymer, °C.	Mol. wt. of polymer (boiling point in benzene)	
1	None	Room	29 days	35–40	1060	1060
2	None	80–85	13 days	52–53	1270	1330
3	K_2CO_3	80–85	5 days	53–54	1840	1820
4	$ZnCl_2$	80–85	5 days	52–54	2230	1846
5	None	150	10 hrs.	52–55	2110	2240
6	Over CH_3COCl	Room	3 days	50–51	1720	1720

The melting points are in general somewhat higher than those reported by Fichter and Beisswenger (1). The polymer is soluble in a variety of organic solvents and is readily crystallized, e. g., from a mixture of petroleum ether and benzene. When allowed to solidify from a melt it forms an opaque, soft, waxy solid. The crystals are poorly developed; they appear under the microscope as tiny irregular particles.

Polymeric δ-valerolactone is acidic. In acetone solution it can be titrated with alkali to a sharp end-point which persists for several minutes. Sample 5 of Table I thus showed a neutral equivalent of 2153 and 2243 in two determinations. The closeness of this value to the observed molecular weights indicates the probable presence of one carboxyl group for each molecule. It is not quite certain that this agreement is not accidental. A product prepared by heating the monomer at 175° showed an equivalent weight of 6320 and a molecular weight of about 1500 (observed 1420 and 1660), but the molecular weight values are under suspicion because of severe foaming. It seems certain however that at least part of the polyester molecules bear carboxyl groups.

The polymeric δ-valerolactone is not homogeneous, but contains molecules of different sizes. Its sodium salts are not soluble in water. A sample of recrystallized polymer formed at ordinary temperature (m. p. 53–56°) showed by titration in acetone an equivalent weight of 3160. The acetone solution was evaporated and the resulting dry sodium salt taken up in hot absolute alcohol, filtered and cooled to crystallize. In this way fractions of different solubilities and sodium content were isolated: (1) 0.38 g. containing 0.22% Na; (2) 0.77 g. containing 0.49% Na; (3) 0.14 g. containing 3.92% Na. The equivalent weights inferred from the sodium contents are: (1) 10,400, (2) 4700, (3) 590. Determination of the molecular weight of fraction 2 by the boiling point in benzene gave the value 3880.

The polyester derived from the lactone (II) of hydroxyethylglycolic acid differs in its behavior from polymeric δ-valerolactone. It cannot be titrated to a sharp end-point with 0.1 N alkali. Attempts to prepare a sodium salt by treating it with sodium bicarbonate under various conditions have led to mixtures from which two distinct fractions are readily separated. One of these is unchanged polyester entirely free of sodium; the other is the pure sodium salt of hydroxyethylglycolic acid. Thus even so mild an alkali as sodium bicarbonate hydrolyzes the polyester, and it is impossible to determine whether the polymeric molecules bear carboxyl groups. Ethylene oxalate (VI) shows a still more exaggerated sensitivity to alkalies. Trimethylene carbonate (V) appears to be neutral.

In this case any terminal carboxyl groups that might arise during the polymerization would be lost spontaneously since they would be linked to oxygen (R—O—CO—OH). The momentary liberation of a small amount of gas at the end of the sudden thermal polymerization of trimethylene carbonate is perhaps due to loss of carbon dioxide from acid carbonic ester groups formed in this way.

For δ-valerolactone, however, as already indicated, the presence of a terminal carboxyl group in the polymeric molecule is fairly clearly demonstrated.

It seems likely that the first step in the polymerization of the cyclic esters involves the intervention of a trace of the corresponding hydroxy acid or one of its derivatives. One can imagine that hydroxyvaleric acid would thus react with valerolactone

$$\text{HO(CH}_2)_4\text{COOH} + \underline{\text{O(CH}_2)_4\text{CO}} \longrightarrow \text{HO(CH}_2)_4\text{CO—O(CH}_2)_4\text{COOH}$$

The dimeric acid would then react in the same manner with valerolactone to form a trimeric acid, and the reaction would continue in this sense until all of the lactone was exhausted or the chains became too long for further reaction. In this mechanism a foreign acid might equally well participate, and it would be bound in the product as the first unit of the polymeric chain. Experiments in this direction were made with chloroacetic acid.

One gram of δ-valerolactone was heated with 0.1 g. of chloroacetic acid for fifteen hours at 150–160°. The reaction mixture, which solidified on standing in a refrigerator, was recrystallized from alcohol and carefully dried. It melted at 42° and contained 3.28% chlorine. It was triturated with an excess of sodium bicarbonate in the presence of a little water, and the product after drying was extracted with warm alcohol. The polyester which separated was thrice recrystallized from alcohol. It now melted at 45–46° and contained 2.3% sodium. The molecular weights calculated respectively from the chlorine and sodium content, assuming a molecule having the formula XII, are 1008 and 1000.

(XII)   ClCH₂CO—[O(CH₂)₄CO—]₂OH

In a similar experiment in which one gram of valerolactone was heated with 0.05 g. of chloroacetic acid the initial product melted at 48° and contained 2.06% chlorine. The sodium salt melted at 50–51° and contained 1.35% sodium. The molecular weights calculated from these data are 1720 and 1705.

Chlorine-containing derivatives were also obtained by heating the polymeric lactone with chloroacetic acid. Two grams of polymer and 0.1 g. of chloroacetic acid were heated for ten hours at 150–160°. The product was thrice crystallized from alcohol. It contained 1.75% chlorine, and this corresponds to a molecular weight of 2030. Its neutral equivalent as indicated by titration with alkali was 2083.

These results are at least consistent with the mechanism suggested above. A mechanism involving the mutual coalescence of two molecules of monomer to form a twelve-atom ring and the growth of this through the progressive absorption of more monomeric molecules seems less likely, but some observations lately made in this laboratory on the polymerization of cyclic anhydrides indicate that this mechanism is not at all impossible.

Lactone (II) of Hydroxyethylglycolic Acid.—Preparation: The method of Hollo (2) was slightly modified. The crude mixture containing the sodium salt of the hydroxy acid, sodium chloride and a little glycol was washed with acetone, suspended in absolute alcohol and treated with less than the calculated amount of hydrochloric acid. The precipitated sodium chloride was removed by filtration and the lactone isolated from the filtrate by distillation. In this way it was readily obtained free of chlorine.

When allowed to stand it gradually solidified to a pasty mass. After five weeks the solid was crystallized five times from ethyl acetate. It then melted at 62–64° and showed a molecular weight in boiling benzene in about 460 (observed, 451, 471). This probably corresponds approximately with Hollo's polymer melting at 56–63°.

A polymer formed by heating the lactone at 150° for five hours after being crystallized four times from ethyl acetate melted at 87–89°. It was very soluble in cold chloroform, hot ethyl acetate and hot alcohol, slightly soluble in ether, cold ethyl acetate and water. Molecular weight determinations in boiling benzene gave the values 1647 and 1788.

Hollo describes another type of polymer obtained when the sodium salt of the hydroxy acid is treated with an excess of hydrochloric acid. This melts at 66–68°, boils at 216 to 220°, and distils without change at atmospheric pressure.

It seems quite impossible however that a polymer should boil only 5° higher than the monomer (210–215°), and the explanation of Hollo's observation probably lies in the fact that the hydrochloric acid present in the polymer distils with the monomer during depolymerization and the polymerization of the distillate is so powerfully catalyzed that it occurs very rapidly. In our experiments a specimen of polymeric lactone originating from a preparation in which a slight excess of hydrochloric acid was used to liberate the hydroxy acid was observed to distil at 215–216° and the distillate solidified immediately on cooling. The solid product after three crystallizations from ethyl acetate melted at 85 to 87°.

This polymer distilled completely, but the distillate was not unchanged polymer. Molecular weight determinations on the distillate made immediately after the completion of the distillation gave the values, 144, 140 and 121 (calcd. for monomer, 102). After two hours the distillate had already begun to crystallize. After twenty-four hours it had solidified, and the solid after recrystallization thrice from ethyl acetate showed a molecular weight of about 900 in boiling benzene (observed, 867, 931).

Polymers originating from preparations in which an excess of hydrochloric acid was carefully avoided behaved in precisely the same way except that the reversion of the distillate was much slower; it remained fluid for twenty-four hours. The melting points of the purified polymers obtained from either source approached 89°.

α-n-**Propyl-δ-valerolactone** was prepared through the steps indicated in the following equations.

$$C_6H_5OCH_2CH_2CH_2Br + n\text{-}C_3H_7CH_2(COOC_2H_5)_2 \longrightarrow$$
$$C_6H_5OCH_2CH_2CH_2(C_3H_7)C(COOC_2H_5)_2 - HBr \longrightarrow BrCH_2CH_2CH_2CH(C_3H_7)COOH$$
$$\longrightarrow BrCH_2CH_2CH_2CH(C_3H_7)COONa \longrightarrow \overline{OCH_2CH_2CH_2CH(C_3H_7)CO}$$

phenoxypropyl-(n-propyl)-malonic diethyl ester: colorless liquid, b. p. (4 mm.) 195–200°; d_4^{20} 1.0246; n_D^{25} 1.4820.

Anal.   Calcd. for $C_{19}H_{28}O_5$: C, 67.85; H, 8.33.   Found: C, 68.60, 68.04; H, 8.03, 8.09.

δ-Bromo-α-n-propylvaleric acid: b. p. (5 mm.) 148–150°; d_4^{20} 1.3851, n_D^{20} 1.4730.

Anal.   Calcd. for $C_8H_{15}O_2Br$: C, 43.05; H, 6.72; neutral equivalent, 223.   Found: C, 44.33; H, 6.84; neutral equivalent, 220, 222.

The high values for carbon are probably due to the presence of some phenol.

α-n-Propyl-δ-valerolactone: b. p. (10 mm.) 118–120°; d_4^{20} 0.9929; n_D^{20} 1.4585.

Anal.   Calcd. for $C_8H_{14}O_2$: C, 67.67; H, 9.85; saponification equivalent, 142. Found: C, 67.59, 67.50; H, 10.01, 10.18; saponification equivalent, 143, 144.

Preparation of Lactide.—The preparation of lactide by methods described in the older literature (22) gave poor yields, but excellent results were obtained by the following method based on recent patents (23).   Two hundred grams of commercial lactic acid was heated at ordinary pressure in a Claisen flask by a metal bath at 120° until water ceased to distil.   The temperature was then raised to 140° and the pressure reduced to 10 mm.   During six hours water continued to distil slowly from the flask.   The pressure in the system was reduced to 5 mm. and the temperature raised sufficiently to cause rapid distillation of the lactide, which solidified in the receiver.   The yield of crude product was 125 g.   It was purified by crystallization from ether; m. p. 128°.

Summary

Several isolated examples of the reversible polymerization of six-membered cyclic esters have been briefly reported in the literature.   Further examples are reported in the present paper, together with some experimental data and speculations on the mechanism of the phenomenon.   The following conclusions are reached.

1.   The ability to undergo reversible polymerization is generally characteristic of six-membered cyclic esters.

2.   Ester rings of five atoms or more than six atoms do not polymerize under the action of heat.

3.   The tendency of six-membered cyclic esters to polymerize is closely related to their great susceptibility toward hydrolysis; both tendencies are diminished by the presence of substituent groups.

4.   The polymers formed from six-membered cyclic esters are linear polyesters and, at least in certain instances, the chains are open and terminated by hydroxyl and carboxyl groups.

5.   Both the polymerization and the depolymerization consist essentially in a process of ester interchange.

6.   The peculiar position occupied by the six-membered cyclic esters is readily explained by stereochemical considerations based on the Sachse-Mohr theory.

Bibliography and Remarks

(1) Fichter and Beisswenger, *Ber.*, **36**, 1200 (1903).

(2) Hollo, *ibid.*, **61**, 895 (1928).

(3) Bischoff and Walden, *ibid.*, **26**, 262 (1893).

(4) Drew and Haworth, *J. Chem. Soc.*, 775 (1927).

(5) *Cf.* Haworth, "The Structure of Sugars," Edward Arnold and Co., London, 1929, p. 78.

(6) Carothers and van Natta, *Journ. Am. Chem. Soc.*, **52**, 314 (1930).

(7) Bischoff and Walden, *Ber.*, **27**, 2939 (1894).

(8) Bischoff, *Ber.*, **40**, 2803 (1907).

(9) Carothers, Arvin and Dorough, *Journ. Am. Chem. Soc.*, **52**, 3292 (1930); *cf.* Bergmann and Wolff, *J. prakt. Chem.*, **128**, 229 (1930); and Carothers and van Natta, *Ber.*, **64**, 1755 (1931).

(10) Bischoff and Walden, *Ann.*, **279**, 71 (1894).

(11) β-Lactones have not been specifically examined from this standpoint, but it appears likely in view of some observations recorded by Johansson [Lunds Universitets Årsskrift II, [2] **12**, 3 (1916)] that simple lactones of this class undergo irreversible polymerization under the action of heat.

(12) Carothers and Dorough, *Journ. Am. Chem. Soc.*, **52**, 711 (1930).

(13) We do not intend to suggest that the polymerization of large cyclic esters is impossible. In fact, since such esters can be hydrolyzed to the corresponding hydroxy acids, it is evident from equation C that such a polymerization can probably be effected under some conditions. The process would consist in hydrolysis of the cyclic ester to the hydroxy acid and the dehydration of this to the poly-ester. Both of these steps might occur in a single operation under appropriate conditions, *e. g.*, at elevated temperature in the presence of a small amount of water plus mineral acid. But the experiments described above do demonstrate that the large cyclic esters, at least qualitatively, are very different from the six-membered esters.

(14) Dietzel and Krug, *Ber.*, **58**, 1307 (1925).

(15) Marvel and Birkheimer, *Journ. Am. Chem. Soc.*, **51**, 260 (1929); Blaise and Koehler, *Compt. rend.*, **148**, 1773 (1909).

(16) No exception to this statement has been observed among the numerous esters we have prepared from dibasic acids and glycols, but we have lately found that in the self-esterification of ω-hydroxy-decanoic acid in the absence of solvent, appreciable amounts of the cyclic dimeric ester are formed. This has already been prepared by a different method and described by Lycan and Adams [*Journ. Am. Chem. Soc.*, **51**, 3450 (1929)].

(17) Abderhalden, *Naturwissenschaften*, **12**, 716 (1924); Bergmann, *ibid.*, **13**, 1045 (1925); Pring-sheim, *ibid.*, **13**, 1084 (1925); Hess, *Ann.*, **435**, 1 (1924).

(18) Hill, *Journ. A. Chem. Soc.*, **52**, 4110 (1930).

(19) But the values for carbon are usually somewhat low and the values for hydrogen somewhat high. This may signify that the chains are open, or it may mean merely that the polyesters in spite of the fact that they are insoluble in water are nevertheless somewhat hygroscopic and difficult to dry.

(20) Lycan and Adams, *Journ. Am. Chem. Soc.*, **51**, 625, 3450 (1929).

(21) Johansson and Sibelius, *Ber.*, **52**, 745 (1919).

(22) Gay-Lussac and Pelouze, *Ann.*, **7**, 43 (1833); Bischoff and Walden, *Ber.*, **26**, 263 (1893).

(23) Chemische Werke, French Patent 456, 824 (1913); Grüter and Pohl, U. S. Patent 1,095,205 (1914).

XI. The Use of Molecular Evaporation as a Means for Propagating Chemical Reactions*

A new design of molecular still is described, the aim being to remove a volatile reaction product of low vapor pressure from another product, which is formed simultaneously and having no volatility. The reaction mixture is heated in a flat pan, a high vacuum being maintained and a cooled condensing plate being disposed in the immediate neighborhood of the evaporating surface.

Reversible reactions involving the simultaneous formation of a volatile and non-volatile product are often forced to completion by causing the volatile product to distil from the reaction mixture as fast as it is formed. The purpose of the present note is to call attention to the possibility of extending the application of this principle to instances in which the effective vapor pressure or escaping tendency of a volatile product or potential product is very small. In the molecular still (1) distillation or continuous evaporation can be effected even when the vapor pressure of the distilling substance is as low perhaps as 10^{-5} mm. The theory of the process has been discussed by Washburn (1b), and we need only to mention that successful operation requires a highly evacuated system comprising a condenser placed very close to the evaporating surface. The temperature of the condenser must be low enough to reduce the vapor pressure of the distillate to a negligible value. Under these conditions the mean free path of the molecules is less than the distance from the condenser to the evaporating surface; consequently most of the molecules that manage to escape from the evaporating surface are caught by the condenser with a negligible probability of return.

Mercury and apparently cane sugar can be evaporated in the molecular still at room temperature (1b) and n-heptacontane can be distilled without decomposition (2). The tendency to distil diminishes with increasing molecular weight, and it appears that, so far as practically useful rates are concerned, the upper limit of distillability for paraffin hydrocarbons may lie at as low a molecular weight as 1100 or 1200. For other types of organic compounds it will in general lie at still lower molecular weights (2). Thus all substances of high molecular weight are practically completely non-volatile. There are many instances of reversible reactions in which

* W. H. Carothers and J. W. Hill; *Journ. Am. Chem. Soc.*, **54**, 1557–59 (1932); Contribution No. 74 from the Experimental Station of E. I. du Pont de Nemours and Co.

Received November 12, 1931. Published April 6, 1932.

only one volatile substance is involved. If this substance has a very low vapor pressure, or if it is strongly held by other substances involved in the reaction, or if its equilibrium concentration is very low, then molecular evaporation may be capable of producing a result not even remotely accessible with the aid of the usual distillation equipment and methods.

Examples of the use of molecular evaporation as a means of propagating chemical reactions are provided in other papers of this series (3). The reactions involved are reversible bifunctional condensations. The starting materials are linear polymers capable, by self-combination, of yielding a still longer molecule with the elimination of some volatile product. The size of the product molecules depends upon the completeness of the reaction. With the aid of the molecular still one can obtain products of much higher molecular weight than with the ordinary distillation equipment. The same principles can doubtless be applied to other kinds of reversible reactions.

The simple stills described by Washburn (1b), function satisfactorily but they do not provide ready access to the residue from the distillation. For this reason we constructed the instrument shown in Fig. 1 and used it in carrying out some of the reactions referred to above. The new instrument has the advantage that the flat pan containing the distillation residue can be lifted out when the instrument is open.

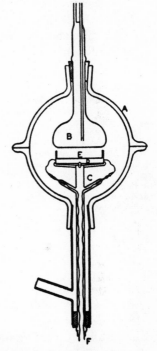

Fig. 1.—Molecular still ($^1/_7$ natural size).

Description of the Instrument

The outer shell (A) of the apparatus is made up of two domes from pyrex vacuum distilling apparatus (Corning Glass Company Catalogue, Item No. 56). The ground surfaces are lubricated with a good vacuum grease. (B) is the condenser provided with water leads. (C) is the glass support for the heater (D) and the distilling pan (E) (4). The heater and distilling pan are contained in an outer copper pan as shown. The heater consists of nichrome wire wound spirally on a sheet of mica which is supported between sheets of thin asbestos board inserted below the distilling pan. The heater leads (F) are brought up through the support (C) and out as shown. Connection with the heater is made with spring clamps which make the heater readily demountable. The lower part of the apparatus is the regular distilling tube provided with the Pyrex vacuum distilling apparatus (Catalogue No. 56). The rubber stoppers at the top and bottom of the apparatus are well covered with a suitable wax such as picein. A thermocouple (not indicated in the drawing) is led in through the lower wax seal and the junction placed under the pan E. The slight bulges on the condenser and the pan support where they enter the apparatus are necessary to obviate the danger of these parts sucking in when the apparatus is evacuated.

Summary

In reversible reactions involving the simultaneous formation of volatile and non-volatile products, the use of molecular evaporation makes it possible to realize chemical effects that cannot be achieved with the aid of the usual distillation equipment. A new design of molecular still is described.

Bibliography and Remarks

(1) (a) Brönsted and Hevesy, *Phil. Mag.*, **43**, 31 (1922); (b) Washburn, *Bur. Standards J. Research*, **2**, 476 (1929); (c) Burch, *Proc. Roy. Soc.* (London), **123**, 271 (1929); (d) Hickman, *Chem. Ind.*, **48**, 365 (1929).

(2) Carothers, Hill, Kirby and Jacobson, *Journ. Am. Chem. Soc.*, **52**, 5279 (1930).

(3) Papers XII, XIII, XIV and XVI.

(4) This pan is conveniently made by cutting a pyrex beaker close to the bottom. The material of which the pan is composed has a considerable effect on the rate of the bifunctional condensations described in Papers XII, XIII and XIV. No polyesterification could be effected in a copper pan. On the other hand, when superpolyesters and polyanhydrides are prepared in a glass pan the products adhere very firmly to the glass so that the dish is frequently shattered on cooling owing to the force of contraction.

XII.   Linear Superpolyesters*

In previous papers[†] polymerization up to molecular weights of about 5000 has been investigated and compared with the tendency to the formation of low molecular rings.   As a general rule it can be stated that if 5- or 6-rings can be formed by esterification, the intra-molecular type of reaction prevails; in the case of 6- and 7-membered rings both monomolecular rings and linear polymers of medium molecular weight are produced.

From now on the main interest is concentrated on higher polymers, which are called superpolymers if the molecular weight exceeds 10,000.   At the same time products with a molecular weight between 800 and 5000 are termed α-esters, while products above 5000 are called ω-esters.

In this paper a series of ω-polyesters was prepared with the use of the mo-

* W. H. Carothers and I. W. Hill; *Journ. Am. Chem. Soc.*, **54**, 1559–66 (1932); Communication No. 75 from the Experimental Station of E. I. du Pont de Nemours and Co.

Received November 12, 1931.   Published April 6, 1932.

† See Contribution I to XI of this series on pages 4 to 156 in this volume.

lecular still described in a previous paper*. Linear α-esters are mostly microcrystalline powders (in some cases opaque, brittle waxes) with melting points around 80°. They are mostly quite soluble in chloroform and ethyl-acetate and on the average represent a polymerization degree around 10.

ω-Superpolyesters are resins with considerable hardness and toughness. If placed in solvents, they first imbibe the latter and swell; later they give solutions of high viscosity. When heated they become transparent around 80°, but do not yet flow at this temperature. Flow only takes place at considerably higher temperatures. In the solid state they give sharp X-ray powder diagrams, which closely resemble the corresponding patterns of the α-esters. A few degrees below the melting point, the rings lose their sharpness and at the melting point a diffuse halo characteristic of a liquid appears. Superpolyesters in the plastic state can be drawn out into very strong, pliable and—as the X-ray investigation shows—highly orientated fibers.†

The following ω-esters are described in this paper:

> ω-trimethylene ester of hexadamethylene dicarboxylic acid
> ω-polyethylene succinate
> ω-polyester from ω-hydroxydecanoic acid
> ω-polyester from ω-hydroxypentadecanoic acid
> ω-ethylene sebacate

In previous papers we have described polyesters having molecular weights ranging from 800 to 5000 derived from dibasic acids of the series $HOOC(CH_2)_xCOOH$ and glycols of the series $HO(CH_2)_yOH$ (2). These esters are microcrystalline solids that dissolve readily in appropriate solvents. Their solutions are not highly viscous and they show no signs of inherently colloidal behavior. In the present paper we describe polyesters of the same series having much higher molecular weights. They exhibit colloidal behavior and simulate to a remarkable degree some of the properties of certain naturally occurring high polymers. For the sake of brevity and convenience we use the designation α-ester or α-form for the polyesters having molecular weights ranging from 800 to 5000 and the designation ω-ester or ω-form for the new superpolyesters.

Nature of the Polyesterification.—The mutual esterification of dibasic acids and dihydric alcohols is a bifunctional reaction (3). As such it presents the formal possibility of yielding (1) cyclic monomeric esters, (2) cyclic

---

* See page 154 to page 156 of this volume.
† Compare the next paper on pages 165 to 168 of this volume.

polyesters, and (3) open chain polyesters. Studies already reported have proved that the first possibility is ordinarily realized only in those comparatively rare instances where the nature of the starting material permits the formation of a ring of five or six atoms. Otherwise reaction generally is intermolecular and the product is of the third type. The polyesterification thus consists in a series of intermolecular couplings resulting in the formation of progressively longer chains as indicated by way of illustration in the following equations.

$$HOOC—R—COOH + HO—R'—OH \longrightarrow HO—R'—O—CO—R—COOH$$
$$2HO—R'—O—CO—R—COOH \longrightarrow$$
$$HO—R'—O—CO—R—CO—O—R'—O—CO—R—COOH$$
$$(n + 1)HO—R'—O—CO—R—COOH \longrightarrow$$
$$HO—R'—O(CO—R—CO—O—R'—O)_n—CO—R—COOH$$

The reaction is reversible and an exceedingly large number of entities are involved in the ester equilibrium. The equilibrium can be displaced by the removal of the liberated water, and the more nearly complete the reaction the longer are the molecules of the polyester product. The reaction becomes formally complete when all the molecules of the initial reactants are combined into a single molecule.

A complicating circumstance arises from the fact that the glycol and the acid need not react in precisely equivalent ratio: at any particular stage n molecules of acid may be involved with $n + 1$ molecules of glycol or, conversely, n molecules of glycol may be involved with $n + 1$ molecules of acid. In the former case the product molecules will bear hydroxyl groups at both ends; in the latter they will bear carboxyl groups at both ends. In either event no further progress is possible by esterification. Under favorable conditions, however, coupling may continue nevertheless. Two molecules may unite by a process of ester interchange involving their terminal ester linkages. This mechanism is realized experimentally (2) when di-(β-hydroxyethyl)-succinate (I) is heated *in vacuo*. Glycol is liberated and the final product of prolonged heating is the same as one obtained by similarly heating succinic acid with a very small excess of glycol.

(I) $HO(CH_2)_2OCO(CH_2)_2COO(CH_2)_2OH + HO(CH_2)_2OCO(CH_2)_2COO(CH_2)_2OH \longrightarrow$
$HO(CH_2)_2OCO(CH_2)_2COO(CH_2)_2OCO(CH_2)_2COO(CH_2)_2OH + HO(CH_2)_2OH,$ etc.

The only factor that could theoretically preclude the possibility of producing exceedingly long molecules as the result of bifunctional esterifications is the loss of terminal groups through ring formation. Since in the polyesters thus far examined the terminal groups are still present, it appears that such ring formation does not occur (4).

Another factor that might be expected to have the same effect is the mutilation of terminal groups, *e. g.*, through the loss of carboxyl as carbon dioxide. But our experience indicates that the loss of terminal groups in this fashion occurs only when patently inappropriate conditions are adopted. More important than this is the fact demonstrated by the behavior of di-(β-hydroxyethyl)-succinate cited above that the coupling can progress through a process of ester interchange involving the last ester linkage. The possibility of further coupling therefore does not absolutely depend upon the integrity of the terminal groups as such.

As a matter of fact, however, as such reactions have been carried out in the past an apparent limit is reached at a comparatively low molecular weight. Thus the glycol and the acid are heated together in a distilling flask provided with a receiver to collect the liberated water, and heating is finally continued at low pressure and considerably elevated temperature. The molecular weight of the polyester product increases during the progress of the heating and finally reaches a value of 3000 to 5000. This value is not noticeably increased if the period of heating is greatly prolonged.

We ascribe the failure of the reaction to progress further under these conditions to the following factors. The concentration of reactive (terminal) groups in esters having molecular weights as high as 3000 is rather low; moreover, such esters are very viscous even at a temperature of 200°. This implies a restricted mobility of the molecules, and a low rate of diffusion of the volatile products to the surface. Beyond this, macromolecular materials, perhaps because of their exaggerated molecular cohesions (5), have a very powerful tendency to retain dissolved or adsorbed liquids or vapors—several days' heating in high vacuum are required to remove benzene completely from macromolecular polystyrenes or water from resinous esters. All these factors affect either the position of the equilibrium or the rate at which the equilibrium is approached, and one may suppose that if some more drastic and effective means could be found for the removal of water or other volatile reaction products, it would be possible to force the reaction further.

Methods of Producing Superpolyesters.—The molecular still, first used by Brönsted and Hevesy (6) for the separation of the isotopes of mercury and later by Washburn (7) for the separation of petroleum hydrocarbons, provides a means for continuously displacing physical equilibria involving very minute vapor pressures, and the application of this to the chemical equilibrium under consideration led to the desired result.

Some of the experiments described below were made in stills of the type described by Washburn (7) and others in a modified still described in the preceding paper (8), where the principles involved are also briefly discussed.

For reasons of a theoretical nature that need not be discussed, our first experiments were made with an ester which has not been described previously, namely, the trimethylene ester of hexadecamethylene dicarboxylic acid. This was obtained from the acid and the glycol by the method used for other α-polyesters (2a).

It was then placed in the molecular still and heated by a bath at 200° for a total time of twelve days. During the first seven days a small amount of distillate collected on the condenser. No distillate was observed during the remaining five days. The viscosity of the molten polyester increased progressively during the heating, and the final product showed an apparent molecular weight of about 12,000.

The same treatment applied to ethylene succinate, ethylene sebacate and to polyesters derived from ω-hydroxydecanoic acid and from ω-hydroxypentadecanoic acid, led to similar transformations.

A part of the effect of the molecular still treatment is evidently due to the greatly prolonged time of heating, and it was found later that a similar, if somewhat less pronounced, effect could be produced by merely heating polyesters such as ethylene sebacate in thin layers at ordinary pressure in a stream of nitrogen for a long period of time, or by bubbling a stream of nitrogen through the molten polyester.

Physical Properties of Superpolyesters.—Linear α polyesters are microcrystalline powders (in certain cases resins) that dissolve readily in certain solvents such as cold chloroform and yield solutions which are quite mobile. The crystalline esters melt fairly sharply and when molten they are exceedingly viscous. On cooling they solidify to opaque masses which range from rather hard, brittle, porcelain-like masses to soft, waxy solids as the length of the polymethylene chain in the acid or glycol from which they are derived increases.

The superpolyesters in the massive state are harder and much tougher. They also dissolve in cold chloroform but the process is slow; they first imbibe solvent and swell, and their solutions are highly viscous. They separate from solution as more or less coherent powdery or curdy masses. When heated they melt at approximately the same temperatures as the α-polyesters from which they are derived. The phenomena associated with the melting, however, are quite different from those observed in the α-polyesters. The solid ester at the melting point suddenly becomes transparent, but it does not lose its shape; a tendency to flow appears only at a considerably higher temperature. In the solid state the superpolyesters furnish sharp x-ray powder diffraction patterns that closely resemble similar patterns obtained from the corresponding α-polyesters. At a temperature a few degrees below the melting point the patterns lose their sharpness. At the melting point the pattern is a diffuse halo characteristic of a liquid. The most remarkable property of the superpolyesters is their capacity to be drawn out into very strong, pliable, highly oriented fibres, and this is discussed in detail in a subsequent paper (9).

By way of summary, the properties of the α- and ω-polyesters from trimethylene glycol and hexadecamethylene dicarboxylic acid are listed in Table I. Similar relations exist between the α- and the ω-forms of other polyesters. One curious property of the ω-esters deserves special mention. They adhere very firmly to the glass vessel (in the molecular still) in which they are prepared, and the force of contraction during cooling often causes the vessel to be completely shattered if the layer of ester is more than two or three millimeters thick.

TABLE I

PROPERTIES OF α- AND ω-POLYESTERS FROM TRIMETHYLENE GLYCOL AND HEXADECA-
METHYLENE DICARBOXYLIC ACID

	α-Ester	ω-Ester
Apparent mol. wt.	3000	12,0000
At 100°C.	Viscous liquid	Soft, sticky resin
At room temperature	White, opaque, brittle wax; d_{20}^{20} 1.061	Cream colored, opaque, horny, elastic; d_{20}^{20}, 1.058
Melting point, °C.	75–76	Becomes transparent at 75, but does not flow
Solubility	Very soluble in cold CHCl₃. Readily soluble in hot ethyl acetate; separates on cooling as a micro-crystalline powder	Swells in cold CHCl₃, then dissolves. Swells and slowly dissolves in hot ethyl acetate; separates on cooling as a white, amorphous, curdy precipitate
Relative viscosity of 7.3% weight solution in chloroform (chloroform, 216 seconds = 1 unit)	8.6 units	166 units

Structure of the ω-Polyesters

The simplest and most reasonable assumption concerning the superpolyesters is that they are formed by a continuation of the same bifunctional esterification that first results in the formation of the α-polyesters, and that they are exceedingly long polymeric chains bearing hydroxyl or carboxyl groups at the ends. Their physical, chemical and analytical behavior is completely consistent with this assumption, but no actual data on the presence of terminal groups are yet available. The average length of the molecules also is still very uncertain. The molecular weights quoted in Table I were obtained by ebullioscopy and in view of the fact that the observed elevations did not greatly exceed the experimental error they can be accepted as signifying only that the molecular weights are quite large—at least as high as 10,000. Comparison of physical properties indicates that molecular weights of the ω-polyesters probably lie in the neighborhood of 20,000. Further work on the determination of the molecular weights of the superpolyesters is in progress.

ω-**Trimethylene Ester of Hexadecamethylene Dicarboxylic Acid.**—This ester was obtained in its α-form by heating the acid together with a 10% excess of the glycol in a distilling flask at 180–200° for three hours, and then heating the residue to 200° for six hours at a pressure less than 1 mm. It was thus obtained in the form of a very viscous liquid which on cooling solidified to a hard, waxy mass. It was readily soluble in cold chloroform and in hot ethyl acetate, from which it separated on cooling as a white microcrystalline powder. It melted rather sharply at 75–76°. Its apparent molecular weight was about 3300.

Anal. Calcd. for —O—(CH$_2$)$_3$—O—CO—(CH$_2$)$_{16}$—CO— = C$_{21}$H$_{38}$O$_4$: C, 71.13; H, 10.81; saponification equivalent, 177.2; mol. wt. 354.3. Calcd. for H(—O—(CH$_2$)$_3$—O—CO—(CH$_2$)$_{16}$—CO—)$_{10}$—O(CH$_2$)$_3$—OH = C$_{213}$H$_{388}$O$_{42}$: C, 70.63; H, 10.80; saponification equivalent, 181; mol. wt. 3619. Found: C, 70.34, 70.40; H, 10.60, 10.69; saponification equivalent, 175.2; mol. wt. (in boiling benzene), 3600, 3200.

A sample (8.5 g.) of this recrystallized ester was placed in a molecular still of the type described by Washburn (10). The condenser was cooled with running tap water, and a trap between the mercury diffusion pump and the still was cooled with liquid air. The still was heated by means of a metal bath kept at about 200°. The pressure of the system as measured by a McLeod gage between the trap and the pump was always less than 10^{-5} mm. Heating was continued for seven days. During the first two days of heating, 0.4 g. of distillate collected on the condenser. This was removed and the heating of the residue was continued for five days more. No distillate collected during this period.

The analytical composition and the saponification equivalent of the residual ester were the same as those of the starting material. Its molecular weight, however, was much greater.

Anal. Calcd. for —O—(CH$_2$)$_3$—O—CO—(CH$_2$)$_{16}$—CO— = C$_{21}$H$_{38}$O$_4$: C, 71.13; H, 10.81; saponification equivalent, 177.2; mol. wt. 354.3. Calcd. for H—(O—(CH$_2$)$_3$—O—CO—(CH$_2$)$_{16}$—CO)$_{34}$—O—(CH$_2$)$_3$—OH = C$_{717}$H$_{1300}$O$_{258}$: C, 70.89; H, 10.83; saponification equivalent, 178.2; mol. wt., 12,122. Found: C, 70.38, 70.52; H, 10.56; 10.53; saponification equivalent, 178.4; mol. wt. (in boiling benzene) 12,100.

The distillate was not homogeneous. By crytallizing it from alcohol there was obtained an apparently homogeneous fraction composed of needles melting sharply at 124–125°. It depressed the melting point of hexadecamethylene dicarboxylic acid (which melts at 122–123°) and was neutral. A single ultimate analysis indicated that it was possibly a monomeric form of the trimethylene ester of hexadecamethylene dicarboxylic acid.

Anal. Calcd. for O—(CH₂)₃—O—CO—(CH₂)₁₆—CO;   C, 71.13;   H, 10.81. Found: C, 70.06; H, 10.63.

A sample of the α-ester and heated at 200–250° for thirty-two hours with a current of dry nitrogen bubbling through the molten mass.   The viscosity of the molten polymer increased very greatly and the product exhibited the phenomenon of cold-drawing described in paper XV.

ω-Polyethylene Succinate.—A sample of polyethylene succinate having the approximate formula HO—(CH₂)₂—O(CO—(CH₂)₂—CO—O—(CH₂)₂—O)₂₁—H (11) was heated in the molecular still as described above for the trimethylene ester of hexadecamethylene dicarboxylic acid.   From the very small amount of distillate no homogeneous fraction could be isolated.   The residue was a tough, horny, somewhat elastic mass (the original material was hard, brittle, rather porcelain-like).   On being heated to 97° is softened to a very viscous and somewhat rubbery mass.   Fibers prepared from this material were short and rather brittle.

Anal. Calcd. for C₆H₈O₄: C, 50.00; H, 5.50. Found: C, 50.30; H, 5.70.

ω-Polyester from ω-Hydroxydecanoic Acid.—ω-Hydroxydecanoic acid was prepared by the method of Lycan and Adams (12).   Five grams was heated under a moderate vacuum for ten hours to bring about incipient polymerization.   If this is neglected and the acid heated directly in the molecular still, it distils practically completely before polymerization sets in.   The material after the preliminary heating was transferred to the molecular still and heated at 150° for twenty-four hours.   Two and four-tenths of a gram of distillate (m. p. 60–65°) collected.   This was not further examined.   The residue was a hard brittle wax which was heated for four days more at 150° and then at 200° for two days.   The final residue was a light gray, translucent, tough, flexible mass. On being heated it suddenly became transparent at 65° but did not lose its shape.   At higher temperatures it could easily be drawn into threads which could be cold drawn.

Microscopic Observation at a Magnification of 180 Diameters.—A thin hazy film was obtained by placing a small specimen of the ester on a slide and covering it with a cover glass.   Between crossed nicols the field appeared as an aggregate of very small, irregular anisotropic particles, each of which showed two extinction positions.   The slide was then warmed to melt the ester and the cover glass moved about 5 mm.   The middle region of the specimen when cold was now transparent and homogeneous; the surrounding portions were unchanged.   This effect is apparently due to the action of stress in moving the slide.   The transparent section showed brilliant interference colors between crossed nicols and extinction parallel and normal to the direction of the stress applied.

Anal. Calcd.: C, 70.59; H, 10.59. Found: C, 70.24, 70.21; H, 10.74, 10.79; mol. wt. in boiling ethylene chloride, 24,600.

ω-Ester from ω-Hydroxypentadecanoic Acid.—One gram of "exaltolide" (the lactone of ω-hyroxypentadecanoic acid) was refluxed with 0.5 g. of sodium hydroxide in 12 cc. of water and 5 cc. of alcohol for five hours.   The solution was evaporated to dryness on a steam-bath, dissolved in 450 cc. of water, acidified with dilute sulfuric acid and extracted with ether.   The ether solution was dried over magnesium sulfate, filtered and evaporated to dryness; yield, 1.075 g.   The product was recrystallized from benzene; m. p. 83–84°.   The acid was put in the molecular still and heated overnight at 150°.   It distilled completely except for a very small residue of hard wax.   The distillate was heated for six hours at 150° at 1 mm. and again placed in the still and heated for seven days. A small amount of distillate which melted at 70–75° was not further examined. The residue consisted of 0.65 g. of a flexible, translucent mass. It became transparent at 95°, yielding a stiff mass which held its shape up to 200°. It could be drawn into thin fibers and cold drawn.

Ethylene Sebacate.—101 g. (0.5 mole) of sebacic acid and 32.5 g. (0.525 mole) of ethylene glycol were heated together at atmospheric pressure in a Claisen flask at 175°. The aqueous distillate was discarded. The residue was then heated at 250° for five hours at 2 mm. pressure. The light gray-buff product was a hard wax. Threads drawn from the molten ester, if pulled immediately while still warm, yielded transparent fibers. The product after recrystallization from ethyl acetate melted at 75° (copper block) and still exhibited the cold drawing phenomenon; molecular weight by cryoscopic method in benzene, 4800, 6000.

Summary

By prolonged heating in a molecular still or in a stream of inert gas, the previously described linear polyesters derived from dibasic acids and glycols or from higher ω-hydroxy acids are caused to react with themselves to produce polyesters of much higher molecular weight. The new super-polyesters (ω-polyesters) are tough, opaque solids which exhibit sharp x-ray powder diffraction patterns and become transparent at a definite temperature. They dissolve in chloroform to form highly viscous solutions. The mechanism of the reaction is discussed.

Bibliography and Remarks

(1) The term "superpolymer" is applied to linear polymers having molecular weights above 10,000.

(2) (a) Carothers and Arvin, *Journ. Am. Chem. Soc.*, **51**, 2560 (1929); (b) Carothers and van Natta, *ibid.*, **52**, 314 (1930); (c) Carothers and Dorough, *ibid.*, **52**, 711 (1930); (d) Carothers, Arvin and Dorough, *ibid.*, **52**, 3292 (1930).

(3) Carothers, *ibid.*, **51**, 2548 (1929).

(4) Valuable indications in this connection are furnished by Lycan and Adams' studies [*Journ. Am. Chem. Soc.*, **51**, 625, 3450 (1929)] of the polyesters derived from ω-hydroxydecanoic acid. We should add that our generalization to the effect that no intramolecular reaction occurs in bifunctional esterifications involving compounds whose structural units are longer than seven atoms is not altogether free from exceptions. Dr. van Natta of this laboratory in preparing polyesters of ω-hydroxydecanoic acid has recently observed the formation of appreciable amounts of the dimeric lactone already obtained by Lycan and Adams by a different method.

(5) Dunkel, *Z. physik. Chem.*, Abt. A, **138**, 42 (1928).

(6) Brönsted and Hevesy, *Phil. Mag.*, **43**, 31 (1922).

(7) Washburn, *Bur. Standards J. Research*, **2**, 476 (1929); see also Burch, *Proc. Roy. Soc.* (London), **123**, 271 (1929); and Hickman, *Chem. Ind.*, **48**, 365 (1929).

(8) Paper XI.

(9) Paper XV.

(10) Washburn, *Bur. Standards J. Research*, **2** 480 (1929).

(11) Carothers and Dorough, *Journ. Am. Chem. Soc.*, **52**, 711 (1930).

(12) Lycan and Adams, *ibid.*, **51**, 625 (1929).

XIII. Polyamides and Mixed Polyester-Polyamides*

Above its melting point ε-aminocaproic acid† splits off water and gives

 a) *a cyclic lactam, which is a seven-membered ring and*
 b) *a linear polyamide with a molecular weight around 3000.*

Linear superpolyamides are harder, tougher, less easily fusible and much less soluble than the corresponding superpolyesters owing to the higher molecular cohesion attributed to the —CONH—group.
In the molecular still the polyamide obtained from ε-aminocaproic acid polymerizes further and exhibits a considerable change in physical properties.
By heating together ε-aminocaproic acid with hexadecamethylene dicarboxylic acid and trimethylene glycol mixed polyester-polyamides are obtained. They lie in their physical properties between the pure polyesters and pure polyamides and can be drawn out into strong and fine transparent fibers.

Above its melting point ε-aminocaproic acid undergoes dehydration with the simultaneous formation of two different products (1). One of these is the cyclic lactam, a seven-membered ring. The other is a polyamide having the formula

$$\dots\text{—NH—}(CH_2)_5\text{—CO—CH—}(CH_2)_5\text{—CO—NH—}(CH_2)_5\text{—CO—}\dots$$

This compound is analogous to the polyesters obtained by the self-esterification of higher hydroxy acids or by the action of glycols on dibasic acids. The binding atom between the units in the case of the esters is —O— and in the case of the polyamide —NH—. In comparison with the esters the polyamide is harder, tougher, less easily fusible and much less soluble. The difference lies in the direction required by the much higher molecular cohesions of amides as compared with esters (2).

The polyamide prepared by dehydration of the amino acid at atmospheric pressure or under diminished pressure in the usual distillation equipment has an apparent molecular weight of about 1000 (the actual value probably lies somewhat higher than this, perhaps in the neighborhood of 3000). It corresponds, therefore, in molecular weight with the α-polyesters that have been described in previous papers (3). The polyesterification reaction

* W. H. Carothers and J. W. Hill; *Journ. Am. Chem. Soc.*, **54**, 1566–69 (1932); Communication No. 76 from the Experimental Station of E. I. du Pont de Nemours and Co.
    Received November 12, 1931. Published April 6, 1932.
    † Compare paper VIII of this series on pages 78 to 81 in this volume.

can be forced further toward completion by the use of molecular distillation, and this process leads to the formation of superpolyesters described in the preceding paper (4). One of the objects of the experiments described in the present paper was to examine the possibility of forcing the amide reaction in a similar manner so as to obtain a polyamide of very high molecular weight.

The polyamide already described was placed in the molecular still and heated for forty-eight hours at 200°. A very small amount of the crystalline cyclic lactam distilled from the reaction mixture and the residue was considerably changed in its properties. It was harder and tougher than before and in thin sections was flexible and elastic. It softened at 210° with considerable decomposition. Like the initial amide it was insoluble in common organic solvents with the exception of hot phenol and hot formamide.

Anal. Calcd. for $C_6H_{11}ON$:   C, 63.71;   H, 9.73.   Found: C, 63.94, 63.94; H, 9.72, 9.76.

The change in properties indicates a considerable increase in molecular weight but no actual measurements of molecular weight are available owing to the lack of any method of sufficient reliability.

The superpolyesters described in the preceding paper are especially interesting because of their ability to furnish strong, pliable, highly oriented fibers. This property is discussed in detail in paper XV. As synthetic silk, however, these materials suffer from the defect of low melting point and considerable solubility in various organic solvents. On the other hand, the polyamide described above is too infusible and insoluble to allow a ready test of its ability to furnish fibers. In the hope of obtaining a compromise between the properties of the polyesters and the polyamides we prepared mixed polyester-polyamides. These compounds were obtained by heating together trimethylene glycol, hexadecamethylene dicarboxylic acid and ε-aminocaproic acid. The glycol was used in a 5% excess over the amount equivalent to the dibasic acid and the amino acid was varied in different experiments in the proportion of 1, 2, 3 and 5 moles per mole of dibasic acid. The mixtures were separately heated in a Claisen flask for three hours in a current of dry nitrogen by means of a bath kept at 200–220°. Heating was continued for five hours more at a pressure of 1 mm. with the bath at 250–260°. The very viscous residue was then removed from the flask and transferred to the molecular still, where it was heated for three days at 200°. So far as could be inferred from the physical appearance of these products the molecular still treatment produced very little effect although in each experiment a small amount of the cyclic lactam from the amino acid was obtained as a distillate.

The products were opaque or translucent solids, hard, very tough and in thin sections flexible and elastic. As the proportion of amino acid increased, the polymers increased in brittleness, hardness, transparency and melting point. The effect of the composition on melting point is indicated below

1 mole of amino acid	ca. 73°	3 moles of amino acid	125°
2 moles of amino acid	100°	5 moles of amino acid	145°

The melting points were determined on a copper block. In the two polymers of lowest amino acid content the temperatures at which the specimens became transparent were taken as the melting points. In the other two cases where the high degree of transparency when cold made this determination extremely uncertain the temperatures at which the sample first began to adhere slightly to the block were taken as the melting points.

The solubility of the mixed polyester-polyamides also diminished with increasing amino acid content. The first member of the series was swelled by hot ethyl acetate and finally completely dissolved. It separated from the cold solution in the form of soft powder. The second was very slightly soluble in hot ethyl acetate, and the higher members were practically insoluble. Since the polyamide derived from ε-aminocaproic acid is not dissolved by hot ethyl acetate, the mixed polyester-polyamides are evidently not merely physical mixtures. From the nature of the reaction also it seems likely that all the components participate in forming each molecule of the product. The different units that may be present in the product molecules are

$$-NH-R-CO- \qquad -O-R'-O- \qquad -CO-R''-CO-$$

which may be joined in any order that leads to ester or amide linkages.

The mixed polyester-polyamides when molten can readily be drawn out into filaments by touching a specimen with a rod and drawing the rod away. The successful production of continuous filaments by this method requires a degree of plasticity in the molten mass that appears only at a temperature somewhat above the melting point. Filaments obtained in this way are brittle and opaque. When slightly warmed (e. g., to 40 to 50°) they can be drawn out by the action of stress into transparent fibers which are exceedingly pliable. Purely qualitative observations indicate that these fibers are considerably stronger than similar fibers derived from the ω-polyesters.

Summary

The polyamide derived from ε-aminocaproic acid when heated in the molecular still undergoes a considerable change in its physical properties, indicating an increase in molecular weight. By heating together ε-aminocaproic acid with hexadecamethylene dicarboxylic acid and trimethylene glycol, mixed polyester-polyamides are obtained. These materials in their physical properties lie between the polyesters and the polyamides and like the superpolyesters described in the preceding paper they can be drawn out into strong, pliable, transparent fibers.

Bibliography and Remarks

(1) Carothers and Berchet, *Journ. Am. Chem. Soc.*, **52**, 5289 (1930); Gabriel and Maass, *Ber.*, **32**, 1266 (1899); Braun, *ibid.*, **40**, 1835 (1907).

(2) Dunkel, *Z. physik. Chem., Abt. A*, **138**, 42 (1928).

(3) Carothers and Arvin, *Journ. Am. Chem. Soc.*, **51**, 2560 (1929); Carothers and van Natta, *ibid.*, **52**, 314 (1930).

(4) Paper XII.

XIV. A Linear Superpolyanhydride and a Cyclic Dimeric Anhydride from Sebacic Acid*

The different products, obtained during the anhydrization of sebacic acid are described in this paper.

α-sebacic anhydride is formed by the action of acetic anhydride on sebacic acid and has a melting point of 79–80°. In the molten state it is very viscous, on cooling it crystallizes in needles; it has a molecular weight around 5200.

β-sebacic anhydride, formed by treating the α-anhydride in the molecular still; is a definitely macrocrystalline solid melting sharply at 68°. It dissolves readily in most of the common solvents and was identified as a twenty-two-membered cyclic dimer.

γ-sebacic anhydride is obtained by heating the β-product to its melting point, cooling down and heating again. Its melting point is 82°, its molecular weight lies in the neighborhood of 600, which shows that it is formed from the β-product by a process of polymerization.

ω-sebacic anhydride is a super polymer, with a rather high molecular weight;† it is formed by heating α-sebacic anhydride in the molecular still. It is a hard and tough resin, which becomes transparent at 83° but remains

* J. W. Hill and W. H. Carothers; *Journ. Am. Chem. Soc.*, **54**, 1569–79 (1932); Communication No. 77 from Experimental Station of E. I. du Pont de Nemours and Co.

† No definite figure can be given owing to the unsolubility of this material.

still hard. At about 130° it gets soft and can be drawn into continuous, strong and pliable filaments.
The reactions of the different anhydrides with aniline are described.

In a previous paper (1) it has been shown that adipic anhydride as ordinarily prepared is a linear polymer of the type formula represented by I and that under the action of heat *in vacuo* it is broken down to the cyclic monomer, a seven-membered ring.

(I)   ...O—CO—R—CO—O—CO—R—CO—O—CO—R—CO—...

Observations have now been extended to sebacic anhydride, and it is shown that the anhydride (α-anhydride) prepared by the action of acetic anhydride or acetyl chloride on sebacic acid is also polymeric. No smooth depolymerization of this polymer can be effected under ordinary conditions, but in the molecular still (2) at elevated temperatures two processes occur simultaneously. The α-anhydride is transformed into a polyanhydride of much higher molecular weight (ω-anhydride) and at the same time depolymerization occurs with the formation of a crystalline product (β-anhydride), which is shown to be not the eleven-membered cyclic monomer, but the twenty-two-membered cyclic dimer. At its melting point the dimer reverts to a higher polymer (γ-anhydride). The anhydrides of different origins are arbitrarily assigned the prefixes α, β, γ and ω to designate them for the purposes of discussion.

Sebacic α-Anhydride.—Voerman (3) obtained this as a microcrystalline solid melting at 74.5° by the action of acetyl chloride on sebacic acid. He seemed unable to decide whether to regard it as monomeric or polymeric. Compared with succinic and glutaric anhydrides (known to be monomeric) it showed a diminished solubility and ability to crystallize, and molecular weight determinations in boiling benzene and boiling acetone gave abnormally high values. The doubt concerning its polymeric character arose from the fact that freezing point determinations in phenol gave values agreeing with those calculated for the monomer, but Voerman overlooked the fact that sebacic anhydride reacts very rapidly with phenol to give phenyl esters of sebacic acid.

We prepared the α-anhydride by heating sebacic acid with excess acetic anhydride, distilling off the volatile material, and precipitating a benzene solution of the residue with petroleum ether. The melting points varied somewhat from one preparation to another and a typical specimen melted at 79–80°. The molten anhydride is exceedingly viscous; on cooling it crystallizes: minute doubly refracting spherulites first separate and grow to what appear to be star-like clusters of needles. This behavior is highly characteristic of crystalline linear high polymers and is observed with such diverse materials as polyesters (4), trimethylcellulose (5) and triacetylinulin (6).

At a temperature of 200° and under a pressure of 0.1 mm. the α-anhydride shows no tendency to distil, and this behavior is also consistent with a highly polymeric structure.

We tentatively assign to sebacic α-anhydride the formula II.

(II) $CH_3CO—[—O—CO—(CH_2)_8—CO—]_x—O—CO—CH_3$

This represents it as a linear polymer and the chains are terminated by acetyl groups derived from the reagent used in bringing about the anhydride formation.   It reacts with water to form sebacic acid and acetic acid.   The latter may conceivably represent adsorbed acetic acid or acetic anhydride not removed in the purification process, but we are inclined to the view that it arises from acetyl groups that actually form a part of the polyanhydride molecule.   This assumption together with the estimation by distillation and titration of the amount of acetic acid formed on hydrolysis furnished a value of 5260 for the molecular weight of a typical specimen of the polymer.

A specimen of the recrystallized α-anhydride which had been stored for three days in a vacuum desiccator over phosphorus pentoxide, potassium hydroxide and paraffin was refluxed with 3 g. of sodium hydroxide in 40 cc. of water, diluted, acidified with sulfuric acid and distilled with the occasional addition of water.   A total of 415 cc. of distillate was collected and titrated with 0.1 N sodium hydroxide.   Sodium acetate was identified in the resulting neutralized solution by microscopic observation of the highly characteristic crystals of sodium uranyl acetate formed upon adding uranyl nitrate.   We are indebted to Mr. W. D. M. Bryant for this identification.   Since it was found that sebacic acid itself tends to steam distil very slowly, a correction was made by repeating the above determination using 6 g. of pure sebacic acid.

Anal. Subs. 5.51 g.: 0.0999 N NaOH, 26.35 cc.   Blank: 0.0999 N NaOH, 5.35 cc.   Found: (assuming two acetyl groups per molecule) mol. wt., 5260.

A different though not strictly independent estimate of molecular weight is found in the quantitative analysis of the behavior of the polymer toward aniline, which is described in the next section, and this method gives a value of 5500.   Attempted molecular weight determinations in boiling benzene gave much lower values than this (as low as 650), but their lack of constancy and reproducibility deprives them of any significance (7).   On the other hand, the α-anhydride in its physical properties closely resembles polyesters derived from sebacic acid and known to have molecular weights in the neighborhood of 5000.

The analytical data presented below are consistent with the suggested structure for the α-anhydride.

	Calcd., %		Found, %	
	C	H	C	H
$(C_{10}H_{16}O_3)_n$	65.18	8.75	64.19	9.07
$CH_3COO(C_{10}H_{16}O_3)_3COCH_3$	62.35	8.31	64.22	9.01
$CH_3COO(C_{10}H_{16}O_3)_8COCH_3$	64.00	8.57		
$CH_3COO(C_{10}H_{16}O_3)_{30}COCH_3$	64.84	8.71		

Behavior of Sebacic Anhydrides toward Aniline.—Theory requires a difference, both qualitative and quantitative, between cyclic monomeric anhydrides and linear polymeric anhydrides in their behavior toward unsymmetrical reagents such as aniline. This requirement was first pointed out by one of us and experimentally verified in the case of adipic anhydrides (1, 8). The analysis has now been extended and further observations made with sebacic anhydrides.

The monomeric anhydride (II) can react with aniline to form only a single product, namely, the monoanilide of sebacic acid.

(II)   ┌─CO—(CH₂)₈—CO—O─┐ + C₆H₅NH₂ ⟶ C₆H₅NH—CO—(CH₂)₈—COOH

In the polymeric form, however, as soon as one anhydride linkage reacts with aniline, reaction at the next linkage will give different products depending upon which side of the oxygen is involved with the reagent. In III we symbolize aniline (RNH—H) as b-a.

(III) .. —CO—(CH₂)₈—CO—O—CO—(CH₂)₈—CO—O—CO—(CH₂)₈—CO—O—...

```
                        .                      .
                                            b-a.
            b-a    ⟶                         .
                        .                    a-b
                        .                      .
                                            b-a.
            a-b    ⟶                         .
                        .                    a-b
```

Considering the two linkages of an interior unit of the chain, if reaction occurs in the direction b—a at the first one it may occur in the directions b—a, and a—b at the second; and if the direction is a—b at the first it may be either b—a or a—b at the second. If we assume that reaction is random, *i. e.*, that the direction of reaction at the second linkage is not affected by the direction that the reaction has already taken at the first linkage, then the probability of each of these four possibilities is the same, and the terminal groups attached to the reaction product derived from the unit under consideration are (1) a b, (2) a a, (3) b b and (4) b a. The first and fourth of these represent monoanilide, and the second and third represent, respectively, dibasic acid and dianilide. Thus each interior unit of the anhydride chain will yield

$1/_4$ molecule of dibasic acid
$1/_4$ molecule of dianilide, and
$1/_2$ molecule of monoanilide

and this total product will contain one atom of acid hydrogen.

If the polyanhydride is cyclic, all the units are interior units, and the ratio of products indicated above will be maintained so long as the anhydride is polymeric (*i. e.*, not monomeric). But if the chains are open this ratio will be modified.

We consider the case IV in which the chains are open and terminated by carboxyl groups.

(IV)   HOOC—(CH$_2$)$_8$—CO—O—[—CO—(CH$_2$)$_8$—CO—O—]$_{x-2}$—CO—(CH$_2$)$_8$—
                                                                                              COOH

The total number of units in the chain is x. Of these, the x-2 interior units will furnish acid, monoanilide and dianilide in the ratios already indicated, while the terminal units will each furnish one-half molecule of acid and one-half molecule of monoanilide. Thus the total products are

$(x - 2)/4 + 1$ molecule of dibasic acid
$(x - 2)/2 + 1$ molecule of monoanilide, and
$(x - 2)/4$ molecules of dianilide

and the number of atoms of acidic hydrogen in the product is

$$[(x - 2)/4 + 1]2 + (x - 2)/2 + 1 = x + 1$$

If M is the gram molecular weight of the polymer, then, since the molecular weight of the structural unit is 184

$$184x + 18 = M \tag{1}$$

and this weight after reacting with aniline will furnish $x + 1$ mole of hydrogen ion. Thus the weight of anhydride required to furnish one mole of hydrogen ion is

$$M/(x + 1) \tag{2}$$

Let g represent the weight of a sample of polyanhydride of the formula IV which is treated with aniline and cc represent the volume in cubic centimeters of normal alkali required to neutralize the product. Then from (2)

$$M/(x + 1) = 1000 \, g(/cc) \tag{3}$$

and from (1)

$$x = (M - 18)/184 \tag{4}$$

Substituting and solving for M, we have

$$M = 166{,}000 \text{ g}/(184 \text{ cc} - 1000 \text{ g}) \qquad (5)$$

If the terminal groups are acetyl as in V

(V) $CH_3CO-O-[-CO-(CH_2)_8-CO-O]_x-COCH_3$

$M = 184 + 102$, and this weight after reacting with aniline will furnish

$x/4$ moles of dibasic acid
$x/4$ moles of dianilide
$x/2$ moles of monoanilide
1   mole of acetic acid, and
1   mole of acetamide

The moles of available hydrogen ion in this product are

$$2x/4 + x/2 + 1 = x + 1$$

In this case equation (5) becomes

$$M = 82{,}000 \text{ g}/(184 \text{ cc} - 1000 \text{ g}) \qquad (6)$$

The manner in which the calculated available acid from the aniline reaction product varies with the molecular weights of different sebacic anhydrides is indicated in Table I.

From the data of Table I it is evident that even if one allows an error of 2% in the titration it should be possible to distinguish an open chain terminated by carboxyl and having a molecular weight of 7500 or less from a cyclic anhydride.   If the terminal groups of the chain are acetyl, a similar distinction is possible only if the molecular weight lies below about 3500.

TABLE I
ACID FURNISHED BY ANILINE REACTION PRODUCT OF SEBACIC ANHYDRIDES

Structural units	Mol. wt. (for cyclic anhydride)	Millimoles of available H^+ in reaction product from one gram of anhydride		
		Cyclic anhydride	Chain terminated by carboxyl	Chain terminated by acetyl
1	184	5.44	9.9	6.95
2	368	5.44	7.75	6.39
3	552	5.44	7.02	6.12
4	736	5.44	6.62	5.97
6	1,104	5.44	6.24	5.82
10	1,840	5.44	5.92	5.66
15	2,760	5.44	5.76	5.59
20	3,680	5.44	5.68	5.55
40	7,360	5.44	5.56	5.49
60	11,040	5.44	5.52	5.48
100	18,400	5.44	5.49	5.46
200	36,800	5.44	5.46	5.45

The data from which the molecular weight of the α-polyanhydride described in the preceding section were calculated are as follows.

Weighed samples of the reprecipitated anhydride, which had been stored for several days in an evacuated desiccator over solid potassium hydroxide, were added to 5 to 8 cc. of aniline and triturated with a stirring rod until a smooth cream was formed. The mixture was then diluted with about 30 cc. of 95% alcohol and titrated with 0.1 N sodium hydroxide using phenolphthalein as the indicator.

Anal. Subs. 0.5869, 0.4814, 0.5632: 0.0999 N NaOH, 32.40, 26.55, 31.12 cc. Calcd. by equation (6): $M = 5532, 5891, 5248$.

Sebacic ω-Anhydride.—Attempts to depolymerize sebacic α-anhydride by heating it under greatly diminished pressure in a Claisen flask resulted merely in thermal decomposition with the formation of tarry products. But in the molecular still (9), at 200° change occurred simultaneously in two directions: a crystalline distillate gradually accumulated on the condenser, and the residue became more viscous. The rate of distillation was about one gram in twenty-four hours (from 8 g. of α-anhydride, and an evaporating surface of about 40 sq. cm.). The final residue when cold was very much harder and tougher than the α-anhydride. It was opaque and when heated to about 83° it suddenly became transparent but remained very stiff. At 130° it was soft enough to be drawn into continuous filaments. These filaments exhibited the phenomenon of cold drawing described in a subsequent paper (10). The resulting fibers were lustrous and exceedingly strong and pliable, but after standing for a few days in a vacuum desiccator they became brittle and fragile. Massive specimens of the ω-anhydride also become brittle under the same conditions and lose their capacity to be drawn out into filaments. No data concerning the molecular weight of ω-polyanhydride are available, but its toughness and viscosity indicate a considerably higher molecular weight than for the ω-polyesters described in paper XII.

The brittleness and loss of tenacity that develop when the ω-polyanhydride is stored are apparently due to hydrolysis. When a sample of the anhydride was stored at ordinary temperature in the still in which it was prepared, it retained its strength and toughness for six days. When the still was opened and the anhydride transferred to a desiccator containing anhydrous calcium chloride, brittleness developed within twenty-four hours.

The ω-anhydride adheres very firmly to the glass dish in which it is prepared, and if the specimen is more than 2 or 3 mm. deep the dish is completely shattered by the force of contraction during cooling. The ω-polyesters manifest the same behavior.

Anal. Calcd. for $(C_{10}H_{16}O_3)_n$: saponification equivalent, 92. Found: 92.0, 92.3.

Sebacic β-Anhydride.—The distillate formed from the α-anhydride during the treatment in the molecular still is a definitely macrocrystalline solid melting sharply at 68°. It dissolves readily in most of the common organic solvents with the exception of petroleum ether and ligroin. When recrystallized from a mixture of petroleum ether and benzene it separates in the form of fine needles and the melting point remains unchanged. The analytical behavior of this material identifies it as the twenty-two-membered cyclic dimer.

Anal. Calcd. for $(C_{10}H_{16}O_3)_n$: C, 65.18; H, 8.75; mol. wt., 368; saponification equivalent, 92. Found: C, 65.08, 64.85; H, 8.90, 8.77; mol. wt. in boiling benzene, 386, 393; saponification equivalent 91.9.

Still more decisive support for the cyclic dimeric structure for sebacic β-anhydride is found in the analysis of its behavior toward aniline when treated in the manner already described for the α-anhydride.

Anal. Subs. 0.939 (after treatment with aniline): 0.0992 N NaOH, 51.2 cc.

Thus one gram of the anhydride furnished 5.41 millimoles of hydrogen ion. The calculated value for a cyclic anhydride is 5.44, and, as the data of Table I show, this agreement demonstrates that the β-anhydride cannot be an open chain unless its molecular weight lies above 3500. But the volatility of the compound indicates that its molecular weight must lie below 1000 (11).

The neutral solution from the above titration contained both monoanilide and dianilide. The alkali used in the titration was neutralized with an equivalent amount of hydrochloric acid; the alcohol was evaporated; the residue was treated with excess hydrochloric acid to dissolve the aniline, and filtered. The residue on the filter was repeatedly extracted with boiling water until no more material dissolved. The combined filtrates on cooling deposited handsome lustrous platelets of the monoanilide, m. p. 122–123°. This compound appears not to have been described before. Recrystallization from water did not raise its melting point.

Anal. Calcd. for $C_{16}H_{23}O_4N$: C, 69.26; H, 8.37. Found: C, 69.51, 69.58; H, 8.26, 8.48.

The insoluble dianilide was transferred to a Gooch crucible and weighed: yield, 0.450 g.; theory requires 0.450 g. After recrystallization from alcohol it melted at 201–202° (12).

Anal. Calcd. for $C_{22}H_{28}O_2N_2$: C, 74.96; H, 8.01. Found: C, 74.49, 74.67; H, 8.34, 8.05.

The fact that dianilide was produced in this reaction demonstrates decisively that the anhydride is not monomeric, and the close agreement between the dianilide calculated and found indicates again that the structure is cyclic.

The β-anhydride is not present as such in more than traces in the α-anhydride before the molecular still treatment. The β-anhydride is exceedingly soluble in cold carbon tetrachloride, whereas rough determinations indicated that the α-compound at 25° dissolves to the extent of only about 0.04 g. in 100 cc. of carbon tetrachloride.

Sebacic γ-Anhydride.—When the β-anhydride is heated to its melting point, cooled and then heated again, its melting point is found to have changed from 68 to 82°. This change is due to polymerization. Samples of the new anhydride were prepared by sealing the β-anhydride in carefully dried glass tubes and heating them in a water-bath. The specimens melted at 68° to an exceedingly mobile fluid which almost instantly became so viscous that it failed to flow when the tube was inverted. When cold, the product was an opaque (or translucent) microcrystalline wax that resembled the α-anhydride. It melted at 82°, and heating at 90–100° for five hours did not raise the melting point.

When the γ-anhydride is heated in the molecular still it behaves in the same manner as the α-anhydride and is converted to the β- and ω-anhydrides.

Determinations of the molecular weight of the γ-anhydride in boiling benzene gave values in the neighborhood of 600, but for reasons already discussed in connection with the α-anhydrides we think that these values merely signify that the material is not monomeric or dimeric.

The behavior of the γ-anhydride toward aniline fails to reveal the presence of terminal carboxyl groups in detectable amounts.

Anal. Subs. 0.2234, 0.2707, 0.1925: (after treatment with aniline) 0.0999 N NaOH, 12.15, 14.70, 10.50 cc. These values correspond to 5.43, 5.43, 5.45 cc. of N NaOH per gram of sample.

Thus one gram of the anhydride furnishes 5.44 millimoles of hydrogen ion, and from Table I it appears that if the polymer is an open chain bearing carboxyl groups at the ends, its molecular weight must lie above 7500.

Discussion

The α-anhydride probably bears terminal groups in the manner already indicated. We suppose that it is made up of chains of slightly differing lengths. Our idea in heating this product in the molecular still was that under these conditions it would condense or couple with itself by a process of dehydration or anhydride interchange involving the elimination of terminal groups between adjacent molecules.

A similar mechanism had already been established (13) for the transformation of the α-polyesters into ω-polyesters. The available facts are all consistent with this mechanism for the transformation of the α-polyanhydride into the ω-polyanhydride. The molecules of the latter compound therefore are very long open chains. Their molecular weights lie perhaps in the neighborhood of 30,000, certainly at not less than 15,000. The transformation of this compound into the β-anhydride evidently involves a process of anhydride interchange.

··· —O—CO—R—CO—O—CO—R—CO—O—CO—R—CO—O—CO—R—CO— ···

An analogous transformation occurs by heating polyesters derived from six-membered cyclic esters (14). But among polyesters smooth depolymerization in this fashion can be effected only if the structural unit is six atoms long. Polyesters whose units are longer than six atoms yield cyclic degradation products only in small amounts and only when they are heated to a temperature sufficiently high to produce complete thermal decomposition (15). The much smoother degradation of the anhydride is consistent with the much greater mobility and reactivity of anhydrides as compared with esters.

A peculiarity of this transformation lies in the fact that the product is not the eleven-membered cyclic monomer but the twenty-two-membered cyclic dimer. A similar peculiarity exists in the nature of the cyclic degradation products from the polyesters (15). The significance of this fact will be discussed in connection with data concerning cyclic anhydrides from other dibasic acids which will be presented in a future publication.

The formation of the γ-anhydride from the β-anhydride apparently involves merely the mutual coalescence of the cyclic molecules of the latter compound. At any rate this transformation occurs under fairly rigorously anhydrous conditions, and, since no terminal groups could be detected in the resulting γ-anhydride, one is almost impelled to conclude that the γ-anhydride is initially a very large ring. This conclusion is a little difficult to reconcile with the fact that in the molecular still the γ-anhydride behaves just like the α-anhydride. According to our hypothesis the transformation of α-anhydride depends upon the presence in this compound of terminal groups capable of being eliminated by condensation between adjacent molecules. There is of course nothing theoretically to preclude the possibility of the mutual coalescence of very large anhydride rings to produce still larger rings. Moreover, it is possible that the ω-anhydride derived from the α-anhydride and that derived from the γ-anhydride are structurally different: the former may be an open chain and the latter a large ring.   On the other hand, it appears that mere heating does not bring about the further polymerization of the γ-anhydride.   The conditions of molecular distillation are required for this transformation.   It is a little difficult to see just why the further growth of the γ-anhydride molecules, if they are rings, should occur only under conditions that favor the simultaneous elimination of smaller cyclic (β-anhydride) residues.   Perhaps the resulting rupture leaves fragments (e. g., bivalent radicals) that are especially prone to unite with one another.

We think it more likely, however, that traces of moisture inevitably acquired by the γ-polymer during its transfer to the molecular still may suffice to transform its molecules into open chains terminated by carboxyl groups. Coupling could then occur by the elimination of water between adjacent molecules.

One further feature of the behavior of the α-anhydride in the molecular still remains to be mentioned.   It has already been indicated that degradation to the β-anhydride and growth to the ω-anhydride occur simultaneously.   The latter process however reaches an apparent limit after a short time, e. g., twelve hours.   But this does not interrupt the formation and distillation of β-anhydride, which continues at an only slightly diminished rate until only a trace of residue remains.

Summary

Sebacic α-anhydride formed by the action of acetyl chloride or acetic anhydride on the acid is a linear polymer.   The chains are probably open and the molecular weights in the neighborhood of 5000.   No smooth depolymerization of this anhydride can be effected by ordinary vacuum distillation, but in the molecular still two different transformations occur: (1) coupling of the α-anhydride with itself yields ω-anhydride, a polymer of much higher molecular weight;   (2) depolymerization of the α- and ω-compounds, which occurs at the same time, yields the definitely crystalline volatile β-anhydride melting at 68°.   The ω-anhydride is very tough and hard and it can be drawn out into exceedingly strong, pliable, lustrous, highly oriented fibers.   The β-anhydride is a cyclic dimer (twenty-two-membered ring).   When heated above its melting point it instantly polymerizes, yielding a γ-anhydride which closely resembles the α-anhydride in its physical properties.   The behavior of these anhydrides toward aniline is described and discussed.   The prefixes α, β, γ and ω used above have been adapted arbitrarily to designate the anhydrides of different origins.

Bibliography and Remarks

(1) J. W. Hill, *Journ. Am. Chem. Soc.*, **52**, 4110 (1930).

(2) Paper XI.

(3) Voerman, *Rec. trav. chim.*, **23**, 265 (1904).

(4) Carothers and Arvin, *Journ. Am. Chem. Soc.*, **51**, 2560 (1929).

(5) Hess, "Die Chemie der Cellulose," Akademische Verlagsgesellschaft, Leipzig, 1928, p. 432.

(6) Pringsheim and Hensel, *Ber.*, **63**, 1096 (1930).

(7) The low and inconsistent molecular weight values obtained for the polymeric anhydrides in boiling benzene are probably due to progressive degradation by hydrolysis. Greer has lately shown [*Journ. Am. Chem. Soc.*, **52**, 4191 (1930)] that completely dry benzene seizes with great avidity sufficient moisture to provide 0.000229 g. of water for one gram of benzene. In a molecular weight determination this would be sufficient to furnish more than one gram of water for each 100 g. of anhydride. The hydrolytic absorption of water in this proportion (1–100) would reduce the average molecular weight of the anhydride by 75% if the initial value were 5400 and the polymer were an open chain. If the initial value were 396 the reduction would be only 14%. If the polymer were cyclic its molecular weight might actually be slightly increased by partial hydrolysis.

(8) We now find that Étaix [*Ann. chim.*, [7] **9**, 356 (1896)] has recorded the fact that the anhydrides of adipic, suberic, azelaic and sebacic acids react with ammonia to give the diamides as well as the amic acids. Einhorn and Diesbach [*Ber.*, **39**, 1222 (1906)] have also observed that the anhydrides of diethylmalonic acid react with ammonia and with diethylamine to form both diamides and amic acids. But apparently none of these investigators recognized the bearing of this behavior on the structure of the anhydrides. Incidentally, it seems certain in view of this behavior that Einhorn and Diesbach's tetrameric diethylmalonic anhydride is actually a sixteen-membered ring. On the other hand, their dodecamer is probably a high polymeric mixture rather than a definite individual.

(9) Carothers and Hill, paper XI.

(10) Paper XV.

(11) Carothers, Hill, Kirby and Jacobson, *Journ. Am. Chem. Soc.*, **52**, 5284 (1930).

(12) Pellizzari, *Gazz. chim. ital.*, **15**, 555 (1885), gives 198°; Barnicoat, *J. Chem. Soc.*, 2926 (1927), gives 200°.

(13) Paper XII.

(14) Carothers, Dorough and van Natta, *Journ. Am. Chem. Soc.*, **54**, 761 (1932).

(15) Carothers, *Chem. Reviews*, **8**, 381 (1931).

XV. Artificial Fibers from Synthetic Linear Condensation Superpolymers*

This publication contains a very interesting and complete description of the mechanical behavior of superpolymers, when they are treated mechanically and especially when drawn into fine filaments.† The experiments refer to the ω-ester of trimethylene glycol and hexadecamethylene dicarboxylic acid. The filaments can be obtained directly by drawing threads from the molten state with a rod; they can also be formed by dissolving the material in chloroform and dry spinning it like cellulose acetate rayon. Diameters less than $1/_{1000}$ inch can be obtained.

* W. H. Carothers and J. W. Hill; *Journ. Am. Chem. Soc.*, 54, 1579–87 (1932); Communication No. 78 from the Experimental Station of E. I. du Pont de Nemours and Co.

Received November 12, 1931.   Published April 6, 1932.

† It may be noted here that these investigations led finally to the development of an all synthetic fiber of very outstanding qualities, which has now been put on the market by E. I. du Pont de Nemours and Co. under the name of "Nylon."

If no stress is applied during spinning, the filaments show properties similar to those of the massive ester from which they are prepared (m. p. about 75°). If stress is applied, the fibers get transparent, lustrous, very strong, pliable and heat resistant.

X-ray investigation shows that in the first case unorientated micellae are present, while the filaments drawn under stress exhibit a fiber diagram which shows that they are built up by a main valence chain lattice.

The strength of such fibers ranges from 16 to 24 kg. per sq. mm., which is comparable with cotton (28 kg. per sq. mm.) and natural silk (35 kg. per sq. mm.).

It is concluded from these observations, that in the case of hydroxydecanoic acid continuous filaments cannot be spun, unless the molecular weight lies above 7000†; the property of cold drawing appears above 9000 and a technically useful degree of strength and pliability of the fibers requires a molecular weight of at least 12,000. This corresponds to an average length of the chains of about 1000 Å or 0.1μ and to a polymerization degree of about 70.

The linear condensation superpolymers described in the three preceding papers of this series (1) can easily be drawn out into strong, pliable, transparent, permanently oriented (2) fibers. So far as we are aware no strictly synthetic material has hitherto been obtained in the form of fibers which thus simulate natural silk.

The superpolyester derived from hexadecamethylene dicarboxylic acid and trimethylene glycol is for brevity referred to below as the 3–16 ω-ester.

Methods of Producing Filaments.—Continuous filaments can be obtained from the molten 3–16 ω-ester by touching it with a stirring rod and drawing the stirring rod away. More uniform filaments are obtained by dissolving the ester in chloroform and extruding the viscous solution through an ordinary rayon spinneret into a chamber warmed to permit the evaporation of the chloroform. The filaments can be picked up and continuously collected on a motor-driven drum at the bottom of the chamber. The production of filaments having a diameter of less than 0.001 inch presents no difficulties. It is also possible to extrude the molten ester through a spinneret that is provided with a heating coil to maintain the ester in a sufficiently fluid condition. When this method is used it is

---

* Meanwhile artificial superpolyamide fibers (Nylon) have been spun with tenacities which considerably exceed the above figures.

† This corresponds to a polymerization degree of about 40 and to a length of the extended chains of about 400 Å or 40μμ.

easy to apply considerable tension to the filaments as they are collected on the drum.

Properties of the Filaments.—The properties of the filaments produced by any of these methods depend upon the amount of tension or stress applied during the spinning operation. If no stress is used the filaments closely resemble the massive ester from which they are produced. They melt at 74–75° and, like the initial mass, they are opaque and devoid of luster. But if sufficient tension is applied during the spinning operation the filaments are very different from the initial mass in their physical properties. Instead of being opaque they are transparent, and they have a very high luster. They

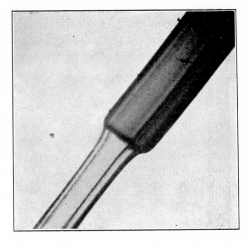

Fig. 1.—Filament from 3-16 ω-ester showing opaque and transparent sections with boundary.

also have a very much higher breaking strength than the initial mass, and they are sufficiently pliable to be tied into hard knots, whereas the opaque

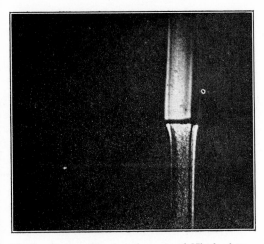

Fig. 2.—Same as Fig. 1 under crossed Nicols showing parallel extinction of oriented section.

filaments produced without stress are so fragile that they can hardly be bent without breaking. The opaque polyester and the transparent filaments produced from it by spinning under tension furnish very different x-ray diffraction patterns. The pattern for the opaque ester (Fig. 4) indicates that it is crystalline, but there is no sign of general orientation. The transparent filaments on the other hand furnish a fiber pattern (Fig. 5) such as one obtains from certain natural silk and cellulose fibers and rayon filaments that have been spun under tension. The character of this pattern indi-

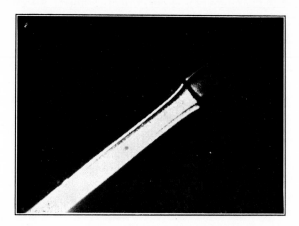

Fig. 3.—Same as Fig. 2, 45° to cross hairs.

cates a very considerable degree of molecular orientation along the axis of the filament (3).

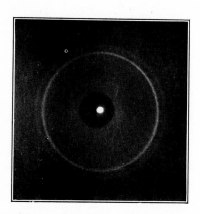

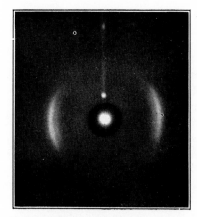

Fig. 4.—x-Ray diffraction pattern of unoriented 3–16 ω-ester.

Fig. 5.—x-Ray diffraction pattern of oriented 3–16 ω-ester.

Cold Drawing.—In connection with the formation of fibers the ω-polymers exhibit a rather spectacular phenomenon which we call cold drawing. If stress is gently applied to a cylindrical sample of the opaque, unoriented

3–16 ω-polyester at room temperature or at a slightly elevated temperature, instead of breaking apart, it separates into two sections joined by a thinner section of the transparent, oriented fiber. As pulling is continued this transparent section grows at the expense of the unoriented sections until the latter are completely exhausted. A remarkable feature of this phenomenon is the sharpness of the boundary at the junction between the transparent and the opaque sections of the filament (Fig. 1). During the drawing operation the shape of this boundary does not change; it merely advances through the opaque sections until the latter are exhausted. This operation can be carried out very rapidly and smoothly, and it leads to oriented fibers of uniform cross section. The oriented and unoriented forms of the polyester are different crystalline states, and in the cold drawing operation one crystalline form is instantly transformed into the other merely by the action of very slight mechanical stress.

Photomicrographs of filaments of the 3–16 ω-ester are reproduced in Figs. 1, 2, 3 and 6. The opaque filament shown in Fig. 1 was obtained by pulling out a specimen of the molten ester, and the transparent section attached to it was produced by cold drawing this filament. This figure shows clearly the sharpness of the boundary between the oriented and the unoriented sections.

Fig. 6.—Filaments of 3–16 ω-ester spun from chloroform solution showing transparent fibers produced by cold drawing (× 15).

Figures 2 and 3 represent the same sample under polarized light. The oriented fiber is birefringent and shows parallel extinction. The opaque filaments of Fig. 6 were obtained by spinning a 23 weight per cent. solution in chloroform of the 3–16 ω-ester through a spinneret having 0.0045 inch holes into a chamber four feet deep heated to about 30°. At the bottom of the chamber the filaments were caught and collected on a motor driven drum. The filaments had a diameter between 0.001 and 0.002 inch. No attempt was made to stretch them during the spinning operation, and they were opaque, devoid of luster and very fragile. Nevertheless they furnished a fiber x-ray diffraction pattern practically identical with that shown in Fig. 5. Thus the x-ray data indicate a high degree of orientation while the physical properties indicate that scarcely any orientation was effected during the spinning operation. When a bundle of the filaments was warmed to about 35° and pulled it was drawn out into thin, transparent fibers which were strong and pliable. Rough determinations of the tenacity of the partially oriented opaque filaments and the oriented transparent filaments prepared from them by cold drawing indicated that the breaking strength of the transparent filaments was about six times that of the opaque filaments. This specimen of oriented fibers was used in some of the physical tests described in the next paragraph.

Tenacity and Elasticity.—Rough determinations of the tensile strength of rather thick fibers of 3–16 ω-ester prepared by pulling filaments from the molten ester and subsequently orienting them by cold drawing gave values ranging from 16 to 24 kg./sq. mm. (24,000 to 36,000 lb /sq. in. These values compare well with those for cotton fibers (*ca.* 28 kg./sq. mm.) and silk (*ca.* 35 kg./sq. mm.). Under gradually increasing stress the fibers show a more or less definite flow point, and then, after considerable elongation, a point of increased resistance to stress. The fibers are sufficiently tough and flexible to be tied into hard knots; thick fibers are sufficiently stiff to be bristle-like.

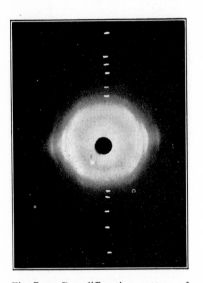

Fig. 7.—x-Ray diffraction pattern of oriented ethylene sebacate.

We are indebted to Dr. W. H. Charch of the du Pont Rayon Company for a series of physical tests on fibers of the 3–16 ω-ester spun from chloroform solution and subsequently oriented by cold drawing. The observed tenacity was about 1.1 g. per denier, but this value is believed to be too low owing to the fact that no account was taken of the considerable number of broken filaments in the specimens tested. The wet tenacity is fully equal to the dry tenacity. (In the actual tests the fibers gave consistently higher values when wet than dry, but the differences probably lay within the experimental error.) A clump of filaments rolled into a small ball and compressed showed a remarkable springiness resembling wool. In their elastic properties these fibers are very much superior to any known artificial silk. In Fig. 7 are presented some slightly idealized curves taken from drawings made by a modified Richards dynamometer.   Bundles of filaments of viscose rayon, natural silk and fibers from the 3–16 ω-ester were stretched for one minute and the curves show the extent and rate of recovery from stretch during the first minute after release from tension.   These curves indicate that the synthetic product is even superior to natural silk, but it is possible that the silk specimen was somewhat deteriorated.

Fibers from Other Linear Condensation Superpolymers.—Fibers closely resembling those described in the preceding section have been obtained in the same way from a variety of other linear condensation polymers in the ω- or superpolymeric state.   The polyesters thus far examined are

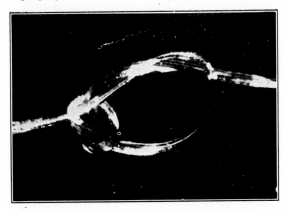

Fig. 8.—Cold drawn fibers from ω-anhydride of decamethylene dicarboxylic acid.   The lack of definition is due to specular reflection caused by high luster.

those derived from ω-hydroxydecanoic acid, ω-hydroxypentadecanoic acid, ethylene glycol and sebacic acid, trimethylene glycol and adipic acid and ethylene glycol and succinc acid.   All of these materials clearly exhibit the phenomenon of cold drawing.   Wide differences in the nature of the structural unit naturally have a considerable effect on the capacity to form fibers and on some of the properties of the fibers.   Thus ethylene succinate in its α-form has a higher melting point and is more brittle than most other α-polyesters derived from dibasic acids and glycols (4), and fibers derived from ω-ethylene succinate are somewhat short and brittle.   On the other hand, α-polyesters derived from adipic acid have rather low melting points, and ω-polyesters derived from the same acid show a tendency to collapse at slightly elevated temperature.

Polyamides such as that derived from ε-aminocaproic acid can also be got in the superpolymeric state (5). Owing to the very high polarity of the amide group and the consequent high molecular cohesion, such polyamides are exceedingly hard and insoluble in most common solvents. They show signs of melting only at temperatures sufficiently high to produce considerable decomposition. These refractory qualities make it very difficult to draw satisfactory filaments from pure polyamides. On the other hand, mixed polyester-polyamides of the type already described (5) yield filaments that are easily cold drawn and, when oriented, have very high tenacity and pliability.

Polyanhydrides derived from dibasic acids of the series $HOOC(CH_2)_x$-COOH are especially easy to obtain in the superpolymeric state. The technique involved and the nature of the reaction is discussed in detail for sebacic acid ($x = 8$) in paper XIV. The behavior described there is characteristic (so far as the formation of superpolyanhydride is concerned) for those acids in which x is greater than 4. (Actual observations thus far include those in which x is 5, 6, 7, 8, 9, 10, 11, 12 and 16.) The fibers obtained from the anhydrides have an especially high degree of strength, pliability and luster (cf. Fig. 8) but they gradually disintegrate on standing owing to hydrolytic degradation.

Discussion

Our studies of polymerization were first initiated at a time when a great deal of scepticism prevailed concerning the possibility of applying the usually accepted ideas of structural organic chemistry to such naturally occurring materials as cellulose; and its primary object was to synthesize giant molecules of known structure by strictly rational methods. The use of synthetic models as a means of approach to this problem had already been undertaken by Staudinger, but the products studied by him (polyoxymethylene, polystyrene, polyacrylic acid, etc.) although unquestionably simpler than naturally occurring polymers, were produced by reactions of unknown mechanism, and their behavior, except in the case of polyoxymethylene, was not sufficiently simple to furnish an unequivocal demonstration of their structure. On the other hand, the development of the principles of condensation polymerization described in preceding papers of this series has led to strictly rational methods for the synthesis of linear polymers, and the structures of the superpolymers III to VI follow directly from the methods used in their preparation. Meanwhile the weight of authoritative opinion has shifted; further evidence has been accumulated (6) and cellulose has been assigned a definite and generally accepted structure (7). Like the synthetic products III to VI it falls in the class already defined as linear superpolymers.

I ...⟨hexagon⟩—O—⟨hexagon⟩—O—⟨hexagon⟩—O—⟨hexagon⟩—O—⟨hexagon⟩—O—
Cellulose (polyacetal)

II ... —NH—R—CO—NH—R'—CO—NH—R—CO—NH—R'—CO—...
Silk (polyamide)

III ... —O—R—CO—O—R—CO—O—R—CO—O—R—CO—O—R—CO—..
Polyester (from hydroxy acid)

IV ... —O—R—O—CO—R'—CO—O—R—O—CO—R'—CO—
Polyester (from dibasic acid and glycol)

V ... —O—R—CO—NH—R'—CO—NH—R'—CO—O—R—CO— ..
Mixed polyester-polyamide

VI ... —O—CO—R—CO—O—CO—R—CO—O—CO—R—CO—...
Polyanhydride

Addition polymers of very high molecular weight have been synthesized in the past, but the capacity to yield permanently oriented fibers of any considerable strength has not been observed hitherto. Why is this, and what conditions of molecular structure are requisite for the production of a useful fiber? We regret that the limitations of space prohibit a detailed discussion of these and accessory questions, and permit only the baldest statement of our conclusions.

We picture a perfectly oriented fiber as consisting essentially of a single crystal in which the long molecules are in ordered array parallel with the fiber axis (Fig. 10). (In actual fibers a considerable number of the molecules fail to identify themselves completely with this perfectly ordered structure.) The high strength in the direction of the fiber axis and the pliability are accounted for by the high cohesive forces of the long molecules and by the absence of any crystal boundaries along the fiber axis (7a). Fiber strength should depend upon molecular length, and recent work by Dr. van Natta in this laboratory indicates that it is not possible to spin continuous filaments from the polyester of hydroxydecanoic acid until its molecular weight reaches about 7000. The property of cold drawing does not appear until the molecular weight reaches about 9000. From these and other facts we conclude that a useful degree of strength and pliability in a fiber requires a molecular weight of at least 12,000 and a molecular length not less than 1000 Å. (The limits for polyamides may perhaps lie at somewhat lower values.)

Besides being composed of very long molecules, a compound must be capable of crystallizing if it is to form oriented fibers, and orientation is probably necessary for great strength and pliability. Linear condensation polymers are quite generally crystalline unless bulky substituents are present to destroy the linear symmetry of the chains; addition polymers, especially those produced from vinyl compounds, are more rarely crystalline. Possible reasons for this have already been discussed in part (8).

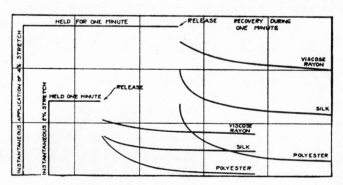

Fig. 9.—Elastic recovery of various fibers.

Three-dimensional polymers are obviously unsuited for fiber orientation, and synthetic materials of this class are besides invariably amorphous. Glyptal resins belong to this class (9). It has been proposed (10) to use glyptal resins for the production of artificial silk, but our attempts to carry out the proposed process led to exceedingly fragile (though lustrous) threads which showed no signs of orientation when examined by x-rays.

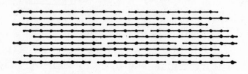

Fig. 10.—Lattice from molecules of unequal length.

Although one will not expect oriented fibers to arise by any process of spontaneous crystallization under the ordinary conditions, the phenomenon of cold drawing is perhaps only accidentally associated with the capacity to yield oriented fibers; it apparently requires a certain degree of softness and suppleness in the molecules; and its mechanism is doubtless analogous to that involved in the mechanical orientation of cellulose preparations (11). (Perhaps however, in the unoriented polyesters the molecules are in spiral form and become extended during orientation.)

It has been suggested repeatedly by Staudinger that the great sensitivity of cellulose and rubber to degradation by heat and by certain reagents is due to the fact that the upper limit of thermal stability of the very long molecules lies close to room temperature. It is of interest in this connection that the synthetic linear superpolyesters, in spite of their very high molecular weights, are formed at 200 to 250°, and that they show no signs of being degraded by repeated exposure to elevated temperature.

Acknowledgment

We are greatly indebted to Dr. W. H. Charch of the du Pont Rayon Company and to Dr. E. O. Kraemer of the Experimental Station for valuable criticism and advice, and we have also to thank Dr. A. W. Kenney of the Experimental Station for the X-ray data.

Summary

The linear condensation ω-polyesters, polyanhydrides and mixed polyester-polyamides described in preceding papers are easily drawn out into very strong, pliable, highly oriented fibers which closely simulate natural silk and cellulose fibers. These materials also resemble cellulose and silk in the essential details of their molecular structure. The significance of these analogies is discussed.

Bibliography and Remarks

(1) Papers XII, XIII and XIV.

(2) The orientation implied in this use of the term is general orientation, with reference to the fiber axis, of the molecules or of some ordered units involving the molecules.

(3) According to some preliminary calculations made by Dr. A. W. Kenney of this laboratory the identity periods in the oriented fibers derived from ethylene sebacate and from the 3–16 ester lie within about 10% of the calculated lengths for one structural unit of the chain.

(4) Carothers and Arvin, *Journ. Am. Chem. Soc.*, **51**, 2560 (1929).

(5) Paper XIII.

(6) Haworth, Long and Plant, *J. Chem. Soc.*, **129**, 2809 (1927); Freudenberg, *Ber.*, **54**, 767 (1921); *Ann.*, **461**, 130 (1928); Freudenberg and Braun, *ibid.*, **460**, 288 (1929); Freudenberg, Kuhn, Durr Bolz and Steinbrunn, *Ber.*, **63**, 1528 (1930).

(7) Sponsler and Dore, *Colloid Symposium Monograph*, **4**, 174 (1926). Chemical Catalog Company, New York; Sponsler, *Nature*, **125**, 633 (1930); Meyer and Mark, *Ber.*, **61**, 593 (1928); Mark and Meyer, *Z. physik. Chem.*, [B] **2**, 115 (1929); Mark and Susich, *ibid.*, **4**, 431 (1929).

(7a) *Cf.* Meyer and Mark, "Der Aufbau der hochpolymeren organischen Naturstoffe," Akademische Verlagsgesellschaft, Leipzig, Germany, 1930.

(8) Carothers, *Chem. Reviews*, **8**, 415 (1931).

(9) Ref. 8, page 402.

(10) British Patents 303,867 and 305,468.

(11) Ref. 8, p. 418.

XVI.   A Polyalcohol from Decamethylene Dimagnesium Bromide*

This is a short description of a polyalcohol made from decamethylene dimagnesium bromide. As this Grignard compound is a bifunctional reactant it can build up a linear polymer. By reaction with methyl formate it yields a crystalline polydecamethylene carbinol. If this is heated in the molecular still a colorless, insoluble, tough, pliable mass of a very considerable molecular weight is obtained.

The action of bifunctional reactants on bifunctional Grignard reagents (e. g., on $BrMg(CH_2)_xMgBr$) presents the possibility of producing cyclic compounds of various types. Cyclopentanone (1), cyclohexanone and methylcyclohexanol (2) have been prepared thus, and also 5- and 6-atom rings containing phosphorus, arsenic (3), lead (4) and silicon (5). Concerning larger rings it is recorded (2) that diacetyl reacts with pentamethylene dimagnesium bromide but yields very little of the product corresponding in composition with the expected 7-ring glycol. The same reagent is said (6), to react with dialdehydes and diketones to give ring compounds, though "not easily"; but none of these compounds are described. The rarity and obscurity of such allusions to reactions which might yield large rings is certainly not due to any difficulty of inducing reaction between —MgX and carbonyl or other groups. On the other hand, bifunctional reactions are not obliged to choose between ring formation and frustration or abortion; they may be, and in fact when the possibility of forming a ring of 5 or 6 atoms is absent, they generally are intermolecular, and they thus lead to linear polymeric chains (7). The diversity of the Grignard reactions should permit the preparation of linear polymers of many different types. Complications due to the usual side reactions of the —MgX group are multiplied when two of these groups are present in the same molecule. Nevertheless, as the following example shows, it is possible by such reactions to prepare linear polymers which are homogeneous in their analytical and chemical behavior.

Methyl formate (0.2 mole) was added dropwise to an ethereal solution (250 cc.) of decamethylene dimagnesium bromide prepared from 0.2 mole of the bromide. Each drop of the formate immediately yielded a heavy, voluminous precipitate. After the addition of all the formate, the mixture was refluxed for one and one-half hours. A

* W. H. Carothers and G. E. Kirby; *Journ. Am. Chem. Soc.*, **54**, 1588–90 (1932); Communication No. 48 from the Experimental Station of E. I. du Pont de Nemours and Co.

Received November 12, 1931.   Published April 6, 1932.

color test (8) then showed that C—MgX was absent from the ethereal layer but present in the insoluble precipitate. The mixture was treated with water and dilute hydrochloric acid, and the undissolved solid was separated by filtration. The yield was 88% of the theoretical. The product was completely freed of magnesium by triturating it with warm dilute hydrochloric acid. It dissolved readily in hot alcohol, acetic acid or ethylene chloride, but not in acetone, ether or benzene. It melted at about 115–120°. More sharply melting samples (e. g., 120–121°) were obtained by repeated crystallization from alcohol, and higher and lower melting samples were obtained in other experiments. The melting points all varied with the rate of heating.

The analytical composition of this solid corresponds with the expected poly secondary alcohol, and its apparent molecular weight indicates an average formula —[(CH₂)₁₀—CHOH]ₐ—. The equation for the reaction may be represented as

$$...—(CH_2)_{10}MgBr \; + \; O{=}C—OCH_3 \; + \; BrMg—... \; \longrightarrow$$
$$|$$
$$H$$
$$...—[—(CH_2)_{10}—CH(OMgBr)—]—...$$

Anal. Calcd. for C₁₁H₂₂O: C, 77.65; H, 12.94. Found: C, 77.35, 77.40; H, 13.04, 12.79. Mol. wt., calcd. for (C₁₁H₂₂O)ₐ: 850. Found (in boiling ethylene chloride): 835, 879.

It is undoubtedly mixed with traces of shorter and longer chains and with analogous derivatives of the coupling products BrMg(CH₂)₂₀MgBr, BrMg(CH₂)₃₀MgBr, etc., which are always formed in small amounts during the preparation of the reagent. The chains are probably all open, but there may be considerable variety in the nature of the terminal groups. However, its lack of homogeneity is probably no greater than that of a purified sample of polyvinyl alcohol (9), of which it is a homolog.

The polyaclohol is readily converted into such acyl derivatives as bromobenzoyl, phthalyl, etc., but all of these products were obtained only in the form of oils or tars. The composition of an oily acetate prepared by refluxing the alcohol with acetic anhydride containing some sodium acetate confirms the empirical structure assigned to the alcohol.

Anal. Calcd. for —(CH₂)₁₀—CH—(OCOCH₃)— = C₁₃H₂₄O₂: C, 73.59; H, 11.32; saponification equivalent, 212. Found: C, 74.09, 73.61; H, 11.27, 11.33; saponification equivalent, 207, 223, 227.

Experiments in other directions remain incomplete.

The behavior of the polyalcohol in the molecular still is noteworthy. A sample melting at 110–113° was heated for a few hours at about 150° under a pressure less than 10⁻⁵ mm. A trace of crystalline solid melting at about 80° collected on the condenser which was within 1 cm. of the evaporating surface. The residue was a colorless, semi-transparent, very tough pliable mass. It was insoluble in the common solvents. On being heated, it gradually became completely transparent between 60 and 100°. At 215–220° it had become somewhat soft and sticky without losing its shape. Above this temperature it first became slightly yellow and finally, at about 250°, still darker with considerable decomposition. Its analytical composition was nearly the same as that of the alcohol from which it was derived. The change in properties indicates a considerable increase in molecular weight, and the absence of solubility and complete fusibility is consistent with the development of a three-dimensional polymeric molecular structure. This might readily occur, with very little change in composition, through cross-linking of the polyalcohol chains by occasional ether formation. When the polyalcohol is heated in the same way at ordinary pressure, it remains quite unchanged in its properties; so this example provides an even more striking illustration than those previously recorded (10) of the powerfulness of the molecular still as a tool for displacing chemical equilibria.

The description of these fragmentary experiments with bifunctional Grignard reagents is presented now because it has become necessary to suspend our work in this field.

Summary

A crystalline polydecamethylene carbinol has been prepared by the action of decamethylene dimagnesium bromide on methyl formate. Its properties are described. It is converted into a colorless, insoluble, tough, pliable mass when it is heated in a molecular still.

Bibliography and Remarks

(1) v. Braun and Sobecki, *Ber.*, **44**, 1918 (1911).

(2) Grignard and Vignon, *Compt. rend.*, **144**, 1358 (1907).

(3) Grüttner and Wiernik, *Ber.*, **48**, 1473 (1915).

(4) Grüttner and Krause, *ibid.*, **49**, 2666 (1916).

(5) Bygden, *ibid.*, **48**, 1236 (1915).

(6) v. Braun, *Chem. Zentr.*, II, 1993 (1909).

(7) See Carothers, *Journ. Am. Chem. Soc.*, **51**, 2548 (1929), and subsequent papers of this series.

(8) Gilman and Schulze, *ibid.*, **47**, 2002 (1925).

(9) Herrmann and Haehnel, *Ber.*, **60**, 1658 (1927); Staudinger, Frey and Starck, *ibid.*, **60**, 1782 (1927).

(10) Papers XI, XII, XIII and XIV.

XVII. Friedel–Crafts Syntheses with the Polyanhydrides of the Dibasic Acids*

This short note deals with the Friedel–Crafts reaction of polyanhydrides of dibasic acids. Such anhydrides react with benzene in the presence of anhydrous aluminum chloride to yield dibenzoyl-alkane, ω-benzoyl fatty acid and dibasic acid. The reaction has been actually carried out with benzene and polymeric adipic and sebacic anhydride; it provides a convenient method of synthesis for ω-benzoyl fatty acids and is presumably quite general.

* J. W. Hill; *Journ. Am. Chem. Soc.*, **54**, 4105–06 (1932); Communication No. 100 from the Experimental Station of E. I. du Pont de Nemours and Co. See also footnote (1) in paper VI on page 63.

Received June 15, 1932. Published October 5, 1932.

It has been shown that the polymeric anhydrides of aliphatic dibasic acids react smoothly and normally as acid anhydrides with aniline (1), with phenol (1a), with ammonia (2a) and with diethylamine (2b).   In each reaction three products are formed.   The course of the reactions is shown by the following scheme, which does not consider the end groups of the polyanhydride

$$(-OC(CH_2)_nCO-O-)_x + RH \longrightarrow \frac{x}{4} R-OC(CH_2)_nCO-R +$$
$$(a)$$

$$\frac{x}{2} R-OC(CH_2)_nCOOH + \frac{x}{4} HOOC(CH_2)_nCOOH$$
$$(b) \qquad\qquad (c)$$

where R is C_6H_5NH-, C_6H_5O-, NH_2- or $(C_2H_5)_2N-$

It has been demonstrated on theoretical grounds that the products of types (a), (b) and (c) should be formed in the molecular ratio of 1:2:1.   This has been verified quantitatively in the aniline reaction (1).

The dibasic acid polyanhydrides have now been found to react typically with benzene in the presence of anhydrous aluminum chloride to yield dibenzoyl alkane, ω-benzoyl fatty acid and dibasic acid.

$$(-OC(CH_2)_nCO-O)_x + C_6H_6 + (AlCl_3) \longrightarrow$$

$$\frac{x}{4} C_6H_5CO(CH_2)_nCOC_6H_5 + \frac{x}{2} C_6H_5CO(CH_2)_nCOOH + \frac{x}{4} HOOC(CH_2)_nCOOH$$

This reaction has been carried out with polymeric adipic and sebacic anhydrides and benzene.   There is no reason to doubt that it is perfectly general and applicable to any polymeric dibasic anhydride and any suitable aromatic hydrocarbon.

This reaction is particularly interesting in providing a convenient method of synthesis for the ω-benzoyl fatty acids which have heretofore been prepared by more elaborate syntheses or in very low and uncertain yields as by-products in the Friedel–Crafts reaction of dibasic acid chlorides with aromatic hydrocarbons (3).

Experimental Part

Friedel–Crafts Reaction between Adipic Polyanhydride and Benzene.—One hundred and forty-six grams (one mole) of adipic acid was refluxed with 400 cc. of acetic anhydride for six hours.   The excess acetic anhydride and the acetic acid formed in the reaction were removed by distillation *in vacuo* up to 120° bath temperature.   The resulting polyanhydride (1a) was dissolved in 400 cc. of warm, dry benzene.   Three hundred grams of anhydrous aluminum chloride was suspended in 1500 cc. of dry benzene contained in a 3-necked 3-liter flask fitted with a reflux condenser and a mechanical stirrer.

The anhydride solution was added with stirring over a period of one hour and the mixture allowed to stand overnight.   The product was decomposed in ice and 250 cc.

of concentrated hydrochloric acid added. The benzene layer was separated and extracted with dilute aqueous sodium hydroxide. The water phase deposited a small amount of crystals on standing which were identified after recrystallization from water as adipic acid by a mixed melting point determination.

The alkaline solution was acidified and the crystalline precipitate of ω-benzoyl-valeric acid filtered off: weight dry, 78 g.; yield, 75%. The product was recrystallized from a benzene–petroleum ether mixture, m. p. 70–71° (4).

Anal. Calcd. for $C_{12}H_{14}O_3$: C, 69.9; H, 6.8. Found: C, 70.1; H, 6.7.

The extracted benzene was distilled to a small volume and chilled; 56.5 g. of dibenzoyl-butane was obtained, yield 85%. Recrystallized from alcohol, it was slightly pink and melted at 105–106° (5). It was identified by means of a mixed melting point determination with an authentic specimen.

Anal. Calcd. for $C_{18}H_{18}O_2$: C, 81.2; H, 6.8. Found: C, 80.6; H, 7.0.

Friedel–Crafts Reaction between Sebacic Polyanhydride and Benzene.—One hundred and one grams (0.5 mole) of sebacic acid was refluxed with 300 cc. of acetic anhydride for five hours. The excess anhydride and the acetic acid formed were distilled off *in vacuo* up to 120°. The residual polyanhydride was dissolved in 250 cc. of warm dry benzene and added to 150 g. of anhydrous aluminum chloride suspended in 750 cc. of dry benzene as in the previous preparation. The products were worked up in the same way. The crude precipitated ω-benzoylnonanoic acid was extracted with hot water to remove sebacic acid. Fifteen grams of sebacic acid separated from the washings and was identified by a mixed melting point determination with a known sample. The ω-benzoylnonanoic acid weighed 50 g., a yield of 78%. Recrystallized from dilute alcohol, it melted at 77–78° (6).

Anal. Calcd. for $C_{16}H_{22}O_3$: C, 73.3; H, 8.4. Found: C, 73.3; H, 8.4.

The dibenzoyloctane was recovered from the benzene solution and weighed 35 g., a yield of 86%. Recrystallized from alcohol, it melted at 92–93° (7).

Anal. Calcd. for $C_{22}H_{26}O_2$: C, 82.0; H, 8.1. Found: C, 81.7; H, 8.1.

Summary

The polymeric anhydrides of adipic and sebacic acids react with benzene in the presence of anhydrous aluminum chloride to yield mixtures of the appropriate dibenzoyl alkane, ω-benzoyl fatty acid, and dibasic acid. The reaction is doubtless general.

Bibliography and Remarks

(1) (a) Hill, *Journ. Am. Chem. Soc.*, **52**, 4110 (1930); (b) Hill and Carothers, *ibid.*, **54**, 1569 (1932).
(2) (a) Étaix, *Ann. Chim.*, [7] **9**, 356 (1896); (b) Einhorn and Diesbach, *Ber.*, **39**, 1222 (1906).
(3) Auger, *Ann. chim.*, [6] **22**, 360 (1891); Étaix, *ibid.*, [7] **9**, 391 (1896).
(4) Grateau, *Compt. rend.*, **191**, 947 (1930), gives 71°.
(5) Étaix, *Ann. chim.*, [7] **9**, 372 (1896), gives 102–103°.
(6) Auger, *ibid.*, [6] **22**, 364 (1891), gives 78–79°.
(7) Auger, *ibid.*, [6] **22** 363 (1891), gives 88–89°.

XVIII.   Polyesters from ω-Hydroxydecanoic Acid*

A series of polyesters from ω-hydroxydecanoic acid is described in this paper.   It represents without doubt the best established set of synthetic high polymers concerning identity, uniformity and structure.

The lower members were prepared by heating ω-hydroxydecanoic acid at 150° in a normal distilling flask; the higher ones were obtained in the molecular still previously described.†

The molecular weights range from 780 to 25,000 and were determined by titration of the terminal acid group; the highest member was also measured in the Svedberg Ultracentrifuge.   The agreement is excellent (25,660 and 25,200).

The polyesters below 10,000 dissolve rapidly and completely in cold chloroform or benzene and in various hot organic solvents.   The highest members show greatly diminished solubility and swell before going slowly into solution.   The melting points increase with the molecular weight until about 1000 (being then around 70°), which corresponds to a polymerization degree of five and to a length of about 100 Å for the extended chain.   Between 1000 and 25,000 there is no further increase of melting points.   All esters are microcrystalline; the lower members being waxy and brittle, the higher ones hard, horny and very tough.

The samples above 10,000 (polymerization degree 50, length of the extended chain around 1000 Å) can readily be spun into fibers.   The initial filaments are opaque and fragile; by stretching they become transparent, pliable and very strong.   The x-ray diagram shows the presence of fiber orientation.   Up to a molecular weight of 5700 (polymerization degree 28) no fibers can be obtained.   The ester with m. w. 7330 furnished filaments but they could not be extended.   The ester 9330 gave stretchable fibers but they were very weak.   Above 10,000 strong extendable filaments are obtained.

*These esters have also been used to test the viscosity equation of Staudinger.**   It was found that this surprisingly simple relation between viscosity and molecular weight holds fairly well up to about 15,000.   Above this point the viscosities rise more rapidly than the equation requires, and the law loses its strict validity.*

* W. H. Carothers and F. J. van Natta; *Journ. Am. Chem. Soc.*, **55**, 4714–19 (1933); Communication No. 129 from the Experimental Station of E. I. du Pont de Nemours and Company.

Received August 8, 1933.   Published November 7, 1933.

† Compare paper XI, pages 154 to 156.

** E. O. Kraemer and F. J. van Natta; *J. Phys. Chem.*, **36**, 3175 (1932).

The obvious importance of simple synthetic models as an aid in studying macromolecular materials has been emphasized repeatedly by Staudinger (1), who has used polystyrene, polyoxymethylene, polyacrylic acid, etc., for this purpose. Our own researches on condensation polymers were started with the idea that the fact of a proposed model's being synthetic is of little value unless the method of synthesis is rational, *i. e.*, unless it is sufficiently clear-cut to leave no doubt concerning the structure of the product. Polystyrene may, for example, serve as a simplified model of rubber, but it has the disadvantage that the method used in its synthesis (a spontaneous polymerization of unknown mechanism) furnishes no certain clue to its structure. The independent demonstration of its structure presents the same difficulties as does rubber; in fact today the formula of rubber can be written with more assurance than that of polystyrene.

In the first paper of this series (2) it was pointed out that bifunctional condensations frequently proceed by known mechanisms. In the second paper (3) it was shown for polyesters derived jointly from dibasic acids and glycols that the reaction consists exclusively in esterification while the average size of the product molecule increases progressively with the completeness of the reaction. Rational, deliberate control over the average molecular weight is thus made possible, and, as was shown later (4), by using more drastic conditions molecules of average weight greater than 20,000 can be obtained. Meanwhile a study of the self-esterification of ω-hydroxydecanoic acid was presented by Lycan and Adams (5), who concluded that the products must be formulated like the polyesters referred to above.

We have now greatly extended the range of polyesters derived from ω-hydroxydecanoic acid and have obtained the series of fractions of different average molecular weights shown in Table I. The structure of these polyesters $HO[-(CH_2)_9CO-O-]_n(CH_2)_9CO-OH$ follows from the method used in their synthesis (see Experimental Part) and the fact that they can be hydrolyzed quantitatively to ω-hydroxydecanoic acid. The only important uncertainty is the distribution, in a given sample, of the molecular weight about the observed average (*i. e.*, the degree of homogeneity). However, since these esters are all crystalline solids and since the mer or unit of the chain is quite long, the homogeneity is probably better than in the case of such materials as polystyrene which can be purified only by fractional precipitation or extraction. Moreover, a determination of the molecular weight of the highest member of the series by the Svedberg ultracentrifugal method indicates that the weight of most of the molecules lies fairly close to the observed average. It is indeed our opinion that this series of polyesters is more definitely and certainly established in identity and structure than any similar series of macromolecular compounds yet described.

TABLE I

POLYESTERS FROM ω-HYDROXYDECANOIC ACID

Mol. wt.	M. p., °C.	d_4^{25}	n_D^{85}	Spinnability	Tensile strength
780	66–67	1.0957	1.4494	Absent	
1720	72–74	1.0935	1.4506	Absent	
3190	74–75	1.0877	1.4517	Absent	
4170	74–76	1.0814	1.4517	Absent	
5670	73–75	1.0751	1.4518	Very short fibers. No cold drawing	
7330	74–75	1.0715	1.4517	Long fibers, but cold drawing absent	Very weak
9330	75–76	1.0668	1.4518	Long fibers which cold draw	Very weak
16900	77–78	1.0627	....	Easily spins and cold draws	13.1 kg./mm.^{2}
20700	77–78	1.0632	....	Spins with difficulty but easily cold draws	12.3 kg./mm.^{2}
25200	75–80	1.0621	1.4515	Spins above 210° and cold draws	7.0 kg./mm.^{2}

TABLE II

MOLECULAR WEIGHTS OF POLYESTERS

Observed mol. wts. (by titration)		Average	Observed mol. wts. (by other methods)	Calculated length of molecule in Å.
776	784	780	930 (in boiling benzene)	60
1707	1722	1720	1620 (in boiling benzene)	123
3188	3201	3190	Not measured	188
4114	4226	4170	Not measured	313
5626	5717	5670	Not measured	440
7327	7329	7330	Not measured	570
9331	9335	9330	Not measured	730
16890	17110	16790	16900	Not measured	1320
20380	20930	20700	Not measured	1610
24240	25760	25660	25200	26700 (ultracentrifuge)	1970

Molecular Weights.—Molecular weights were estimated by titration with standard alcoholic potash of the polyesters dissolved in a chloroform–alcohol mixture. Phenolphthalein was used as an indicator. This method applied to pure lauric acid gave values agreeing sharply with the theoretical (200.4, 199.6 and 199.2 as against 200.2). Observed values for the polyesters are shown in Table II. It is interesting to note that no difficulty was encountered in titrating the highest member of the series where the acid hydrogen is only one part in 25,000.

The average equivalent weight measured by titration will of course be identical with the average molecular weight only if each molecule bears a terminal carboxyl in the manner required by the indicated structure.

The accidental loss of terminal carboxyls under the conditions of preparation used seems rather improbable, but indication of the absence of such loss is provided by independent estimations of molecular weight. The boiling point method furnished values for the first two members agreeing, within the probable experimental error, with the much more sharply reproducible values determined by titration. For compounds above molecular weight 3000, in our experience, boiling-point or freezing-point methods are not self-consistent within 10%, and above 10,000 they are practically worthless. We were, however, very fortunate in being able to obtain a value for the highest polymer by the Svedberg ultracentrifugal method (6). The agreement is all that could be desired.

Physical Properties.—The polyesters below 10,000 dissolve rapidly and completely in cold chloroform or benzene and in hot acetone, ethyl acetate and acetic acid. They are practically insoluble in hot alcohol, ligroin or water. The highest members show diminished solubility in benzene and in hot acetone and ethyl acetate. They dissolve copiously in chloroform, but solution occurs only slowly and is preceded by some swelling. At *ca.* 110° the first member of the series is a highly viscous liquid while the highest member is a transparent resin that is too stiff to flow and sufficiently elastic to offer resistance to permanent deformation.

Lycan and Adams have pointed out (5) that the melting point of self-esters of hydroxydecanoic acid increases with increasing molecular weight up to 1000, but changes little between 1000 and 9000. As the data of Table I show, there is also no further increase between 9000 and 25,000. The polyesters separate from solution in the form of white powders which give sharp x-ray powder diffraction patterns. At least in the lower members of the series crystallinity can also be demonstrated by microscopic observation. A very dilute solution of the 3190 ester in butyl acetate, when examined at a magnification of 400, showed the separation of tiny flat glittering plates. The molten esters in thin layers crystallize very rapidly, but with the lower members one can observe the crystallization to start with the emergence and growth of innumerable doubly refracting centers, apparently spherulites. At a magnification of 900 the growth appears to involve the intermeshing of radiating clusters of needles.

The masses resulting from crystallization of the molten polyesters are opaque solids. The lower members are waxy and brittle; when fractured they show no planes of cleavage. The highest members are harder and so horny and tough that they can scarcely be fractured.

In Table I are listed the densities of the solid esters at 25°. The values *diminish* as the molecular weight rises, quite rapidly at first and then more slowly until at a molecular weight of 16,900 they become almost constant. This at first sight is very surprising. Polymerization usually involves an increase in density. There is, for example, an increase of 23% in passing from chloroprene to polychloroprene (7). The interpretation of the present case can scarcely be attempted in the absence of data on the molten esters, which are not yet available; but it is easy to imagine that the longer the molecules are the more difficulty they will have in lining themselves up perfectly in the crystal lattice. The refractive indices of the molten esters at 85° are presented in Table I. There is a slight increase from 780 to 1720, a smaller increase from 1720 to 3190, and beyond that no further change.

Fiber Formation.—In a previous paper (8) it was shown that linear polyesters of molecular weight above 10,000, when melted or dissolved, can be spun into fibers. The initial filaments are opaque and fragile, but when stress is applied to them they are readily elongated several fold and then remain *permanently extended*. The stretching is accompanied by a loss of opacity, and an enormous increase in tensile strength and pliability. Examination by x-rays shows the presence of fiber orientation.

These fibers are, we believe, the first examples of a synthetic material being obtained in the form of fibers having any considerable degree of strength, orientation and pliability. The analogies in chemical structure with cellulose and silk are especially interesting, and the esters of the present paper provide some data (Table I) on the relation between molecular weight and fiber-forming ability. Until a molecular weight of 5670 is reached, the viscosity and coherence of the molten esters are so low that they do not yield continuous filaments. The ester of molecular weight 7330 furnished continuous filaments which, however, could not be stretched and oriented. The 9330 ester could be stretched, but the oriented fibers were too weak to permit the determination of tensile strength. Oriented fibers from the 16,900 ester had a tensile strength of 13.1 kg./sq. mm. or 1.36 g. per denier, which is in the same range as good regenerated cellulose fibers. The value for the 20,700 ester (12.3 kg./sq. mm.) differs from that for the 16,900 ester by an amount that probably lies within the experimental error. The tensile strength of the 15,200 ester is, however, definitely much lower. It is exceedingly improbable that the fiber strength of completely oriented molecules rises to a maximum and then falls off as the length of the molecule increases. On the other hand, the degree of orientation that can be produced by cold-drawing probably depends upon other factors besides molecular weight. An unusually high temperature (210°) was required to soften the 25,200 ester sufficiently to permit spinning, and its relatively low tensile strength may therefore reasonably be ascribed to factors associated with orientation. It may be observed that the ability to form strong, highly oriented fibers does not appear until the molecular length reaches some value lying between 700 and 1300 Å.

Viscosity and Other Properties.—The viscosities of dilute solutions of these polymers in tetrachloroethane have been carefully measured. The results already reported and discussed (9) show that Staudinger's simple empirical equations relating viscosity to molecular weight (1) are satisfied fairly well until the molecular weight reaches 16,900; beyond this point the viscosities rise more rapidly than the equations require. Staudinger has assumed that the relations between viscosity and molecular weight established for compounds below 10,000 will hold for compounds of higher molecular weight. The data referred to above provide the first experimental test of this assumption, and for the polyesters under consideration it is shown to be not strictly valid. Molecular weights that have been assigned to cellulose, rubber, high polystyrenes, etc., on the basis of viscosity measurements must therefore be considered as subject to considerable uncertainty.

Study of the physical properties of polyesters derived from hydroxydecanoic acid is being continued, and further results will be reported in future papers.

Experimental Part

Preparation of Polyesters.—The lowest members of the series were obtained by heating ω-hydroxydecanoic acid at 150° in an ordinary distilling flask provided with a receiver. Diminished pressure and higher temperatures were used for higher members of the series; the highest members (above 10,000) were obtained by heating the hydroxydecanoic acid or its lower polyesters in a molecular still consisting essentially of a suction flask into which a water-cooled test-tube was inserted to act as a condenser. The products were crystallized several times to increase their homogeneity. Typical procedures are indicated below.

Polyester of Molecular Weight 4170.—Twenty grams of the acid was heated at 150–175° under atmospheric pressure for one and one-half hours, then at 200° at 1 mm. pressure for eight hours. The resulting waxy product was crystallized by dissolving in a small amount of boiling chloroform and adding several volumes of hot acetone. The product had an apparent equivalent weight of 3906. A second crystallization from hot acetone by slow cooling raised the equivalent weight to 4170. The ester was obtained as a chalky powder, soluble in chloroform and benzene and in hot acetone, ethyl acetate and acetic acid. Hot alcohol, ligroin or water did not dissolve it appreciably.

Anal. Calcd. for $HO—[(CH_2)_9—CO—O]_{24}—H$: C, 70.22; H, 10.66; mol. wt. 4101; saponification equivalent, 170.8. Found: C, 70.35, 70.70; H, 10.69, 10.88; mol. wt. by titration, 4114, 4226; saponification equivalent, 170.7.

Polyester of Molecular Weight 9330.—Thirty-six grams of the acid was heated for seven hours at 120–175° at 1 mm. pressure, then for twenty-five hours at 225° at 1 mm. It was crystallized several times from hot acetone by slow cooling and was obtained as a pure white powder. It did not differ appreciably from polymer 4170 in solubility.

Anal. Calcd. for HO—[(CH₂)₉—CO—O]₅₅—H: C, 70.39; H, 1066; mol. wt., 9376; saponification equivalent, 170.5. Found: C, 70.56; H, 10.87; mol. wt. by titration, 9335, 9331; saponification equivalent, 169.6.

Polyester of Molecular Weight 20,700.—Fifteen grams of hydroxydecanoic acid was heated at 230° in a molecular still for thirty hours. During the first few hours a considerable amount of distillate (dimer and unchanged acid) collected on the condenser. This was removed and the residue in the flask was stirred frequently. At the end of the reaction the mass was plastic when hot. It was purified by dissolving in a small amount of hot chloroform, then adding several volumes of acetone and allowing the product to crystallize by cooling. This polymer was less soluble than lower members in benzene or in hot acetone or ethyl acetate. Solution was slow and was preceded by some swelling.

Anal. Calcd. for HO—[(CH₂)₉—CO—O]₁₂₁—H: C, 70.47; H, 10.66; mol. wt.. 20,605; saponification equivalent, 170.3. Found: C, 70.72, 70.29; H, 10.62, 10.47; mol. wt. by titration, 20,380, 20,930; saponification equivalent, 170.8.

Saponification of the polyesters by alcoholic alkali always resulted in complete solution, indicating the absence of any appreciable amount of non-ester ingredient, and the following experiment showed that the product of saponification was the initial hydroxydecanoic acid: 0.3097 g. of the 13,600 polyester was saponified with alcoholic sodium hydroxide; the alcohol was removed and the solution was acidified and extracted with ether. Evaporation of the ether yielded 0.34 g. (99.3% of the theoretical amount) of hydroxydecanoic acid.

During the preparation of the polyesters a small amount of the cyclic dimeric lactone, a 22-membered ring $\overline{O—(CH_2)_9—CO—O—(CH_2)_9—CO}$, was always formed. It was obtained in the form of needles from dilute alcohol; m. p. 95–96°.

Anal. Calcd. for C₂₀H₃₆O₄: C, 70.58; H, 10.67. Found: C, 70.07, 70.04; H, 10.53, 10.55.

This lactone has already been prepared by Lycan and Adams (5) indirectly from the potassium salt of hydroxydecanoic acid and acetic anhydride followed by dry distillation at 400–500°.

Summary

A series of polyesters prepared from ω-hydroxydecanoic acid and ranging in molecular weight from 780 to 25,200 is described. Strong, oriented fibers are obtained only from members having molecular weights above 9330. The influence of molecular weight on some other physical properties is discussed.

Bibliography and Remarks

(1) Staudinger, "Die hochmolekularen organischen Verbindungen," Julius Springer, Berlin, 1932.
(2) Carothers, *Journ. Am. Chem. Soc.*, **51**, 2548 (1929).
(3) Carothers and Arvin, *ibid.*, **51**, 2560 (1929).

(4) Carothers and Hill, *ibid.*, **54**, 1559 (1932).
(5) Lycan and Adams, *ibid.*, **51**, 625, 3450 (1929).
(6) Kraemer and Lansing, *Journ. Am. Chem. Soc.*, **55**, 4319 (1933).
(7) Carothers, Williams, Collins and Kirby, *Journ. Am. Chem. Soc.*, **53**, 4203 (1931).
(8) Carothers and Hill, *ibid.*, **54**, 1579 (1932).
(9) Kraemer and van Natta, *J. Phys. Chem.*, **36**, 3175 (1932).

XIX.　Many-Membered Cyclic Anhydrides (1)*

This paper contains first some definitions:

Linear polymers are those the molecules of which are built up from a recurrring bivalent **structural unit**.

Superpolymers are linear polymers having molecular weights above 10,000.

Unit length is the number of atoms in the chain of the structural unit.

Macrocyclic compounds are rings of more than seven atoms.

Monomers are compounds containing only one structural unit.

Dimers contain two structural units.

Bifunctional compounds are molecules bearing two groups capable of mutual reaction.

Intramolecular reaction leads to ring closure,

Intermolecular reaction to chain formation.

α-*Anhydrides*† *of a series of dicarboxylic acids were prepared by the action of acetic anhydride or acetylchloride on*

pimelic acid	dodecandioic acid
suberic acid	brassylic acid
azelaic acid	tetradecandioic acid
undecanedioic acid	octadecandioic acid

They are all linear polymers with molecular weights between 3000 and 5000. When heated in the molecular still**, they disproportionate, yielding

(a) ω-*anhydrides (residue). (These are superpolymers with very high molecular weight) and*

(b) β-*anhydrides (distillate), which are cyclic monomers or dimers.*

The latter are converted by heat or time into γ-*anhydrides, which are very similar to the* α-*modification.*

* J. W. Hill and W. H. Carothers; *Journ. Am. Chem. Soc.*, **55**, 5023–31 (1933); Communication No. 131 from the Experimental Station of E. I. du Pont de Nemours and Co.
Received September 2, 1933.　Published December 14, 1933.
† Compare paper XIV on page 168.
** See paper XI on page 154.

Terminology.—To clarify the text of subsequent papers the following definitions are presented. Some of the terms here defined were first introduced in previous papers of this series (2), but they have not yet gained very wide currency, while in some cases they have been used in a sense different from that suggested.

Linear Polymers, e. g.

$$\ldots -CH_2CH_2O-CH_2CH_2O-CH_2CH_2O-CH_2CH_2O-CH_2CH_2O-CH_2CH_2O-\ldots$$

are those whose molecules are built up from a recurring bivalent radical or *structural unit, e. g.*, —CH$_2$CH$_2$O—. Linear polymers are not necessarily open chains; they may be rings. *Superpolymers* are linear polymers having molecular weights above 10,000. The *unit length* is the number of atoms in the chain of the structural unit; in polyethylene glycol (or oxide) the unit length is three. *Macrocyclic compounds* are rings of more than seven atoms. *Monomers* are compounds containing only one structural unit; ethylene oxide and ethylene glycol are both monomers, since each has one —CH$_2$CH$_2$O— group. *Dimers* contain two units: dioxane and diethylene glycol are both dimers. *Bifunctional compounds* are chains bearing two groups capable of mutual reaction with the formation of a new bond. Bifunctional compounds always formally present two possibilities of self-reaction: *intramolecular* leading to ring closure, and *intermolecular* leading to chain formation.

Cyclic Anhydrides.—In previous papers, studies of adipic (3) and sebacic (4) anhydrides have been reported. The present paper describes the extension of these studies to the anhydrides of pimelic, suberic, azelaic, undecanedioic, dodecanedioic, brassylic, tetradecanedioic and octadecanedioic acids. The results closely resemble those already reported.

The anhydrides obtained by the action of acetic anhydride or acetyl chloride on the acids are linear polymers of the type formula —O—CO—R—CO—O—CO—R—CO—O—CO—R—CO— . . . These products are called α-anhydrides to distinguish them from other forms (β, γ, ω) that originate in other ways. They are very reactive, microcrystalline powders which are only slightly soluble in organic solvents and have molecular weights in the neighborhood of 3000 to 5000. They react with aniline to yield a mixture of the dianilide, the monoanilide and the dibasic acid in the ratio 1:2:1 (3, 4). This reaction serves to distinguish any sort of polymeric dibasic acid anhydride from the cyclic monomer, which yields exclusively with monoanilide.

When the α-anhydrides are heated in a high vacuum with a condenser placed close to the evaporating surface (molecular still) (5), they undergo the transformations summarized in the following scheme:

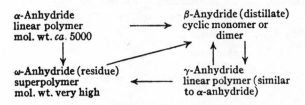

The α-anhydride yields β-anhydride and ω-anhydride simultaneously. As the β-anhydride collects on the condenser, the residue increases progressively in viscosity and molecular weight. The resulting ω-anhydride when cold is a very tough, opaque, solid; it becomes transparent (melts) at a definite temperature without flowing; and at still higher temperatures it can be drawn into pliable, highly oriented fibers (6). The ω-anhydride depolymerizes just as the α-anhydride does, and if heating in the molecular still is continued long enough complete conversion to β-anhydride finally occurs. The β-anhydrides on being heated or allowed to stand readily revert to a polymeric form, the γ-anhydride. In their physical properties the γ-anhydrides are generally practically indistinguishable from the α-anhydrides. However, the latter structurally are probably open chains terminated by acetyl groups while the former at least when freshly formed under anhydrous conditions are perhaps giant rings (4).

Adipic anhydride differs from the higher homologs in that the α-anhydride depolymerizes relatively easily even in an ordinary distillation apparatus. The other anhydrides differ from each other only in the nature of the volatile β-anhydride which they yield on depolymerization. The facts in this connection are shown in Table II. It will be observed that those anhydrides whose unit lengths are 7, 8, 10, 12, 14, 15 and 19 yield monomeric β-anhydrides and that those whose unit lengths are 9, 11 and 13 yield only dimeric β-anhydrides. These relations are represented graphically in Table I.

The three dimeric anhydrides (suberic, sebacic and dodecanedioic) are sharply crystalline solids sufficiently stable that their molecular weights can be determined cryoscopically in benzene. When allowed to react with aniline they furnish the dibasic acid, its monoanilide and its dianilide in the ratio 1:2:1. When heated above their melting points the dimeric anhydrides polymerize almost instantly to γ-anhydrides.

The monomeric anhydrides are not sufficiently stable to permit cryoscopic molecular weight determinations, but their identity as monomers is established by the fact that they react with aniline to yield pure monoanilide.   The first and last members of the series are low-melting crystalline solids; the others are all liquids.

The monomers show characteristic differences in stability. Adipic β-anhydride, the seven-membered ring, polymerized completely in about seven hours at 100° under rigorously anhydrous conditions and fairly rapidly at room temperature in the presence of traces of moisture.   The 8-, 10- and 12-membered monomers polymerize so rapidly even at very

TABLE I

NATURE AND STABILITY OF β-ANHYDRIDES

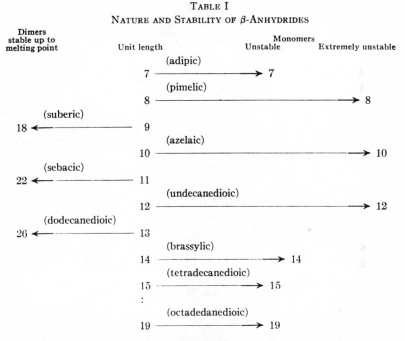

low temperature that a special technique was required to demonstrate their temporary existence. When distilled in the molecular still onto a condenser cooled by tap water, they condensed as transparent fluid drops which in the course of an hour or less became opaque, and in several hours set to hard waxes.   Distillate collected under these conditions invariably contained polymer, since its reaction with aniline always yielded dianilide. In the method devised, the condenser was cooled by means of liquid air. At this temperature the monomers condensed as solids. When, after several hours, a sufficient quantity of distillate had collected, a small reservoir of aniline (Fig. 1) was connected with the vacuum system by opening a stopcock, and a layer of crystalline aniline was deposited by evaporation on top of the anhydride distillate. The condenser was then allowed to warm up gradually, and as soon as the aniline started to melt, was quickly removed from the still and the lower part, bearing the distillate, was submerged in aniline. When the reaction was completed, the mixture was examined for dianilide and monoanilide.

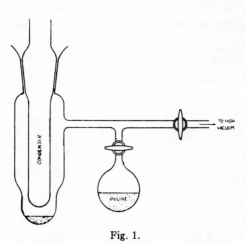

When this method was applied to pimelic anhydride (8-atom unit) it yielded pure monoanilide. The next two members, azelaic and undecanedioic anhydrides (10- and 12-atom units) gave mixtures of acid, monoanilide and dianilide. However, the presence of some monomer in the distillate was established by the fact that the ratio of monoanilide was considerably higher than that required by the theory for dimer or other polymer. Moreover, when the condenser was operated at a higher temperature, these anhydrides first collected as transparent fluid drops with no evidence of the presence of crystalline material (dimer). It seems very probable therefore that the distillates

Fig. 1.

TABLE II

CYCLIC ANHYDRIDES

Acid	Structural unit of anhydride	Product of depolymerization and size of ring		Stability	M. p., °C.
Adipic	$-OC(CH_2)_4CO-O-$	Monomer	7	Unstable	20
Pimelic	$-OC(CH_2)_5CO-O-$	Monomer	8	Extremely unstable	Liq.
Suberic	$-OC(CH_2)_6CO-O$	Dimer	18	Stable up to m. p.	56–57
Azelaic	$-OC(CH_2)_7CO-O$	Monomer	10	Extremely unstable	Liq.
Sebacic	$-OC(CH_2)_8CO-O$	Dimer	22	Stable up to m. p.	68
Undecanedioic	$-OC(CH_2)_9CO-O-$	Monomer	12	Extremely unstable	Liq.
Dodecanedioic	$-OC(CH_2)_{10}CO-O$	Dimer	26	Stable up to m. p.	76–78
Brassylic	$-OC(CH_2)_{11}CO-O-$	Monomer	14	Unstable	Liq.
Tetradecanedioic	$-OC(CH_2)_{12}CO-O-$	Monomer	15	Unstable	Liq.
Octadecanedioic	$-OC(CH_2)_{16}CO-O-$	Monomer	19	Unstable	36–37

were initially pure monomers and that the presence of dianilide in the aniline reaction product was due to subsequent polymerization. The next three members of the monomer series were much more stable than those of 10- and 12-atoms. Brassylic anhydride (14-atom unit) yielded pure monoanilide when the condenser was cooled with solid carbon dioxide and acetone. The liquid distillates from the 15- and 19-membered anhydrides (tetradecanedioic and octadecanedioic) when condensed at the temperature of tap water yielded pure monoanilide if allowed to react with aniline within a few hours of distillation. These two monomeric anhydrides, like that of adipic acid, could also be preserved for several days at room temperature without complete polymerization.

Experimental Part

Preparation of α-Anhydrides.—The α-anhydrides were prepared by the following method. A small quantity of the acid (5 to 20 g.) was refluxed with three parts by weight of acetic anhydride for four to six hours. In the case of the less soluble octadecanedioic acid six parts of acetic anhydride was used. The volatile material was distilled off under the vacuum of a water aspirator. The crude anhydrides were dissolved in hot dry benzene and precipitated, after filtration of the solutions, with petroleum ether. They were then preserved in a vacuum over potassium hydroxide, phosphorus pentoxide and paraffin. The α-anhydrides separate from solution as white microcrystalline powders. In the molten state they are very viscous liquids which crystallize on cooling in the form of small radiating clusters of microscopic needles and finally solidify to hard waxes.

TABLE III

ANALYTICAL DATA FOR α-POLYANHYDRIDES

α-Anhydride	Empirical formula	M. p., °C.	Calcd. C	Calcd. H	Found C	Found C	Found H	Found H
Pimelic	$C_7H_{10}O_3$	53–55	59.11	7.11	...	...	...	...
Suberic	$C_8H_{12}O_3$	65–66	61.50	7.75	61.67	61.04	7.68	7.42
Azelaic	$C_9H_{14}O_3$	53–53.5	63.49	8.29	63.04	63.09	7.86	7.91
Undecanedioic	$C_{11}H_{18}O_3$	69–70	66.60	9.18	65.90	65.71	9.31	9.29
Dodecanedioic	$C_{12}H_{20}O_3$	86–87	67.86	9.52	66.88	67.01	9.63	9.84
Brassylic	$C_{13}H_{22}O_3$	76–78	68.97	9.81	68.80	68.98	9.96	10.05
Tetradecanedioic	$C_{14}H_{24}O_3$	89–91	69.94	10.08	69.17	69.32	9.94	9.79
Octadecanedioic	$C_{18}H_{32}O_3$	94–95	72.90	10.90	72.69	72.02	10.69	10.49

Reaction of the Anhydrides with Aniline.—A small sample of the anhydride (ca. 2 g.) was added to 5 to 10 cc. of aniline and triturated with a stirring rod until a smooth cream was formed. The mixture was then treated with 10% hydrochloric acid to dissolve the excess aniline, cooled and filtered. The mixtures derived from the anhydrides below undecanedioic were separated by treatment with boiling water, in which the dianilides are completely insoluble. The monoanilides separated from the filtrate on cooling. Sufficient water was used to keep the dibasic acids in solution. The separation of the mixtures from the anhydrides above sebacic was accomplished by means of dilute aqueous sodium hydroxide, which dissolved the monoanilide and the dibasic acids as sodium salts and left the dianilide. The monoanilide and the dibasic acid were precipitated from the filtered solution by acidification, and separated by means of boiling water. In the cases of tetradecanedioic and octadecanedioic anhydrides, the alkaline separation was carried out hot, as the sodium salts of these monoanilides are difficultly soluble in the cold. Up to and including undecanedioic α-anhydride, the dianilide was estimated quantitatively and in each case was obtained in 25% yield, as required by theory. A clean separation was difficult with the higher homologs as the alkaline solutions were increasingly soapy. The properties of the anilides are given in Table IV.

TABLE IV

MONOANILIDES

	M. p., °C.	Cryst. from	Empirical formula	Calcd. C	H	Found C	H
Pimelic	108–109	H₂O	C₁₃H₁₇O₃N	66.35	7.27	66.23 ...	7.55 ..
Suberic	128–129	Benzene	C₁₄H₁₉O₃N	67.42	7.70	67.51 ...	7.86 ..
Azelaic	107–108	Dil. EtOH	C₁₅H₂₁O₃N	68.39	8.05	68.05 68.32	7.89 8.02
Undecanedioic	112.5–113	50% EtOH	C₁₇H₂₅O₃N	70.06	8.65	70.28 70.10	8.94 9.03
Dodecanedioic	123	50% EtOH	C₁₈H₂₇O₃N	70.77	8.91	70.85 71.13	8.96 8.72
Brassylic	118.5–119.5	50% EtOH	C₁₉H₂₉O₃N	71.41	9.18	71.71 71.46	9.60 9.37
Tetradecanedioic	124–125	60% EtOH	C₂₀H₃₁O₃N	72.01	9.39	71.97 72.27	9.42 9.10
Octadecanedioic	128–129	60% EtOH	C₂₄H₃₉O₃N	73.98	10.10	74.15 74.09	10.02 9.92

DIANILIDES

Pimelic	155–156	MeOH–H₂O	C₁₉H₂₂O₂N₂	73.50	7.16	73.16 ...	7.11 ..
Suberic	186–187	MeOH	C₂₀H₂₄O₂N₂	74.03	7.46	73.87 73.95	7.52 7.29
Azelaic	186–187	Xylene	C₂₁H₂₆O₂N₂	74.51	7.75	74.03 ...	7.94 ..
Undecanedioic	160–161	EtOH	C₂₃H₃₀O₂N₂	75.35	8.27	75.44 75.32	8.28 8.44
Dodecanedioic	170–171	EtOH	C₂₄H₃₂O₂N₂	75.73	8.49	76.28 76.09	8.47 8.46
Brassylic	160–161	EtOH	C₂₅H₃₄O₂N₂	76.08	8.70	75.86 76.16	8.84 8.74
Tetradecanedioic	169.5–170	EtOH	C₂₆H₃₆O₂N₂	76.41	8.89	76.41 ...	8.91 ..
Octadecanedioic	162–163	EtOH	C₃₀H₄₄O₂N₂	77.52	9.56	77.38 77.64	9.76 9.78

Depolymerization.—The molecular still (Fig. 1) used in these experiments was a cylindrical vessel, 18 cm. high and 5 cm. in diameter, with a rather flat curved bottom and an outlet to a high vacuum system. Into this vessel was fitted, by means of a large ground joint at the top, another cylinder 3 cm. in diameter, the rounded bottom of which was 3 cm. from the bottom of the larger vessel. This inner vessel constituted the condenser. A sample of α-anhydride was introduced into the outer vessel, the condenser was placed in position and the apparatus was evacuated by means of a mercury diffusion pump backed by a Hyvac oil pump. A trap cooled by solid carbon dioxide in acetone was placed in the system. The still was heated by means of a metal bath.

Pimelic Anhydride.—The α-anhydride was heated at 150°. The β-anhydride collected on the water-cooled condenser as a dew which solidified to a pasty gel in about one hour and to a hard wax overnight (γ-anhydride). The saponification equivalent of the wax was 70.7 [$(C_7H_{10}O_3)_n$ requires 71.0]. The experiment was repeated with liquid air in the condenser and the heating bath at 125°. The heating was continued for six hours, after which the still was isolated from the vacuum system by closing a stopcock and put in communication with a small evacuated bulb containing aniline by opening a stopcock (see Fig. 1). Aniline was distilled into the still until a layer of crystalline aniline completely covered the distillate on the condenser. To accomplish this, it was necessary to let the liquid air evaporate almost completely from the condenser. The liquid air was finally allowed to evaporate completely. As soon as the condenser had warmed up to a point where the aniline started to melt, the vacuum was relieved and the condenser removed and immersed in aniline to a level slightly above the coating of distillate. When the mixture had come to room temperature, it was treated with dilute hydrochloric acid. Complete solution indicated the absence of any dianilide in the reaction product. The solution was made alkaline and extracted three times with ether. It was then concentrated and acidified to Congo Red. The precipitate was filtered off and treated carefully with cold water to remove sodium chloride. The residue of mono-anilide was recrystallized from water; m. p. 107–108°. It did not depress the melting point of an authentic sample of melting point 108–109°. The absence of any dianilide in the aniline reaction product demonstrates that the β-anhydride was monomeric.

Suberic Anhydride.—A sample of α-anhydride was heated at 160° in the molecular still. The β-anhydride collected as a crystalline solid on the water-cooled condenser at the rate of about 0.1 g. a day. It melted at 55–57°. This compound proved to be the cyclic dimer of suberic anhydride.

Anal. Calcd. for $C_{16}H_{24}O_6$: C, 61.50; H, 7.75; mol. wt., 312.2; saponification equiv., 78.0. Found: C, 61.57, 61.67; H, 7.72, 7.89; mol. wt. (cryoscopic in benzene), 343, 355, 346; saponification equiv., 77.5.

It reacted with aniline to form the monoanilide (m. p. 125–127°) and the dianilide (m. p. 186–187°) of suberic acid, which were identified by mixed melting points. When heated above its melting point it rapidly polymerized to the γ-anhydride, a waxy solid melting at 65–68°; mol. wt. observed in boiling benzene, 703, 718.

Azelaic Anhydride.—The α-anhydride was heated in the molecular still at 150°. The β-anhydride collected on the water-cooled condenser as a liquid and soon solidified to a gel and then in about twelve hours to a wax (γ-anhydride). The observed saponification equivalent of the wax was 84.8, and 84.5 [$(C_9H_{14}O_3)_x$ requires 85]. Two runs were made in which the condenser was cooled with liquid air and the cold distillate was treated with aniline as described under pimelic anhydride, but products free of dianilide were not obtained. The amounts of the two anilides were determined quantitatively, taking advantage of the insolubility of the dianilide in hot water and the insolubility of the monoanilide in cold.

(1) *Four hours:* Dianilide, 0.18 g.; monoanilide, 0.35 g.—A polymeric anhydride yields 2 moles of monoanilide for one of dianilide; a monomeric anhydride yields only monoanilide. The dianilide found indicates an amount of polyanhydride that could produce only 0.28 g. of monoanilide. The excess, 0.07 g., must arise from monomeric anhydride, and this amount corresponds with 11% of monomer in the total anhydride sample.

(2) *Six hours:* Dianilide, 0.22 g., equivalent to 0.34 g. of monoanilide (from poly-anhydride). Monoanilide found, 0.49 g.; excess due to monomeric anhydride, 0.15 g., equivalent to 18% of monomer in the total anhydride sample.

Since there was no evidence of any dimer (which should be a crystalline solid) in the distillate, the failure to demonstrate that the distillate was initially pure monomer was probably due to the fact that the latter polymerized to a considerable extent before the examination could be completed.

The distillate if removed when still liquid or pasty, had a spicy, aromatic odor. This disappeared when the distillate solidified completely.

¹ **1,11-Undecanedioic Anhydride.**—The α-anhydride was heated in the molecular

still with a water-cooled condenser. The β-anhydride condensed first as a dew which soon became pasty and finally after a few hours set to a hard wax, m. p. 85–88°. Before complete solidification it had a spicy odor. The saponification equivalent of the wax was 98.8 [$(C_{11}H_{18}O_3)_n$ requires 99.1]. The experiment was repeated using liquid air in the condenser and the aniline technique described under pimelic anhydride. As the reaction product was found to contain dianilide, the amounts of dianilide and monoanilide formed were estimated quantitatively. The product from the aniline reaction was treated with a slight excess of warm dilute aqueous sodium hydroxide and the insoluble dianilide was filtered off and weighed (0.079 g.). The filtrate was acidified, cooled and filtered (weight of crystalline precipitate 0.281 g.). This material was shown by a determination of the neutralization equivalent to be pure monoanilide (calcd. 291; found, 289). The dianilide found (0.079 g.) indicates an amount of polymeric anhydride capable of yielding only 0.125 g. of monoanilide. The excess of the latter (0.156 g.) must have come from monomeric anhydride, and calculation indicates 38% of monomeric anhydride in the mixture.

1,12-Dodecanedioic Anhydride.—The α-anhydride was heated in the molecular still at 110°. A beautifully crystalline distillate of melting point 76–78° collected on the condenser at the rate of about 0.1 g. in two days. This β-anhydride was identified as the cyclic dimeric anhydride of dodecanedioic acid.

Anal. Calcd. for $C_{24}H_{40}O_6$: C, 67.86; H, 9.52; mol. wt., 424.4; saponification equiv., 106.1. Found: C, 67.15, 67.54; H, 9.46, 9.60; mol. wt. (cryoscopic in benzene), 496, 450; saponification equiv., 105.5.

It polymerized at the melting point and then melted again at 85–87°. It reacted with aniline in the usual way to yield monoanilide of m. p. 123° and dianilide of m. p. 169–170°.

Brassylic Anhydride.—The α-anhydride was heated in the molecular still for four hours at 150° with the condenser cooled with solid carbon dioxide and acetone. The distillate of β-anhydride was shown to be pure monomer by its reaction with aniline. The product was completely soluble in dilute aqueous sodium hydroxide. The monoanilide separated on acidification of the alkaline solution and was recrystallized from 50% alcohol. It melted at 118.5–119.5° and showed no depression when mixed with an authentic sample.

When the depolymerization of the anhydride was carried out using a water-cooled condenser, the β-anhydride collected as a liquid which changed in the course of a day to a pasty mass and in the course of two days to a hard wax (saponification equivalent found 112.7, calculated 113.1). The liquid was fragrant and aromatic and when allowed to react with aniline shortly after distillation yielded only a small amount of dianilide. The odor disappeared during the change to the wax.

1,14-Tetradecanedioic Anhydride.—The α-anhydride was heated four and one-half hours at 145–150° in the molecular still using solid carbon dioxide in acetone as the refrigerant in the condenser. The distillate of β-anhydride was shown to be pure monomer by its reaction with aniline. The product was completely soluble in a large volume of warm, dilute sodium hydroxide and consequently consisted of monoanilide free of dianilide. The monoanilide separated on acidification of the alkaline solution and was recrystallized from 60% alcohol. It melted at 124–125° and did not depress the melting point of an authentic sample.

When the depolymerization of the anhydride was carried out using a water-cooled condenser, the distillate, like that from brassylic anhydride, collected as a liquid which changed in the course of a day to a pasty mass and in the course of two to a hard wax, m. p. 88–91°. The distillate, before it changed completely to the hard wax, possessed a strong odor like that of musk. This odor was completely lost on saponification (saponification equivalent found, 120.4, 119.1; calcd., 120.1) and on heating to 100° which brought about the change to the γ-anhydride instantly.

1,18-Octadecanedioic Anhydride.—The behavior of this α-anhydride was identical in every respect with that of tetradecanedioic anhydride. The fresh liquid distillate likewise possessed the odor of musk but was rather fainter. It polymerized instantly on being heated to 100°, to a wax of m. p. 98–100° (γ-anhydride), losing its odor in the change. About 1 cc. of β-anhydride was collected using a still adapted for the collection of liquids. It crystallized on chilling or seeding and melted at 36–37° (saponification equivalent found, 146.5; calcd. for $C_{18}H_{32}O_3$, 148.1). After two weeks it had changed to the wax of m. p. 98–100°.

Summary

Data are presented on the anhydrides of dibasic acids $COOH(CH_2)_n$-COOH where n is 4, 5, 6, 7, 8, 9, 10, 11, 12 and 16. The anhydrides are all linear polymers and when heated in a molecular still they are depolymerized yielding volatiles products (β-anhydrides). The latter are either cyclic monomers or dimers depending upon the unit length, $n + 3$. The compounds thus obtained are rings of 7, 8, 18 (dimeric) 10, 22 (dimeric), 12, 26 (dimeric), 14, 15 and 19 atoms. The dimers are crystalline solids which polymerize instantly when heated above their melting points. The monomers are liquids or low melting solids which polymerize at lower temperatures than the dimers. The monomers of 8, 10 and 12 atoms are exceedingly unstable and polymerize rapidly even below room temperature.

Bibliography and Remarks

(1) An abstract of papers XIX, XX, XXI and XXII was presented at the Washington meeting of the American Chemical Society, March 28, 1933.

(2) Carothers, *Journ. Am. Chem. Soc.*, **51**, 2548 (1929); Carothers, *Chem. Rev.*, **8**, 353 (1931); Carothers and Hill, *Journ. Am. Chem. Soc.*, **54** 1559 (1932).

(3) Hill, *ibid.*, **52**, 4110 (1930).

(4) Hill and Carothers, *ibid.*, **54**, 1569 (1932).

(5) *Cf.* Carothers and Hill, *Journ. Am. Chem. Soc.*, **54**, 1557 (1932). The Washburn type of still was used in this work.

(6) Carothers and Hill, *ibid.*, **54**, 1579 (1932).

XX.   Many-Membered Cyclic Esters*

Only one general method of producing cyclic esters is described in the literature and this gives very low yields.   In the present study a new and very effective way for the preparation of cyclic esters has been found.
If linear polyesters are heated in vacuo and in the presence of a catalyst just below their point of thermal destruction, the monomer or the dimer cyclic ester is formed in good yield.   Sodium or other ester interchange catalysts are most effective.   No fewer than thirty new cyclic esters are described; in some cases (ethylene carbonate, decamethylene malonate, etc.) they were exclusively monomeric, in others (pentamethylene carbonate) they were only dimeric, in others again (tetramethylene carbonate, etc.) they were mixtures between monomers and dimers.   The ratio in which the two forms are obtained is determined in part by the experimental conditions and in part by the nature of the ester, especially by its unit length.

The only generally applicable method known for the synthesis of macro-cyclic esters consists in oxidation of cyclic ketones with Caro's acid.   This

$$(\overset{\lceil------\rceil}{\underset{\lfloor------\rfloor}{CH_2}})_n \quad C{=}O \quad \longrightarrow \quad (\overset{\lceil------\rceil}{\underset{\lfloor------\rfloor}{CH_2}})_n \quad \overset{\overset{O}{|}}{\underset{}{C}}{=}O$$

I   II $(n = 12, 13, 14, 15, 16)$

method, discovered by Baeyer and Villiger (1), has been applied by Ruzicka and Stoll (2) to the synthesis of the lactones, II.

The reaction is far from clean-cut, while the requisite ketones (I) are obtained in yields not exceeding 5% (3).   The necessity for adopting this devious and extravagant method for synthesizing macrocyclic lactones is due to the fact, repeatedly illustrated in previous papers (4) of this series, that bifunctional esterifications involving unit lengths greater than seven yield almost exclusively linear polyesters instead of the desired cyclic esters.   When linear polyesters of unit length greater than seven are heated, e. g., to 275°, there is generally no evidence of depolymerization or distilla-tion (5), but at temperatures somewhat above 300° destructive general de-composition occurs, and from the complicated mixture of distillable prod-ucts in four cases (6) true depolymerization products have been isolated.

* J. W. Hill and W. A. Carothers;   *Journ. Am. Chem. Soc.*, **55**, 5031–39 (1933); Communication No. 132 from the Experimental Station of E. I. du Pont de Nemours and Co.
Received September 2, 1933.   Published December 14, 1933.

These cyclic esters however are not monomers but dimers, and the yields are very poor (5% or less).

When linear polyesters of unit length greater than seven are heated (e. g., to 200–250°) under the conditions of molecular distillation (7), the long chains couple to form still longer chains (8). The products (superpolyesters) have molecular weights above 10,000 and are capable of being drawn out into tough, pliable, highly oriented fibers (9).

It was recognized in advance that the conditions of the molecular still at high temperature would be likely to favor either this type of coupling or a depolymerization by ester interchange (10):

···—ORCO—|—ORCO—|—ORCO—|—ORCO—|—ORCO—|—ORCO—|—ORCO—|—ORCO—···

Evidences of such depolymerization, at least in traces, were in fact frequently observed in the formation of superpolyesters, and after methods had been developed for the smooth depolymerization of polyanhydrides, attention was again turned to the polyesters. The result was the development of the method presently described by means of which it became possible to prepare with good yields and without unreasonable difficulty a whole series of macrocyclic esters, both monomeric and dimeric. Briefly, the method consists in heating linear polyesters *in vacuo* at a temperature just below the point of thermal destruction under conditions that permit any volatile product to be removed by distillation as fast as it is formed.

The success of the new method, practically, depends upon numerous factors not all of which have yet been completely isolated and defined; the two most important however are the identity of the polyester and the use of catalysts. On the first point it may be said that esters of carbonic acid and of oxalic acid depolymerize more readily and smoothly than any others yet examined. On the second point, ester interchange catalysts (e. g., sodium added as metal in the preparation of the initial polyester) are almost indispensable.

After some experimentation it was discovered that esters of carbonic acid and of oxalic acid can be depolymerized merely by heating them (with catalyst) under diminished pressure in an ordinary distilling flask. Most of the experiments now reported were however made in a simplified molecular still (described below) operated at pressures ranging from 0.1 to 2 or 3 mm.

The depolymerization of the polyester in favorable cases progresses smoothly and fairly rapidly, the cyclic ester distilling to the condenser and being collected as it is formed. The residual ester at the same time progressively increases in viscosity (formation of superpolymer); if this increase in viscosity does not proceed too far, depolymerization still continues and is ultimately almost complete and quantitative. In many cases, however, the residue, before complete depolymerization, becomes converted to a gel; even at 250° it is completely immobile and resembles a piece of porous, vulcanized, gum rubber. Depolymerization then practically ceases. This residue incidentally is extraordinarily resistant to attack by solvents and chemical agents generally. It evidently results from a polymerization which has progressed beyond the linear superpolymer stage. It seems likely that some quantitatively minor side-reaction (dehydrogenation at a venture) occurs permitting accessory polymerization to form a three-dimensional macromolecule.

The product of the depolymerization is generally a mixture of cyclic monomer and cyclic dimer although in many cases one of these forms predominates to the practical exclusion of the other. The ratio of the two forms is in some cases quite sensitive to the experimental conditions (temperature, pressure, shape of apparatus) but the data on this point recorded in Table I were all obtained under closely similar conditions.

Preparation of Polyesters.—Polymeric carbonates derived from the glycols $HO(CH_2)_nOH$ where n is 3, 4, 6 and 10 and from diethylene glycol have already been described (11). The new polymeric carbonates prepared as intermediates in the present work include those derived from the glycols $HO(CH_2)_nOH$ where n is 5, 7, 8, 9, 11, 12, 13, 14 and 18, and from diethylene and triethylene glycols. The fact that these compounds are lacking in crucial physical properties (e. g., sharply characteristic melting points) makes it unnecessary to describe them individually. They are all insoluble in water and soluble in certain organic solvents such as chloroform. They separate from solvents in the form of soft powders (microcrystalline). The molten polyesters are very viscous liquids which crystallize on cooling in the form of small radiating clusters of microscopic needles or spherulites and finally solidify to more or less hard, tough waxes. The polymeric carbonate derived from triethylene glycol, however, failed to solidify and was obtained only as a thick sirup.

The general method of preparation used for the new polycarbonates was the same as that already described (11), but, on account of the boiling points involved, dibutyl carbonate was found to be a more convenient source of the acid radical than diethyl carbonate. To the mixture of glycol and alkyl carbonate a small amount of sodium was added; the mixture was heated at 170–220° until the distillation of alcohol ceased, and removal of the alcohol was completed by continuing the heating for two hours or more *in vacuo*. The residue was usually depolymerized without any purification. The alkylene oxalates and malonates were prepared from the glycols and the diethyl esters of

TABLE I

NATURE AND PHYSICAL PROPERTIES OF CYCLIC ESTERS

	Unit length	Proportions of monomer and dimer in distillate	M. p. of monomer, °C.	B. p. of monomer, °C.	n_D of monomer	d_4 of monomer	M. p. of dimer, °C.
Ethylene carbonate	5	Exclusively monomer	39	238	1.4158 (50°)	1.3079 (50°)	
Trimethylene carbonate	6	Exclusively monomer	47-48	135 at 4 mm.	1.4409 (50°)	1.2282 (50°)	
Tetramethylene carbonate	7	Mixture of dimer and tetrahydrofuran					175-176
Pentamethylene carbonate	8	Exclusively dimer					117-118
Hexamethylene carbonate	9	Almost exclusively dimer; odor of monomer					128-129
Heptamethylene carbonate	10	Almost exclusively dimer; odor of monomer					97-98
Octamethylene carbonate	11	Almost exclusively dimer; odor of monomer	21.5-23	74-76 at 0.5 mm.	1.4665 (20°)	1.0727 (20°)	116-117
Nonamethylene carbonate	12	Almost exclusively dimer; odor of monomer	34-35	63-64 at 0.1 mm.	1.4528 (50°)	1.0240 (50°)	95-95.5
Decamethylene carbonate	13	Mixture of monomer and dimer	10-11	92-93 at 1 mm.	1.4659 (20°)	1.0354 (20°)	105-106
Undecamethylene carbonate	14	Mixture of monomer and dimer	40-41	104.5 at 7 mm.	1.4544 (50°)	0.9968 (50°)	97-97.5
Dodecamethylene carbonate	15	Almost exclusively monomer; small amount of dimer identified					93-95
Tridecamethylene carbonate	16	Almost exclusively monomer; no dimer isolated	11-12	118-119 at 3 mm.	1.4639 (20°)	1.0036 (20°)	
Tetradecamethylene carbonate	17		23-24.5	149-150 at 4.5 mm.	1.4622 (25°)	0.9888 (25°)	
Octadecamethylene carbonate	21		21-22	144-146 at 2 mm.	1.4622 (20°)	0.9814 (20°)	
			36-37	165-169 at 1 mm.	1.4537 (50°)	0.9273 (50°)	
Triethylene glycol carbonate	11	Mixture of monomer and dimer	Liq.	128-130 at 1 mm.	1.4569 (50°)	1.1961 (50°)	
Tetraethylene glycol carbonate	14	Exclusively monomer	42-44	125-126 at 0.2 mm.	1.4730 (20°)	1.0812 (20°)	
Decamethylene oxalate	14	Exclusively monomer	Liq.	120-123 at 0.5 mm.	1.4700 (25°)	1.0623 (25°)	
Undecamethylene oxalate	15	Exclusively monomer	23-24.5	117-118 at 0.5 mm.	1.4695 (20°)	1.0599 (20°)	
Decamethylene malonate	15		Liq.				
Decamethylene succinate	16	Almost exclusively dimer; no monomer isolated					108-109
Ethylene sebacate	14	Almost exclusively dimer; trace of monomer isolated	40-41				80-81
Ethylene undecanedioate	15	Almost exclusively dimer;	35				143
Ethylene dodecanedioate	16	no monomer isolated					95-96
Ethylene brassylate	17						145-146
Ethylene tetradecanedioate	18						102-103
Trimethylene sebacate	15						108-110
Self ester of ω-hydroxypentadecanoic acid	16	Almost exclusively dimer; odor of monomer	31-32[a]				83-84

[a] Ruzicka and Stoll, *Helv. Chim. Acta.*, 11, 1159 (1928).

the acids in the same manner as the carbonates. The other esters were prepared directly from the acids and the glycols.

Depolymerization.—The apparatus used in the depolymerizations for which data are listed in Table I consisted simply of a 250-cc. Pyrex suction filter flask. Through a rubber stopper in the neck of the flask was inserted a test-tube about 1.5 cm. in diameter. Its bottom was about 3 cm. distant from the bottom of the flask. The outside of this test-tube served as the condenser and receiver; the inside was cooled with a stream of tap water (in some cases a mixture of solid carbon dioxide and acetone); the distillate collected on the outside. At intervals the test-tube was removed and the solid or pasty distillate was scraped from it. When the distillate was sufficiently fluid to flow, a small glass thimble was hung on the end of the test-tube to catch the drip.

The side-tube of the flask was connected to a vacuum line. This line was connected to an oil pump and the pressure in the line was about 0.1 to 2 mm. No attempt was made to secure an exceedingly high vacuum. The flask was immersed to a depth of about 2 cm. in a metal bath which was kept at 210–240° by means of an electric heater.

Nature of the Depolymerization Products.

—For the sake of completeness Table I includes the physical constants of ethylene and trimethylene carbonates. The former, a 5-atom ring, is known only as the monomer; the latter, which has a unit length of 6 atoms, can be obtained either as monomer or polymer, but the polymer depolymerizes so rapidly and smoothly on distillation that the use of a molecular still is quite unnecessary (11).

The rest of the compounds listed in Table I are obtained by the ordinary methods of preparation only as linear polyesters; and the polyesters were all depolymerized in the apparatus and under the conditions described above.

The behavior of tetramethylene carbonate (7-atom unit) was exceptional: the distillate was found to contain a considerable amount of tetrahydrofuran, which obviously might arise by the loss of carbon dioxide from the structural unit. The chief product, however, was the dimer, a 14-membered ring which has already been described (11). No detectable amount of monomeric ester was formed. The products from the next five members of the series (unit lengths 8 to 12 atoms) also were chiefly dimeric. Pentamethylene carbonate (8-atom unit) gave no detectable amount of monomer. The presence of some monomer in the distillate from hexamethylene carbonate was inferred from the odor, but the attempt to obtain isolable amounts of monomer by carrying out the depolymerization in ordinary distillation equipment gave only indefinite unsaturated products. The odors of the distillates from heptamethylene, octamethylene and nonamethylene carbonates also indicated the presence of monomer, and in the last two of these cases monomer was actually isolated and identified when the depolymerization was carried out in ordinary distillation equipment.

The next member of the series, decamethylene carbonate, showed a sharp change in the nature of the depolymerization products: considerable amounts of the monomer were formed even in the molecular still. Undecamethylene carbonate (14-atom unit) behaved similarly. Beyond this point the ratio was reversed: dodecamethylene carbonate (15-atom unit) gave only a small amount of dimer, and with higher members of the carbonate series the isolated products were exclusively monomeric.

The oxalates (decamethylene and undecamethylene) showed a greater tendency to yield monomers than did the carbonates of the same unit length. Decamethylene malonate also gave almost exclusively the monomer.

The rest of the compounds listed in Table I, compared with the carbonates, exhibited a peculiar reluctance toward the formation of monomers. Even ethylene tetradecanedioate yielded a 36-membered dimer and no appreciable amount of the 18-membered monomer. Similarly ω-hydroxypentadecanoic acid yielded the 32-membered dimer instead of the 18-membered monomer which has already been obtained by oxidation of the corresponding cyclic ketone (12). It should be added that the depolymerization of all the esters referred to in this paragraph is especially slow and difficult. Depolymerization of carbonates, oxalates, and even malonates, proceeds much more rapidly and completely.

Effect of Conditions on the Ratio of Monomer to Dimer.—The data on the carbonates listed in Table I indicate that polyesters of this series on depolymerization yield dimers almost exclusively when the unit length is 7 to 12 inclusive, both monomer and dimer when the unit length is 13 and 14, and monomers almost exclusively when the unit length is more than 14. It will be shown later that this characteristic change in the nature of the products under a given set of conditions is probably due to stereochemical factors inherently associated with the structure of the cyclic esters. It is also true, however, that the ratio of monomer to dimer can be controlled within certain limits by the experimental conditions. Thus octamethylene and nonamethylene carbonates in the modified molecular still yield almost exclusively the cyclic dimers, but when the depolymerization is conducted in an ordinary distilling flask the product is almost entirely the monomer. The distilling flask (unlike the molecular still) permits refluxing, so that while most of the monomer escapes most of the dimer is returned to the residue, where it is either cracked to monomer or converted to higher polymer. Limitations of this method of experimental control are indicated by the fact that when it was applied to hexamethylene carbonate no smooth depolymerization occurred and only indefinite unsaturated products were obtained. Esters of dibasic acids above malonic also depolymerize very slowly if at all in an ordinary distilling flask.

The depolymerization of polymeric decamethylene carbonate in an ordinary distilling flask gave a much higher yield of monomer than dimer and the examination of a large sample of crude product showed the presence of a by-product, decen-9-ol-1, $CH_2\!\!=\!\!CH(CH_2)_7CH_2OH$. The following data are typical.

The depolymerization was conducted in ordinary distilling flasks in batches of various sizes up to 100 g. and at (bath) temperatures up to 290°. The product was a mixture of colorless liquid and crystalline material. The crystals (a mixture of dimeric carbonate and decamethylene glycol) were removed by filtration, and the filtrate (2425 g.) was distilled, yielding 1276 g. of pure monomer, 400 g. of crystalline residue (chiefly dimer) and 742 g. of low-boiling material. The latter by redistillation was separated into four fractions of which the two largest were: A, b. p. 76–81° (2 mm.), 81%, and B, b. p. 87–89° (2 mm.), 9%. The latter was practically pure monomer. Analytical data for B indicated that it was a mixture of decamethylene carbonate (monomer) and decenol (apparently a constant-boiling mixture). The ester was destroyed by saponification with alcoholic sodium hydroxide, and the recovered alcohol was purified by distillation.

Decen-9-ol-1.—B. p. 85–86° (2 mm.); n_D^{20} 1.4480; d_4^{20} 0.8446; M D calcd., 49.53; M D found, 49.45.

Anal. Calcd. for $C_9H_{18}O$: C, 76.9; H, 12.8. Found: C, 76.51; H, 13.09.

Its structure was established by the fact that it was oxidized to azelaic acid by neutral aqueous permanganate (in one experiment a small amount of suberic acid was found) and hydrogenated to decanol-1 which was identified by comparison of the phenylurethan with a known specimen (crys. from 80% alcohol, m. p. 61–62°).

Decen-9-ol-1 yields a phenylurethan of m. p. 49–50° (crys. from 80% alcohol).

Polymerization of Macrocylic Esters.—Macrocyclic esters, unlike 6-membered cyclic esters (11), show no tendency to polymerize spontaneously. They do, however, polymerize at elevated temperatures especially in the presence of catalysts for ester-interchange, and the following observations are typical.

Small samples of monomeric decamethylene, dodecamethylene, tridecamethylene, and tetradecamethylene carbonates were heated for twenty hours at 200° together with parallel samples each containing a trace of potassium carbonate. The uncatalyzed samples of tridecamethylene and tetradecamethylene carbonates showed a considerable increase in viscosity; the decamethylene and dodecamethylene carbonates a much larger increase. The catalyzed samples of decamethylene and dodecamethylene carbonates were completely changed to solid, waxy polymers; while the catalyzed samples of the other two esters were still semi-solid.

Samples of dimeric hexamethylene and decamethylene carbonates, both with and

TABLE II

ANALYSIS OF CYCLIC ESTERS

Compound	Calculated, %			Found, %			
	C	H	Mol. wt.	C	H	Mol. wt. in freezing benzene	
Pentamethylene carbonate *dimer* [—(CH₂)₅OCOO—]₂	55.4	7.7	260	55.4	8.3	258 (b. p.)	
Hexamethylene carbonate *dimer* —[(CH₂)₆OCOO—]₂	58.3	8.3	288	58.2	8.4	284	286
Heptamethylene carbonate *dimer* [—(CH₂)₇OCOO—]₂	60.8	8.9	316	61.2	8.9	313	312 (b. p.)
Octamethylene carbonate *monomer* [—(CH₂)₈OCOO—]	62.8	9.3	172	62.2	9.4	174	
Octamethylene carbonate *dimer* [—(CH₂)₈OCOO—]₂	62.8	9.3	344	63.2	9.6	325	329 (b. p.)
Nonamethylene carbonate *monomer* [—(CH₂)₉OCOO—]	64.5	9.7	186	64.8	9.9	171	
Nonamethylene carbonate *dimer* [—(CH₂)₉OCOO—]₂	64.5	9.7	372	64.6	9.7	330	329 (b. p.)
Decamethylene carbonate *monomer* [—(CH₂)₁₀OCOO—]	66.0	10.0	200	66.3	10.1	216	204
Decamethylene carbonate *dimer* [—(CH₂)₁₀OCOO—]₂	66.0	10.0	400	66.4	10.1	395	391
Undecamethylene carbonate *monomer* [—(CH₂)₁₁OCOO—]	67.3	10.3	214	67.5	10.3	213	211
Undecamethylene carbonate *dimer* [—(CH₂)₁₁OCOO—]₂	67.3	10.3	428	67.2	10.4	400	409
Dodecamethylene carbonate *monomer* [—(CH₂)₁₂OCOO—]	68.4	10.5	228	68.2	10.6	249	223
Dodecamethylene carbonate *dimer* [—(CH₂)₁₂OCOO—]₂	68.4	10.5	456	68.2	10.4	265	238
Tridecamethylene carbonate *monomer* [—(CH₂)₁₃OCOO—]	69.4	10.7	242	69.2	10.5	242	242
Tetradecamethylene carbonate *monomer* [—(CH₂)₁₄OCOO—]	70.3	10.9	256	69.6	10.9	268	273 (b. p.)
Octadecamethylene carbonate *monomer* [—(CH₂)₁₈OCOO—]	73.1	11.5	312	73.3	11.8		
Triethylene glycol carbonate [—(CH₂CH₂O)₃COO—]ₙ probably mixture of monomer and dimer	47.7	6.8	(176)n	47.6	6.8	266	284 (b. p.)
Tetraethylene glycol carbonate *monomer* [—(CH₂CH₂O)₄COO—]	49.1	7.3	220	48.9	7.3	216	211
Decamethylene oxalate *monomer* [—(CH₂)₁₀OCOCO—]	63.2	8.8	228	63.4	8.7	220	222
Undecamethylene oxalate *monomer* [—(CH₂)₁₁OCOCO—]	64.5	9.1	242	64.4	9.1	253	
Decamethylene malonate *monomer* [—(CH₂)₁₀OCOCH₂CO—]	64.5	9.1	242	64.5	9.1	238	
Decamethylene succinate *dimer* [—(CH₂)₁₀OCOCH₂CH₂CO—]₂	65.6	9.4	512	65.4	9.3	478	
Ethylene sebacate *monomer* [—(CH₂)₂OCO(CH₂)₈CO—]	63.1	8.9	228	63.1	8.9		
Ethylene sebacate *dimer* [—(CH₂)₂OCO(CH₂)₈CO—]₂	63.1	8.9	456	63.3	9.0	431	433 (b. p.)
Ethylene 1,11-undecanedioate *monomer* [—(CH₂)₂OCO(CH₂)₉CO—]	64.5	9.1	242	64.2	9.4		
Ethylene 1,11-undecanedioate *dimer* [—(CH₂)₂OCO(CH₂)₉CO—]₂	64.5	9.1	484	64.3	9.3	451 (b. p.)	
Ethylene 1,12-dodecanedioate *dimer* [—(CH₂)₂OCO(CH₂)₁₀CO—]₂	65.6	9.4	512	65.6	9.4	481 (b. p.)	
Ethylene brassylate *dimer* [—(CH₂)₂OCO(CH₂)₁₁CO—]₂	66.7	9.6	540	66.7	9.6	494 (b. p.)	
Ethylene 1,14-tetradecanedioate *dimer* [—(CH₂)₂OCO(CH₂)₁₂CO—]₂	67.6	9.6	568	67.6	9.5		
Trimethylene sebacate *dimer* [—(CH₂)₃OCO(CH₂)₈CO—]₂	64.5	9.1	484	63.8	9.2		
Self-ester of ω-hydroxypentadecanoic acid *dimer* [—(CH₂)₁₄COO—]₂	75.0	11.7	480	75.0	11.8		

without traces of potassium carbonate, were heated for eight hours at 200°. The catalyzed samples changed to very viscous liquids which solidified to hard waxes; the uncatalyzed samples were unchanged.

Summary

By heating linear polyesters with catalysts under certain conditions it is possible in many cases to bring about a smooth depolymerization to the corresponding monomeric and/or dimeric esters. This method makes it possible for the first time to prepare macrocyclic esters in good yields. Thirty new macrocyclic esters are described, mostly esters of dibasic acids. The cyclic carbonates and oxalates are obtained most easily. The ratio in which the two forms, monomer and dimer, are obtained is determined in part by the experimental conditions and in part by the nature of the ester—especially by its unit length. Monomers of 7 to 12 atoms are especially difficult to obtain.

Bibliography and Remarks

(1) Baeyer and Villiger, *Ber.*, **32**, 3625 (1899).

(2) Ruzicka and Stoll, *Helv. Chim. Acta*, **11**, 1159 (1928).

(3) Since this paper was prepared for publication Ziegler, Eberle and Ohlinger [*Ann.*, **504**, 94 (1933)] have described an ingenious method based on Ruggli's dilution principle for the preparation of large cyclic ketones in good yields. This principle has been referred to in previous papers of the present series [*e. g.*, *Journ. Am. Chem. Soc.*, **51**, 2551 (1929)] and we hope to describe its application to the synthesis of cyclic esters in future papers.

(4) Carothers, *Journ. Am. Chem. Soc.*, **51**, 2548 (1929); Carothers and Arvin, *ibid.*, **52**, 711; Carothers, Arvin and Dorough, *ibid.*, 3292; Carothers, *Chem. Reviews*, **8**, 353 (1931). *Cf.* Chuit and Hausser, *Helv. Chim. Acta*, **12**, 463 (1929); Lycan and Adams, *Journ. Am. Chem. Soc.*, **51**, 625, 3450 (1929).

(5) Compounds of molecular weight higher than 1000 cannot be distilled even under the highest vacua, Carothers, Hill, Kirby and Jacobson, *Journ. Am. Chem. Soc.*, **52**, 5279 (1931).

(6) The cases referred to are ethylene succinate, Tilitschejew, *J. Russ. Phys.-Chem. Soc.*, **57**, 143 (1925); Carothers and Dorough, *Journ. Am. Chem. Soc.*, **52**, 711 (1930); tetramethylene carbonate, Carothers and van Natta, *ibid.*, **52**, 314 (1930); trimethylene oxalate, Tilitschejew, *J. Russ. Phys.-Chem. Soc.*, **58**, 447 (1926); Carothers, Arvin and Dorough, *Journ. Am. Chem. Soc.*, **52**, 3292 (1930); self-ester of hydroxydecanoic acid, Lycan and Adams, *ibid.*, **51**, 625, 3450 (1929).

(7) Carothers and Hill, *ibid.*, **54**, 1557 (1932).

(8) *Ibid.*, p. 1559.

(9) *Ibid.*, p. 1579.

(10) *Cf.* the discussion of 6-membered cyclic esters and their polymers in Carothers, Dorough and van Natta, *ibid.*, **54**, 761 (1932).

(11) Carothers and van Natta, *Journ. Am. Chem. Soc.*, **52**, 314 (1930).

(12) Ruzicka and Stoll, *Helv. Chim. Acta*, **11**, 1159 (1928).

XXI. Physical Properties of Macrocyclic Esters and Anhydrides. New Types of Synthetic Musks*

L. Ruzicka has shown that some large ring lactones have very valuable properties as perfume ingredients; this paper investigates the odor as a function of the molecular structure of multi-membered rings.

Rings of 5 and 6 atoms smell like bitter almonds and menthol; from 9 to 12 they exhibit the odor of camphor; 14 and 15 give musk, 17 and 18 civet. The molecular refractions and melting points of the carbonate and oxalate series are determined.

Odors.—The monomeric cyclic anhydrides and cyclic esters described in the two preceding papers have highly characteristic odors. In particular some of the higher members have odors closely resembling musk. This observation is especially interesting because of the bearing of odor on the general problem of macrocyclic compounds.

The essential principles of musk and civet are the macrocyclic ketones I and II. Ruzicka's demonstration (1) of this fact was followed by the discovery (2) that the lactones III and IV are odorous principles of angelica oil and musk-seed oil. These materials are highly valued as perfume ingredients. In spite of the great difficulties involved in their synthesis, a synthetic ketone ("Exaltone," cyclopentadecanone) and a lactone "Exaltolide") have been placed on the market as substitutes for the natural musks.

I	II	III	IV

The observations on the anhydrides and carbonates are assembled in Table I, together with Ruzicka's data on the ketones and lactones. It will be noted that in each of the four series, with the possible exception of the ketones, odors are rather vague and indefinite until the number of atoms in the ring reaches 9. A camphoraceous or minty note then appears, and at about 13 atoms a woody or cedar-like quality. Beyond this point there is a nuance of musk which however in the anhydride series does not be-

* J. W. Hill and W. H. Carothers; *Journ. Am. Chem. Soc.*, 55, 5039–43 (1933); Communication No. 133 from the Experimental Station of E. I. du Pont de Nemours and Co.

Received September 2, 1933. Published December 19, 1933.

come definite and pronounced until the 15-atom compound is reached. At 15 or 16 atoms the musk quality approaches a maximum of fullness and homogeneity. Tetradecamethylene carbonate (17 atoms) shows a remarkable resemblance to "Exaltolide" (16-atom lactone). Beyond 18 or 19 atoms the odors in each series practically disappear.

The structural feature common to the four series is the presence of one or more C=O groups as a member of a ring. It is rather extraordinary that the manner in which the C=O group is linked in the ring should make so little difference in the quality of the odor. On the other hand it appears that any modification of the C=O group itself completely changes the odor. Ruzicka, Schinz and Seidel report (3) that the alcohol corresponding to civetone has a faint and only slightly characteristic odor.

The fact that the only requirement (there are no doubt other limits not yet known) for musk-like odor is the presence of a C=O group in a ring of approximately 15 atoms is further illustrated by the following compounds not included in Table I (other physical properties of these compounds are listed in Table I of Paper XX)

$\overline{(-CH_2CH_2O-)_4CO-O}$ tetraethylene carbonate, 14 atoms, fresh, faint, musk-like

$\overline{(CH_2)_{10}-O-CO-CO-O}$ decamethylene oxalate, 14 atoms, fresh, musk-like

$\overline{(CH_2)_{11}-O-CO-CO-O}$ undecamethylene oxalate, 15 atoms, musk-like

$\overline{(CH_2)_{10}-O-CO-CH_2-CO-O}$ decamethylene malonate, 15 atoms, faint, musk-like

$\overline{CO-(CH_2)_8-CO-O-CH_2CH_2-O}$ ethylene sebacate, 14 atoms, musk-like

$\overline{CO(CH_2)_9-CO-O-CH_2CH_2-O}$ ethylene undecanedioate, 15 atoms, musk-like

The first of these contains six oxygen atoms in the ring of which two are directly connected to the carbonyl group; the second and third have two adjacent carbonyls to which annular oxygens are attached, in the fourth a methylene has been interposed between the two carbonyls, and in the fifth and sixth eight and nine methylenes are inserted between the carbonyls. It would be of great interest to have information on similar compounds in which the carbonyls are replaced by methylenes; unfortunately macrocyclic ethers are as yet entirely unknown.

From the practical standpoint the cyclic anhydrides are of no interest as odorous materials since they polymerize spontaneously on standing and the odors then disappear. (This fact incidentally demonstrates that the odors of the cyclic anhydrides are not due to any traces of the corresponding cyclic ketones which might conceivably be present as impurities.) On the

TABLE I

ODORS OF CYCLIC COMPOUNDS

Atoms in ring	Ketones $(CH_2)_x$ $C=O$	Lactones $(CH_2)_x$ $C=O$	Carbonates $(CH_2)_x$ $C=O$	Anhydrides $(CH_2)_x$ $C-O-C$
5	Bitter almond and menthol	Fruity	Faint	Odorless
6	Bitter almond and menthol	Faint[a]	Faint	Odorless
7	Transition	Faint, spicy and floral[b]		Faint, pungent
8	Transition			
9	Camphoraceous		Minty, empyreumatic	Spicy
10	Camphoraceous		Minty, less empyreumatic	Spicy
11	Camphoraceous		Earthy, camphoraceous	Spicy
12	Camphoraceous		Earthy, camphoraceous	
13	Cedarwood, then musk		Cedar, faint rose and camphor	Aromatic
14	Musk	Musk	Musk, camphoraceous	Musk
15	Pure musk	Musk and ambergris	Musk	
16	Transition	Musk	Musk	
17	Civet	Civet	Musk	
18	Faint civet	Faint		
19	Faint			Musk
21		Faint		

Observation on a specimen very carefully purified by F. J. van Natta.   [b] From unpublished work of F. J. van Natta.

This compound has not yet been described.

other hand the cyclic esters, with the exception of the oxalates, are quite resistant to hydrolysis or polymerization and from the practical standpoint they have the advantage over the previously described ketones and lactones that they are formed in relatively high yields.

Molecular Refractions.—Ruzicka and Stoll have shown that the molecular refractions of macrocyclic lactones (4) and hydrocarbons (5) are lower by about 0.6 unit than the calculated values. The macrocyclic carbonates exhibit the same peculiar negative exaltation and to about the same degree. Typical data are assembled in Table II.

TABLE II
MOLECULAR REFRACTIONS OF CYCLIC ESTERS

Compound	Atoms in ring	M_D calcd.	M_D found	$E\ M_D$
Ethylene carbonate	5	17.15	16.87	−0.28
Trimethylene carbonate	6	21.77	21.92	+ .15
Octamethylene carbonate	11	44.86	44.45	− .41
Nonamethylene carbonate	12	49.48	49.05	− .43
Decamethylene carbonate	13	54.20	53.49	− .71
Undecamethylene carbonate	14	58.71	58.17	− .54
Dodecamethylene carbonate	15	63.33	62.66	− .67
Tridecamethylene carbonate	16	67.95	67.32	− .63
Tetradecamethylene carbonate	17	72.57	71.74	− .83
Octadecamethylene carbonate	21	91.04	91.05	+ .01
Tetraethylene glycol carbonate	14	49.79	50.21	+ .42
Decamethylene oxalate	14	58.72	59.12	+ .40
Undecamethylene oxalate	15	63.34	63.56	+ .22
Decamethylene malonate	15	63.34	63.63	+ .29

The last four compounds of the table appear to have a positive exaltation, but the amounts of these materials available were quite small and their purity was somewhat uncertain. The compounds for which negative values are listed were for the most part purified by crystallization. No significance can be attached to the fluctuations in these negative values from one member of the series to the next since the molecular refractions were not all taken at the same temperature.

Melting Points.—The melting points of the known macrocyclic compounds show little regularity in the nature of the change produced by increasing molecular weight but in the range of 8 to 14 atoms there is generally an oscillation from one member to the next (5). The cyclic carbonates show a similar oscillation, the melting points and ring size for some of the monomeric polymethylene carbonates being

11	12	13	14	15	16	17
23°	35°	11°	41°	12°	25°	22°

Summary

Macrocyclic esters and anhydrides have odors closely resembling those of the ketones and lactones of the same ring size. The rings in the neighborhood of fifteen atoms have musk-like odors. The molecular refractions show a negative exaltation. Melting points in the carbonate series oscillate from one member to the next.

Bibliography and Remarks

(1) Ruzicka, *Helv. Chim. Acta*, **9**, 230, 716, 1008 (1926).
(2) Kerschbaum, *Ber.*, **60**, 902 (1927); Ruzicka and Stoll, *Helv. Chim. Acta*, **11**, 1159 (1928).
(3) Ruzicka, Schinz and Seidel, *Helv. Chim. Acta*, **10**, 695 (1927).
(4) Ruzicka and Stoll, *Helv. Chim. Acta*, **11**, 1159 (1928).
(5) Ruzicka, Stoll, Huyser and Boekenoogen, *ibid.*, **13**, 1152 (1930).

XXII. Stereochemistry and Mechanism in the Formation and Stability of Large Rings*

The first systematic investigation of large rings was carried out by Ruzicka. His method gives low yields and does not allow a reliable insight into the mechanism of the reaction. The new data† on polyesters and anhydrides make it possible to discuss more thoroughly the formation of large rings. This is done in the present paper.

First the thermalysis of thorium octadecanedioate was investigated as carried out by Ruzicka. During this reaction first a linear polymer—a polyketone—is formed; if this is heated in the molecular still, it cracks and gives appreciable amounts of the monocyclic ketone. As was found** in the case of the polyesters and polyanhydrides the formation of the macrocyclic product proceeds by way of the linear polymer. The cracking of the chains may be monomolecular or bimolecular.

To explain the easiness of ring closure, the density of large ring compounds and the stability of the rings, a thorough discussion of the sterical conditions and interferences is made. If a radius of 0.77 Å. is assumed for the carbon atom and a covering sphere with a radius of 1.1 Å. for the hydrogen atoms attached to the carbons, models representing to an appreciable degree the actual conditions are obtained. There is a minimum of

* W. H. Carothers and J. W. Hill; *Journ. Am. Chem. Soc.*, **55**, 5043–52 (1933); Communication No. 134 from the Experimental Station of E. I. du Pont de Nemours and Co.
Received September 2, 1933. Published December 19, 1933.
† Compare paper number XII on page 156.
** Compare paper number XIII on pages 165 to 168.

probability for the formation of rings between 10 and 17 carbon atoms owing to the fact that in such molecules a considerable strain is effected through the compression of the hydrogen domains inside the ring; if the rings get larger this stress decreases and the ease of formation increases.

A great deal of discussion has been devoted to stereochemistry and mechanism in the formation of rings, but on account of the limited range of experimental facts available, fruitful discussion has been largely restricted to rings containing fewer than 8 atoms. The only important series exemplifying closure of long chains hitherto has been the macrocyclic ketones which Ruzicka obtained by heating salts of the higher dibasic acids. As a basis for theoretical inferences this general reaction suffers from two disadvantages. The macrocyclic ketones are formed in such small yields (0.1 to 5%) that they can hardly be regarded as major reaction products, and the nature of the reaction (thermal destruction at high temperatures) is such that its mechanism is inherently obscure. Data on the polyesters and anhydrides now provide the possibility for a much clearer insight into the mechanism of the formation of large rings.

Following the demonstration of the stable existence of large carbon rings, Baeyer's theory of negative strain has been generally abandoned and replaced by the idea of Sachse and Mohr (1) that large rings may exist in strainless and non-planar forms. A carbon chain constructed from conventional wire tetrahedra in such a way as to allow free rotation about each single bond clearly shows that the chain can assume a great multiplicity of shapes. If the number of atoms is 5 or 6, the model is readily rotated so that the ends collide once in each complete rotation. If the number is more than 6 the ends can be brought together arbitrarily without any difficulty to produce a non-planar ring, which is quite flexible and can be bent into a variety of shapes without any appreciable strain. Considering the chain model as a representation of the bifunctional molecule, it is evident why rings of 5 and 6 atoms are readily formed and stable. Larger rings should be equally stable, but it is obvious that their formation may present some difficulties. The chain can assume a great multiplicity of shapes; the particular configurations requisite for ring closure are relatively few. If then the molecule is placed under conditions where mutual reaction of its terminal groups can occur, the probability of *inter*molecular reaction is very much greater than that of *intra*molecular reaction. Hence, as has been demonstrated in previous papers of this series, reactions that might conceivably yield large rings from open chains almost invariably yield linear polymers instead. It is necessary again to emphasize this point since even some of the most recent writings on the subject of forming large rings still convey the impression that attempts to close long chains do not result in any clear-cut reaction at all. In fact, in most cases, reaction occurs perfectly smoothly without any difficulty but the reaction is intermolecular not intramolecular.

What means are available for controlling this situation? Obviously nothing much can be expected from any modification of the nature of the terminal groups. Even if these groups are of such a nature (*e. g.*, NH₂ and COOH) as to exercise a strong attraction for each other, this pre-existing attraction may itself be intermolecular rather than intramolecular (2).

There is in fact no method known for controlling experimentally the shape that molecules assume. The possibility of such control may perhaps exist in the use of surface forces, but nothing is known about this matter. There are, however, two possible methods of controlling the result of the reaction. (1) High dilution will increase the *relative* probability of intramolecular reaction (3). (2) If a series of mutually dependent and quantitatively reversible reactions is involved, constant removal of any traces of cyclic product will cause a displacement of the equilibrium with the ultimate conversion of the entire sample into the cyclic product. This is the principle involved in the synthesis of the cyclic esters and anhydrides described above.

In speculations devoted to Ruzicka's ketone synthesis it has been suggested (2, 4) that the peculiarity of the reaction which makes possible this very exceptional closure of large rings lies in the ability of the metal ion (*e. g.*, thorium) to bring the ends of the chain into a position of close intramolecular approach. But no reason is offered to explain why the metal ion should have such a peculiar effect; and the force of this suggestion is moreover considerably weakened by the claim (5) that macrocyclic ketones are obtained by thermal destruction not only from salts of dibasic acids but also from the acids themselves and their anhydrides. It appears to have been taken for granted in these speculations that reaction *is* intramolecular and leads directly to the cyclic ketone. This is a point that appears to be open to test and the following experiment was accordingly made.

Thermolysis of Thorium Octadecanedioate in Dixylylethane.—Twenty-five grams of thorium octadecanedioate, prepared by the method of Ruzicka, and 150 cc. of unsymmetrical dixylylethane were placed in a 300-cc. flask fitted with a stirrer and thermometer. The mixture was heated by means of a metal bath to 325°. In the course of ten minutes the suspended solid became gummy and attached itself to the stirrer.

At the end of fifty minutes the mixture had become homogeneous but very viscous.   At the end of two hours, heating was stopped.   On cooling, the melt solidified to a slightly elastic gel.   Some solid material (apparently unchanged salt) around the top of the flask was discarded.   The gel was continuously extracted with ether for eighteen hours, whereupon it disintegrated to a light gray powder.   It was further extracted for four hours with benzene, dried, heated with concentrated hydrochloric acid for three hours, separated, ground in a mortar, extracted for three hours with hot hydrochloric acid, then twice with hot alcohol and once with ether.   The dried residue (10 g.) was an almost pure white powder.   It was practically free of ash and melted at 126–128°; soluble in hot toluene, butyl alcohol and acetylene tetrachloride.

Anal.   Found: C, 78.22, 78.89; H, 12.29, 12.41.

When triturated with aqueous sodium carbonate and thoroughly washed and dried it was converted to a salt (Na found, 1.16, 1.36%).   The analytical data are consistent with the formula $HOOC[(CH_2)_{16}CO]_7OH$, the calculated values for C and H being 78.9 and 12.4% while a monosodium salt would contain 1.25% Na.

A sample of this material was placed in a molecular still and heated by a metal bath at 300–305°.   At the end of one day a film of white solid distillate had collected on the condenser.   It had a very pronounced fragrant musky odor.

Our interpretation of this experiment is that the thorium salt of the acid, as in other bifunctional reactions involving long chains, breaks down with the formation of a linear polymer

$$\ldots-RCO-RCO-RCO-RCO-RCO-\ldots$$

The resulting polyketone comprises the solid product remaining from the extraction.   When the polyketone is heated in the molecular still, it cracks and appreciable amounts of the monomeric cyclic ketone (cycloheptadecanone) are produced; the characteristic musk-like odor therefore first makes its appearance at this point in the experiment.

The facts recited above place the macrocyclic ketones, esters (including lactones) and anhydrides on a common basis for discussion so far as the stereochemistry and mechanism of formation are concerned.

The α-polyanhydrides for example may be represented by the formula $\ldots-CORCOO-CORCOO-CORCOO-CORCOO-\ldots$ They are apparently open chains, and contain no more than traces of cyclic anhydrides of low molecular weight.   The possibility of converting the polymeric α-anhydrides into β-anhydrides of low molecular weight depends in the first place on the very great reactivity of carboxylic anhydrides and the fact that they are capable of reacting with themselves.   A mixed anhydride such as that derived from acetic and butyric acids will, at least at elevated temperatures, pass into an equilibrium mixture containing a considerable proportion of the two simple anhydrides (6).   The process is analogous to ester interchange and, like that, doubtless proceeds through the formation of an addition product involving the ether oxygen of one molecule and the carbonyl carbon of another (A). A linear polyanhydride

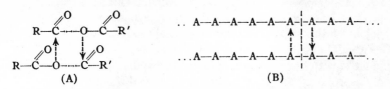

is not a chemical individual. It is a mixture of long chains of slightly differing lengths each of which bears a series of anhydride linkages. It presents a very complicated series of possibilities of reacting with itself. Adjacent chains can react with themselves to produce simultaneously longer and shorter chains (B). Reaction in a similar manner at two points will yield large rings and these may mutually coalesce by the same mechanism to produce still larger rings. Intramolecular reaction may result in the formation of cyclic monomers and dimers, etc.

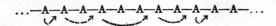

The potentialities of the situation are sufficiently complex to suggest that at equilibrium the number of entities involved will be limited only by the magnitude of the sample. No doubt a condition of genuine equilibrium is impossible to achieve; nevertheless, experiment shows that at elevated temperatures quite a considerable series of transformations occurs, and it leads chiefly to the formation of very large molecules. At the same time appreciable amounts of smaller cyclic fragments (β-anhydride) are produced. The actual concentration of these β-anhydrides present in the reaction mixture at any time must be small, since the β-anhydrides polymerize almost instantly at the temperature involved; and their rate of formation cannot be exceedingly great because even at elevated temperatures where the speed and amplitude of molecular vibrations are greatly increased, the relative probability of the configurations necessary for the formation of such cyclic compounds must be rather low. However, in the molecular still a mechanism is provided for removing and isolating the β-anhydrides as fast as they are produced. The equilibrium is thus continuously displaced and the entire specimen is finally converted into the β-anhydride.

A precisely similar mechanism is unquestionably involved in the formation of macrocyclic esters from polyesters and it is significant in this connection that smooth transformation requires the presence of ester-interchange catalysts.

The ketones obviously present a more difficult case. No mechanism corresponding to ester interchange exists for the smooth rupture of the linkages joining the structural units in a chain of the type . . . —CO—R—CO—R—CO—R—. . .; nor would one expect a macrocyclic ketone to polymerize with the formation of the corresponding polyketone. Since the reactions involved are not strictly reversible and there are many side reactions, the formation of cyclic ketones offers scarcely any possibilities for rational and deliberate control. The yields are therefore generally only a small fraction of those obtained with the cyclic carbonates, oxalates and anhydrides.

Steric Interferences.—The outline presented above is incomplete since the possible influence of atoms attached to the carbon chain has been ignored. Such atoms are capable of acting as obstacles to ring closure, and they may also introduce strains into rings. For the series under consideration hydrogen is the most numerous and important peripheral atom. The internuclear C–H distance is known from spectroscopic data to be 1.08 Å., and since the (aliphatic) carbon radius is 0.77 Å., the distance from the center of the hydrogen to the surface of the carbon is 0.31 Å. This indicates an atomic diameter of 0.62 Å. for hydrogen attached to carbon. But hydrogens not mutually joined will be expected to exercise a mutual repulsion preventing close approach, and data on the densities of hydrocarbons, collision areas, etc., show that the average distance between the centers of hydrogens belonging to separate molecules is always greater than 0.62 Å. The combined hydrogen atom must therefore be assigned, in addition to its internal radius of 0.31 Å., a larger external radius, which defines the closest average approach of other atoms (7). This external radius will vary with the compound and the conditions; it will decrease with increasing temperatures and will be larger in a crystal than a gas. The most elaborate experiments and speculations on the external radius of hydrogen are those of Mack (8), who in different cases uses values ranging from 0.49 to 1.26 Å. Stoll and Stoll-Comte (9) had, however, already made specific application of the external domain of hydrogen atoms in connection with macrocyclic hydrocarbons. They pointed out that the cyclic paraffins exhibit two anomalies. (1) When density is plotted against number of CH_2 groups a maximum appears in the range of 10 to 17 atoms, and (2) it is within this range that the yields of the cyclic ketones fall to an exceedingly low minimum. The explanation which they offer is very briefly this. Consideration of the densities of cyclic and open-chain hydrocarbons indicates a domain for the CH_2 group that can be accounted for by representing the hydrogen as spheres of diameter 2.3 Å. (compared with 1.54 Å. for carbon).   Rings of 5, 6 or 7 members therefore consist of an approximately flat cyclic chain of carbon atoms with a shell of much larger hydrogen atoms around the periphery.   In rings of 8 to 15 atoms the geometrical limitations imposed by the valence angles of the carbon atoms force some of the hydrogens toward the center of the ring.   The space available is not sufficient to receive them; the "domain" of the hydrogens (or of the CH_2 group) is therefore reduced or compressed.   The resulting strain explains the minimum in the yield of the cyclic ketones, and the compression explains the maximum in the density curve of the hydrocarbons. The turning in of hydrogens toward the center of the ring is illustrated for cyclononane by Fig. 1 in which the diameter of the hydrogens (1.18 Å.) is much smaller than that assumed by Stoll and Stoll-Comte (2.3 Å.).   This configuration is quite rigid and it is evident that if the hydrogens were twice as large, the space available would not be adequate to receive them.   As the size of the ring increases the number of hydrogens forced toward the center increases; above 15 atoms half of them are forced toward the inside of the ring, but there is sufficient space to accommodate them and no strains are developed.

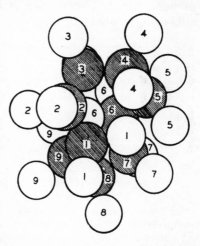

Fig. 1.—Cyclononane (carbon, d = 1.54 Å.; hydrogen, 1.1).   This model illustrates the cramped nature of the ring and the turning of hydrogen toward the center.

This idea of steric interferences due to "external" radii is capable of many interesting applications to the cyclic esters and anhydrides.   It is unfortunately for this purpose impossible to assign any exact value to the external radius of hydrogen.   Results obtained in the diphenyl problem (10) suggest that the value implied in a spherical hydrogen of 2.3 Å. is probably much too large; however, for immediate qualitative purposes the exact value adopted is not particularly important.   The following discussion is based on observation of models in which the hydrogen is represented as a sphere of radius 2.2 Å.

When a zig-zag hydrocarbon chain is constructed with such large hydrogens, it is immediately evident that the mobility of the chain is greatly reduced. The hydrogens interfere with many rotational movements that would present no difficulty if the hydrogens were absent. The interferences toward ring closure become exaggerated as the length of the chain is increased beyond 6 or 7 atoms. For a cycloparaffin of 9 atoms the interferences are so serious that the model is not constructible.

If an oxygen atom is inserted in the chain, the flexibility of the model is considerably increased, since this insertion is practically equivalent to the removal of two of the interfering hydrogens (11). Actually also oxygen probably presents less resistance to the deflection of its valence angles, although this is not illustrated by the models. In the anhydrides and esters under consideration each structural unit contains in its chain at least one oxygen and at least one carbonyl carbon (which also bears no hydrogens). The result is a great increase in the constructibility of the models. Construction of models of the cyclic hydrocarbons in the range of 9 to 15 atoms requires either a compression of the hydrogen spheres or a considerable deflection of the angles. In the carbonates and anhydrides the entire series of monomers from the 5-atom ring up can be constructed from spherical wooden atoms without more than very slight deflection of the angles. From this one may infer that no maximum should appear in the curve relating density to ring-size of the carbonates. The experimental curve is shown in Fig. 2. Unfortunately data are lacking in the range of 7 to 10 atoms, but the nature of the curve makes it very improbable that any maximum exists.

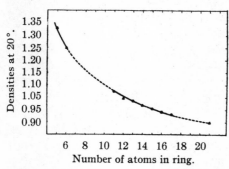

Fig. 2.—Densities of monomeric cyclic polymethylene carbonates at 20°: ⊙, values determined at 20°; ▢, values obtained by extrapolation via molecular refractions from determinations of density made at 25°; △, values obtained by extrapolation via molecular refractions from determinations made at 50°.

Although it appears from the models that no compression of the hydrogen domains is involved in any of the cyclic ester or anhydride molecules, the manipulation of the models shows that there is a great difference in ease of ring closure depending upon the length of the chain. In the range of 8 to 14 atoms the interferences are so numerous that many trials and errors must occur before the particular configuration that permits ring closure is found; and the ring when closed is then very rigid. In the carbonate series with the 15-membered ring the model acquires considerable flexibility.

The greater ease in constructibility of rings of 15 atoms or more explains why in the preparation of carbonates in the range of 7 to 12 atoms the products are almost exclusively the dimeric forms. At equilibrium the concentration of dimer will be large compared with the concentration of monomer. But as the ring size increases not only does the ease of monomer formation approach (and ultimately exceed) that of the dimer, but the latter becomes relatively more and more difficult to remove by evaporation. The ring-size at which the two forms begin to appear in equal amounts will depend partly upon the experimental conditions; but it will also be controlled to a certain extent by the nature of the ring. It is interesting in this connection to compare the three 14-membered rings undecamethylene carbonate, tetraethylene glycol carbonate and decamethylene oxalate. The first has two annular oxygens and one carbonyl, the second two oxygens and two carbonyls and the third five oxygens and one carbonyl. The first compound under the conditions used gave a mixture of monomer and dimer, the last two gave exclusively monomer.

The alkylene esters of dibasic acids above malonic yield chiefly dimers even when the unit length is as great as 18. The models do not furnish any very clear explanation of this fact although it appears that some advantage in ease of ring formation may be expected if the oxygens and carbonyls are all adjacent (as in oxalic esters).

The cyclic anhydrides present the same reluctance toward the formation of rings of intermediate size as do the esters, but they show some peculiarities. The products appear to be invariably either monomer or dimer, not mixtures of the two. The range of dimer formation is from 9 to 13 atoms (unit length). Very peculiar is the fact that the two even membered compounds (10 and 12 atoms) in this range appear to yield exceedingly unstable monomers rather than dimers. The result is the alternating effect shown graphically in Table I (p. 205 . . . . .). The manipulation of models in this range furnished the impression that even-membered rings were more readily constructed than odd, but the geometrical peculiarity responsible for this effect was not identified. All of the cyclic anhydrides are exceedingly unstable at the high temperatures used in their formation, and the nature of the β-anhydrides produced might therefore be expected to be very sensitive to very slight differences in the ease of constructibility.

Ring Stability.—Ruzicka showed (12) that his macrocyclic paraffins were not destroyed by the action of phosphorus and hydriodic acid at 250°

and his cyclic ketones resisted the action of fuming hydrochloric acid at 180–190°. This was an indication that large rings are no less stable than those of 5 or 6 atoms and a refutation of the idea that large rings are strained. It appears, however, in view of the results obtained with the cyclic esters and anhydrides, that this conclusion requires some revision. The higher cyclic anhydrides all polymerize very readily. In this respect the large rings are very unstable as compared with those of 5 to 6 atoms, which do not polymerize at all. The instability rises to a maximum with the rings of 10 to 12 atoms, which polymerize rapidly even at temperatures below 0°. At elevated temperatures (e. g., 200°) the macrocyclic esters also polymerize. It is therefore very difficult to accept the conclusion that large rings are entirely free from strain. Our interpretation of the facts is as follows.

Rings of 3 or 4 atoms have very large strains owing to the necessarily large deflection of the annular valences. Rings of 5 atoms are practically free of strain. Most rings of 6 atoms are strained. It is true that cyclohexane can be represented as existing in two strainless forms (cis and trans) but since it has not been possible to isolate two cyclohexanes, it seems likely that the two forms are in dynamic equilibrium. On each conversion of one form into the other the ring must pass through a nearly planar position of strain. The existence of such strain is indicated by the fact that all simple 6-membered cyclic esters polymerize very readily. (Glutaric anhydride does not polymerize but the oxygen valences in this case may permit sufficient deflection to avoid strain.) Larger rings are all strained. In the range of 7 to 14 atoms where the models are very rigid the strain may be pictured as due to the mutual repulsion of non-linked peripheral atoms that are crowded against one another. In larger, more flexible rings the vibrations due to thermal agitation constantly present the possibility of introducing momentary strains. This effect is similar to that pictured for the cyclohexane ring but is probably less pronounced. At any rate, 6-membered cyclic esters polymerize more readily than macrocyclic esters.

The ease of polymerization of the macrocyclic anhydrides is unquestionably associated with the extraordinary reactivity of anhydrides generally. A facile mechanism for the rupture of the ring is provided by the nature of the anhydride linkage and hence very slight strains or distortions, which may arise merely through small interferences among substituent atoms, need not be tolerated. The macrocyclic esters polymerize by a similar mechanism (i. e., by ester interchange) but less readily because they are less reactive. The apparent high stability of the macrocyclic hydrocarbons and ketones is due to the fact that they present no point of easy chemical attack; if a sufficiently delicate chemical probe were available they would probably prove to be somewhat less stable than those of 5 atoms.

Summary

It is shown that the formation of macrocyclic ketones from salts of the dibasic acids probably involves first a linear polyketone which is subsequently cracked or decomposed. The ketones thus follow a course already established for esters and anhydrides. The characteristic analogies and differences in the three series can be explained by taking into account the nature of the reactions involved and the steric effects of peripheral atoms. Rings of more than 5 atoms cannot be regarded as entirely strainless. The probable nature of the strains in large rings is indicated.

Bibliography and Remarks

(1) Mohr, *J. prakt. Chem.*, **98**, 348 (1918).

(2) The idea that such attractions may favor intramolecular reaction has been suggested by Mills, "Proceedings, Fourth International Solvay Conference," 1931, p. 20.

(3) *Cf.* Ruggli, *Ann.*, **392**, 92 (1912).

(4) Ruzicka, Stoll and Schinz, *Helv. Chim. Acta*, **11**, 670 (1928).

(5) Ruzicka, Brugger, Seidel and Schinz, *ibid.*, **11**, 496 (1928).

(6) *Cf.* Autenrieth, *Ber.*, **34**, 168(1901).

(7) *Cf.* the excellent review by Sidgwick in "Annual Reports of the Progress of Chemistry for 1932."

(8) Melaven and Mack, *Journ. Am. Chem. Soc.*, **54**, 888 (1932); Sperry and Mack, *ibid.*, 904; Mack, *ibid.*, 2141.

(9) Stoll and Stoll-Comte, *Helv. Chim. Acta*, **13**, 1185 (1930).

(10) *Cf.* Adams and Yuan, *Chem. Reviews*, **12**, 261 (1933).

(11) This effect is probably considerably exaggerated in the models since the oxygens are represented only by their internal diameters.

(12) Ruzicka, Brugger, Pfeiffer, Schinz and Stoll, *Helv. Chim. Acta*, **9**, 499 (1926).

XXIII.* ϵ-Caprolactone and Its Polymers

Bifunctional esterifications yield either cyclic monomers or linear polyesters.† Choice between these possibilities is controlled by

  (a) *the unit length of the reactant,*
  (b) *the nature of the unit,*
  (c) *the experimental conditions (especially dilution).*

* F. J. van Natta, J. W. Hill and W. H. Carothers; *Journ. Am. Chem. Soc.*, **56**, 455–7 (1934); Communication No. 118 from the Experimental Station of E. I. du Pont de Nemours and Co.
Received October 20, 1933.
† Compare paper No. XII on page 156.

In the present paper these conditions are studied during the self esterification of ε-hydroxycaproic acid. Under certain experimental conditions the principal primary product is the monomeric lactone; a trace of dimeric ester is formed, but little if any of the high polymers.

Under the action of heat (about 150°) the lactone polymerizes to a linear polymer with a molecular weight around 4000.

Bifunctional esterifications (1) generally yield either cyclic monomers or linear polyesters. Choice between these possibilities is controlled by (a) the unit length of the reactant, (b) the nature of the unit and (c) the experimental conditions (especially dilution). Factor (a) is generally by far the most important and its effect has been illustrated in previous papers. Unit lengths of 7 and 8 however constitute transition cases and factor (b) may here become the controlling one. It is well known that substitution (*e. g.*, by methyl) favors ring closure but otherwise the effect of variations in the nature of the unit are not easy to foresee. The simplest possible structural situation for self-esterification is found in the ω-hydroxy acids, $HO(CH_2)_{n-2}COOH$, and information concerning them is available for all values of *n* from 3 to 22 (2) excepting 7 and 8. These acids have never been isolated or their self-esterification studied (3).

A

The experiments presently reported were prompted by the considerations outlined above and by the fact that several grams of ε-hydroxycaproic acid had become available as a by-product in the preparation of hexamethylene glycol by the reduction of diethyl adipate. The acid could neither be distilled nor crystallized, and it was therefore impossible to isolate it as such in a state of purity. It was however found possible, as described in **B** (below), to isolate an oil composed essentially of the acid (80%) and its lactone (20%). This mixture was dehydrated by heating it in a distilling flask at 150 to 210°. The residue was completely volatile, and, when purified by redistillation, it was found to consist of the lactone of ε-hydroxycaproic acid, a colorless liquid having a pleasant, spicy odor. It crystallized when strongly cooled and melted at about −5°. The yield of purified lactone was about 63% of the theoretical. The only other product of the reaction consisted of a very small amount (1%) of a volatile crystalline solid melting at 111 to 113°. This was identified as the dimeric, cyclic self-ester of ε-hydroxycaproic acid, a 14-membered ring.

The monomeric lactone showed no appreciable tendency to polymerize spontaneously when allowed to stand at the ordinary laboratory conditions; but when heated at 150° in a sealed tube it gradually became more viscous and, after twelve hours, when cooled to room temperature, it solidified to an opaque mass. When a trace of potassium carbonate was added to the lactone the same result was obtained in five hours at 150°. The product crystallized from alcohol as a white powder melting at 53 to 55°. It was very soluble in ethyl acetate, acetone and benzene but only slightly soluble in alcohol or ether. The analytical composition and chemical behavior of this material demonstrated that it was a linear polyester, and molecular weight determinations in freezing benzene gave values about 4000.

Anal. Calcd. for HO—[—$(CH_2)_5$—CO—O—]$_{35}$—H: C, 62.83; H, 8.84; mol. wt., 4008. Found: C, 62.15; H, 8.86; mol. wt., 3660, 4300.

All three of the above esters (lactone, dimer and polyester) were actually derivatives of ε-hydroxycaproic acid, and no shift of the hydroxyl oxygen was involved in their formation (4), since they all yielded the same hydrazide when treated with hydrazine hydrate. This hydrazide was also obtained from the ethyl ester described in C.

To test its susceptibility to depolymerization the polyester was placed in a molecular still and heated by a bath at 250° and at a pressure of 1 to 2 mm. for ninety hours (5). During this time only a very small amount of distillate was collected—a viscous, dark-colored oil containing a few minute crystals of the cyclic dimer. The polymeric residue was darker in color but otherwise appeared to be unchanged.

Conclusions.—Under the conditions described, the principal primary product of the self-esterification of ε-hydroxycaproic acid is the monomeric lactone; a trace of the dimeric ester is formed at the same time but little if any of the higher polyester. Like 6-membered cyclic esters, the lactone of ε-hydroxycaproic acid is polymerized by the action of heat. (Apparently it polymerizes only slightly less readily than δ-valerolactone.) The polyester thus obtained can be depolymerized only with great difficulty under the action of heat. In this respect it differs from the polyesters that result from 6-membered cyclic esters, and resembles polyesters derived from the higher ω-hydroxy acids.

The following comparisons with other compounds having 7-atom units are also of interest. Tetramethylene carbonate and trimethylene oxalate are obtained only in the form of linear polyesters. These are depolymerized with great difficulty and the only products identified are the cyclic dimers. The lactone of 3,7-dimethyl-6-hydroxyoctanoic acid is reported (6) to exist in two forms, a liquid and a solid. The authors suggest that these are stereoisomers, but no molecular weight determinations are recorded, and it seems more likely that they represent a monomeric and a dimeric form. Another ε-lactone results from tetrahydrocarvone by oxidation with Caro's acid (7). It is hydrolyzed to the acid, HO—CH-(CH_3)—$(CH_2)_2$—CH(C_3H_7)—CH_2—COOH, from which the lactone is regenerated by the action of heat. A simple lactone is also obtained from ε-hydroxyoctanoic acid by direct distillation (5). When ε-aminocaproic acid is heated it is partly converted to the monomeric lactam (about 30%) and partly to polyamide (about 70%). These are not directly interconvertible.

B

Preparation of ε-Hydroxycaproic Acid.—The acid was isolated from the product obtained by reducing a large amount of ethyl adipate. After the hexamethylene glycol had been removed by ether extraction of the completely saponified reaction mixture, the latter was acidified with sulfuric acid and continuously extracted with ether. From the concentrated ethereal extract, a part of the adipic acid was removed by filtration. Attempts to remove the ε-hydroxycaproic acid from the filtrate by distillation were unsuccessful. The mixture was therefore acetylated (8), and the acetate of the hydroxy acid was isolated by distillation (b. p. 134 to 145° at 2 mm.). This was saponified, acidified with dilute sulfuric acid, extracted with ether and concentrated *in vacuo*. The acetic acid was removed by evaporation *in vacuo* at room temperature in an all glass apparatus, the condenser bulb being cooled with carbon dioxide snow and acetone. After four days the bulbs were opened. The distillate consisted of dilute acetic acid. The residue was a pale yellow, viscous liquid having a slightly rancid odor. It solidified to a glass when cooled with solid carbon dioxide. Titration indicated that it consisted of a mixture of ε-hydroxycaproic acid and its self-ester containing about 80% of the free acid.

Anal. Calcd. for hydroxycaproic acid: neutral equivalent or saponification equivalent, 132. Found: neutral equivalent, 164.1, 164.3; saponification equivalent, 130.5.

ε-Caprolactone.—The lactone prepared as described in A was very soluble in alcohol, benzene, ether, ethyl acetate and water, but insoluble in petroleum ether; b. p. 98 to 99° at 2 mm.; d_4^{24} 1.0698; n_D^{24} 1.4608; M_R calcd., 29.44; M_R found, 29.15.

Anal. Calcd. for $C_6H_{10}O_2$: C, 63.11; H, 8.84; mol. wt., 114; saponification equivalent, 114. Found: C, 62.81, 63.39; H, 8.68, 9.07; mol. wt. (in freezing benzene), 120, 122; saponification equivalent, 113.4, 113.3.

Dimeric ε-Caprolactone.—Obtained as described in A: granular crystals; soluble in most organic solvents, but insoluble in petroleum ether or water; m. p. 112 to 113°.

Anal. Calcd. for $C_{12}H_{20}O_4$: C, 63.11; H, 8.84; mol. wt., 228. Found: C, 62.98, 63.39; H, 8.84, 9.09; mol. wt. (in freezing benzene), 243, 226.

Hydrazide of ε-Hydroxycaproic Acid.—The monomeric and dimeric lactones as well as the polyester described in A, and the ethyl ester described in C (below) were separately warmed with hydrazine hydrate for several hours on a steam-bath. In each case the mixture solidified on being cooled; and after crystallization from ethyl acetate or alcohol, the hydrazide was obtained in the form of white crystals melting at 114 to 115°. It was very soluble in water.

Anal. Calcd. for $C_6H_{14}O_2N_2$: N, 19.18. Found: N, 18.68, 18.74.

C

Attempts to Prepare ε-Caprolactone from ε-Bromocaproic Acid.—Prior to the experiments described above, attempts had been made to prepare ε-caprolactone by the action of sodium ethylate on ε-bromocaproic acid. By this method Marvel and Birkhimer (9) obtained a small amount of material "which seemed to be slightly impure ε-caprolactone," but its identity was not established.

ε-Bromocaproic acid with an equivalent amount of sodium ethylate in absolute alcohol was refluxed for eight hours. The mixture was made very slightly acid with a few drops of hydrochloric acid, then filtered, concentrated and distilled *in vacuo*. After a small preliminary fraction, a halogen-free product distilling at 104 to 106° at 4 mm. was obtained in 37% yield.

This, presumably, is similar to the product described by Marvel and Birkhimer, but it proved to be the ethyl ester of ε-hydroxycaproic acid. Unlike ε-caprolactone it was insoluble in water; and it did not crystallize on being strongly cooled but merely became very viscous. It was soluble in most organic solvents; d_4^{25} 0.9944; n_D^{25} 1.4381; M_R calcd., 42.32; M_R found, 42.24.

Anal. Calcd. for $C_8H_{16}O_3$: C, 60.0; H, 10.0; mol. wt., 160; saponification equivalent, 160. Found: C, 59.98; H, 10.08; mol. wt. (in boiling acetonitrile) 151, 154; saponification equivalent, 158.7, 158.8.

When treated with hydrazine hydrate it yielded the hydrazide already described in **B** (above).

The residue from the distillation of the ethyl ester was distilled further and yielded a small fraction boiling at 110–200° at 4 mm. From this halogen-free distillate granular crystals of the caprolactone dimer described in **B** separated (identified by mixed melting point).

The residue still remaining (41%) solidified to a paste on standing, and was obtained as a light colored powder melting at 51 to 53° after several crystallizations from alcohol. It was similar to the polyester described in **A**, but it had a somewhat lower apparent molecular weight.

Anal. Calcd. for HO—[—(CH₂)₅—CO—O—]₁₆—H: C, 62.7; H, 8.8; mol. wt., 1842. Found: C, 63.56; H, 9.08; mol. wt. (in freezing benzene) 1980, 1660.

When treated with hydrazine hydrate it yielded the hydrazide already described.

From the above described reaction of sodium ethylate on bromocaproic acid no monomeric lactone was isolated. It is, however, not permissible to infer that no caprolactone was formed, since hydrochloric acid was present, and this, doubtless, would strongly catalyze the polymerization of any caprolactone that might have been formed.

Summary

ε-Caprolactone has been prepared for the first time. It is the principal product of the self-esterification of the corresponding acid. A small amount of the cyclic dimeric ester (14-membered ring) is formed at the same time. Under the action of heat ε-caprolactone is converted to a polyester of high molecular weight. The process is not easily reversible. This behavior is compared with that already observed for other cyclic and polyesters.

Bibliography and Remarks

(1) For terminology.

(2) Chuit and Hausser, *Helv. Chim. Acta*, **12**, 463 (1929); Bougault and Bourdier, *Compt. rend.*, **147**, 1311 (1908); Lycan and Adams, *Journ. Am. Chem. Soc.*, **51** 625, 3450 (1929).

(3) Some of their derivatives are meagerly described in the following references: Baeyer and Villiger, *Ber.*, **33**, 863 (1900); Helferich and Malkomes, *ibid.*, **55**, 704 (1922); Marvel and Birkhimer, *Journ. Am. Chem. Soc.*, **51**, 260 (1929).

(4) *Cf.* Blaise and Koehler, *Compt. rend.*, **148**, 1772 (1909).

(5) Under these conditions polyesters having 6-atom units depolymerize very rapidly and smoothly Those having longer units depolymerize very slowly and incompletely if at all, although in many such cases a smooth depolymerization can be effected in the presence of an ester-interchange catalyst.

(6) Baeyer, *Ber.*, **32**, 3619 (1899); Baeyer and Villiger, *ibid.*, 3628.

(7) Baeyer, *ibid.*, **29**, 27, 30 (1896); Baeyer and Villiger, *ibid.*, **32**, 3629 (1899).

(8) *Cf.* Chuit and Hausser, *Helv. Chim. Acta*, **12**, 463 (1929).

(9) Marvel and Birkhimer, *Journ. Am. Chem. Soc.*, **51**, 260 (1929).

XXIV. Cyclic and Polymeric Formals*

Polymerization and ring formation follows the general scheme.†

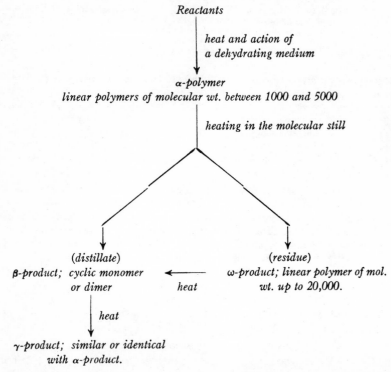

Reactants

heat and action of
a dehydrating medium

α-polymer
linear polymers of molecular wt. between 1000 and 5000

heating in the molecular still

(distillate)
β-product; cyclic monomer ← ——— ω-product; linear polymer of mol.
or dimer   heat   wt. up to 20,000.

heat

γ-product; similar or identical
with α-product.

It is to be expected that a similar scheme holds for the acetals derived from glycols. In the present paper the action of glycols on formals is described.

A new class of linear polymers and large rings is obtained.

Heating a glycol with dibutylformal and an acidic catalyst at about 150° yields an α-polyacetal. The molecular weight is around 2200. When α-polyacetals are heated at 230 to 250° in the molecular still, β- and ω-products are formed. The cyclic monomers (β-products) are liquids with characteristic odors fitting completely in the scheme developed by

* J. W. Hill and W. H. Carothers; *Journ. Am. Chem. Soc.*, **57**, 925–8 (1935); Communication No. 152, from the Experimental Station of E. I. du Pont de Nemours and Co.
Received March 21, 1935.
† Compare paper No. I on page 4 and No. XII on page 156.

Ruzicka and discussed in a previous paper. The ω-polymers are hard and tough microcrystalline masses, which can be drawn out into strong, pliable, silk-like filaments. X-ray diagrams indicate high orientation. Depolymerization was studied. The relative rate of hydrolysis of the ethylene acetals derived from formaldehyde, acetaldehyde and acetone is approximately 1:4000:44,000.*

Macrocyclic esters and anhydrides can be obtained by depolymerizing the corresponding linear polymers (1). The various relations involved are shown in the following diagram.

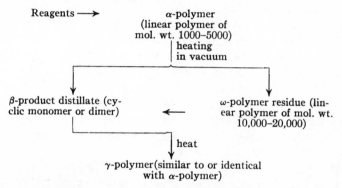

Reagents ——➤   α-polymer
(linear polymer of
mol. wt. 1000–5000)
heating
in vacuum

β-product distillate (cyclic monomer or dimer)   ⬅—   ω-polymer residue (linear polymer of mol. wt. 10,000–20,000)

heat

γ-polymer(similar to or identical with α-polymer)

Heating the α-polymer causes (a) formation of traces of cyclic monomer and dimer derived from one and two structural units of the molecular chain and (b) coupling of the α-polymer chains to form the still longer chains of ω-polymer. Linear polyesters and polyanhydrides result from reversible bifunctional condensations. In the ideal case, it would be possible to establish an equilibrium among all the species of α-, β- and ω-forms and constant removal of the β-forms by distillation should result in a complete transformation of the sample into cyclic monomer and/or dimer. This ideal is closely approached in some cases, the chief critical factors involved being inherent mobility of the link, catalysis, temperature and speed with which possible volatile products are withdrawn.

The fact that acetal interchanges are smoothly reversible reactions suggests that it should be possible to realize all these transformations among the acetals derived from glycols. For formals this is indeed true, and the compounds now reported constitute a new family of linear polymers and large rings. Here also, as with the esters and anhydrides, a single member may be obtained in the form of a macrocrystalline solid, an odorous (*e. g.,*

* Compare paper No. XX on page 212 and No. XXI on page 221.

musk-like) liquid, or a tough microcrystal line mass capable of being drawn into strong, pliable, highly oriented, silk-like filaments.

Preparation and Behavior of Formals. —Heating of a glycol with dibutyl formal and an acidic catalyst at about 150° results in acetal interchange with the distillation of butanol

$$HO(CH_2)_nOH + BuOCH_2OBu \longrightarrow \ldots-CH_2O(CH_2)_nO-\ldots + 2BuOH$$

Trimethylene or tetramethylene glycol thus yields a mobile liquid easily distilled *in vacuo*, and the major primary product is, therefore, presumably the cyclic monomer. When the glycol is pentamethylene, or a higher one the residue remaining from the removal of the alcohol is a viscous liquid. To ensure complete removal of volatile products, it is heated to 200–220° at low pressure. The remaining non-volatile product is then the α-poly-acetal. That derived from decamethylene glycol, for example, is a waxy solid which crystallizes as a powder from hot ethyl acetate and then melts at 56.5–57°. Its observed apparent molecular weight was 2190. Similar α-polyformals were obtained from pentamethylene, hexamethylene, tetra-decamethylene and octadecamethylene glycols as well as from triethylene glycol. The last gave a sirupy product which showed no tendency to crystallize; the others were all solids.

When the α-polyformals were heated to 230–250° at low pressure in a still provided with a condenser placed close to the evaporating surface (3), conversion to the β and ω forms occurred. Compared with the polyesters derived from carbonic acid, the rate of distillation was quite slow; in this respect, the polyformals resembled the previously described (2) polyesters derived from the higher dibasic acids such as sebacic; the tendency toward ω-polymer was greater than toward the β forms, and as the viscosity of the residue increased, the rate of distillation became less. The ultimate yield of distillate was, therefore, relatively small, and, as in the case of those polyesters that manifested a similar behavior, the distillates were largely the cyclic dimers which were without exception definitely crystalline solids of sharp melting points. The presence of cyclic monomer in the distillate could be inferred from the characteristic odor, and the monomer from pentamethylene formal was obtained in sufficient quantity to permit isolation and purification. The α-polyformal from triethylene glycol differed from the other formals of similar unit length. It was a viscous liquid and when heated in vacuum at 200–250° it depolymerized very rapidly. The product apparently consisted essentially of monomer, which was isolated in a state of purity and in considerable quantity by fractional crystallization of the distillate.

Polymerization of Cyclic Formals.—The possible polymerization of cyclic acetals has occupied an important place in speculations concerning cellulose, starch, etc. (3), but no clear example of a polymerization originating in an acetal linkage *per se* has been adduced. Among cyclic esters, rings of more than 5 atoms generally polymerize on being heated with catalysts and those of 6 atoms occupy a peculiar position because this transformation occurs with especial facility and is easily reversible (4). It is of interest in this connection that trimethylene formal (6-ring) could not be induced to polymerize. The monomeric tetramethylene, pentamethylene and triethylene glycol formals, however, quickly became more viscous when heated (*e. g.*, at 150°) in the presence of a trace of sulfonic acid. Dimeric decamethylene formal (26-ring) when treated in this manner was converted to a microcrystalline solid having approximately the same melting point and molecular weight (2500) as the α-polymer from which the dimer was originally derived. Results obtained with monomers are indicated in the table.

VISCOSITY CHANGE (IN ARBITRARY UNITS) OF MONOMERIC FORMALS HEATED WITH A TRACE OF CAMPHOR SULFONIC ACID

Formal	Ring size	Successive heating intervals	Time of flow, sec.
Trimethylene	6	Initial	4.5
		+2 hrs. at 100°	4.5
		+1.5 hrs. at 150°	4.5
Tetramethylene	7	Initial	4.5
		+2 hrs. at 100°	4.5
		+0.5 hr. at 150°	35
		+1.0 hr. at 150°	∞
Pentamethylene	8	Initial	4.5
		+2 hrs. at 100°	13
		+0.5 hr. at 150°	16

Odors.—The remarkable parallelism between the odors of macrocyclic ketones, lactones, carbonates, malonates, oxalates, sebacates, etc., of similar ring size previously reported (5) suggested that for musk-like odor the only requirement is a C=O group in a ring of suitable size. Meanwhile, Ruzicka (6) has extended his own researches and observed that the cyclic imine ⌐—(CH₂)₁₆—NH—⌐ has a musk-like odor, thus demonstrating that the presence of the carbonyl group is not necessary. The odors of the cyclic formals indicated in Table I now point to the same conclusion. Only the compounds marked* were actually isolated, but there is no doubt that the characteristic odor of the crude distillate was in each case due to cyclic monomer. The odors of the formals I were so strikingly similar to those of the corresponding carbonates II as to be almost indistinguishable from them.

$$\begin{matrix} \overset{\displaystyle\Gamma\!\!-\!\!O}{\underset{\displaystyle L\!\!-\!\!O}{(CH_2)_n CH_2}} \end{matrix} \qquad \begin{matrix} \overset{\displaystyle\Gamma\!\!-\!\!O}{\underset{\displaystyle L\!\!-\!\!O}{(CH_2)_n C\!\!=\!\!O}} \end{matrix}$$

(I)   (II)

TABLE I

ODORS OF MONOMERIC FORMALS

Glycol from which formal is derived	Ring size	Odor
*Tetramethylene	7	Sweet and penetrating
*Pentamethylene	8	Minty, camphoraceous
Hexamethylene	9	Minty
Nonamethylene	12	Earthy, camphoraceous
Decamethylene	13	Cedar, camphoraceous
Tetradecamethylene	17	Musk-like
Octadecamethylene	21	No odor
*Triethylene glycol	11	Faint, flowery

Fibers from ω-Polyformals.—ω-Polyesters and polyanhydrides can be drawn out into continuous filaments which readily accept permanently a high degree of orientation along the fiber axis and have very good strength and pliability (7). These materials are in fact the only truly synthetic fibers for which any measured strengths have been reported although it appears that continuous oriented filaments can also be drawn from polyoxymethylene and polyethylene oxide (8) when their molecular weights are sufficiently high. In all these classes of compounds as in cellulose itself, very long molecules are made up of units joined through C–O bonds. In the ω-polyformals as in cellulose, this linkage is actually an acetal linkage. It is not surprising then that the ω-polyformals can also be drawn into oriented filaments. X-ray diagrams for unoriented and oriented ω-polydecamethylene formal are shown in Figs. 1 and 2.

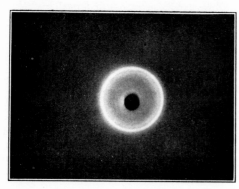

Fig. 1.—x-Ray diffraction pattern of ω-decamethylene formal.

Ease of Depolymerization.— The most obvious factor influencing ease of depolymerization is the reactivity characteristic of the type of linkage involved. Polyanhydrides are depolymerized much more readily than polyesters. The relative ease of hydrolysis of the ethylene acetals derived from formaldehyde, acetaldehyde and acetone is approximately 1:4000:44,000 (9). That the alkylene formals depolymerize with difficulty is therefore not surprising. One might expect that it would be very much easier to form macrocyclic acetals from other aldehydes and ketones; unfortunately, various other complications arise in these cases.

Rings of 9 to 12 atoms are especially difficult to form and in some cases exceptionally unstable. This may be attributed to repulsions arising from methylene hydrogens whose external radii are forced by the shape of the molecule into a space too small to receive them (10). As we have already pointed out (11), oxygens in a chain may relieve strains of this type since they carry no hydrogens and their valences are probably more flexible than those of

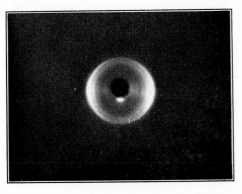

Fig. 2.—x-Ray diffraction pattern of cold-drawn ω-decamethylene formal.

carbon (12). Further presumed illustrations of the oxygen effect: polyformals (III) are definitely more difficult to depolymerize than are polycarbonates (IV), and triethylene glycol formal (V) is very much more easily depolymerized than alkylene formals of similar unit length.

$$..—(O—R—O—CH_2)_x—.....—(O—R—O—CO)_x—...$$
$$(III) \qquad\qquad\qquad (IV)$$
$$...—(OCH_2CH_2OCH_2CH_2OCH_2CH_2OCH_2)_x—...$$
$$(V)$$

Experimental Part

Tetramethylene Formal.—Difficultly separable mixtures were formed when the interchange method was applied to this compound. The most convenient method was to distil the glycol (30 g.) with trioxymethylene (10 g.) and a trace of camphor sulfonic acid (bath temperature, 210°). Fractionation of the distillate gave some tetrahydrofuran, and then a liquid boiling at 112–117° which was washed with strong caustic and redistilled at low pressure. It had d_4^{20} 1.0022; n_D^{20} 1.4310; M_D found, 26.34; M_D calcd., 26.38.

Decamethylene Formal.—Dibutyl formal (0.2 mole) with a 5% excess of decamethylene glycol and 0.1 g. of ferric chloride gave fairly rapid reaction at 165° (bath). The temperature was raised to 200° during two hours and heating continued for one and one-half hours in a good vacuum. The distillate was 98% of the theoretical calculated as butyl alcohol; the yield of residual *α-polymer* was 103%. When cold, it was a light brown rather hard wax. When dissolved in hot ethyl acetate (150 cc. for 17.5 g.), it separated in the form of a microcrystalline powder; soluble in chloroform, benzene, carbon tetrachloride and xylene; insoluble in alcohol, ether, petroleum, hydrocarbons and acetone.

β-**Product.**—Eight grams of the crude α-polymer was heated in a 250-cc. suction flask provided with a test-tube through which water could be circulated to act as an internal condenser (13); temperature, 230–250° (bath); pressure, about 1 mm. After forty-eight hours 2 g. of distillate had collected. It was a pasty mixture of liquid and crystals having a pleasant camphoraceous odor. The solid portion after crystallization from alcohol was odorless and melted at 93–94°. It was the *cyclic dimer*.

ω-**Polymer.**—The residue from the above was a hard, very tough, opaque, leather-like mass. It melted (became transparent) at 58–63°, but at this temperature it was too stiff to flow and showed considerable resistance to deformation. At slightly higher temperatures, it could be drawn out into thin strips or filaments which could be stretched and cold-drawn (14). The product then showed fiber orientation (Fig. 2) and also exhibited parallel extinction between crossed Nicols. The cold-drawn material was exceedingly strong, tough and pliable.

TABLE II

DATA ON FORMALS

Name of formal	M. p., °C.	Formula	Calcd. C	H	Mol. wt.	Found C	H	Mol. wt. in freezing benzene
Tetramethylene, monomer	B. p. 112–117	C$_5$H$_{10}$O$_2$	58.8	9.9	102	59.6	10.0	103
Decamethylene, α-polymer	56–57	(C$_{11}$H$_{22}$O$_2$)$_x$	70.9	11.9	(186)$_x$	68.9	11.7	2190
Decamethylene, dimer	93–94	(C$_{11}$H$_{22}$O$_2$)$_2$	70.9	11.9	372	70.8	12.1	368
Pentamethylene, dimer	55–56	(C$_6$H$_{12}$O$_2$)$_2$	62.1	10.4	232	61.8	10.5	262^a
Pentamethylene, monomer	B. p. 40–44 (11 mm.)	C$_6$H$_{12}$O$_2$	62.1	10.4	...	62.0	10.8	...
Hexamethylene, dimer	71–72	(C$_7$H$_{12}$O$_2$)$_2$	64.6	10.8	260	64.0	10.6	257
Nonamethylene, dimer	68–69	(C$_{10}$H$_{20}$O$_2$)$_2$	69.8	11.6	344	69.8	11.6	334^a
Tetradecamethylene, α-polymer	68–69	(C$_{15}$H$_{30}$O$_2$)$_x$	74.4	12.4	(242)$_x$	73.1	12.1	2480
Tetradecamethylene, dimer	103.5–104	(C$_{15}$H$_{30}$O$_2$)$_2$	74.4	12.4	484	74.4	12.5	503
Triethylene glycol, monomer	18–20	C$_7$H$_{14}$O$_4$	51.9	8.6	162	51.6	8.4	161

^{a} In boiling benzene.

γ-**Polymer.**—The cyclic dimer (0.5 g.) with a trace of camphor sulfonic acid heated at 150° soon became very viscous and the characteristic odor of the cyclic monomer appeared. After an hour, the melt when cooled set to a hard wax, easily electrified when powdered. Purified out of benzene, it separated as a microcrystalline powder, m. p. 58–59°; molecular weight observed in freezing benzene, 2580.

Other Formals.—The other α-polyformals were for the most part brittle waxy solids, and the observed melting points were: pentamethylene 38–39°, hexamethylene 38°, nonamethylene 54–55°, tetradecamethylene 68–69°, octadecamethylene 71–72° and triethylene, sirup. The β-polymers were generally pasty solids having the odors indicated in Table I and, when purified by crystallization from alcohol, yielded the odorless crystalline dimers whose melting points are shown in Table II. Pentamethylene formal depolymerized more readily than its higher homologs, and the monomer was isolated from the β-product as a colorless liquid of camphoraceous odor; b. p. 40–44° at 11 mm. Triethylene glycol formal depolymerized more readily than any of the others and gave a 70% yield of β-product which apparently consisted largely of monomer melting at 18–20°.

Summary

A new class of linear polymers represented by the general formula
. . .—[CH$_2$—O—R—O]$_x$—. . . is obtained by the action of alkyl formals on the higher glycols (above tetramethylene). These α-polyformals can in part be depolymerized to the β-forms (cyclic monomer and dimer) and in part converted to the higher ω-polyformals. The latter can be drawn out into strong, pliable, highly oriented fibers. The β-forms constitute a new type of large rings; the monomers have odors scarcely distinguishable from the corresponding carbonates ⌐O—R—O—CO⌐ and in particular tetradecamethylene formal, the 17-membered ring, has a musk-like odor. The dimers are odorless crystalline solids. Trimethylene formal (6-membered ring) does not polymerize, and no polymeric form is known, but tetramethylene formal (7-membered ring) and the higher ones polymerize rapidly (e. g., at 150°) when catalyzed by acid.

Bibliography and Remarks

(1) Hill and Carothers, ibid., 54, 1569 (1932); 55, 5023, 5031 (1933).

(2) Ibid., 55, 5035 (1933).

(3) See, for example, Hibbert and Timm, Journ. Am. Chem. Soc., 45, 2433 (1923); Hill and Hibbert, ibid., 3108 3124; Helferich and Sparmberg, Ber., 64, 104 (1931); Bergmann and Miekeley, ibid., 62, 2297 (1929).

(4) Carothers and van Natta, Journ. Am. Chem. Soc., 52, 314 (1930); Hill and Carothers, ibid., 55, 5037 (1933).

(5) Ibid., 55, 5039 (1933).

(6) Ruzicka, Salomon and Meyer, Helv. Chim. Acta, 17, 882 (1934).

(7) Journ Am. Chem. Soc., 54, 1579 (1932).

(8) Staudinger, "Die hochmolekularen organischen Verbindungen," Julius Springer, Berlin, 1932, p. 262; Sauter, Z. physik. Chem., 21B, 161 (1933).

(9) Leutner, Monatsh., 60, 317 (1932).

(10) Stoll and Stoll-Comte, Helv. Chim. Acta, 13, 1185 (1930); Hill and Carothers, Journ. Am. Chem. Soc., 55, 5023, 5031 (1933).

(11) Journ. Am. Chem. Soc., 55, 5050 (1933).

(12) Cf. Sidgwick, "Annual Reports of the Progress of Chemistry for 1932," p. 73.

(13) Journ. Am. Chem. Soc., 55, 5035 (1935).

(14) Ibid., 54, 1580 (1932).

XXV.   Macrocyclic Esters*

*Cyclic esters can be prepared† with alkaline catalysts from linear poly-
esters derived from carbonic, oxalic or malonic acid, but not from higher
members of the homologous series.*

*It has been found that by depolymerization at exactly 270° at a pressure
below 1 mm. Hg in the presence of hydrous metal chlorides, such as SnCl₂·-
2H₂O, KnCl₂·4H₂O, FeCl₂·4H₂O, or of magnesium powder good yields
of macrocyclic esters are obtaine l.*

*Thirty-six new esters of this type—partly monomeric, partly dimeric—
derived from succinic acid and from other, higher dibasic acids, have been
prepared and are described.*

*The molecular refractions of large rings are generally considerably less than
the calculated values, the depression, ranging from 0.4 to 0.7, being most
marked in the region between 8 and 15 carbon atoms. This is attributed
to the strain and interference of the peripheral atoms described in a previous paper** and connected with the relatively large sphere of interference
attributed to the hydrogen atoms of the chain.*

The depolymerization of linear polyesters derived from carbonic oxalic,
or malonic acid to the corresponding cyclic monomers and dimers proceeds
smoothly and rapidly in the presence of alkaline catalysts (1), but the same
conditions give very poor results when applied to polyesters derived from
succinic acid or from higher acids of the series.   We have, however, now
found a number of catalysts that act effectively in these cases.   The result
is a considerable extension of the useful range of the interchange method
in the preparation of macrocyclic esters.   Since n different glycols and an
equal number of dibasic acids may give $2n^2$ different cyclic monomers and
dimers, the number of possible compounds is very large.   In this paper,
we describe thirty-six new macrocyclic esters.   Their properties are listed
in Table I and are discussed in a later paragraph.   Details of procedure are
presented in the Experimental Part, but points of essential importance are
as follows.

The depolymerizations are carried out in the glass apparatus depicted
in Fig. 1 (2).   The outer flask contains a liquid whose refluxing vapors
heat the inner chamber where the depolymerization occurs.   This makes it

* E. W. Spanagel and W. H. Carothers; *Journ. Am. Chem. Soc.*, **57**, 929–34 (1935);
Communication No. 153 from the Experimental Station of E. I. du Pont de Nemours
and Co.

Received March 21, 1935.

† Compare paper No. XX on page 212.

** Compare paper No. XXII on page 225.

possible to control the temperature very exactly and ensures an adequate heat input. The optimum temperature appears to lie in the neighborhood of 270°; the pressure should be about 1 mm. or lower. Materials that act as effective catalysts with esters from higher acids are $SnCl_2.2H_2O$, $MnCl_2.4H_2O$, $FeCl_2.4H_2O$, $MgCl_2.6H_2O$, $CoCl_2.6H_2O$, $MnCO_3$, MgO, $MgCO_3$ and Mg powder.

By way of specific example, it may be mentioned that 20 g. of polymeric hexamethylene sebacate with 0.2 g. of $MgCl_2.6H_2O$, in two hours gave 15 g. of distillate from which 11.4 g. of pure crystalline monomer was isolated. In the preparation of other esters listed in Table I, the crude yields generally ranged from 40 to 85%, while in favorable cases the yields of pure monomers approached 70%. Presumably both monomers and dimers are always present in the crude depolymerizate. In fact, for unit lengths of 8, 9, 10 and 11, the dimers tend to predominate whereas for unit lengths above 13 very little dimer, if any, is ordinarily isolated. The ratio of dimer to monomer can be controlled within certain limits since if refluxing in the depolymerization vessel is permitted relatively little dimer can escape.

Physical Properties.—The molecular refractions of large rings are generally considerably less than the calculated values (3), the depressions commonly ranging from about 0.4 to 0.7. This peculiarity is, however,

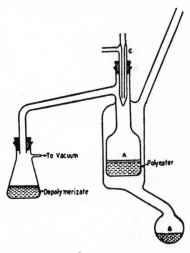

Fig. 1.—Apparatus for depolymerizing.

for the most part restricted to rings of 8 to 15 atoms, and some of the largest rings (e. g., 30–34 members) even show considerable exaltations (3). In Table I molecular refractions for 26 new macrocyclic esters are listed. The average depression is 0.32. The values fluctuate rather widely, and this may be due in part to experimental error since the measurements had to be made at a relatively high temperature. It must, however, be regarded as a significant fact that, in general, the largest depressions are found for the smaller rings (9 to 14 atoms) where the strains or interferences of the peripheral atoms are greatest, while depressions very close to zero are found only in three cases. These are listed below together with one of the cyclic carbonates (4) which shows a similar peculiarity.

Ring size	Formula	ΔM_D
21	$\boxed{\quad-O(CH_2)_{18}OCO\quad}$	+0.01
20	$\boxed{\quad-O(CH_2)_{14}OCO(CH_2)_2CO\quad}$	.00
16	$\boxed{\quad-(OCH_2CH_2)_2OCO(CH_2)_4CO\quad}$	− .09
17	$\boxed{\quad-(OCH_2CH_2)_2OCO(CH_2)_8CO\quad}$	+ .03

The first two of these are larger rings than any other esters for which values are available. The other two have in the ring extra oxygens which are capable of relieving steric interferences (5).

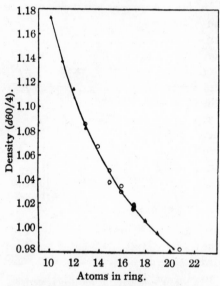

Fig. 2.—Densities (60°/4°) of cyclic esters: ▲, succinates; ○, other cyclic esters.

Densities of the new esters for which values are available are plotted in Fig. 2. The curve shows no maximum, and the densities of isomers lie quite close together.

The odors of the macrocyclic esters are especially interesting, but characterizations are not sufficiently exact to justify a detailed discussion. It may be pointed out, however, that Table I includes 3 new rings of 14 atoms, 3 of 15, 4 of 16, 7 of 17, 2 of 18, and one each of 19 and 20 atoms. Those of 18, 19 and 20 atoms are practically odorless; the odors most prominent in the others are woody or cedary, earthy, camphoraceous and musk-like. The musk-like odor is very pronounced in all of the 17-atom rings.

Data on melting points are rather incomplete, but here, as in the series previously examined, there is little to indicate any regular relation between ring size and melting point. Values for succinates are shown in Fig. 3. As the ring size increases, the melting point first falls to a minimum, then it rises to a maximum, falls again and becomes almost constant. The isomeric 17-membered rings have the general formula $\boxed{\quad-OCO(CH_2)_nCOO-(CH_2)_m\quad}$ where $n = 17 - (m + 4)$. The melting points for various values of n are

n........	3	4	6	7	8	11
M. p., °C.	14	26	47	59	37	−8

Ease of Ring Formation.—As measured by yields, it has been found for every series thus far examined that rings of 9 to 12 atoms are more difficult to form than rings of 15 to 20 atoms. Stoll and Stoll-Comte (6) have suggested that this is due to a type of steric hindrance caused by mutual re-

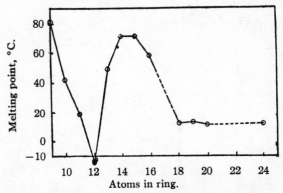

Fig. 3.—Melting points of monomeric alkylene succinates.

pulsions of peripheral hydrogens which are crowded against one another in rings of intermediate sizes. The position of the minimum in the yield *vs.* ring-size curve is not the same in different series. For cyclic ketones it lies at 10 to 11 atoms; for esters derived from dibasic acids, it apparently lies at 7 to 8 atoms. At any rate, monomers of this size have not yet been obtained among the dibasic esters, while, for example, the 7-atom lactone is obtained as a major primary product from ε-hydroxycaproic acid (7).

Another point of interest is that in the intermediate range odd-membered rings are relatively more difficult to produce than the adjacent even ones. An alternating effect of this kind was first observed in the dibasic acid anhydride series (8). Although rings of 8, 10 and 12 atoms were formed, those of 9, 11 and 13 atoms were not (the corresponding dimers were formed instead). More recently, an alternation in yield of cyclic ketones in passing from one member to the next has also been observed by Ziegler and Aurnhammer (9) in syntheses by the dilution method. The type of alternation observed in the present study is illustrated by Fig. 4 where the yield of dimer is plotted against unit length for glycol esters of succinic acid. The material not dimer is mostly monomer, and so by inverting the ordinate scale, a rough plot of monomer yield is obtained. The alternating effect is more clearly brought out by the inset of Fig. 4 which shows the rate of change of dimer yield with increasing unit length. One is tempted to compare this behavior with the well-known alternation in physical properties of certain series of open chain compounds, but the responsible factors are probably quite different in the two cases. Examination of models (with large hydrogens) shows that the interferences to ring closure in chains of 9 to about 13 atoms appear to be greater for the

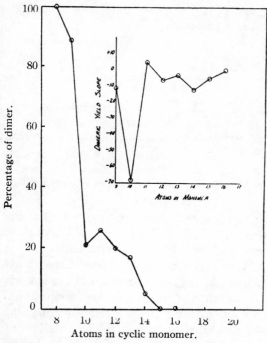

Fig. 4.—Yield *vs.* ring size in the preparation of alkylene succinates.

odd members (10), and it is probable that these interferences are still operative after the chains are closed so that the odd-membered rings are less stable than the even ones.

Since the rates at which different rings are formed are sure to be differently affected by changes in conditions, the inherent relative ease of ring formation is a concept to which no quantitative significance can be attached. Nevertheless, the effect of structure and particularly of chain length is so pronounced that even crude data permit a qualitative comparison of the inherent relative ease of forming rings of different sizes. A comparison of this kind for glycol esters of dibasic acids is shown in Fig. 5, and it includes a similar plot for the stability of cyclic anhydrides. Ease of ring formation and stability will, in general, run parallel, but 6-membered cyclic esters furnish a notable exception to this rule. They are both more easily formed and less stable than larger ester rings.

Methods of Ring Formation.—For the synthesis of large rings, there are now available two methods based upon rational principles: the dilution method first explicitly formulated and applied by Ruggli in 1912 (11) and the interchange method described above.

Ruggli's dilution method was cited in early papers of this series (12) where the general theory of bifunctional reactions was developed, but it

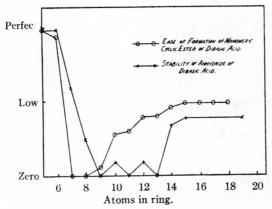

Fig. 5.—Ease of formation and stability *vs.* ring size.

received no further published attention until very recently. Ziegler and his co-workers (13) have now applied it in a very ingenious fashion to the synthesis of cyclic ketones in good yields, and further successful applications have been made by various investigators to the preparation of macrocyclic amides (14), imines (15) and lactones (16).

In a recent discussion of ring formation (17), Ziegler suggests that the interchange method will be severely restricted in the range of its applicability. On the contrary, as we have shown in this and the preceding paper, it presents extensive possibilities, and it may be appropriate to point out some of the peculiar advantages of this method.

It is true, of course, that the interchange method is inherently restricted to reversible bifunctional condensations, but almost all condensations are

TABLE I

PROPERTIES OF CYCLIC ESTERS

Cyclic ester	Number of atoms in monomeric ring	M. p. of monomer	B. p. of monomer °C mm.	Density of monomer d_4^{60}	Refractive index of monomer n_D^{60}	Mol. ref. M_D Obsd.	Mol. ref. M_D Calcd.	Diff. EM_D	M. p. of dimer
Ethylene succinate	8	81	94–100 2	1.1732	1.4567	39.91	40.56	− 0.65	131
Trimethylene succinate	9	42	95–96 2	1.1373	1.4583	44.66	45.16	− .50	138
Tetramethylene succinate	10	19	88–89 1	1.1140	1.4606	49.21	49.77	− .56	121
Pentamethylene succinate	11	−15	108–110 2	1.0821	1.4576	53.92	54.37	− .45	87
Hexamethylene succinate	12	49	116–118 1–2	1.0540 (80°)	1.4528 (80°)	58.46	58.97	− .51	110
Heptamethylene succinate	13	71		1.0357 (80°)	1.4529 (80°)	63.15	63.58	− .43	86
Octamethylene succinate	14	71	135–140 2	1.0308	1.4592	67.91	68.18	− .27	109
Nonamethylene succinate	15	58	156–159 2	1.0060	1.4588	77.14	77.38	− .24	109[a]
Decamethylene succinate	16	12	154 1–2	0.9958	1.4579	81.62	81.99	− .37	
Dodecamethylene succinate	18	13	167	0.9807	1.4568	86.59	86.59	.00	
Tridecamethylene succinate	19	11	199–201 2		1.4553				
Tetradecamethylene succinate	20	13	136–139 1						
Octadecamethylene succinate	24	14	117						
Decamethylene glutarate	17	70	162 2	1.0168	1.4585	72.51	72.78	− .27	
Hexamethylene adipate	14	59	144–146 2	1.0535 (80°)	1.4542 (80°)	58.64	58.97	− .33	
Triethylene glycol adipate	16	26	158–160 1–2	1.1289 (80°)	1.4545 (80°)	64.35	64.44	− .09	
Nonamethylene adipate	17	47	123–124 2	1.0186	1.4594	72.53	72.78	− .25	
Heptamethylene suberate	17	52		1.0188	1.4592	72.46	72.78	− .32	145
Ethylene azelate	13	9	119–123 2	1.0851	1.4593	53.96	54.37	− .41	
Tetramethylene azelate	15	59	130–133 2	1.0471	1.4595	63.23	63.58	− .35	
Hexamethylene azelate	17	42[a]	136–138 2	1.0032 (80°)	1.4520 (80°)	72.59	72.78	− .19	
Ethylene sebacate	14	7	159–160 2	1.0669	1.4599	58.51	58.97	− .46	81[a]
Trimethylene sebacate	15	6	156–157 2	1.0372	1.4560	63.43	63.58	− .15	110[a]
Tetramethylene sebacate	16	37	139–141 2	1.0344	1.4605	67.84	68.18	− .34	
Pentamethylene sebacate	17	15	139–142 1	1.0176	1.4594	72.60	72.78	− .18	
Diethylene glycol sebacate	17			1.0635	1.4586	69.89	69.86	+ .03	
Hexamethylene sebacate	18	47		1.0053	1.4589	77.20	77.38	− .18	
Ethylene decamethylene dicarboxylate	16	18		1.0303	1.4588	67.89	68.18	− .29	
Ethylene brassylate	17	−8		1.0180	1.4582	72.38	72.78	− .40	96[a]
Decamethylene octadecanedioate	30	60			1.4576			Av. .32	146[a]

[a] Previously reported in *Journ. Am. Chem. Soc.*, **55**, 5034 (1933).

reversible to a certain extent. We have already presented some evidence (18) indicating that even polyketones can be depolymerized and that this is what is involved in Ruzicka's thorium salt method for the synthesis of large carbon rings. Practically, the interchange method will be restricted to those bifunctional condensations that are *easily* reversible, but, as the present paper shows, much can be accomplished in that direction by the choice of suitable catalysts, and the formation of esters and anhydrides by no means represents the limit of the possibilities.

One other point that deserves mention is this: there are two general types of bifunctional reactions symbolized in the two formulas

$$x—R—y \longrightarrow \text{products, and}$$
$$x—R—x + y—R'—y \longrightarrow \text{products}$$

In the first type (simple bifunctional), both the mutually reactive groups are present on the same molecule; in the second (bifunctional) (12) the mutually reactive groups are initially present on separate molecules. An example of the first type is an hydroxy acid, of the second type, a dibasic acid plus a glycol. The second type is much the more numerous, and it is one to which the theoretical advantages of the dilution method are not applicable with full efficiency since the initial step toward ring formation necessarily involves an intermolecular reaction. Practical advantages of the interchange method in connection with such problems as the preparation of lactones and p-rings will be illustrated in future papers.

Experimental Part

The apparatus used in the present work is shown in Fig. 1. The flask B contains a liquid whose refluxing vapors heat the chamber A. This method makes it possible to control the temperature very exactly and ensures an adequate heat input. The dephlegmator C may be cooled with steam if reflux is desired to restrict the distillation of dimer, or it may be omitted entirely. For amounts of polymer in the neighborhood of 50 g., the chamber A should be of about 800 cc. capacity since considerable foaming occurs at the start of the depolymerization.

Preliminary experiments were made with decamethylene carbonate using a sodium catalyst. The importance of low pressure was soon demonstrated, and in further work a pump with high capacity was used and the pressure kept at 1 mm. or below. The rate increased, but the purity of the distillate dropped off somewhat as the temperature was raised above 250°. A temperature of 270° appeared to be about the optimum, and it was conveniently supplied by boiling o-chlorodiphenyl. These observations were applied to the preparation of monomeric tetradecamethylene carbonate on a one hundred gram scale using an alkaline catalyst; a 93% yield of monomer having a purity of 97% was obtained in less than two hours.

These conditions, however, gave no satisfactory results with polyesters derived from higher dibasic acids, and attention was therefore turned to a further exploration of catalysts. The polyesters used were prepared from the appropriate dibasic acid and a slight excess of glycol by heating at 200° (bath) finally at a pressure of 2–3 mm. Products obtained in this manner were gray waxy masses of varying degrees of hardness. One of the first catalysts tried was stannous chloride, and the following results are typical.

TABLE II
ANALYTICAL DATA FOR NEW CYCLIC ESTERS

Compound	Calculated			Found		Mol. wt. in freezing benzene
	C, %	H, %	Mol. wt.	C, %	H, %	
Trimethylene succinate, Monomer	53.16	6.32	158	53.10	6.42	162 159
Trimethylene succinate, Dimer	53.16	6.32	316	53.52	6.45	270
Tetramethylene succinate, Monomer	55.81	6.97	172	55.56	6.76	170 166
Tetramethylene succinate, Dimer	55.81	6.97	344	56.33	6.87	332
Pentamethylene succinate, Monomer	58.06	7.52	186	57.59	7.88	177 182
Pentamethylene succinate, Dimer	58.06	7.52	372	57.86	7.42	395 376
Hexamethylene succinate, Monomer	60.00	8.00	200	59.76	8.04	199 197
Hexamethylene succinate, Dimer	60.00	8.00	400	60.41	8.14	418 393
Heptamethylene succinate, Monomer	61.68	8.41	214	60.61	8.67	206
Heptamethylene succinate, Dimer	61.68	8.41	428	61.91	8.82	428
Octamethylene succinate, Monomer	63.15	8.77	228	63.32	8.76	228 228
Octamethylene succinate, Dimer	63.15	8.77	456	63.40	8.83	498
Nonamethylene succinate, Monomer	64.46	9.09	242	64.04	9.08	236 229
Decamethylene succinate, Monomer	65.62	9.37	256	65.36	9.35	250 246
Dodecamethylene succinate, Monomer	67.60	9.85	284	67.77	10.03	283 271
Tridecamethylene succinate, Monomer	68.45	10.06	298	68.98	10.27	290 277
Tetradecamethylene succinate, Monomer	69.23	10.25	312	69.24	10.20	314 300
Octadecamethylene succinate, Monomer	71.74	10.88	368	71.58	10.73	365 348
Decamethylene glutarate, Monomer	66.67	9.63	270	67.14	9.64	271 265
Hexamethylene adipate, Monomer	63.16	8.77	228	63.21	8.81	214 217
Triethylene glycol adipate, Monomer	54.96	8.39	262	55.26	7.74	283 275
Nonamethylene adipate, Monomer	66.67	9.63	270	66.54	9.10	266 256
Heptamethylene suberate, Monomer	66.67	9.63	270	66.92	9.79	272 269
Ethylene azelate, Monomer	62.15	8.41	214	61.93	8.25	216 212
Ethylene azelate, Dimer	62.15	8.41	428	62.13	8.81	466 431
Tetramethylene azelate, Monomer	64.46	9.09	242	64.55	9.21	244 234
Hexamethylene azelate, Monomer	66.67	9.63	270	66.98	9.44	260 269
Ethylene sebacate, Monomer			228			232 224
Trimethylene sebacate, Monomer	64.46	9.09	242	64.05	8.89	248 236
Tetramethylene sebacate, Monomer	65.62	9.37	256	65.55	9.58	268 254
Pentamethylene sebacate, Monomer	66.67	9.63	270	66.08	9.37	264 258
Diethylene glycol sebacate, Monomer	61.76	8.82	272	62.37	9.37	257 258
Hexamethylene sebacate, Monomer	67.60	9.85	284	67.41	9.75	260 256
Ethylene decamethylene dicarboxylate, Monomer	65.62	9.37	256	65.41	9.45	256 249
Ethylene brassylate, Monomer	66.67	9.63	220	66.88	9.93	242 252
Decamethylene octadecanedioate, Monomer	74.33	11.50	452	74.72	11.83	465 443

Fifty grams of polymeric hexamethylene succinate with 0.5 g. of SnCl$_2$.2H$_2$O was heated at 270° at 1 mm. or less. The polymer became soft and bubbled, and after about ten minutes distillation started. The rates observed were: after fifteen minutes, 12 drops/min.; after thirty minutes, 14 drops/min. At this point the residue became a stiff porous gel occupying about half the volume of the flask, but distillation continued: after forty-five minutes, 10 drops/min.; after sixty minutes, 8 drops/min.; after seventy-five minutes, 3 drops/min. The ultimate residue was a light porous mass of tough, insoluble, yellow resin. The distillate (40 g.), consisting of a light yellow liquid and a white solid, was filtered. The solid on recrystallization from alcohol yielded 8 g. of dimer, white plates melting at 110°. Any catalyst present in the monomer was removed by dissolving the filtrate in ether and washing with water. The dried ether solution was concentrated and distilled. The yield of cyclic monomeric hexamethylene succinate boiling at 108–110° (2 mm.) was 21 g. This general procedure was used in isolating other cyclic esters except that when the monomer was a solid it was usually purified by crystallization from alcohol at low temperature. Yields of crude distillate varied from 40 to 85%.

For further study of catalysts, experiments were made with hexamethylene sebacate since its monomer is a readily purified crystalline solid. The polyester (20 g.) was heated with 0.2 g. of the possible catalyst in a glass still at 270° (1 mm.) for two hours. The crude distillate was dissolved in 50 cc. of alcohol, cooled, and the pure monomer isolated by filtration. Results are shown in Table III.

TABLE III

CATALYSTS FOR DEPOLYMERIZATION

Catalyst	Distillate, %	Pure monomer, %
$SnCl_2.2H_2O$	65	45
$MnCl_2.4H_2O$	75	55
$FeCl_2.4H_2O$	75	57
$MgCl_2.6H_2O$	75	57
$CoCl_2.6H_2O$	80	65
$Co(NO_3)_2.6H_2O$	70	55
Mg (powd.)	75	60
$MnCO_3$	60	40
MgO	70	45
$MgCO_3$	70	55
$PbCl_2$	15	8
$FeCl_3$	25	18
Tl_2CO_3	15	8
$SbCl_3$	15	8
$Th(NO_3)_4.12H_2O$	10	5
None (control)	5	..

The following substances were also tried but gave very small distillates, from which no monomer could be isolated: $NiCl_2.6H_2O$, $FeSO_4$, $TiCl_4$, tin dust, $Mg_3(PO_4)_2$, $CrCl_3$, $CaCO_3$, $CrCl_2$, $ZnCl_2$.

Typical yields of cyclic esters obtained at 270°/1 mm. using 1 to 3% $SnCl_2.2H_2O$ as catalyst are shown below.

Losses in purification are due in part to polymerization during redistillation, and these can be largely avoided by first washing out the catalyst. Considerable improvements can also be effected by suitable precautions in preparing the polymer.

TABLE IV
YIELDS OF CYCLIC ESTERS

Ester	Unit length	Time, hrs.	Crude distillate %	Distillate isolated as monomer %	dimer %
Ethylene succinate	8	4	80	0	95
Trimethylene succinate	9	4	46	9	89
Tetramethylene succinate	10	4	48	70	21
Pentamethylene succinate	11	4	77	46	26
Heptamethylene succinate	13	4	68	30	17
Octamethylene succinate	14	4	81	55	5
Nonamethylene succinate	15	4	84	83	0
Octadecamethylene succinate	24	6	60	76	0
Decamethylene glutarate	17	5	81	30	0
Nonamethylene adipate	17	3	75	48	0
Heptamethylene suberate	17	7	70	58	0
Ethylene azelate	13	4	68	79	4
Trimethylene sebacate	15	7	52	84	0
Tetramethylene sebacate	16	6	40	70	0
Pentamethylene sebacate	17	7	51	60	0
Hexamethylene sebacate	18	4	73	73	0
Diethylene glycol sebacate	17	5	67	81	0
Ethylene brassylate	17	4	72	58	0

Summary

The optimum conditions for the depolymerization of linear polyesters have been more clearly defined and new catalysts have been found which make it possible to apply this method generally to the rapid preparation of macrocyclic esters in good yields. Thirty-six new cyclic esters, monomeric and dimeric, derived from succinic acid and from other higher dibasic acids are described. Conclusions developed in the study of other macrocyclic compounds have been confirmed and extended.

Bibliography and Remarks

(1) Hill and Carothers, *ibid.*, **55**, 5031 (1933).

(2) This design was suggested to us by Mr. C. H. Greenewalt.

(3) Ruzicka and Stoll, *Helv. Chim. Acta,* **11**, 1159 (1928); Ruzicka, Stoll, Huyser and Boekenoogen, *ibid.*, **13**, 1152 (1930); Ruzicka and Boekenoogen, *ibid.*, **14**, 1319 (1931); Ruzicka, Hürbin, and Furter, *ibid.*, **17**, 78 (1934); Hill and Carothers, *Journ. Am. Chem. Soc.*, **55**, 5042 (1933).

(4) *Journ. Am. Chem. Soc.*, **55**, 5042 (1933).

(5) Hill and Carothers, *ibid.*, **57**, 925 (1935); **55**, 5049 (1933).

(6) Stoll and Stoll-Comte, *Helv. Chim. Acta*, **13**, 1185 (1930).

(7) van Natta, Hill and Carothers, *Journ. Am. Chem. Soc.*, **56**, 455 (1934).

(8) Hill and Carothers, *Journ. Am. Chem. Soc.*, **55**, 5025 (1933).

(9) Ziegler and Aurnhammer, *Ann.*, **513**, 43 (1934).

(10) Hill and Carothers, *Journ. Am. Chem. Soc.*, **55**, 5050 (1933).

(11) Ruggli, *Ann.*, **392** 92 (1912).

(12) *E. g., Journ. Am. Chem. Soc.*, **51**, 2551 (1929).

(13) Ziegler, Eberle and Ohlinger, *Ann.*, **504**, 94 (1933); Ziegler and Aurnhammer, *ibid.*, **513**, 43 (1934).

(14) Reid and Lippert, St. Petersburg Meeting of the A. C. S., March, 1934.

(15) Salomon, *Helv. Chim. Acta*, **17**, 851 (1934); Ruzicka, Salomon and Meyer, *ibid.*, **17**, 882 (1934).

(16) Stoll, Rouvé and Stoll-Comte, *ibid.*, **17**, 1289 (1934).

(17) Ziegler, *Ber.*, **67**, 139 (1934).

(18) *Journ. Am. Chem. Soc.*, **55**, 5045 (1933).

XXVI. Meta and Para Rings*

This paper deals with rings closed through the m- and p- positions of the benzene nucleus. Six meta rings were prepared by combining resorcinol diacetate with

> *ethylene glycol*
> *trimethylene glycol*
> *tetramethylene glycol*
> *hexamethylene glycol*
> *nonamethylene glycol and*
> *decamethylene glycol*

Five para rings were obtained from hydroquinone diacetate with

> *ethylene glycol*
> *trimethylene glycol*
> *tetramethylene glycol*
> *hexamethylene glycol and*
> *decamethylene glycol*

Again there is formed first a polyester, which gives the required ring by depolymerization. Meta rings much smaller than 13 atoms and para rings much smaller than 16 atoms are not likely to be obtained. All samples prepared were pure white sharply melting macrocrystalline solids. They are easily soluble in most organic solvents.

The closure of rings through the *m*- and *p*-positions of the benzene nucleus is one of the conventional problems of organic chemistry that long resisted solution. As soon as a rational theory of ring closure had been developed (1), it became apparent that success might easily be achieved by the use of either the dilution or the interchange principle. Meanwhile,

* E. W. Spanagel and W. H. Carothers; *Journ. Am. Chem. Soc.*, **57**, 935–6 (1935); Communication No. 154 from the Experimental Station of E. I. du Pont de Nemours and Co.

Received March 21, 1935.

Ruzicka, Buijs and Stoll (2) applied their thorium salt method to the acids p-$C_6H_4[(CH_2)_5COOH]_2$ and m-$C_6H_4[(CH_2)_6COOH]_2$ and from the latter obtained a small amount of the 16-membered cyclic ketone, while Ziegler and Luttringhaus (3) have applied the dilution method to the nitriles m- and p-$C_6H_4[O(CH_2)_6CN]_2$. The cyclic iminonitriles of 18 and 19 atoms were obtained in good yields.

In the experiments presently reported, the acids m- and p-$C_6H_4(OCH_2$-$COOH)_2$ were esterified with glycols of the series $HO(CH_2)_nOH$ and the resulting polyesters depolymerized. In this manner, we have obtained m-rings (I) of 13, 14, 15, 17, 20 and 21 atoms, in yields ranging from 16 to 35%. In the p-series (II) none of the 14- or 15-membered ring was obtained, but those of 16, 18 and 22 atoms were isolated in yields of 12 to 18%.

Data concerning yields and properties are shown in Table I.

TABLE I

PROPERTIES AND SUMMARY OF PREPARATION OF META AND PARA RINGS

Polyester diacetate	Polyester, g.	Heating, hrs.	Crude yield, %	Pure yield, %	M. p. of monomer, °C.	Ring size of monomer
Ethylene resorcinol	23	2.5	30	21	100	13
Trimethylene resorcinol	29	3.5	41	24	134	14
Tetramethylene resorcinol	22	5	23	16	112	15
Hexamethylene resorcinol	22	3	45	35	115	17
Nonamethylene resorcinol	20	5	45	35	86	20
Decamethylene resorcinol	20	5	55	35	86	21
Ethylene hydroquinone	48	14	9	0	..	..
Trimethylene hydroquinone	35	6.5	10	0	..	..
Tetramethylene hydroquinone	28	4	42	12	140	16
Hexamethylene hydroquinone	50	7	30	12	124	18
Decamethylene hydroquinone	50	7	38	18	58	22

These results demonstrate clearly the formation and stable existence of a 13-membered m-ring, and they suggest that in the p-series a ring of 16 atoms is the smallest possible, but caution must be used in extending or generalizing these conclusions. On the one hand, it has already been shown (4) that the replacement of —CH₂— by —O— in a chain considerably increases the ease of ring formation; thus, in the carbocyclic series the limits may lie at values different from those obtained for rings containing two ester groups and two ether oxygens. On the other hand, the failure to obtain a ring by no means demonstrates that its formation is impossible or that it would be very unstable if formed. Nevertheless, in view of the observed facts and the implications of space models, it seems that *m*-rings much smaller than 13 atoms and *p*-rings much smaller than 16 atoms are not likely to be obtained.

Experimental

Preparation and Properties of Polymers.—Polymeric resorcinol diacetates were prepared by heating equivalent amounts of the acid and glycol at 190–200° for about three hours and finally heating the residue to 210° *in vacuo* one or two hours. The polymers were light brown viscous resins. Nonamethylene resorcinol diacetate, however, crystallized on long standing; the melting point of the crude polymer was 35–40°.

Owing to the high melting point of the acid, polymeric hydroquinone diacetates were prepared by heating equivalent amounts of the glycol and the ester (ethyl hydroquinone diacetate) with a small crystal of stannous chloride to 190° for about three hours. Final traces of alcohol were removed by heating the mixture in a vacuum to 210°. Ethylene and trimethylene hydroquinone diacetates are low-melting brown glassy resins. The remaining polymers were solids which had the following melting points:

Tetramethylene hydroquinone diacetate	45–50°
Hexamethylene hydroquinone diacetate	50–55°
Decamethylene hydroquinone diacetate	60–65°

Depolymerization.—The polyesters were depolymerized at 270° (1 mm.) in an 800-cc. vapor-heated still or depolymerizer of the type described in the preceding paper (5), using 1 to 2% of SnCl₂.2H₂O as catalyst. Rates, yields and melting points are given in Table I. The monomers, purified by crystallization from alcohol, are all pure white sharply macrocrystalline solids. They are very soluble in ethyl acetate, benzene, acetone and ether; moderately soluble in petroleum ether and carbon tetrachloride. In the latter solvent, the higher members are more soluble than the lower ones. The compounds are all neutral (*i. e.*, they do not decompose potassium carbonate), and they react only slowly with a carbon tetrachloride solution of bromine. Two of the monomers, hexamethylene hydroquinone diacetate and hexamethylene resorcinol diacetate, were saponified; the corresponding dibasic acids were obtained in good yields and identified by mixed melting points.

Summary

Polyesters prepared from the acids m- and p-$C_6H_4(OCH_2COOH)_2$ by causing them to react with glycols $HO(CH_2)_nOH$ have been depolymerized. Cyclic monomers were thus obtained in the m-series, having rings of 13, 14, 15, 17, 20 and 21 atoms. In the p-series none of the 14- or 15-membered rings could be isolated, but those of 16, 18 and 22 atoms were readily formed.

TABLE II
ANALYTICAL DATA FOR META AND PARA RINGS

	C	H	Mol. wt.[a]		C	H	Mol. wt.[a]
Ethylene resorcinol diacetate				Decamethylene resorcinol diacetate			
Calcd. for $C_{12}H_{12}O_6$	57.14	4.76	252	Calcd. for $C_{20}H_{28}O_6$	65.92	7.69	364
Found	57.37	4.76	252	Found	66.02	7.75	364
Trimethylene resorcinol diacetate				Tetramethylene hydroquinone diacetate			
Calcd. for $C_{13}H_{14}O_6$	58.64	5.96	266	Calcd. for $C_{14}H_{16}O_6$	60.00	5.71	280
Found	58.69	5.38	260	Found	60.33	5.86	268
Tetramethylene resorcinol diacetate				Hexamethylene hydroquinone diacetate			
Calcd. for $C_{14}H_{16}O_6$	60.00	5.71	280	Calcd. for $C_{16}H_{20}O_6$	62.33	6.49	308
Found	60.04	5.65	290	Found	62.40	6.84	307
Hexamethylene resorcinol diacetate				Decamethylene hydroquinone diacetate			
Calcd. for $C_{16}H_{20}O_6$	62.33	6.49	308	Calcd. for $C_{20}H_{28}O_6$	65.92	7.69	364
Found	61.96	6.29	302	Found	66.25	7.84	356
Nonamethylene resorcinol diacetate							
Calcd. for $C_{19}H_{26}O_6$	65.14	7.43	350				
Found	65.02	7.31	360				

[a] Determinations made by freezing point in benzene.

Bibliography and Remarks

(1) *Journ. Am. Chem. Soc.*, **51**, 2548 (1929); **54**, 1569 (1932); **55**, 5043 (1933).

(2) Ruzicka, Buijs and Stoll, *Helv. Chim. Acta*, **15**, 1220 (1932).

(3) Ziegler and Luttringhaus, *Ann.*, **511**, 1 (1934).

(4) *Journ. Am. Chem. Soc.*, **55**, 5050 (1933).

(5) *Ibid.*, **57**, 929 (1935; this volume, page 248).

XXVII.   Polydecamethylene Oxide*

During the course of the investigations which belong to this series it was observed† that the depolymerization of polydecamethylene carbonate gave a rubbery residue. This material was hydrolyzed and gave decamethylene glycol, decene-9-ol-1 and polydecamethylene oxide. The latter has a molecular weight of about 1200.

In a previous paper of this series (1) it was shown that polyesters, when heated under appropriate catalytic conditions in an evacuated vessel designed for the quick and irreversible removal of volatile material, undergo the series of transformations represented in the scheme

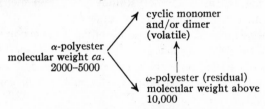

In the case of the polymethylene carbonates, the end-products under favorable circumstances were almost all obtained as volatile depolymerizate and very little residue remained. However, in certain instances in which it is now believed that the pressure rose too high on account of inadequate pumping, the residue became rubbery early in the experiments and distillation soon practically ceased. During the course of a large number of experiments on the depolymerization of polymeric decamethylene carbonate, a considerable amount of these residues accumulated, and it was thought worth-while to attempt the recovery of decamethylene glycol from them by hydrolysis. Comparatively little glycol was recovered in this way. The major product isolated from the hydrolysis mixture was a wax-like material which examination showed to be polydecamethylene oxide (2)

$$\ldots(CH_2)_{10}-O-(CH_2)_{10}-O-(CH_2)_{10}-O-(CH_2)_{10}-O\ldots$$

The hydrolysis of the rubbery residue was carried out by means of alcoholic potassium hydroxide. The resulting solution was filtered from a small amount of insoluble matter. Most of the alcohol was distilled and

* J. W. Hill; *Journ. Am. Chem. Soc.,* **57**, 1131–2 (1935); Communication No. 156 from the Experimental Station of E. I. du Pont de Nemours and Co.
Received April 26, 1935.
† Compare paper No. III on page 29.

replaced by hot water. The insoluble upper layer was allowed to solidify and separated. It was then heated under vacuum in a Claisen flask until the distillation of decamethylene glycol ceased. The residue was repeatedly extracted with boiling water until no more glycol could be removed in this way. It was then recrystallized once from acetone, once from alcohol, dried and analyzed.

Anal. Calcd. for $(CH_2)_{10}O$: C, 76.92; H, 12.82; mol. wt., 156. Found: C, 76.18, 76.31; H, 12.44, 12.37; mol. wt. (cryoscopically in benzene), 1200, 1200.

It was soluble in benzene, carbon tetrachloride, chloroform and concentrated sulfuric acid, insoluble in cold alcohol, ethyl acetate and acetone, and insoluble, hot or cold, in petroleum fractions. From recrystallizing solvents, it separated as a microcrystalline powder of melting point 58–60°. From a melt it was obtained as a soft wax.

The probable course of the reaction leading to the polyether may be represented by the following scheme in which it is supposed that the polyester undergoes scission and gives carbon dioxide and decamethylene oxide radicals. These may rearrange to decene-9-ol-1 or combine to give the polymeric ether.

$$(-O-(CH_2)_{10}-OCO-)_n \xrightarrow{-CO_2}$$
α-polydecamethylene
carbonate

$$n[-(CH_2)_{10}-O-] \longrightarrow (-(CH_2)_{10}-O-)_n$$
$$\downarrow$$
$$CH_2=CH-(CH_2)_1OH \qquad \text{polydecamethylene oxide}$$
decene-9-ol-1

Support for this mechanism is the fact that in the depolymerization experiments yielding considerable polyether residues, the distillates were always contaminated with decene-9-ol-1 (3).

The constitution of the material was established by its analyses and molecular weight and by its transformation by the following reactions to decamethylene glycol.

$$(-(CH_2)_{10}-O-)_n \xrightarrow{HI} I(CH_2)_{10}I- \xrightarrow{KOAc}$$
$$AcO(CH_2)_{10}OAc \xrightarrow{H_2O} HO(CH_2)_{10}OH$$

The intermediate compounds were not purified.

Twenty grams of recrystallized polymer, 40 cc. of glacial acetic acid, and 75 cc. of constant boiling hydriodic acid were refluxed together for six hours. The resulting dark red lower layer was separated and refluxed briefly with a suspension of calcium carbonate which removed the color.

The heavy oil was recovered by means of an ether extraction and then re-fluxed with 40 g. of powdered freshly fused potassium acetate, 15 cc. of glacial acetic acid and 3 cc. of acetic anhydride for four hours. This mixture was drowned in water and the product recovered by ether extraction. This was then hydrolyzed by refluxing for ten hours with a solution of 15 g. of sodium hydroxide in 150 cc. of 50% alcohol. The alcohol was removed by steam distillation which was continued for several hours to remove a very small amount of oil, which smelled like decene-9-ol-1. The oil on top of the residual liquid solidified and from it was isolated, by two crystallizations from benzene, 5 g. of pure decamethylene glycol, m. p. 71–72°. It showed no depression in melting point when mixed with a known sample of decamethylene glycol.

Summary

The depolymerization of polydecamethylene carbonate, under certain experimental conditions, pursues an abnormal course and yields a distillate contaminated with decene-9-ol-1 together with a large amount of residue. This residue has been examined and found to consist largely of a polymeric substance which has been characterized as polydecamethylene oxide. A mechanism for the side reaction has been suggested.

Bibliography and Remarks

(1) *Journ. Am. Chem. Soc.*, **55**, 5031 (1933).

(2) It is of interest to mention that Franke [*Monatsh.*, **53–54**, 577 (1929), and earlier papers] obtained, by the dehydration of decamethylene glycol with sulfuric acid, not a decamethylene oxide, but α-amyl pentamethylene oxide.

(3) *Journ. Am. Chem. Soc.*, **55**, 5037 (1933).

XXVIII. Preparation of Macrocyclic Lactones by Depolymerization*

The depolymerization method† is used in this publication to prepare macrocyclic lactones. A yield of 70% of pure monomer could be obtained from the polyester of hydroxy tetradecanoic acid. Depolymerization was carried out with the aid of catalysts, mostly hydrous magnesium chloride at 270° in vacuo. The lactones of the following acids were prepared:

* E. W. Spanagel and W. H. Carothers; *Journ. Am. Chem. Soc.*, 58, 654–6 (1936); Communication No. 166 from the Experimental Station of E. I. du Pont de Nemours and Co.

Received January 18, 1936.

† Compare *e. g.* paper No. XXV on page 248.

14-hydroxy-12-oxatetradecanoic (mono and dimer)
16-hydroxy-12-oxahexadecanoic (monomer).

Lactones of the higher ω-hydroxy fatty acids were first successfully synthesized by oxidizing the corresponding cyclic ketones (1). Preparation by the conventional methods is impossible because the acids tend to react intermolecularly yielding linear polyesters. Once this fact was clearly recognized it became evident (2) (p. 8 . . .) that direct lactonization might be favored by application of the dilution principle first utilized by Ruggli (3); and Stoll and Rouvé (4) have showed experimentally that this is indeed the case.

A third method for the preparation of large ester rings consists in depolymerizing the corresponding linear polyester. This was first realized with esters of carbonic and oxalic acids (5). Later it was shown that, by the proper control of temperature and selection of catalysts, excellent results could also be obtained with glycol esters of other dibasic acids (6).

We have now applied this method to the preparation of several lactones. The possibilities are indicated by the fact that a 70% yield of pure monomer was obtained from the polyester of hydroxytetradecanoic acid. Stoll and Rouvé (4) in a similar case report yields by the dilution method considerably higher than this, but their scale of operation was small (10 g.), the volume large (10 liters) and the time long (six days). Our depolymerization required only three and one-half hours for 32 g. of polyester. It appears therefore that this method has some advantages over the use of high dilution.

One of the objects of the present work was to obtain some lactones which had not been reported previously. Meanwhile Stoll and Rouvé have published a much more extended study (4) of lactonization by the dilution method covering in part the same ground. The overlapping results of the two investigations are in good agreement, but in several cases we are able to report slightly higher melting points than were found by Stoll and Rouvé.

As new compounds we report

$$\overline{O(CH_2)_2O(CH_2)_{10}CO}$$

$$\overline{O(CH_2)_4O(CH_2)_{10}CO} \quad \text{and}$$

$$\overline{O(CH_2)_2O(CH_2)_{10}COO(CH_2)_2O(CH_2)_{10}CO}$$

The first two are rings of 15 and 17 atoms and their odors are definitely musk-like. These compounds are also of interest because the required hydroxy acids are relatively easily accessible from undecylenic acid through the addition of hydrogen bromide followed by reaction with the sodium derivative of the glycol.

The greater ease of forming rings of large size compared with intermediate size is again illustrated in the present study by the fact that hydroxytetradecanoic acid gave monomer and dimer in the ratio of 15/1 while for hydroxydecanoic acid the corresponding ratio was 0.17/1. Further evidence of specificity in the catalysis of ester depolymerizations was also found. Whereas in most of the cases previously examined, stannous chloride and various magnesium salts were almost equally effective, in the present work magnesium chloride was much more effective than any other material tested (cf. Table I).

TABLE I
EFFECT OF CATALYST ON YIELDS

Catalyst	Remarks	Crude yield, %	% of distillate dimer	% of distillate monomer
MgCl$_2$.6H$_2$O	No reflux	73	36	64
MgCl$_2$.6H$_2$O	Steam cooled reflux	53	3	97
MgO	No reflux	66	40	60
MnCl$_2$.4H$_2$O	No reflux	63	47	53
SnCl$_2$.2H$_2$O	No reflux	40	75	25
CoCl$_2$.6H$_2$O	No reflux	27	62	48
Mg (powd.)	No reflux	20	83	27

TABLE II
EFFECT OF TEMPERATURE ON YIELDS

Temp., °C.	Time, hours	% crude yield	% dimer
270	2	73	26
260	2	30	12
260	5	58	15
250	2	28	10
250	5	52	12

Experimental Part

Polyesters were prepared by heating the hydroxy acids at 180–250° for three or four hours in a Claisen flask without added catalyst but with diminished pressure during the last hour.

Depolymerizations were carried out in the vapor heated still already described (6) at a pressure of 1 mm. or less. In some experiments a dephlegmator cooled with steam was inserted at the top of the still. It lowered the rate of distillation and increased the ratio of monomer to dimer.

Catalysts were explored using polyester (15 g.) from hydroxyundecanoic acid with 0.2 to 0.3 g. of the proposed catalyst at 270° during two hours. The distillate was dis-

TABLE III

YIELDS OF LACTONES

Polyester from	Polyester used, g.	Catalyst added	Time of heating to 270° (1 mm.) hrs.	Distillate, %	Distillate isolated as monomer, %	Distillate isolated as dimer, %
10-Hydroxydecanoic acid	20	MgCl₂. 6H₂O	2	65	12	70
13-Hydroxytridecanoic acid	95	SnCl₂. 2H₂O	4	55	Trace (odor)	50
14-Hydroxytetradecanoic acid	32	MgCl₂. 6H₂O	3.5	77	90	6
HO(CH₂)₂O(CH₂)₁₀COOH	75	MgCl₂. 6H₂O	4	64	66	6
HO(CH₂)₃O(CH₂)₁₀COOH	40	MgCl₂. 6H₂O	4	70	50	0
HO(CH₂)₄O(CH₂)₁₀COOH	60	MgCl₂. 6H₂O	3	55	76	0

TABLE IV

PROPERTIES OF LACTONES

Monomeric lactone from	Atoms in monomeric ring	M. p. of monomer, °C.	B. p. of monomer, °C.	Density of monomer d_4^{33}	Refractive index of n_D^{33}	Molecular refraction, Md Obsd.	Calcd.	Diff. EMd	M. p. of dimer, °C.
10-Hydroxydecanoic acid	11	6.0	113–15/15	0.9926	1.4655	47.40	47.90	−0.50	96[b]
11-Hydroxyundecanoic acid[a,c]	12	3.0	126–7/15	.9812	1.4662	51.97	52.50	−.53	74
13-Hydroxytridecanoic acid	14	....	....	....	....	....	....	....	84[c]
14-Hydroxy-12-oxatetradecanoic acid	15	8.0	108–11/1	.9916	1.4645	63.52	63.39	+.13	106–107
15-Hydroxy-12-oxapentadecanoic acid[c]	16	12.0	119–20/2	.9762	1.4622	68.13	67.99	+.14	......
16-Hydroxy-12-oxahexadecanoic acid	17	−19.0	129–31/1	.9724	1.4646	72.68	72.60	+.08	......

[a] Cf. Stoll, Rouvé and Stoll-Comte, Helv. Chim. Acta, 17, 1307 (1934).   [b] Cf. Lycan and Adams, Journ. Am. Chem. Soc., 51, 3450 (1929); Carothers and van Natta, ibid., 55, 4719 (1933).   [c] Cf. Stoll and Rouvé, Helv. Chim. Acta, 18, 1087 (1935).

solved in 50 cc. of alcohol and the crystalline dimer which separated on cooling was filtered off and weighed. The accumulated filtrates on distillation were shown to be largely monomer, and in the last column of Table I the indicated yields are based on the assumption that all not dimer was monomer.

The effect of *temperature* is indicated in Table II.   In each case 20 g. of polyester from hydroxyundecanoic acid was heated with 0.5 g. of $MgCl_2.6H_2O$.   The ratio of monomer to dimer rises as the temperature falls, but the rate falls off quite rapidly at the same time.

The results for the depolymerization of polylactone derived from 10-hydroxy-decanoic, 13-hydroxytridecanoic, 14-hydroxytetradecanoic acid and the ether acids are listed in Table III.   Properties and analyses are indicated in Tables IV and V.

TABLE V

ANALYTICAL DATA

	C	H	Mol wt.[a]
Lactone of 10-hydroxydecanoic acid			
Calcd. for $C_{10}H_{18}O_2$	70.58	10.58	170
Found	70.31	10.13	162
Dimeric lactone of 13-hydroxytridecanoic acid			
Calcd. for $C_{26}H_{48}O_4$	73.24	11.26	426
Found	73.46	11.30	407, 432
Dimeric lactone of 14-hydroxytetradecanoic acid			
Calcd. for $C_{28}H_{52}O_4$	74.33	11.50	452
Found	74.29	11.79	414
Lactone of 14-hydroxy-12-oxatetradecanoic acid			
Calcd. for $C_{13}H_{24}O_3$	68.42	10.52	228
Found	68.57	10.17	232
Dimeric lactone of 14-hydroxy-12-oxatetradecanoic acid			
Calcd. for $C_{26}H_{48}O_6$	68.42	10.52	456
Found	68.16	10.36	466
Lactone of 15-hydroxy-12-oxapentadecanoic acid			
Calcd. for $C_{14}H_{21}O_3$	69.42	10.74	242
Found	69.76	11.00	234
Lactone of 16-hydroxy-12-oxahexadecanoic acid			
Calcd. for $C_{16}H_{28}O_3$	70.3	10.93	256
Found	70.31	11.01	258

[a] Determinations made in freezing benzene.

Preparation of Materials

11-Hydroxyundecanoic was prepared from undecylenic acid and hydrobromic acid following Ashton and Smith (7).   Our best yields were 72% of the theoretical.   Conversion of this to 11-hydroxyundecanoic acid was carried out as follows: a solution of 60 g. (1.5 moles) of sodium hydroxide and 132 g. (0.5 mole) of the bromo acid in one liter of water was refluxed for five hours. The filtered solution was cooled to about 5° for several hours where upon the sodium salt of the acid separated. It was filtered off and redissolved in hot water. Acidification liberated the hydroxy acid as an oil which crystallized when cooled. One recrystallization from benzene gave 74 g. (72% of the theoretical amount) of fine crystals melting at 70°.

The Ether Hydroxy Acid $HO(CH_2)_2O(CH_2)_{10}COOH$.—One mole of sodium (23 g.) was dissolved in 248 g. of ethylene glycol. The mixture was then heated to 110–115° under reflux and stirred while 133 g. (0.5 mole) of 11-bromoundecanoic acid was added in four portions during one hour. Stirring and heating were continued for four hours and most of the glycol was removed by further heating *in vacuo*. The residue was dissolved in water, acidified and extracted with ether. The crude acid after crystallization from petroleum ether was obtained as a white powder melting at 48–50°.

Anal. Calcd. for $C_{13}H_{26}O_4$: C, 63.41; H, 10.56; neut. equiv., 246. Found: C, 63.27; H, 10.36; neut. equiv., 244.

The ether hydroxy acid $HO(CH_2)_3O(CH_2)_{10}COOH$ was obtained similarly, m. p. 51°.

Anal. Neutral equivalent calcd. for $C_{14}H_{28}O_4$: 260. Found: 263.

The ether-hydroxy acid $HO(CH_2)_4O(CH_2)_{10}COOH$, m. p. 53°.

Anal. Calcd. for $C_{15}H_{30}O_4$: C, 65.69; H, 10.95; neut. equiv., 274. Found: C, 65.39; H, 11.01; neut. equiv., 281.5, 281.3.

Summary

The interchange method for preparing macrocyclic esters is shown to be applicable to the preparation of many-membered lactones and to have advantages in speed and simplicity over the high dilution method.

Three new large cyclic esters are described: the monomeric and dimeric lactones of 14-hydroxy-12-oxatetradecanoic acid and the monomeric lactone of 16-hydroxy-12-oxahexadecanoic acid.

Bibliography and Remarks

(1) Ruzicka and Stoll, *Helv. Chim. Acta*, **11**, 1159 (1928).
(2) Carothers, *Journ. Am. Chem. Soc.*, **51**, 2548 (1929).
(3) Ruggli, *Ann.*, **392**, 92 (1912).
(4) Stoll and Rouvé, *Helv. Chim. Acta*, **17**, 1283 (1934).
(5) Hill and Carothers, *Journ. Am. Chem. Soc.*, **55**, 5031 (1933).
(6) Spanagel and Carothers, *ibid.*, **57**, 929 (1935).
(7) Ashton and Smith, *J. Chem. Soc.*, 1308 (1934).

PART TWO

ACETYLENE POLYMERS
AND THEIR DERIVATIVES

PART TWO

ACETYLENE POLYMERS AND THEIR DERIVATIVES

I. Introduction

This introduction, by drawing to the reader's attention the salient and most significant features of Carothers' series of papers on Acetylene Polymers and their Derivatives, will, it is hoped, add to his satisfaction in perusing the papers themselves, which are reprinted hereafter.

The outstanding element of interest and importance in the work described in the series is the discovery of a synthetic rubber, polychloroprene, which has been manufactured since 1933 and represents one of the most striking achievements of industrial chemistry in recent years. In addition however, to providing the basis for this industrial development, the work also makes a brilliant and important contribution to our knowledge of (1) the influence of substitution on the polymerization of conjugated systems and (2) the chemical behaviour of conjugated systems in which an ethylenic and an acetylenic bond are disposed in a conjugated relationship to one another.

In the first paper of the series Acetylene Polymers and their Derivatives, by Nieuwland, Calcott, Downing and Carter (1) there is described the discovery that, by means, as a catalyst, of cuprous chloride (preferably together with ammonium chloride) acetylene can be polymerized in high yield to (1) a dimer, vinyl acetylene, $CH_2:CH.C:CH$, b. p. 5° and (2) a trimer, divinylacetylene, $CH_2:CH.C:C.CH:CH_2$, b. p. 83.5°. With these two highly reactive substances thus made readily available, Carothers and his co-workers proceeded to an extensive study of their chemistry, the results of which are described in subsequent papers of the same series.

Chloroprene

Of outstanding interest was the discovery that 2-chloro-1,3-butadiene, $CH_2:CCl.CH:CH_2$, obtainable by the action of aqueous hydrogen chloride on vinyl acetylene under appropriate conditions in the presence of cuprous and ammonium chlorides, polymerizes readily to a rubber-like product (Paper II, p. 281). By analogy with isoprene, the compound is commonly referred to as chloroprene. It polymerizes far more rapidly than does isoprene, thanks to the activating effect of the β-chlorine atom, and, con-

(Publications listed in the Bibliography, p. 423, *et seq.*, are referred to by Reference numbers in large Roman corresponding to the Serial Numbers of the papers.)

trary to what might perhaps have been expected (by, *e. g.*, analogy with poly vinyl chloride) the product turns out to be highly elastic and indeed similar in elastic properties to vulcanized natural rubber. By interrupting the polymerization before it is complete, it is possible to isolate an intermediate polymeric material (the so-called α-polymer) which, being plastic, can be handled by much the same techniques as raw rubber and its stocks are handled, and which having thus been fabricated into rubber goods of various shapes, can be converted into the final elastic material (the so-called μ-polymer) by the further application of heat, which completes the polymerization.

Polychloroprene is now being manufactured on a substantial scale, because, despite the fact that it is more costly than natural rubber, it has special properties which make it better adapted than the latter to certain applications. Chief of these properties is its lower imbibition of aliphatic hydrocarbons, which, presumably, is dependent on its high content of chlorine. It is, further, more stable than vulcanized rubber. This stability is exhibited in its resistance to deterioration on aging, by heat, by ozone, etc., and is probably due largely to the fact that in it the polymerization process to which it owes its formation is substantially complete, whereas vulcanized rubber is susceptible to further polymerization or—if views now in vogue as to the nature of vulcanization are adopted—to further cross-linking.

Under certain special conditions chloroprene yields a polymer of different properties, distinguished as the ω- or granular polymer. It is lacking in plasticity and imbibes organic liquids hardly at all. It can be produced, for example, by exposing chloroprene vapour to light from a mercury arc, and after its formation has been thus initiated, it will without further irradication continue to grow in the vapour or in liquid chloroprene. Carothers (2) in some interesting comments calls attention to the curious and perhaps suggestive analogy of such a process to vital growth.

Influence of Substituents on Polymerization

Carothers' studies afford much valuable information as to the influence of substitution in the butadienoid system on the readiness with which polymerization occurs and the degree to which it proceeds. Considering first halogen substitution: chloroprene, with chlorine in the 2-position, polymerizes about 700 times as quickly as isoprene and yields a product of excellent rubber-like properties; the analogous bromo derivative (Paper V, p. 314) polymerizes somewhat more rapidly, but the product, although having good extensibility and strength, shows, presumably owing to the high percentage by weight of halogen in the molecule, less completely recovery from extension than does polychloroprene, and the lower limit of the temperature range within which it is elastic is higher than for polychloroprene; 2-iodo-1,3-butadiene (Paper XV, p. 361) polymerizes at a markedly higher rate than either of the preceding, but the product (which contains 70 per cent of iodine) is rubber-like only under certain conditions (3).

The introduction of a second chlorine atom to one of the interior carbon atoms of the butadienoid system yields a compound $CH_2:CCl.CCl:CH_2$, which polymerizes even more rapidly than chloroprene $CH_2:CCl.CH:CH_2$ (Paper XI, p. 340). The product, either because of the high degree to which polymerization has proceeded or because of its high chlorine content, is a hard tough mass lacking in rubber-like properties. (The high speed of polymerization of $CH_2:CCl.CCl.:CH_2$ is perhaps somewhat unexpected, if one were to judge by analogy with the effect of chlorine substitution in the ethenoid system, for, whereas here the introduction of one atom of chlorine, which renders the system highly polar, gives a compound (vinyl chloride) which is highly polymerizable, the introduction of a second atom of chlorine, symmetrically disposed with respect to the first, gives a compound (sym.-dichloroethylene) in which the ability to polymerize has been lost. It is, however, to be noted that in 2,3-dichloro-1,3-butadiene unsubstituted terminal $:CH_2$ groups are present and that the presence of such may well be a condition for chlorine to exert an "activating" effect on polymerizability.) The substitution of chlorine in the terminal positions of the butadiene has no such striking effect on polymerization as its substitution in the interior positions. 1-Chloro-1,3-butadiene, $ClCH:-CH.CH:CH_2$, polymerizes not much more quickly than isoprene and the product has only inferior rubber-like properties (Paper XI, p. 340) (3). Similarly, 1,2,3,-trichloro-1,3-butadiene, $ClCH:CCl.CCl:CH_2$ polymerizes much more slowly than 2,3-dichloro-1,3- butadiene, $CH_2:CCl.CCl:CH_2$ (Paper XI, p. 340).

Observations on a number of chlorine compounds prepared from divinylacetylene by steps involving the addition and the removal of the elements of hydrogen chloride provide further data on the influence of chlorine-substitution on the polymerization of conjugated systems (Paper XIII, p. 348). The compounds in question, each containing a conjugated system, are as follows:

1. $CH_2:C:CCl.CCl:C:CH_2$
2. $CH_2:C:C:CCl.CH:CH_2$

3. Cl CH$_2$.CH:C:CCl.CH$_2$:CH$_2$
4. Cl CH$_2$.CH:CCl.CCl:C:CH$_2$
5. Cl CH$_2$.CH:CCl.CCl:CH.CH$_2$Cl

Of these, 1 showed a strong tendency to polymerize: it changed to a hard resin when allowed to stand for 24 hours; 2 and 3 polymerized only slowly (3 changed to a viscous syrup on standing for three months); 4 and 5, in which one end or both ends of the molecule carries chlorine and in which a terminal vinyl group is lacking, showed no tendency at all to polymerize.

The effect of introducing other groups into the 2-chloro-butadienoid system, especially their introduction into the terminal positions, is to depress the polymerizability. 3-Methyl-2-chloro-1,3-butadiene, CH$_2$:-CCl.C(CH$_3$):CH$_2$, polymerizes somewhat more slowly than chloroprene, and the polymer is somewhat inferior to polychloroprene in rubber-like properties: although tough and elastic, it has a rather low extensibility (Paper XXI, p. 384). The introduction to the last-mentioned butadiene of a second, terminal methyl group has a more profound effect, 3-4-dimethylchloroprene, CH$_2$:CCl.C(CH$_3$):CH.CH$_3$, polymerizing not much more rapidly than isoprene and yielding a produce which, although elastic, recovers only sluggishly from deformation (Paper XXI, p. 384). As contrasted with the relatively slight effect of a 3-methyl group on the polymerization of chloroprene, a terminal methyl group, as in 1-methylchloroprene, CH$_3$CH:CCl.CH:CH$_2$, reduces the speed of polymerization greatly and detracts markedly from the rubber-likeness of the polymeric product (Paper IX, p. 331). Increase in the magnitude of the terminal alkyl group magnifies the effect in the same direction, n-heptylchloroprene, C$_7$H$_{15}$.CH:CCl.CH:CH$_2$, yielding on polymerization only a sticky solid with very slight elasticity (Paper IX, p. 331). Such observations are in accord with previous findings that the introduction of terminal alkyl groups to butadiene reduces polymerizability and that, the larger the alkyl group, the greater is the reduction (4).

In papers of the Acetylene Polymers series published subsequent to Carothers' association with it, the influence of certain other substituents on the polymerizability of chloroprene is recorded. The introduction of a dialkylmethylamino group in a terminal position depresses the polymerization of the chloroprene system very greatly, the 1-(dialkylmethylamino)-chloroprenes, R$_2$N.CH$_2$.CH:CCl.CH:CH$_2$, polymerizing very slowly indeed and yielding no rubber-like product (5). Alkoxy-methyl or alkoxy-(methyl)methyl groups in the terminal position have some but a far smaller effect on the polymerizability of chloroprene, $CH_3O.CH_2.$- $CH:CCl.CH:CH_2$ polymerizing at one-sixth the rate of chloroprene and yielding a product with somewhat rubber-like properties (6).

In view of the profound effect on polymerization of the presence of chlorine in the 2-position of the butadienoid system, the effect of other substituents in this position was examined. As compared with isoprene, which has a methyl group in the 2-position, 2-heptyl-1,3-butadiene was found to polymerize rather less readily and to yield a weaker and softer rubber (Paper XVI, p. 368). 2-Phenyl-1,3-butadiene was found to polymerize considerably more rapidly than isoprene but to yield under ordinary conditions only a dimeric product (Paper XVI, p. 368). In continuation of Carothers' studies, the effect of introducing (a) alkoxy groups, (b) aliphatic acid residues with the 2-position has been examined. 2-Ethoxy-1,3-butadiene, $CH_2:C(OC_2H_5).CH:CH_2$, was found to polymerize at about one-third the rate of isoprene and to give a product of inferior rubber-like properties (7). 2-Acetoxy-1,3-butadiene, $CH_2.C(O.COCH_3).$- $CH:CH_2$, and analogous compounds on the other hand were found to polymerize at a rate not vastly different from that of chloroprene and to yield rubber-like products (8).

4-Cyano-1,3-butadiene, $CH_2:CH.CH:CH.N:C$, despite the fact that the substituent group is in a terminal position, has been found to polymerize about twenty times as quickly as isoprene (9). Perhaps the extra conjugation which the cyano-group provides is responsible for this result. The final product of polymerization, although rubber-like, is markedly inferior to polychloroprene or polyisoprene: it could be stretched 1300 per cent without breaking, but ten minutes after release still had an extension of 200 per cent.

Chemical Behaviour of Vinylacetylene and Divinylacetylene

Turning attention now to the acetylene polymers, vinylacetylene and divinylacetylene, note may be made of the salient features of observations regarding (a) the polymerization of these substances, (b) their addition reactions other than self-addition (i. e., polymerization), (c) their other reactions.

Polymerization.—In the presence of cuprous chloride, vinylacetylene gives a liquid dimer, which is probably octatriene-1,5,7-ine-3, $CH_2:CH.$- $C:C.CH:CH.CH:CH_2$ (10, 11), and which, on exposure to air, becomes converted into an insoluble product which explodes violently when heated (11). When heated in the absence of a catalyst, as, e. g., at 105° for six hours (11) or in the presence of peroxide catalysts (10), vinylacetylene polymerizes first to viscous oils and finally to hard, resinous solids. The available evidence (11) suggests that these polymers, which contain acetylenic hydrogen, are cyclobutane and cyclobutene derivatives, as follows:

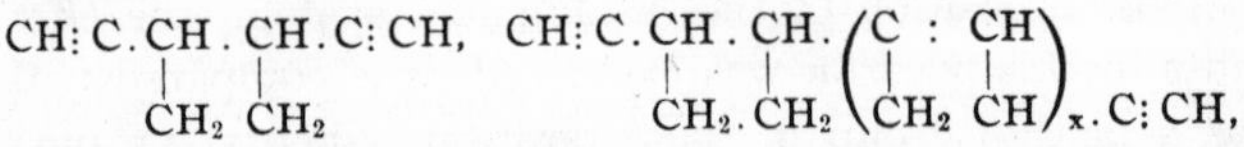

$$\begin{array}{ccc} \text{CH}_!\text{C.CH.CH.C}_!\text{CH}, & \text{CH}_!\text{C.CH.CH.}\left(\begin{array}{cc}\text{C} & : & \text{CH}\\ | & & | \\ \text{CH}_2 & \text{CH}\end{array}\right)_x.\text{C}_!\text{CH}, \\ \quad | \quad | & \quad\quad | \quad | \\ \text{CH}_2 \; \text{CH}_2 & \text{CH}_2.\text{CH}_2 \end{array}$$

their formation involving only the ethylenic linkages of vinylacetylene.

When heated in the presence of acids, acid anhydrides or phenols, vinylacetylene, in addition to forming resinous products, yields, unexpectedly, styrene in amount corresponding to about one-half of the vinylacetylene used (11). Styrene, C_8H_8, in this connection figures as a dimer of vinylacetylene, C_4H_4. Its formation can be represented as, analogously to the dimerization of butadiene, involving first the addition, in a 1,4-sense, of the acetylenic portion of one molecule of vinylacetylene to the conjugated system of another, and then a rearrangement of bond. Thus:

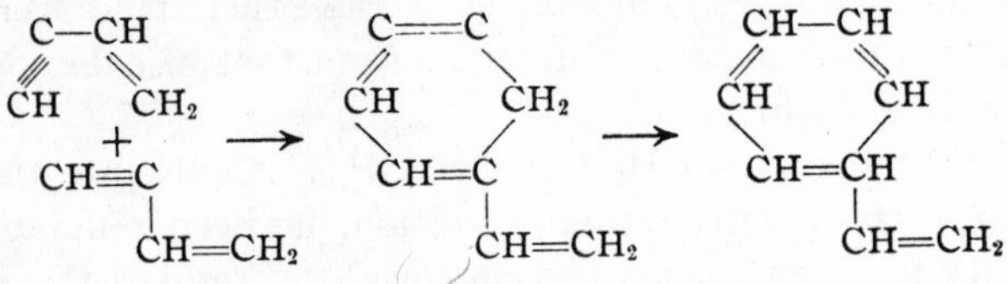

Divinylacetylene, when heated in the absence of air (in the presence of air it absorbs oxygen and becomes dangerously explosive) polymerizes to first a viscous liquid and finally a hard, brittle, insoluble resin. The intermediate, oily material, when exposed as a film to air, takes up oxygen and "dries" to a hard, insoluble product (12) (Paper XIX, p. 378). It has been referred to as a "synthetic drying oil." From the intermediate, oily polymeric material it was possible to isolate a dimer of vinylacetylene, which was shown to be divinylethinyl-1,2-cyclobutane, $CH_2\!:\!CH.C\!:\!C.CH.CH.C\!:\!C.CH\!:\!CH_2$ (Paper XIX, p. 378), its formation

$$\begin{array}{cc} | & | \\ \text{CH}_2 & \text{CH}_2 \end{array}$$

depending as in the case of the analogous dimer of vinylacetylene (*supra*) on the mutual addition of an ethylenic part of each of two molecules of the monomer.

The work provides some information regarding the polymerization of certain substitution products of vinyl- and divinyl-acetylene. 1-Halo-2-vinyl acetylenes, $CH_2\!:\!CH.CH\!:\!C$ Hal., on standing for several months, polymerize to black, highly explosive solids (Paper XVIII, p. 375).

1-Alkyl-2-vinyl acetylenes, $CH_2:CH.CH:CR$, polymerizes only slowly; they become viscous syrups after 2–3 months' standing (Paper VIII, p. 329). Replacement of the acetylenic hydrogen of vinylacetylene by a secondary carbinol residue has a favourable effect on the speed of polymerization, the tertiary carbinols all polymerizing spontaneously with considerable rapidity (Papers VI, p. 321; VII, p. 323). Thus, *e. g.*, (vinylethinyl) methylethyl carbinol, $CH_2:CH.C:C(OH)(C_2H_5)CH_3$, on standing in a stoppered bottle, had become a thick syrup in one week, then passed through a tough elastic, rather rubberlike stage, and in six weeks had become a very hard mass (Paper VII, p. 323).

Addition Reactions.—Prior to Carothers' study of the chemistry of vinyl- and divinyl-acetylenes little was known about the additive behaviour of -enine systems—or, alternatively, enyne systems—in which contiguous carbon atoms carry respectively double and triple bonds, thus: $—.\dot{C}:C.\overset{..}{C}:C$. Can such a system of fonds behave as a conjugated system? Yes; for it was shown rather conclusively that the first result of treating vinylacetylene with hydrochloric acid is to form 4-chloro-1,2-butadiene (Paper III, p. 306).

$$HC:C:CH:CH_2 + HCl \longrightarrow H_2C:C:CH.CH_2Cl$$

This compound, which can readily be isolated, can be put through a series of methathetical reactions without any rearrangement of the bonds (Paper XV, p. 361). Thus, *e. g.*, by means of hot water, preferably in the presence of a mild alkali, the chlorine is replaced by a hydroxyl group (Paper XV, p. 361; U. S. Patent 2,073,363, p. 431; 2,136,178, p. 432). It readily rearranges, however, under many conditions of treatment, especially in the presence of cuprous chloride, and gives 2-chloro-1,3-butadiene, $CH_2:CCl.CH:CH_2$, *i. e.*, chloroprene, the allene arrangement changing to the more stable conjugated one, in which the chlorine atom, attached to a doubly bonded carbon, has lost its mobility (Paper III, p. 306). Carothers discusses the mechanism of the α,γ-shift involved and concludes that it is dependent, not on ionization, but on the formation of a complex (coördination compound) and chelation (Paper XV, p. 361).

In the presence of a little sodium alcoholate, alcohols readily react with vinylacetylene to yield acetylene ethers of the type, $RO.CH_2.C:C.CH_3$ (Paper XX, p. 381). This reaction is considered to involve first 1,4-addition, and then a rearrangement similar to the rearrangement of monosubstituted allenes to disubstituted acetylenes which Favorsky found to be produced by sodium alcoholates. Thus:

$$CH_2:CH.C:CH, \text{ i. e., } .CH_2.CH:C:CH. \longrightarrow (RO.CH_2.CH:C:CH_2) \longrightarrow$$
$$RO.CH_2.C:C.CH_3$$

When two atoms of chlorine are added to divinylacetylene, the product is reasonably concluded to have the structure $ClCH_2.CH:C:CCl.CH:CH_2$, and hence to have been formed by 1,4-addition. When to this product two more atoms of chlorine are added, the tetrachloride formed has apparently the structure $ClCH_2.CH:CCl.CCl:CH.CH_2.Cl$, and to be found by a further 1,4-addition (Paper XIII, p. 348). This last conclusion makes it appear that in a system $.\dot{C}:C:\dot{C}.\dot{C}:\dot{C}.$ a carbon atom with twinned double bonds can act as one of the ends of a conjugated system (cf. the remarks on the polymerization of chlorine compounds derived from divinylacetylene, p. 378).

It is to be remarked that some of the chlorides derived from divinyl-acetyelene and also certain derivatives of vinylacetylene, despite the fact that they contain conjugated double bonds, fail to react with maleic anhydride or naphthoquinone (Paper XIII, p. 348).

Although in most of their addition reactions vinyl- and divinylacetylenes behave as conjugated systems, two exceptions were encountered. (1) In reaction with thiophenols, only the ethylenic bond of the -enine system is involved, and in view of this Carothers made considerable use of thio-p-cresol in studying the constitution of acetylene polymers and their derivatives. Divinylacetylene readily adds, at room temperature, two molecules of thio-p-cresol to give a crystalline product (Paper XII, p. 344), thus: $CH_2:CH.C:C.CH:CH_2 \rightarrow C_7H_7S.CH_2.CH_2.C:C.CH_2.CH_2S.C_7H_7$. (2) A reaction dependent on addition to the acetylenic bond of vinylacetylene is the formation of 1,3-butadienyl esters by treating vinylacetylene with an aliphatic acid in the presence, as catalyst, of a mercuric salt or boron fluoride (13). Thus:

$$CH_2:CH.C:CH + R.COOH \longrightarrow CH_2:CH.C(O.COR):CH_2$$

Other Reactions.—Reactions of vinylacetylenes dependent on the reactivity of the acetylenic hydrogen $(CH_2:CH.C:CH)$ are as follows:

(a) With Grignard reagents, vinylethinyl magnesium halides, e. g., $CH_2:CH.C:CMgBr$, are formed, and the latter react in a way typical of organo-magnesium compounds, giving, with acetone, a carbinol, $CH_2:CH.C:C(OH)(CH_3)_2$, and with carbon dioxide, an acid, vinyl-propiolic acid, $CH_2:CH.C:C.COOH$ (Paper VI, p. 321).

(b) With sodium or sodamide, there is formed sodium vinylacetylide, $CH_2:CH.C:CNa$, which is very reactive; giving with aldehydes secondary carbinols, $CH_2:CH.C:C.(OH)CHR$; with ketones, tertiary carbinols, $CH_2:CH.C:C(OH)CRR'$ (Paper VII, p. 323), and with alkyl halides, alkyl-vinylacetylenes, $CH_2:CH.C:CR$ (Paper VIII, p. 329).

(c)   With potassium mercuric iodide or with mercuric acetate in acetic acid, vinylacetylene yields di-vinylethinyl mercury $(CH_2\!:\!CH.C\!:\!C)_2Hg$ (Paper XVII, p. 372).

(d)   Treatment of vinylacetylene with alkali hypohalides replaces the acetylenic hydrogen by halogen and yields the 1-halo-vinylacetylenes, $CH_2\!:\!CH.C\!:\!C$ Hal. (Paper XVIII, p. 375).

(e)   By treating vinylacetylene with formaldehyde and a secondary amine, the acetylenic hydrogen is replaced by a secondary-amino-methyl residue (14,15), thus:

$$CH_2\!:\!CH.C\!:\!CH + CH_2O + HNR_2 \longrightarrow CH_2\!:\!CH\ C\!:\!C.CH_2NR_2 + H_2O$$

Bibliography and Remarks

(1) J. A. Nieuwland, U. S. Pat. 1,811,959 (1931); Journ. Am. Chem. Soc., 53, 4197–4202 (1931).
(2) W. H. Carothers, Trans. Farad. Soc., 32, 39 (1936).
(3) W. H. Carothers, Ind. Eng. Chem., 26, 30 (1934).
(4) Whitby and Gallay, Can. Jour. Res., 6, 280 (1932); Whitby and Crozier, ibid., 6, 203 (1932).
(5) D. D. Coffman, Journ. Am. Chem. Soc., 57, 1978 (1935).
(6) H. B. Dykstra, ibid., 58, 1747 (1936).
(7) H. B. Dykstra, ibid., 57, 2255 (1935).
(8) J. H. Werntz, ibid., 57, 204 (1935).
(9) D. D. Coffman, ibid., 57, 1981 (1935).
(10) Nieuwland, Calcott, Downing and Carter, ibid., 53, 4197 (1931).
(11) H. B. Dykstra, ibid., 56, 1625 (1934).
(12) Nieuwland, Calcott, Downing and Carter, ibid., 53, 4197 (1931).
(13) J. H. Werntz, ibid., 57, 204 (1935).
(14) D. D. Coffman, ibid., 57, 1978 (1935); also U. S. Patent 2,136,177.
(15) Journ. Am. Chem. Soc., 53, 4197 (1931).

G. S. W.

II.   A New Synthetic Rubber: Chloroprene and Its Polymers*

Study of the reactions of vinylacetylene, a compound which has become available through discoveries described in the preceding paper (1), has led to the synthesis of a series of new analogs and homologs of isoprene. The present paper is concerned with one of the simplest of these, namely, chloro-2-butadiene-1,3 (I).   This compound is especially interesting for the following reasons.   It is easily prepared in quantity in a state of purity; it differs structurally from isoprene only in having a chlorine atom instead of a methyl group;   like isoprene it reacts with itself to yield a synthetic

* W. H. Carothers, I. Williams, A. M. Collins and J. E. Kirby, Journ. Am. Chem. Soc., 53, 4203–25 (1931); Contribution from the Experimental Station of the Central Chemical Department (Communication No. 83) and from the Jackson Laboratory of the Dyestuffs Department (Communication No. 26), E. I. du Pont de Nemours and Co. Received October 3, 1931.   Published November 5, 1931.

rubber; but the transformation occurs with much greater velocity than in the case of isoprene; and the product is distinctly superior to natural rubber in some of its properties.

In order to recognize the analogy in structure and behavior which exists between isoprene and chloro-2-butadiene-1,3, we call the latter compound *chloroprene*, and this name also serves to distinguish it from other chlorobutadienes that will be described in future papers.

Preparation of Chloroprene.—Chloroprene is obtained by the addition of hydrogen chloride to vinylacetylene

$$CH\equiv C-CH=CH_2 + HCl \longrightarrow CH_2=C-CH=CH_2 \atop \qquad\qquad\qquad\qquad\qquad | \atop \qquad\qquad\qquad\qquad\qquad Cl \qquad (I)$$

Other products, which will be described in future papers, are also formed by the action of hydrogen chloride on vinylacetylene under certain conditions; but under the conditions indicated in the following example, chloroprene is practically the only product.

Fifty grams of cold vinylacetylene is placed in a pressure bottle containing a thoroughly chilled mixture composed of 175 g. of concd. hydrochloric acid (sp. gr. 1.19), 25 g. of cuprous chloride and 10 g. of ammonium chloride. The bottle is placed in a water-bath the temperature of which is held at approximately 30°, where it is shaken for a period of four hours. The contents of the bottle are placed in a separatory funnel, the lower aqueous layer is drawn off and the oily layer is washed with water, dried with calcium chloride, mixed with a small amount of catechol or pyrogallol and distilled *in vacuo* through an efficient column provided with a refrigerated dephlegmator and receiver. Pure chloroprene is thus obtained in yields of about 65% of the theoretical based on the vinylacetylene applied. Some vinylacetylene is recovered in the distillation. The yields can be considerably improved if the chloroprene is separated from the reaction mixture by steam distillation *in vacuo* (100–250 mm.).

Physical Properties and Analysis.—Chloroprene is a colorless liquid with a characteristic ethereal odor, somewhat resembling ethyl bromide. It is miscible with most of the common organic solvents, but only slightly soluble in water. Some of its other properties are boiling point (2), 59.4° at 760 mm., 46.9° at 500 mm., 40.5° at 400 mm., 32.8° at 300 mm., 6.4° at 100 mm.; vapor pressure, $\log_{10}$ v. p. (mm. Hg) $= -1545.3/T(\text{abs}) + 7.527$; calculated molal latent heat of evaporation, 7090 cal.; density, d_{20}^{20} 0.9583; refractive index, n_c^{20}, 1.4540, n_D^{20} 1.4583, n_F^{20}, 1.4690.

	M_c 25.06	M_D 25.26
Found		
Calcd.	24.67	24.66
Difference	0.39	0.60

Viscosity at 25°, 0.394 centipoise.

Anal. Calcd. for C_4H_5Cl: C, 54.25; H, 5.69; Cl, 40.06; mol. wt., 88.5. Found: C, 54.37; H, 5.95; Cl, 39.51, 38.81; mol. wt. (in freezing benzene) 89.0, 89.0.

Chemical Properties and Proof of Structure.—The structure of chloroprene as chloro-2-butadiene-1,3 is established by its analytical composition and by the following reactions.

It reacts readily with maleic anhydride and yields, after hydrolysis with water, a crystalline product to which we assign the structure chloro-4-tetrahydro-1,2,3,6-phthalic acid (II). The chlorine atom of this product, in accordance with its assumed structure, is very resistant to the action of concentrated boiling alkali, and oxidation with boiling nitric acid yields a crystalline compound identical in melting point and composition with the known acid, butane-$\alpha,\beta,\gamma,\delta$-tetracarboxylic acid (III).

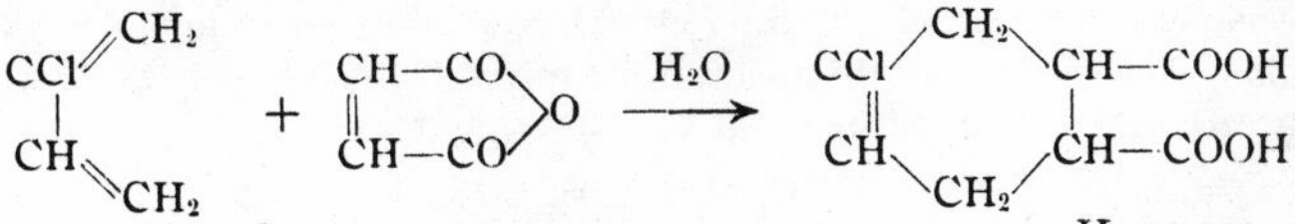

I II

$CH_2 \cdot COOH$
$CH \cdot COOH$
$CH \cdot COOH$
$CH_2 \cdot COOH$

III

Chloroprene further reacts readily with naphthoquinone, and the primary product, which presumably has the structure chloro-2-tetrahydro-1,-4,4a,9a-anthraquinone-9,10 (IV), is smoothly oxidized by air in the presence of alkali to β-chloroanthraquinone (V). The identity of this is established by the method of mixed melting point.

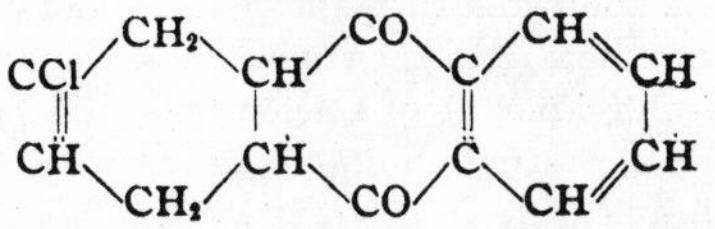

IV

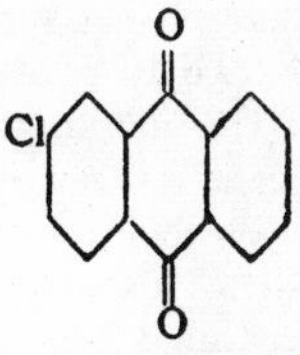

V

$CH_3CCl{=}CH{-}CH_2Cl$

VI

In view of the recent studies of Diels and Alder (3) this result decisively demonstrates the presence in chloroprene of a pair of conjugated double bonds, and it fixes unequivocally the position of the chlorine atom.

In chloroform solution chloroprene readily adds approximately two atoms of bromine before substitution begins. It rapidly decolorizes alkaline permanganate solution. In the presence of cuprous chloride it reacts with aqueous hydrochloric acid. The reaction consists in 1,4-addition and the product is dichloro-1,3-butene-2 (VI), which will be described in a future paper. The chlorine atom of chloroprene is very firmly bound. Only traces of chloride ion appear on boiling with alcoholic silver nitrate, alcoholic sodium hydroxide, or pyridine.

Reaction of Chloroprene with Maleic Anhydride. Preparation of Chloro-4-tetrahydro-1,2,3,6-phthalic Acid (II).—21.2 g. of chloroprene was warmed with 19.6 g. of maleic anhydride. The anhydride dissolved readily and when 50° was reached sufficient heat was developed from the reaction to maintain this temperature for some time. After standing overnight the reaction product was boiled with 200 cc. of water to remove unchanged chloroprene and filtered. On cooling stout rectangular plates separated; yield 31.5 g. or 77% of the theoretical; m. p. 171–172° (corr.). Recrystallization from water raised the melting point to 173–175°.

Anal. Calcd. for $C_8H_9O_4Cl$: C, 46.94; H, 4.43; Cl, 17.34; neutral equivalent, 102.3. Found: C, 47.54; H, 4.78; Cl, 17.24, 17.71; neutral equivalent, 103.5.

The acid was boiled with 25% potassium hydroxide for three hours. No significant quantity of chloride ion was produced. This indicates that the chlorine is attached to a double-bonded carbon atom.

Oxidation to Butane-$\alpha,\beta,\gamma,\delta$-tetracarboxylic Acid (III).—A sample (8.2 g.) of the above-described acid was warmed with 30 g. of 70% nitric acid until a rather violent reaction took place with the evolution of nitrogen oxides. The unused nitric acid was removed *in vacuo* and the partly crystalline residue taken up in a small volume of hot water. On cooling a thick mass of flat needles with square ends separated. After a second crystallization, the product melted at 192–193° with effervescence.

Anal. Calcd. for $C_8H_{10}O_8$: C, 41.05; H, 4.27; neutral equivalent, 58.5. Found: C, 41.32, 41.46; H, 4.66, 4.67; neutral equivalent, 58.8.

This acid has already been described by Auwers and Jacob (4) and also by Farmer and Warren (5).

Action of α-Naphthoquinone on Chloroprene. Conversion to β-Chloroanthraquinone.—To 10 g. of naphthoquinone dissolved in benzene 12 g. of chloroprene was added. The mixture was refluxed for three hours and then allowed to stand overnight. The benzene was removed under reduced pressure, and the residual mass was dissolved in warm alcohol and cooled. A considerable amount of unchanged naphthoquinone separated. This was filtered off. Dilution of the mother liquor with water gave a solid which separated from alcohol in fine needles melting at 76°. It was still contaminated with naphthoquinone. It was suspended in alcohol containing a little sodium hydroxide, and air was bubbled through the suspension for twenty minutes. The suspended solid was crystallized three times from amyl alcohol; small needles, m. p. 209.5°; mixed melting point with β-chloroanthraquinone, 209.5°.

Spontaneous Polymerization of Chloroprene.—The following example is typical of the spontaneous polymerization of chloroprene.

About 40 cc. of chloroprene is placed in a 50-cc. bottle of soda glass, closed with a cork stopper, and allowed to stand at the laboratory temperature (about 25°) in the absence of direct light. After twenty-four hours the viscosity of the sample has considerably increased; after four days it has set to a stiff, colorless, transparent jelly, which still contains a considerable amount of unchanged chloroprene. As the polymerization proceeds further this jelly contracts in volume and becomes more tough and dense. After ten days all the chloroprene has polymerized. We call this product μ-polychloroprene to distinguish it from other chloroprene polymers that will be described later in this paper.

Properties of μ-Polychloroprene.—The product of the above described reaction is a colorless or pale yellow, transparent, resilient, elastic mass resembling a completely vulcanized soft rubber. Its density at 20° is about 1.23, and its refractive index (n_D^{20}) is about 1.5512. It has a tensile strength of about 140 kg./sq. cm. and an elongation at break of about 800%. It is not plastic; that is, it does not sheet out smoothly on the rolls of the rubber mill nor break down on continued milling. It is not thermoplastic. It swells strongly but does not dissolve in carbon tetrachloride, carbon disulfide, benzene, nitrobenzene, pyridine, aniline, ethyl acetate and ether. Compared with natural rubber the tendency of this material to imbibe gasoline and lubricating oil is very slight. When a stretched sample is immersed in liquid air for a moment and then struck with a hammer it shatters into fibrous fragments (6).

The properties of the μ-polymer vary somewhat depending upon the conditions under which it is formed. When the chloroprene has access to large amounts of air or oxygen during the polymerization the product is dark in color and harder and stiffer than otherwise. The polymer formed at elevated temperature is inclined to be soft and it has a distinct terpene-like odor. This is due to the presence of the volatile β-polymer, which will be described in a subsequent paragraph.

x-Ray Diffraction Pattern.—Although the x-ray diffraction pattern of unstretched rubber shows only a single diffuse ring, characteristic of a liquid or an amorphous solid, stretched rubber shows a point diagram (7). On the other hand, according to Mark (8), all synthetic, polymerized products from isoprene or other unsaturated hydrocarbons so far investigated have given, even when stretched, a diffraction pattern analogous to that of a liquid.

It is therefore a matter of considerable interest that the μ-polychloroprene described above (as well as the cured plastic polymer described in a later paragraph), when stretched about 500%, exhibits a fully developed fiber diagram showing a number of definite layer lines. One of these diffraction patterns is reproduced in Fig. 1, together with a diagram of stretched rubber (Fig. 2). The identity period along the fiber axis is 4.8 Å. This length corresponds rather closely with the calculated length for one chloroprene unit. The agreement is better if one assumes a *trans* instead of a *cis* configuration since the calculated identity period in a *cis* polyprene chain is about 2×4.1 Å., whereas in a *trans* chain it is about 4.8 Å. (9). Incidentally, 4.8 Å. is exactly the identity period observed for β-gutta percha by Hauser and v. Susich (10). Unstretched samples of polychloroprene give an amorphous ring (Fig. 3) entirely like natural rubber. The spacing corresponding to this ring is 4.86 Å. We are indebted to Dr. A. W. Kenney for these observations.

Chemical Properties of μ-Polychloroprene.—The μ-product has the composition required for an addition polymer of chloroprene.

Anal. Calcd. for $(C_4H_5Cl)_x$: C, 54.25; H, 5.69; Cl, 40.06. Found: C, 53.74, 54.83; H, 5.70, 5.93; Cl, 40.06, 39.32.

Molecular weight determinations are not possible on account of its lack of solubility.

The μ-polymer is unsaturated toward bromine but no quantitative data on this point are yet available. The chlorine atoms are very firmly bound. Only slight traces of chloride ion are liberated when the compound is heated for six hours in boiling alcoholic potash or boiling pyridine. This fact suggests that the chlorine atoms of the polymer are still attached to carbon atoms bearing double bonds.

The oxidation of the μ-polymer with hot nitric acid leads to the isolation of succinic acid.

No attempts have yet been made to degrade the μ-polymer with ozone completely, but when stretched it is much more resistant than natural rubber to the deteriorating effect of ozone-containing air.

It is well known that purified rubber hydrocarbon is very susceptible to autoxidation. A similar and perhaps more exaggerated sensitivity is characteristic of synthetic rubbers derived from diene hydrocarbons. In this respect μ-polychloroprene appears to be considerably more resistant. Nevertheless it does not long remain completely unaltered when freely exposed to air and light. It gradually becomes darker in color and finally after two or three weeks is dark brown. At the same time, it becomes harder, especially on the surface. These changes are accompanied by the liberation of traces of hydrogen chloride. The autoxidation can be suppressed by treating the polymer with small amounts of antioxidants.

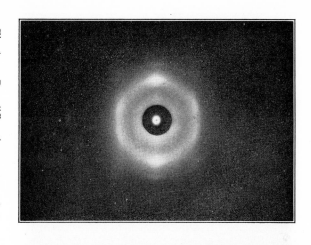

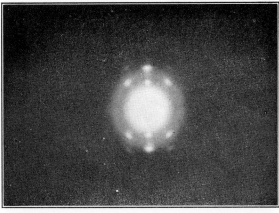

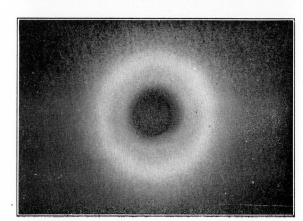

Fig. 1.—x-Ray diffraction pattern of μ-polychloroprene (from latex) stretched 500%.

Fig. 2.—x-Ray diffraction pattern of lightly cured smoked sheet rubber stretched 500%.

Fig. 3.—x-Ray diffraction pattern of α-polychloroprene (unstretched).

Chemical Structure of μ-Polychloroprene.—The molecules of natural rubber are long chains built up from the unit (VII) derived (formally) from isoprene (VIII). This structure follows from the fact that the ozoni-

$$-CH_2-C=CH-CH_2- \qquad\qquad CH_2=C-CH=CH_2$$
$$\mathrm{\ \ \ \ \ \ \ |} \qquad\qquad\qquad\qquad\qquad \mathrm{|}$$
$$CH_3 \qquad\qquad\qquad\qquad\qquad CH_3$$
$$\text{VII} \qquad\qquad\qquad\qquad\qquad \text{VIII}$$

zation of rubber (IX) leads to levulinic acid and levulinic aldehyde (X) as the principal products (11).

$$\ldots-CH_2-C=CH-CH_2-CH_2-C=CH-CH_2-\ldots \xrightarrow{O_3}$$
$$\mathrm{\ \ \ \ \ \ |} \qquad\qquad\qquad\ \ \mathrm{|}$$
$$CH_3 \qquad\qquad\qquad CH_3 \qquad\qquad\qquad OCH-CH_2-CH_2-CO-CH_3$$
$$\text{IX} \qquad\qquad\qquad\qquad\qquad\qquad\qquad \text{X}$$

In their behavior toward ozone the so-called *normal* synthetic rubbers from isoprene very closely resemble the natural products (12), and their molecules must therefore for the most part be built up on the same general plan.

Analogy suggests that the molecules of the chloroprene polymer are similarly built up from the units (XI) derived from chloroprene (XII).

$$-CH_2-C=CH-CH_2- \qquad\qquad CH_2=C-CH=CH_2$$
$$\mathrm{\ \ \ \ \ \ |} \qquad\qquad\qquad\qquad\qquad \mathrm{|}$$
$$Cl \qquad\qquad\qquad\qquad\qquad\qquad Cl$$
$$\text{XI} \qquad\qquad\qquad\qquad\qquad\qquad \text{XII}$$

The resulting chains would have the formula XIII.

$$\ldots-CH_2C=CHCH_2CH_2C=CHCH_2CH_2C=CHCH_2-\ldots \xrightarrow{O} HOOC(CH_2)_2COOH$$
$$\mathrm{\ \ \ |} \qquad\qquad\quad \mathrm{|} \qquad\qquad\quad \mathrm{|}$$
$$Cl \qquad\qquad\quad Cl \qquad\qquad\quad Cl$$
$$\text{XIII} \qquad\qquad\qquad\qquad\qquad\qquad \text{XIV}$$

This formula readily accounts for the fact that oxidation of the μ-polychloroprene yields succinic acid (XIV). It also explains why the chlorine atom is very resistant to the action of alkalies: as in vinyl chloride, the chlorine is attached to a carbon atom bearing a double bond. This situation is changed however by autoxidation. This must lead to some such grouping as $\begin{smallmatrix} -CCl-CH- \\ \diagdown_{O}\diagup \end{smallmatrix}$, in which the chlorine atom would be exceedingly mobile.

Some evidence for this formula is also found in the physical properties of the μ-polychloroprene. The molecular refractivity calculated for this formula (22.95) agrees exactly with the experimental value (22.95). The x-ray diffraction pattern indicates an identity period of 4.8 Å., which corresponds quite well with that calculated for one chloroprene unit.

It appears to be generally true that the presence of a chlorine atom at a double bond decreases the tendency of the double bond to react with ozone, and in this connection it is significant that μ-polychloroprene is much more resistant than natural rubber to the deteriorating action of ozone.

In the formulas IX and XIII the isoprene and chloroprene units have been represented as being united regularly in 1,4-1,4- . . . order. The units however are not symmetrical and in joining of two units one or both of them might be inverted. This would lead to the arrangements 1,4-4,1- . . . and 4,1-1,4- . . . . It has been demonstrated that such inversions (13) do occur in the polymerization of isoprene in the presence of sodium and alcohol. On the other hand isoprene rubber formed by thermal polymerization, since its behavior toward ozone is normal (14), must be free from any considerable proportion of such inversions in its molecules.

The oxidation of μ-polychloroprene to succinic acid gives no indication as to whether the arrangement of the units is normal as represented in XIII or inverted as in XV and XVI, since the latter would also yield succinic acid.

$$...—CH_2—CCl=CH—CH_2—CH_2—CH=CCl—CH_2—... \qquad XV$$

$$...—CH_2—CH=CCl—CH_2—CH_2—CCl=CH—CH_2—... \qquad XVI$$

On the other hand the fact that μ-polychloroprene like natural rubber yields a sharp x-ray diffraction pattern whereas this property is absent from other synthetic rubbers perhaps indicates that the polychloroprene is freer from irregularities in the structure of its molecules than other synthetic rubbers.

The spontaneous polymerization of isoprene requires several years for its completion; with chloroprene the transformation is complete in a few days. The great difference in speed may be ascribed, in part at least, to the activating influence of the chlorine atom. The methyl group is too feebly polar to exert any such effect. A similar difference exists between vinyl chloride and propylene in their tendency to polymerize. The chlorine atom here functions not only to powerfully activate the double bond, it also exerts a greater effect than methyl on the direction of addition reactions at the double bond: it more effectively controls the polarity of the molecule. A similar directive effect in chloroprene is demonstrated by its behavior toward hydrogen chloride. Thus the relation between chloroprene and isoprene may be symbolized by the formulas XVII and XVIII.

$$^-CH_2{=}C{-}CH{=}CH_2{}^+$$
$$\mid$$
$$Cl$$
XVII

$$^-CH_2{=}C{-}CH{=}CH_2{}^+$$
$$\mid$$
$$CH_3$$
XVIII

It seems highly probable therefore on theoretical grounds not only that the polymerization of chloroprene will proceed much more rapidly than the polymerization of isoprene, but that there will be much less chance of inversions of the units in the polychloroprene chains.

Formula XIII adequately represents the chemical behavior of μ-polychloroprene, but is not sufficiently complete to account for the remarkable physical behavior of this material. The difficulties in this connection are precisely the same as those presented by natural rubber. The linear polymeric structure partially represented in formula IX furnishes a sufficient basis for describing the chemical behavior of rubber. It is known further that the molecular weight of rubber is exceedingly high—perhaps in the neighborhood of 70,000 (15); but no entirely adequate explanation of the elastic properties of rubber in terms of this structure has been offered. It seems scarcely necessary to review the numerous speculations that have been devoted to this subject (16). We merely point out that the units in a substituted polyprene chain (e. g., rubber or polychloroprene) present the possibility of geometrical isomerism and that they may be arranged in *cis-cis-cis-* . . . order or *trans-trans-trans-* . . . order; or both arrangements may be present in a single chain. The molecules may be coiled into spirals rather than rigidly extended. On these questions we have no data concerning polychloroprene (see however the above paragraph entitled x-Ray Diffraction Pattern). Moreover, we have no direct information concerning the molecular weight of polychloroprene. It seems certain, however, that the chains must be very long.

We observe finally that μ-polychloroprene resembles vulcanized rather than unvulcanized rubber. It is not plastic; it does not become plastic when heated; and it does not dissolve but merely swells in rubber solvents such as benzene and chloroform. This behavior is much more consistent with a three-dimensional polymeric structure than with a simple linear structure. We assume therefore that in μ-polychloroprene chains of the type already described are chemically linked together at occasional points. The resulting structure as we conceive it may be symbolized by formula XIX in which A stands for the structural unit. The cross-linking may occur through the mediacy of oxygen atoms, but it seems more likely that the double bonds of parallel chains mutually saturate one another directly. Since the chains are exceedingly long they need to be linked together only at occasional points to produce a non-plastic structure.

β-Polychloroprene.—When chloroprene is polymerized at elevated temperature, *e. g.*, at 60° especially in the absence of air, the product is somewhat less dense and softer than that formed at ordinary temperature, and it has a pronounced terpene-like odor.   This odor is due to the presence of volatile chloroprene polymers (β-polymer).   This product can be prepared in quantity by storing or heating chloroprene in the presence of substances such as pyrogallol or trinitrobenzene that inhibit the transformation of chloroprene into the μ-polymer.   By distillation the β-polymer can be separated into two fractions, one boiling at 92 to 97° at 27 mm. and the other boiling chiefly at 114 to 118° at 27 mm.   The odor of the fractions is very similar—fragrant and terpene-like.   The constitution of these products has not been determined, but there is little doubt that they are cyclic dimers of chloroprene.   It is already known that analogous products are formed from isoprene (17), butadiene (18) and dimethylbutadiene (19).   The β-polychloroprenes are stable substances, which show no tendency to polymerize further.   They have therefore no direct bearing on the formation of the rubber-like polymers, and they are relatively unimportant, especially since they appear in significant amounts only under rather exceptional conditions.

Influences Affecting the Polymerization of Chloroprene.—A few typical data are assembled in Table I.

(a)   **Catalysts.**—Oxygen is an exceedingly powerful catalyst for the transformation of chloroprene into the μ-polymer.   Samples of chloroprene distilled in high vacuum and sealed off in glass tubes without exposure to the air show an appreciable increase in viscosity only after a period of one or two months, and the transformation to μ-polymer is still incomplete after twelve months.   From some recent studies of the behavior of isoprene (20) it appears that the active catalyst in such transformations is a volatile peroxide.   Since it is practically impossible to prepare a sample of chloroprene without exposing it to air at some time during the course of its preparation, it seems probable that even the products distilled in high vacuum are not altogether free from catalyst.

The amount of oxygen necessary to produce an optimum catalytic effect is quite small.   At ordinary temperatures the presence of a volume of air equal to about 10% of the volume of the chloroprene sample causes the transformation to μ-polymer to be completed in about eight to ten

TABLE I

ESTIMATED TIME REQUIRED FOR 90% OF A SAMPLE OF CHLOROPRENE TO POLYMERIZE
UNDER VARIOUS CONDITIONS (ABSENCE OF DIRECT LIGHT)

No.	Temp., °C.	Air	Pressure, atm.	Other added substances	Time, days	Character of product
1	25	Present	1	None	8	Colorless, strong, tough
2	25	Absent	1	None	400	Soft, low density, strong odor of dimer
3	62	Present	1	None	2	Strong, tough, slight odor of dimer
4	62	Absent	1	None	10	Strong, tough, odor of dimer
5	100	Absent	1	None	<1	Semi-fluid, black, much dimer
6	25	Present	4500	None	<2	Transparent, rather hard, very tough
7	25	Present	6000	None	0.7	Transparent, rather hard, very tough
8	60	Absent	6100	None	2	Rather soft, odor of dimer
9	62	Absent	1	1.5% Benzoyl peroxide	1	Product variable
10	62	Present	1	0.5% Benzoyl peroxide	1	Strong, tough, colorless
11	25	Absent	1	0.1% Catechol		Still fluid after 65 days
12	25	Present	1	1.6% Thiodiphenylamine		Still fluid after 13 months; strong odor of dimer

days. If the volume of air is much smaller than this the time required
for the transformation is somewhat greater, but much larger ratios of air
or oxygen do not greatly increase the velocity. Large quantities of oxygen
do however affect the character of the final product. In general they
lead to a product which, instead of being colorless or only slightly yellow,
is dark brown and considerably harder and stiffer than the usual products.

Peroxides such as benzoyl peroxide also function as catalysts. Their
use, however, presents no practical advantages, and is in fact somewhat
hazardous. In samples containing benzoyl peroxide there is frequently
a considerable induction period, and then reaction suddenly starts at
some point in the sample and spreads very rapidly through the mass.
The heat of reaction may be sufficient to char the sample.

The rate of formation of β-polychloroprene is not appreciably accelerated by oxygen or peroxides.

(b) **Temperature, Pressure and Light.**—Catalytic and anticatalytic
effects in the polymerization of chloroprene are very powerful and difficult
to regulate exactly; for this reason it is impossible to obtain precise quantitative correlations concerning the effect of temperature, pressure and
light on the reaction velocity. It appears, however, that in the presence
of air the transformation of chloroprene into the μ-polymer occurs about
four times as fast at 62° as at 25°. Thus the temperature coefficient of
the catalyzed reaction is abnormally low. The relative rate of the for-

mation of β-polymer, which is negligible at ordinary temperature, is more strongly affected by rise in temperature. Polymers produced at temperatures above 50° contain appreciable proportions of β-polymer. These proportions are still further increased if the reaction is carried out in the absence of air since this greatly reduces the speed with which μ-polymer is formed without affecting the formation of β-polymer. In the absence of air the effect of increased temperature on the rate of transformation of chloroprene into μ-polymer appears to be much greater than in the presence of air.

When chloroprene is polymerized at temperatures above 80° (in the absence of solvents) considerable decomposition occurs with liberation of appreciable amounts of hydrogen chloride, and the product is dark in color and tarry in consistency.

At a pressure of 6000 atmospheres the polymerization of chloroprene occurs about ten times as rapidly as at ordinary pressure.

Light has a considerable accelerating effect on the transformation of chloroprene into the μ-polymer. The rate of formation of β-polymer is not affected. The active wave lengths lie in the blue, violet and near ultraviolet.

(c) **Inhibitors.**—Substances that generally function as antioxidants act as powerful inhibitors for the transformation of chloroprene into the μ-polymer. Under ordinary conditions a sample of chloroprene will set in four days to a stiff jelly containing about 40% polymer but the presence of 0.1% of catechol will permit the sample to remain fluid for several months. This fact confirms indications already mentioned that the spontaneous transformation of chloroprene into μ-polymer is normally dependent upon the presence of traces of autoxidation products of the chloroprene. The formation of β-polymer is not thus dependent upon oxidation. Samples of chloroprene containing inhibitors, after several months at the ordinary temperature, are found to contain several per cent. of β-polymer, and frequently they are quite free of μ-polymer. A sample of chloroprene containing 0.2% of pyrogallol yielded 49% of crude β-polymer after being heated for forty days at 62°.

The following types of compounds generally function as inhibitors: phenols, quinones, amines, mercaptans, thiophenols, aromatic nitro compounds, halogens. Some compounds in each of these classes function as powerful inhibitors, others have a feebler effect. It is somewhat surprising to find aromatic nitro compounds in this list. Trinitrobenzene is among the most powerful of the inhibitors.

In the presence of relatively feeble inhibitors or small amounts of the more powerful inhibitors the polymerization of chloroprene can be effected at a somewhat diminished rate. The non-volatile polymer formed under these conditions, however, differs very considerably in its properties from that formed in the absence of inhibitors.

(d) **Solvents.**—The polymerization of chloroprene can be effected in the presence of solvents. If the solvent is one such as benzene, toluene, ethylene chloride, or carbon disulfide that powerfully swells μ-polychloroprene, the resulting polymer remains dissolved. The polymerization of solutions containing as much as 50% by volume of chloroprene leads to the formation of stiff jellies. Even as little as 10% of chloroprene leads to highly viscous solutions. The solutions are generally colorless and transparent. The polymers contained in these solutions are somewhat different in their properties from the μ-polychloroprenes produced under ordinary conditions. They are softer, and unless the solution is very old they can usually be redissolved in benzene.

The presence of the solvent considerably diminishes the rate of the polymerization, and dilute solutions polymerize more slowly than concentrated ones. Solvents also frequently exert a specific effect. Chloroprene dissolved in benzene polymerizes very much more rapidly than chloroprene dissolved in ether or pyridine.

Chloroprene may also be polymerized in the presence of non-volatile solvents, inert fillers and foreign materials of various kinds.

Granular Polymer (ω-Polymer).—The polymerization of chloroprene occasionally leads to a coherent mass of glistening, hard, rubbery granules or globules (ω-polymer). This material is non-plastic and it shows scarcely any tendency to imbibe solvents. The conditions favoring its formation are not very clearly understood, since it occasionally appears under the most diverse conditions. It seems certain, however, that its formation is autocatalytic. When a speck of this polymer appears in a sample of chloroprene during the early stages of its polymerization the granular growth continues to spread through the whole sample. Because of its cell-like structure it occupies more volume than the same amount of μ-polymer, and if the growth begins to spread laterally through a sample it may burst the walls of a heavy Pyrex container even when the total volume of the container is much greater than the volume of the product. The presence of metallic sodium especially favors the formation of the granular polymer. It frequently appears under other conditions that result in very slow polymerization.

According to experiments made by Dr. H. W. Starkweather the formation of the ω-polymer is initiated (or accelerated) by light of 3130 Å. wave length. The following observation is especially interesting.

Chloroprene containing pyrogallol to inhibit polymerization was placed in the bottom of a long Pyrex tube. The chloroprene was cooled to −80°, and the tube was evacuated and sealed off. The lower half of the tube was covered with black friction tape to exclude light and the upper part was exposed to light from a mercury arc. During the exposure the lower part of the tube was kept in a bath at 10°; the upper half was at 60–65°. After twelve hours there was a white deposit at the top of the tube. This deposit gradually increased during two and one-half days. Exposure to the light was then discontinued. The solid deposit, however, continued to form at the top of the tube as a white, crinkly mass, until the liquid in the bottom of the tube was completely exhausted.

It is interesting to observe that products similar to this granular polymer have been obtained from other dienes. Kondakow (21) observed that dimethylbutadiene in a closed flask in diffused daylight is gradually transformed into a white, insoluble mass, and Harries (22) obtained a similar product by the action of ultraviolet light on isoprene.

The great resistance of the ω-polychloroprene as compared with the ω-polymer to the swelling action of solvents indicates a considerably higher degree of cross-linking of the chains in the ω-compound. If such a cross-linking should occur in a sufficiently regular fashion, it would lead to a three-dimensional primary valence lattice, a type of structure which is illustrated by the diamond, but is not known among synthetic organic compounds. The conditions under which the ω-polymer is formed are such as might be especially favorable to the development of a regular three-dimensional structure. The formation of ω-polymer is catalyzed by an ω-polymer surface; the process is one of heterogeneous autocatalysis. It seems most probable that the function of the ω-polymer surface in this connection is not (or at least not wholly) to activate adsorbed molecules of the monomer, but rather to orient the adsorbed molecules into a configuration favorable for mutual union. The incidence of activating energy could then bring about the combination of a very large number of molecules in a single act.

As a matter of fact the granular polymer at first sight gives the impression of being definitely macrocrystalline, but on closer observation the crystals turn out to be globules. x-Ray examination gives only an amorphous pattern.

It is interesting to note that the granular polymer never appears in samples of α-polychloroprene (described later) that contain phenyl-β-naphthylamine.

Progressive Changes during the Spontaneous Polymerization of Chloroprene.—The following table illustrates in more detail the changes in properties and composition that occur when a sample of chloroprene is allowed to stand under ordinary conditions in the presence of a little air.

TABLE II
CHANGES DURING THE POLYMERIZATION OF CHLOROPRENE

Time, days	Polymer, %	Density	Viscosity in centipoises
0	0	0.952	0.4
1	4	..	6.0
2	14	0.98	550.0
4	45	1.06	Stiff jelly
10	99+	1.23	Non-plastic

The polymer formed during the early stages of the reaction can be isolated by precipitation with alcohol, or by distilling off the unchanged chloroprene *in vacuo*. This material is very different in its properties from the final product, the μ-polychloroprene already described. It is soft, plastic, and completely soluble in benzene. We call this plastic polymer α-polychloroprene. When allowed to stand at the ordinary temperature it slowly reacts with itself and in the course of a day or two is transformed into a product apparently identical with the μ-polymer.

Mechanism of the Formation of α- and μ-Polymers.—The isolation of the α-polymer demonstrates that the transformation of chloroprene into the μ-polymer is a step-wise reaction. Some of the facts concerning the two polymers and their relation to each other are best correlated by a brief discussion of mechanism.

The transformation of chloroprene into the α-polymer is evidently a chain reaction. It is enormously susceptible to catalytic and anticatalytic effects; it is accelerated by light; and although a large number of molecules is combined to form a single larger molecule, the apparent order of the reaction is low. The reaction probably first involves the coupling of an activated molecule of chloroprene with another chloroprene molecule. The activating energy persists in the polymeric chain until it has been built up to a considerable length. The molecules of α-polymer thus formed doubtless have the linear structure already suggested in formula XIII. The formation of a molecule of α-polymer involves a series of separate acts, but these follow one another in very rapid succession Under ordinary conditions the α-polymer present when 4% of a sample of chloroprene has polymerized is indistinguishable from the polymer present when 20% of the chloroprene has polymerized.

The transformation of the α-polymer into the μ-polymer consists in the cross-linking of the long chains into a three-dimensional structure of the type represented in formula XIX. In a sample of chloroprene undergoing spontaneous polymerization this process becomes noticeable when the concentration of polymer has reached about 25%. It is marked by an abrupt change in properties. The viscosity increases very rapidly and the sample soon sets to a stiff jelly. If the polymer is isolated just before this point is reached, it is found to be soft and plastic. Polymer isolated just after this abrupt change is still soft, but the manner in which it resists permanent deformation indicates the presence of a considerable proportion of the μ-polymer.

The reactions, (1) chloroprene ⟶ α-polymer, and (2) α-polymer ⟶ μ-polymer, are not merely two stages of a single process, but are different reactions. The polymerization of chloroprene is rather strongly inhibited by primary aromatic amines, such as aniline, the naphthylamines, and benzidine; but these same compounds when mixed with isolated α-polymer accelerate its conversion into μ-polymer. The temperature coefficients of the two reactions are different. For reaction (2) the ratio of the velocity constants for a temperature increase of 10° is about two; for reaction (1) the ratio is considerably less than two.

Other Polymers; Balata-like Polymer.—The α-, μ- and ω-types are not chemical individuals but rather qualitatively different species of polymeric mixtures. The properties of each type may vary over a considerable range and in practice no doubt one generally has to do not with a pure species but with a mixture in which one of the species may preponderate. A consideration of the formulas assigned to the α- and μ-polymers will suggest some of the complications that might arise. The molecules of the α-polymer are no doubt chains of very great length, but in the polymerization of chloroprene under certain conditions, e. g., at elevated temperature, the process of cross-linking may set in before the chains have attained the usual length of α-polymer chains. One will then have a product very different in its properties from that produced by the vulcanization of α-polymer. Stereochemical factors (e. g., cis-trans isomerism) may also produce great variations in the character of the products.

The α-, β-, μ- and ω-polymers by no means exhaust the different types of polychloroprenes. Anything that influences the velocity of the polymerization has some effect on the properties of the product, and the modifications produced by inhibitors and catalysts are especially marked. The phenomena in this connection are very complex. It would be useless to attempt to recognize as distinct species all the distinguishably different polymeric products derived from chloroprene.

There is, however, one type of product that appears to be qualitatively different from the α-, β-, μ- and ω-polymers. This material rather closely resembles balata in its properties. It is obtained more or less contaminated with the other types of polymers under various conditions, but especially by the polymerization of chloroprene in the presence of inhibitors such as iodine or the tetraalkyl thiuramdisulfides.

A typical specimen of this balata-like material when cold is a hard, amorphous, non-brittle mass. When warmed to 60° it becomes soft and plastic. At higher temperatures it is quite sticky. When heated under vulcanizing conditions the plasticity is partly lost, but the transformation to the elastic condition is very incomplete. We make no attempt to suggest a structure for this material.

Conditions for the Isolation of α-Polymer.—Owing to the effect of changing concentrations, the rate of formation of α-polymer progressively decreases during the polymerization of chloroprene, and the rate of the conversion of α-polymer into μ-polymer progressively increases. For this reason if pure α-polymer is to be obtained, the reaction must be interrupted before all of the chloroprene has polymerized.

Under the most favorable conditions the concentration of the α-polymer in the polymerizing mixture can be built up to 30 or 40% before any appreciable transformation to μ-polymer occurs. The reaction is best conducted in glass vessels under strong illumination from a Mazda lamp or a mercury arc in glass. The most effective wave lengths lie in the long ultraviolet, but the use of a quartz container with mercury arc radiation is not advisable on account of the danger of forming granular polymer. The temperature should be kept in the neighborhood of 35°. Under these conditions about 30% of the chloroprene is polymerized in sixteen to twenty-four hours. The product is a thick, colorless, transparent sirup. If this sirup is poured into a large volume of alcohol, the α-polymer separates as a colorless mass and the unchanged chloroprene remains dissolved in the alcohol. The α-polymer can also be separated by allowing the unchanged chloroprene to distil out of the mixture under diminished pressure. The mixture is preferably stirred during the distillation.

Properties of the α-Polymer.—In density and refractive index the α-polymer lies very close to the μ-polymer. The α-polymer resembles milled smoked sheets in its physical properties and mechanical behavior. It is plastic and it dissolves completely in benzene to form highly viscous solutions. It can be calendered into thin sheets or extruded with the usual rubber machinery

At 30° the α-polymer loses its plastic properties and becomes completely changed to the elastic form (μ-polymer) in about forty-eight hours. At 130° the transformation is complete in about five minutes. This process corresponds to the vulcanization of natural rubber, but sulfur is not needed and when present it takes no part in the process. The speed of this transformation can be greatly modified by the addition of various substances, some of them materials that are used in the vulcanization of natural rubber.

Zinc oxide brings about the vulcanization of α-polymer in eight to ten hours at 30°. Zinc chloride, zinc butyrate and ferric chloride are even more active catalysts. The most effective organic catalysts are primary aromatic amines such as aniline, the naphthylamines and benzidine. Diphenylguanidine, which is a relatively active vulcanization accelerator for natural rubber, is a mild accelerator for α-polymer. On the other hand mercaptobenzothiazole and tetraalkylthiuram sulfides, which are active natural rubber accelerators, have no accelerating action on the α-polymer. Basic inorganic materials such as lime and magnesium oxide, which may accelerate natural rubber through their action with sulfur, have a slight retarding influence on the vulcanization of α-polymer. Strong acids and acidic materials that retard the vulcanization of natural rubber have no influence on the curing of plastic polymer.

Secondary aromatic amines such as phenyl-β-naphthylamine powerfully inhibit the vulcanization of α-polymer at ordinary temperature. This fact is of considerable practical importance since it brings about the possibility of storing the plastic polymer over long periods of time. The phenyl-β-naphthylamine also acts as an antioxidant and confers age-resisting properties on the final product. The inhibiting effect of the phenyl-β-naphthylamine on the curing of the α-polymer largely disappears above 100°.

Behavior of α-Polymer in Compounding and Properties of the Cured Rubber.—The compounding ingredients that can be used with α-polymer are similar to those used with natural rubber, but there are a number of important additions. Materials such as ground leather and cork which strongly retard the vulcanization of natural rubber act as inert ingredients in α-polymer. Carbon black and zinc oxide act as reinforcing agents as they do in natural rubber and impart good abrasion resistance. In contrast to their action in rubber, whiting and clay are perfectly wet by α-polymer, and they produce compounds having good tear resistance. Cotton and other vegetable fibers are also much more perfectly wet by α-polymer than by rubber. Most plasticizing and softening materials such as mineral oil, stearic acid and pine tar are insoluble in α-polymer and have little true softening action. Milling also produces little softening other than a temporary thermal effect. Mineral rubber and similar asphaltic materials act as diluents with little effect on the physical properties of the vulcanized material.

Natural rubber can be successfully milled into α-polymer, although there is little affinity between the two. Sheets of the two rubbers before vulcanization may be firmly pressed together and easily separated. A reasonably firm union can be obtained between natural and chloroprene rubber when they are vulcanized together under sufficient pressure. Benzene solutions of rubber and α-polymer are not compatible; when thoroughly mixed they quickly separate into two layers.

Table III gives the composition of compounded stocks prepared from α-polychloroprene and from smoked sheets. These were used for a series of parallel tests to compare the behavior of the two rubbers. All the processing and testing were carried out with the usual rubber laboratory equipment.

TABLE III

COMPOSITION OF COMPOUNDED STOCKS FROM α-POLYCHLOROPRENE AND FROM SMOKED SHEETS

| | Amount in grams | |
Materials	Compound from α-polychloroprene	Compound from smoked sheets
α-Polychloroprene	100	...
Smoked sheet rubber	...	100
Zinc oxide	10	10
Sulfur	...	3
Stearic acid	2	2
Diphenylguanidine	...	1
Benzidine (accelerator)	0.5	..
Phenyl-β-naphthylamine	1	1

The effect of different times and temperatures of vulcanization on the physical properties of the two compounds is shown in Table IV. The chloroprene rubber reaches a maximum tensile strength after only five minutes at 140°; but the strength is not adversely affected if the curing time is extended to sixteen hours. In contrast to this, the natural rubber compound vulcanizes more slowly and softens rapidly under the action of prolonged vulcanization. The maximum tensile strength for the chloroprene compound is slightly lower than that for the natural rubber compound. In contrast to the smoked sheet compound the chloroprene compound shows no reversion and the load supported at 500% elongation continues to increase slowly throughout the curing range. When the polychloroprene compound is heated longer than sixteen hours at 140° a material resembling hard rubber is formed.

TABLE IV

EFFECT OF VULCANIZATION ON PHYSICAL PROPERTIES OF COMPOUNDED STOCKS

Vulcaniza-tion temp., °C.	Minutes vulcaniza-tion time	Load at 500% elongation, kg. per sq. cm.		Tensile strength at break, kg. per sq. cm.		% Elongation at break	
		Chloroprene rubber	Smoked sheet	Chloroprene rubber	Smoked sheet	Chloroprene rubber	Smoked sheet
110	20	16.0	..	166.9	...	920	...
110	40	28.1	..	177.5	...	860	...
120	20	28.2	..	169.3	...	860	...
120	40	30.2	..	171.2	...	820	...
140	5	29.9	..	170.5	...	825	...
140	10	33.4	..	170.5	...	780	...
140	15	38.6	12.2	172.2	12.6	770	860
140	20	38.6	16.0	170.5	15.2	760	830
140	30	42.2	21.0	172.2	175.0	750	820
140	60	42.2	35.1	167.0	210.0	750	760
140	90	43.9	46.2	167.0	192.0	720	680
140	120	45.7	42.0	181.0	205.0	740	720
140	480	54.4	14.0	165.2	87.0	700	800
140	960	63.3	11.9	151.1	82.1	640	820

The chloroprene compound is very resistant to the action of ozone. The two compounds were stretched about fifteen per cent. and exposed to ozone-containing air. The natural rubber compound was ruptured in three minutes; the chloroprene compound was not detectably affected during an exposure of three hours.

Table V shows the results of artificial aging tests on the two compounds of Table III. The chloroprene compound was cured for fifteen minutes and the natural rubber compound for sixty minutes at 140°. The tests were carried out at 70° in oxygen at twenty atmospheres. Under these conditions twenty-four hours is generally considered to approximate one year of natural aging for rubber. These data indicate that the chloroprene rubber is considerably more resistant to oxidation than natural rubber. Natural aging tests have not been carried out for a length of time sufficient to confirm this conclusion, but samples of the chloroprene rubber compound that have been kept for one year show no deterioration.

Chloroprene rubber is much more resistant than the natural product to the action of solvents and many chemicals. After seventy-two hours the chloroprene compound had increased 7% in weight by immersion in

TABLE V

AGING PROPERTIES OF COMPOUNDS FROM SMOKED SHEETS AND FROM
α-POLYCHLOROPRENE

Days in oxygen bomb at 70°	Tensile strength, kg. per sq. cm.		% Elongation at break	
	Chloroprene rubber	Smoked sheets	Chloroprene rubber	Smoked sheets
0	172.2	232.0	890	720
1	212.6	195.0	845	660
2	181.0	163.4	820	660
3	193.3	159.9	805	670
8	209.1	116.1	720	595
14	165.2	54.5	690	510

light machine oil and 25% by immersion in kerosene, and it had retained more than half of its original tensile strength in each case. The tensile strength of the natural rubber was destroyed under these conditions. In contrast to natural rubber, chloroprene rubber is not attacked by hydrogen chloride, hydrogen fluoride, sulfur chloride, ozone and many other chemicals. The high chlorine content of the chloroprene rubber also renders it very resistant to combustion. Measurements of diffusion of both hydrogen and helium through a polychloroprene membrane show it to be only 40% as permeable as natural rubber. The absence of water-soluble materials in chloroprene rubber makes it very resistant to penetration by water.

Synthetic Latex.—Chloroprene is readily emulsified by shaking or stirring it with water containing an emulsifying agent such as sodium oleate. The resulting emulsion polymerizes very rapidly and completely. The polymer remains suspended or emulsified and constitutes an artificial latex. When the water is allowed to evaporate from a layer of this latex, a thin coherent, strong, elastic film remains. This film in its physical and mechanical properties very closely resembles the μ-polychloroprene already described: it is strong, extensible, elastic, resilient, non-plastic and not thermoplastic, and it is swelled but not dissolved by benzene.

The following example illustrates the preparation of a synthetic latex. Four hundred grams of chloroprene is slowly added with vigorous stirring to 400 g. of water containing 8 g. of sodium oleate in a wide-mouthed bottle. A smooth emulsion results. After a time (usually about thirty minutes) the temperature of the mixture begins to rise and it may quickly reach the boiling point of the chloroprene unless cooling is applied. After standing for two to eight hours at room temperature the polymerization is complete. The mixture is then practically odorless.

More uniform products are obtained if the temperature is carefully controlled during the emulsification and polymerization. At a temperature of 10° the process is complete in about twenty-four hours—always in less than forty-eight hours. The reaction is always characterized by an induction period, which at 10° usually lasts forty to sixty minutes. It is evident that the speed of polymerization of chloroprene is much greater (apparently at least 20-fold) in emulsion than otherwise. The particular nature of the interface appears to be of great importance in determining the rate of polymerization. The rate is much more rapid with sodium oleate than with egg albumen although both of these emulsifying agents produce very small particles.

A small amount of free acid is developed during the polymerization of the emulsions, and this gradually brings about coagulation during storage. However, if a little ammonia (e. g., 5 g. of NH_3 per liter) is added to the latex after completion of the polymerization this tendency is avoided. Latex stabilized in this way can be stored indefinitely without change. In addition to the ammonia it is ordinarily desirable to add an antioxidant such as phenyl-β-naphthylamine since this greatly prolongs the life of articles prepared with the latex.

The particle size of latex prepared according to the above example is very small and remarkably uniform. Figure 4 gives the results of some measurements made by Dr. J. B. Nichols with the ultracentrifuge. When sodium oleate is used as the emulsifying agent the mean radius of the particles is about 0.063μ and more than 60% of the particles lie between 0.05 and 0.07μ. It appears that the ultracentrifugal method has not been applied to natural latex, but according to Hauser (23) the latex from mature *Hevea* trees contains particles ranging in diameter from 0.5 to 3μ as well as a considerable proportion of smaller particles. The particle size of the synthetic latex can be controlled to a certain extent by suitably modifying the nature and the amount of the emulsifying agent. The use of lithium oleate in the ratio of two grams to one hundred grams of chloroprene gives particles having a mean radius of about 0.087μ.

In the preparation of the synthetic latex the ratio of chloroprene to water can be varied over a wide range. As long as the concentration lies below 55% by weight of polychloroprene, the latices are very fluid. Above this concentration there is a sharp increase in viscosity, and a 60% latex is quite thick.

The synthetic latex is rapidly coagulated by acids, alcohol, acetone and many salts. The polychloroprene separates as a coherent mass, which is at first quite soft and plastic. However, as soon as the water is squeezed out, this plasticity is lost. The mass then has the properties already indicated for μ-polychloroprene—it is analogous to a soft, vulcanized natural rubber.

Applications of the Latex.—The chloroprene latex can be directly applied to many uses after the manner of vulcanized natural latex. In this connection it has some special advantages owing to its peculiar properties. Thus on account of its small particle size it penetrates porous articles such as leather and wood in a manner that can hardly be approached with natural latex.

Shaped articles are readily prepared by dipping forms of glass, metal or porcelain into the latex and coagulating the resulting film or allowing it to dry. By repeated dipping, articles of any desired thickness can be built up.

The latex can be mixed with dyes, fillers and modifying and protective agents of various kinds to adapt it to specific uses.

Polymerization of Chloroprene in Porous Materials.—Attempts to impregnate such porous materials as leather, wood and tile with natural rubber are unsuccessful, whether the rubber is used in the form of latex or dissolved in a solvent such as benzene; but a very intimate impregnation of these materials with

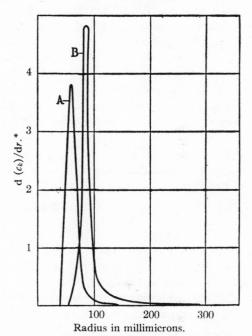

Radius in millimicrons.

Fig. 4.—Weight distribution curve for chloroprene lattices. The units are such that the area under the curves for any radius interval equals the fraction of the total weight of particles whose radii lie in that interval. Curve A, latex made with sodium oleate. Curve B, latex made with lithium oleate.

chloroprene rubber can be accomplished by soaking them in chloroprene and then allowing the rubber to be formed in place. Chamois or kid leather saturated with its own weight of chloroprene and sealed to prevent evaporation until polymerization is complete becomes translucent and assumes a rubber-like flexibility without extensibility. Impregnated spruce be-

* Fraction of total weight (c_k) corresponding to a certain radius (r).

comes water resistant but its appearance is unchanged. This process may be used with any porous or bibulous material that does not contain inhibitors for the spontaneous polymerization of chloroprene.

Conclusion.—If space permitted it would be possible to review the literature on synthetic rubber from diene hydrocarbons and to show that almost every recorded peculiarity and complication in this field finds some analogy in the behavior of chloroprene. Chloroprene is therefore capable of serving adequately as a representative diene in studying as a scientific problem the synthesis of rubber-like materials, and for this purpose it has the great advantage of its very high speed of polymerization as compared with dienes previously available.

On the economic side the greatly diminished costs of producing natural rubber have obviated the need for an artificial material having the same properties. There remains, however, the need for a synthetic rubber that is free from some of the inherent defects of the natural product. The differences between polychloroprene and natural rubber are sufficient to suggest considerable potentialities for the new synthetic product.

Summary

Chloro-2-butadiene-1,3 (chloroprene) is described and its structure established through reactions leading to its conversion into butane-α, β,γ,δ-tetracarboxylic acid, and into β-chloroanthraquinone.

Within ten days under ordinary conditions in a closed vessel containing a little air, chloroprene spontaneously changes into a transparent, resilient, strong, non-plastic, elastic mass resembling vulcanized rubber. This product is called μ-polychloroprene. By interrupting the polymerization before it has proceeded to completion one obtains a soft plastic product (α-polymer) that resembles unvulcanized rubber. Under the action of heat the α-polymer rapidly changes to the μ-polymer. Other polymers of chloroprene described are volatile (β-) polymer, granular (ω-) polymer, and balata-like polymer. The structures of the polymers are discussed as well as the effect of conditions on the formation of each type.

Unlike any previously described synthetic rubbers, μ-polychloroprene resembles natural rubber in the fact that when it is stretched its x-ray diffraction pattern shows a point diagram.

The transformation of chloroprene into μ-polychloroprene occurs very rapidly in aqueous emulsion. The resulting product constitutes a synthetic (vulcanized) latex. It has a much smaller particle size than natural latex and it penetrates porous materials more readily.

Chloroprene can also be polymerized in the pores of porous or bibulous materials. The materials thus become intimately impregnated with synthetic rubber.

Compared with natural rubber the new synthetic rubber is more dense, more resistant to absorption or penetration by water, less strongly swelled by petroleum hydrocarbons and less permeable to many gases. It is much more resistant to attack by oxygen, ozone, hydrogen chloride, hydrogen fluoride and many other chemicals.

Bibliography and Remarks

(1) Nieuwland, Calcott, Downing and Carter, *Journ. Am. Chem. Soc.*, **53**, 4197 (1931).

(2) These data are based on vapor pressure measurements made with an isoteniscope by Dr. H. W. Starkweather.

(3) Diels and Alder, *Ber.*, **62**, 2337 (1929).

(4) Auwers and Jacob, *ibid.*, **27**, 1114 (1894).

(5) Farmer and Warren, *J. Chem. Soc.*, 897 (1929).

(6) The same behavior has already been observed in rubber by Hock, *Gummi-Ztg.*, **39**, 1740 (1925).

(7) Katz, *Chem.-Ztg.*, **49**, 353 (1925); Meyer and Mark, *Ber.*, **61**, 1939 (1928).

(8) "Die Röntgentechnik in der Materialprüfung," Eggert and Schiebold, Akademische Verlagsgesellschaft, Leipzig, **1930**, p. 142.

(9) Meyer and Mark, "Der Aufbau der hochpolymeren organischen Naturstoffe," Akademische Verlagsgesellschaft, Leipzig, **1930**.

(10) Hauser and v. Susich, *Kautschuk*, **7**, 145 (1931).

(11) Harries, *Ber.*, **37**, 2708 (1904); **38**, 3985 (1905); Pummerer, Ebermayer and Gerlach, *ibid.*, **64**, 809 (1931).

(12) Harries, "Untersuchungen," Julius Springer, **1910**, p. 222.

(13) Midgley and Henne, *Journ. Am. Chem. Soc.*, **52**, 2077 (1930).

(14) *Cf.* Pummerer and Koch, in Memmler's "Handbuch der Kautschukwissenschaft," S. Hirzel, Leipzig, **1930**, p. 270.

(15) Staudinger and Bondy, *Ann.*, **488**, 127 (1931).

(16) Some of the most suggestive are Staudinger, *Kautschuk*, **5**, 911, 1261 (1929); Meyer and Mark, "Der Aufbau der hochpolymeren organischen Naturstoffe," Akademische Verlagsgesellschaft, Leipzig, **1930**; Fikentscher and Mark, *Kautschuk*, **6**, 2 (1930).

(17) Pummerer and Koch, *loc. cit.*, p. 284.

(18) Hofmann and Tank, *Z. angew. Chem.*, **25**, 1465 (1912).

(19) Van Romburgh and Van Romburgh, *Proc. Roy. Acad. Amsterdam*, **34**, 224 (1931).

(20) Conant and Peterson, private communication.

(21) Kondakow, *J. prakt. Chem.*, [2] **64**, 109 (1901).

(22) Pummerer and Koch, *loc. cit.*, p. 268.

(23) Hauser, "Latex," Theodor Steinkopff, Leipzig, **1927**, p. 56.

III.   The Addition of Hydrogen Chloride to Vinylacetylene*

Vinylacetylene (I) constitutes the simplest possible example of a conjugated enine system. Recorded information concerning the addition reactions of such systems is exceedingly meager. It has already been reported (1) that chloroprene (chloro-2-butadiene-1,3, III) can be obtained by the addition of (aqueous) hydrogen chloride to vinylacetylene, and the present paper is concerned with a further description of the mechanism of this reaction and the nature of the products to which it leads.

It is shown that the initial step consists in 1,4 addition, and the primary product thus formed is chloro-4-butadiene-1,2 (II) (b. p. 88°), a new compound of rather unusual structure and curious properties. Under certain conditions this chloro-4-butadiene-1,2 can be isolated as the major reaction product, but it readily undergoes an isomerization involving migration of the chlorine atom and a shift of a double bond†. Chloroprene (b. p. 59.4°) is formed thus, and the transformation occurs with such facility in the presence of hydrogen chloride that chloroprene always constitutes a part of the reaction product. Certain salts reinforce the catalytic effect of hydrogen chloride on this transformation, and when cuprous chloride is present no chloro-4-butadiene-1,2 is found in the reaction product. When sufficient amounts of hydrogen chloride are present the reaction proceeds further with the formation of dichloro-2,4-butene-2 (IV).

$$CH{\equiv}C{-}CH{=}CH_2 \xrightarrow{\text{HCl}} CH_2{=}C{=}CH{-}CH_2Cl \longrightarrow$$
$$\text{I} \hspace{4cm} \text{II}$$

$$CH_2{=}C{-}CH{=}CH_2 \xrightarrow{\text{HCl}} CH_3{-}C{=}CH{-}CH_2Cl$$
$$\quad\ \ |\hspace{6cm}|$$
$$\quad\ \ Cl\hspace{5.6cm}Cl$$
$$\quad\ \ \text{III}\hspace{5.3cm}\text{IV}$$

Influence of Conditions on the Reaction.—The reaction between vinylacetylene and hydrogen chloride is conveniently carried out in the following manner. Fifty grams of vinylacetylene and 175 cc. of concentrated hydrochloric acid (about 2.2 moles of hydrochloric acid) are placed in a pressure bottle, and the bottle is shaken to promote contact between the aqueous and the hydrocarbon layers. After the completion of the reaction the oily layer is separated, dried, mixed with a small amount of an anti-

* W. H. Carothers, G. J. Berchet and A. M. Collins, *Journ. Am. Chem. Soc.*, **54**, 4066-70 (1932); Contribution No. 96 from the Experimental Station of E. I. du Pont de Nemours and Co.

Received June 9, 1932. Published October 5, 1932.

† For a further study of the chemical behavior of chloro-4-butadiene-1,2 and for a discussion of its rearrangement to chloroprene, see this volume, page 335.

oxidant such as catechol or pyrogallol, and distilled *in vacuo* through an efficient column. Data from a very large number of experiments of this type are available. Owing to the fact that in most cases neither the temperature nor the speed of shaking was precisely controlled these data cannot be used as a basis for a quantitative description of reaction velocities; nevertheless, they give a clear idea of relative rates.

In a typical experiment of the kind described above, about 43% of the vinylacetylene was utilized in seven hours, and analysis of the reaction product yielded chloro-4-butadiene-1,2 and chloroprene in the ratio 2.2:1. In general this ratio is diminished by increase in the temperature, concentration of hydrogen chloride, or time of contact; and the proportion of the chloro-4-butadiene-1,2 in the product is less the more completely the vinylacetylene is utilized. This fact demonstrates that part at least of the chloroprene is formed by the isomerization of the chloro-4-butadiene-1,2 during the course of the reaction, and it seems reasonable to conclude that all of it is formed by this demonstrated mechanism.

The reaction is considerably accelerated by the presence of certain salts. Thus when 25 g. of calcium chloride is present in the reaction mixture the time required to obtain 40% conversion is decreased by about one-half, but the ratio of the two isomeric chlorobutadienes present in the reaction product at a given percentage conversion remains practically unaffected. Cuprous chloride is a much more powerful catalyst. When 25 g. of this salt is present in the reaction mixture, about 90% of the vinylacetylene reacts in four hours at 20°. In this case the product consists for the most part of chloroprene, and no chloro-4-butadiene-1,2 is present. It is, however, not necessary to assume that the cuprous chloride directs the reaction so that addition occurs at the acetylenic linkage. Separate experiments show that cuprous chloride reinforces the catalytic effect of hydrogen chloride on the isomerization of chloro-4-butadiene-1,2 and this effect seems adequate to explain the absence of chloro-4-butadiene-1,2 in the reaction product.

Chloroprene reacts further with hydrogen chloride to produce dichloro-2,4-butene-2. This reaction is also catalyzed by cuprous chloride, and the relative velocities are such that any conditions of concentration, temperature, and time of contact that suffice to convert all of a given sample of vinylacetylene result in the formation of a certain amount of the dichlorobutene. The following experiment is illustrative. Fifty grams of vinylacetylene, 175 cc. of concentrated hydrochloric acid, 25 g. of cuprous chloride, and 10 g. of ammonium chloride were placed in each of forty bottles. The bottles were gently shaken in a bath at 20° for four hours and then allowed to stand for twelve hours at 0°. The contents of all the bottles were combined and the mixture was steam distilled *in vacuo* into a receiver placed at the bottom of a 2-meter jacketed, carborundum-packed column provided with a dephlegmator and a second receiver each cooled to −80°. The pressure was kept at about 150 mm. until all of the unchanged vinylacetylene had collected in the second receiver, and the pressure was then gradually reduced to 10 mm. until all of the chloroprene had collected in the second receiver. The dichlorobutene remained in the first receiver. The yields were: unchanged vinylacetylene, 115 g.; chloroprene, 2862 g.; dichlorobutene, 117 g. In mole percentages these values are 5.7, 84.2 and 2.5, respectively. The deficit amounting to 7.6 mole per cent. was mostly comprised in intermediate fractions. When this deficit is distributed proportionately among the three major fractions, the percentage yields become: unreacted vinylacetylene, 6.1%; chloroprene, 91.2%; dichlorobutene, 2.7%. The corresponding figures for the calculated yields based upon unrecovered vinylacetylene are chloroprene, 97%, and dichlorobutene, 3%. Further experiments indicate that the conditions of this experiment lie very close to the optimum for the conversion of vinylacetylene to chloroprene in a batch process: a higher ratio of chloroprene to dichlorobutene can be obtained only by utilizing a smaller proportion of the applied vinylacetylene, and a more complete utilization of the vinylacetylene results in a larger proportion of dichlorobutene.

The Properties of Chloro-4-butadiene-1,2 and the Proof of Its Structure.—Chloro-4-butadiene-1,2 is a colorless liquid boiling at 87.7 to 88.1°. It is only slightly soluble in water but miscible with most of the common organic solvents. It has a peculiar, sharp odor. Some other properties are: n_D^{20} 1.4775; d_4^{20}, 0.9891; M_R calcd., 24.61; M_R found, 25.30.

Anal. Calcd. for C_4H_5Cl: C, 54.23; H, 5.64; Cl, 40.11. Found: C, 55.04, 55.11; H, 5.70, 5.90; Cl, 39.75, 40.03.

Its chlorine atom is exceedingly reactive. When mixed with alcoholic silver nitrate it rapidly yields a copious precipitate of silver chloride. This fact in itself indicates that the compound is not a 1,3-diene, since in such a structure the chlorine atom would, of necessity, be attached to a doubly bonded carbon. Furthermore, the compound does not react with maleic anhydride or with naphthoquinone. It is not a true acetylenic compound either since it does not yield any derivative with ammoniacal cuprous chloride. When treated with ozone it yields formaldehyde and (after oxidation with potassium permanganate) chloroacetic acid. The compound has also been directly oxidized with potassium permanganate. The only product obtained was chloroacetic acid. Acetic acid and oxalic acid were absent. This behavior demonstrates the presence of the groups $CH_2=$ and $=CH-CH_2Cl$, and the compound must therefore have the structure chloro-4-butadiene-1,2. This structure is further confirmed by the fact that under the action of cold concentrated sulfuric acid, chloro-4-butadiene-1,2 is readily converted into chloro-4-butanone-2 (2).

The transformation of chloro-4-butadiene-1,2 into chloroprene exemplifies a type of reaction that is common to many substituted allyl halides. Such halides (e. g., $CH_3CHXCH=CH_2$ or $CH_3CH=CHCH_2X$) arise quite generally by the addition of halogens or hydrogen halides to 1,3-dienes, and in these cases the possibility of isomerization frequently makes it difficult or impossible to determine whether the primary product is the result of 1,2 or 1,4 addition. Chloro-4-butadiene-1,2, however, differs from other allyl halides: the α,γ shift brings the adjacent double bonds into the more stable conjugated configuration and the chlorine atom becomes attached to a doubly bonded carbon where its mobility is lost. A reversal of the isomerization is therefore impossible, and chloro-4-butadiene-1,2 cannot be other than a primary product of the addition of hydrogen chloride to vinylacetylene.

The transformation of chloro-4-butadiene-1,2 into chloroprene has been observed under a variety of conditions: by the action of powdered potassium hydroxide, by the action of hot quinoline (140–150°), by the action of heat (290°) in the presence of silica gel, and by the action of hot dilute hydrochloric acid (3). However, the isomerization occurred most smoothly and rapidly in the presence of hydrochloric acid containing cuprous chloride. Fifty grams of chloro-4-butadiene-1,2 was refluxed for three and one-half hours with 20 g. of cuprous chloride in 100 cc. of 18% hydrochloric acid. The oily layer was decanted, dried and distilled. The entire specimen except for a small amount of undistillable residue came over between 59 and 63° and the distillate was pure chloroprene. When the chloro-4-butadiene-1,2 was similarly treated with aqueous cuprous chloride alone it was recovered unchanged.

Chloro-4-butadiene-1,2 unlike its isomer chloroprene shows no tendency to polymerize. It can be distilled unchanged at ordinary pressure, and specimens stored under the ordinary laboratory conditions for many months remain unaltered. It undergoes no change even when submitted to a pressure of 6000 atmospheres for forty-five hours at 50° (4).

Experimental Part

Oxidation of Chloro-4-butadiene-1,2.—To a mixture of 30 g. of chloro-4-butadiene-1,2 with 250 cc. of water containing a little sodium carbonate was added in small portions with constant stirring 214 g. of potassium permanganate. The mixture was filtered, the filtrate acidified and continuously extracted with ether for several hours. The ether solution on distillation gave a liquid boiling at 185° which solidified on cooling. This was chloroacetic acid, identified by its melting point, neutralization equivalent (found, 96; calcd., 94.5) and transformation into chloroacetamide, m. p. 119°. No acetic or oxalic acid was found.

Ozonization of Chloro-4-butadiene-1,2.—A solution of 20 g. of chloro-4-butadiene-1,2 in 20 cc. of chloroform was treated with ozone for twelve hours at 0°. The solvent and the unchanged material were evaporated *in vacuo* and the remaining ozonide. was decomposed with water. Formaldehyde was detected in the aqueous solution by its strong odor and the formation of methylene-di-β-naphthol; white needles melting at 204° (corr.).

Chloroacetaldehyde was not detected directly. The aqueous solution was treated gradually with 50 g. of potassium permanganate, the excess permanganate destroyed with sulfur dioxide, and the filtrate extracted with ether. Distillation of the ether solution left a residue which crystallized on cooling. This product was chloroacetic acid. identified by its melting point and neutralization equivalent.

Hydration of Chloro-4-butadiene-1,2.—Into 250 cc. of concentrated sulfuric acid 88.5 g. of chloro-4-butadiene-1,2 was added dropwise with stirring, the temperature being maintained at −5 to 3°. The dark reaction product was poured onto cracked ice, partly neutralized with sodium carbonate and extracted with ether. The ethereal solution was washed, dried and distilled, yielding 58 g. of crude chloro-4-butanone-2, b. p. 110–123°. On redistillation it boiled at 120 to 122° at 760 mm.

Anal. Calcd. for C_4H_7OCl: C, 45.07; H, 6.57; Cl, 33.33. Found: C, 45.42, 45.42; H, 6.81, 6.47; Cl, 32.26, 32.42.

When treated with phenylhydrazine it gave a derivative having the correct melting point (77°) and analysis for phenylmethylpyrazoline (5).

Anal. Calcd. for $C_{10}H_{12}N_2$: C, 75.00; H, 7.50; N, 17.50. Found: C, 74.32; H, 7.60; N, 17.10.

Dichloro-2,4-butene-2.—This material is obtained as a by-product in the preparation of chloroprene and it is readily prepared in quantity by shaking vinylacetylene with an excess (4 moles) of hydrochloric acid containing cuprous chloride. It is a colorless liquid having a characteristic odor; other properties are: boiling point 127–129° at 756 mm., 61–63° at 70 mm., 53 to 54° at 50 mm., d_4^{20} 1.1591, n_D^{20} 1.47239, n_C^{20} 1.46988, n_F^{20} 1.48187, M_R calcd. 29.94, M_R found 30.27.

Anal. Calcd. for $C_4H_6Cl_2$: C, 38.40; H, 4.80; Cl, 56.80. Found: C, 38.53; H, 4.87; Cl, 56.90.

The proof of the structure of this compound will be presented in a future paper dealing with its reactions.

Acknowledgment.—The writers are indebted to Mr. O. R. Kreimeier for assistance in the experiments on the addition of hydrogen chloride to vinylacetylene.

Summary

The results of experiments on the action of aqueous hydrogen chloride on vinylacetylene are described. The initial step consists in 1,4 addition and the primary product is chloro-4-butadiene-1,2. This readily undergoes isomerization, yielding chloroprene, which always constitutes a part of the reaction product. When cuprous chloride is present in the reaction mixture the isomerization proceeds more rapidly and no chloro-4-butadiene-1,2 is found in the reaction product. When sufficient hydrogen chloride is present the reaction proceeds further, yielding dichloro-2,4-butene-2.

Bibliography and Remarks

(1) Carothers, Williams, Collins and Kirby, *Journ. Am. Chem. Soc.*, **53**, 4203 (1931); this volume, page 281.

(2) *Cf.* Gustavson and Demjanoff, *J. prakt. Chem.*, [2] **38**, 201 (1888); Bouis, *Ann. chim.*, [10] **9**, 402 (1928).

(3) We are indebted to Dr. D. D. Coffman for some of these observations.

(4) We are indebted to Dr. H. W. Starkweather for this observation.

(5) Maire, *Bull. soc. chim.*, [4] **3**, 272 (1908).

IV. The Addition of Hydrogen Bromide to Vinylacetylene, Bromoprene and Dibromobutene*

Observations on the combination of vinylacetylene with hydrogen chloride (1) have been extended to the analogous case of hydrogen bromide. The two reactants are closely similar in their behavior, but hydrogen bromide appears to act somewhat more slowly than hydrogen chloride. Concentrated aqueous hydrobromic acid containing cuprous bromide, when shaken with vinylacetylene at the ordinary temperature, yields the two products, bromo-2-butadiene-1,3 (bromoprene, II) and dibromo-2,4-butene-2 (III). It seems likely, in view of the results already described for the hydrogen chloride reaction (1b) that the primary product of reaction between hydrogen bromide and vinylacetylene is bromo-4-butadiene-1,2 (I), which then rearranges to yield bromoprene, but no decisive direct evidence for the formation of this primary product is yet available. Its presence among the reaction products has not been established—even when no cuprous bromide (catalyst) was used. The structure of the dihydrobromide has not yet been directly established either, but formula III, in view of the results with hydrogen chloride, is not open to serious doubt.

* W. H. Carothers, A. M. Collins and J. E. Kirby, *Journ. Am. Chem. Soc.*, 55, 786–8 (1933); Contribution No. 106 from the Experimental Station of the E. I. du Pont de Nemours and Co.
Received August 11, 1932. Published February 9, 1933.

$$CH\equiv C-CH=CH_2 \xrightarrow{\text{HBr}} CH_2=C=CH-CH_2Br \longrightarrow CH_2=C-CH=CH_2 \xrightarrow{\text{HBr}}$$

$$\underset{I}{} \qquad \underset{\underset{Br}{|}}{\underset{II}{}}$$

$$CH_3-CBr=CH-CH_2Br$$
$$III$$

The third step in this series of reactions has a relatively high velocity, and appreciable amounts of the dihydrobromide (III) are present in the reaction mixture even at an early stage when the major part of the vinyl-acetylene applied remains unchanged. In this respect also the behavior of hydrogen bromide appreciably differs from that of hydrogen chloride.

Bromoprene is an oil having a faint greenish-yellow color and an odor rather closely resembling that of butyl bromide. It boils at 42 to 43° at 165 mm. The proof of its structure follows the course already indicated for chloroprene. It reacts with maleic anhydride to yield, after hydrolysis, a product whose composition agrees with that required for bromo-6-cyclohexene-5-dicarboxylic-2,3 acid (IV). Bromoprene furthermore reacts readily with naphthoquinone. The primary product is a crystalline solid, which probably has the formula bromo-2-tetrahydro-1,4,4a,9a-anthra-quinone-9,10 (V). It is rapidly oxidized by air in alkaline solution to β-bromoanthraquinone (VI).

IV

V   VI

Experimental Part

Preparation of Bromoprene.—Fifty grams of cold vinylacetylene was placed in a pressure bottle containing 225 cc. of a thoroughly chilled solution prepared by dissolving 75 g. of moist, freshly prepared cuprous bromide in 200 g. of concentrated hydrobromic acid (sp. gr. 1.55). The bottle was allowed to warm up to room temperature and was then mechanically shaken for seven hours. After standing overnight and shaking for another two hours the unused vinylacetylene was allowed to evaporate. The residual oil was separated, washed with water, dried over calcium chloride and distilled from hydroquinone under reduced pressure. Dry, oxygen-free nitrogen was led through the capillary tube during the distillation. The yield of bromoprene boiling at 42–43° at 165 mm. was 30 g. (24%); d_4^{20}, 1.397; n_D^{20} 1.4988; M_R calcd., 27.50; M_R found, 27.94.

Anal. Calcd. for C_4H_5Br: C, 36.11; H, 3.78; Br, 60.15. Found: C, 36.32, 36.47; H, 4.13, 4.21; Br, 60.91, 61.43.

Higher yields were obtained by the use of more concentrated hydrobromic acid. For example, by using 2 moles of hydrobromic acid (sp. gr. 1.66) for each mole of vinyl-acetylene a yield of 44.8% of bromoprene was obtained.

Dibromo-2,4-butene-2.—After the distillation of the bromoprene a considerable amount of higher-boiling residue remained. From this residue there was obtained 12 g. (6%) of a strongly lachrymatory, light yellow oil corresponding in analysis to a dibromo-butene. It had the following physical constants: b. p. (760 mm.) 168 to 169° with loss of HBr; b. p. (23 mm.) 73°; d_4^{20} 1.8768; n_D^{20} 1.5485; M_R calcd., 35.74; M_R found, 36.25.

Anal. Calcd. for $C_4H_6Br_2$: C, 22.43; H, 2.80; Br, 74.77. Found: C, 22.98, 23.06; H, 3.05, 2.95; Br, 74.94, 75.34.

Reaction of Bromoprene with Maleic Anhydride. Preparation of Bromo-6-cyclo-hexene-5-dicarboxylic-2,3 Acid.—To 5 g. (0.037 mole) of bromoprene was added 3 g. (0.030 mole) of maleic anhydride. After the mixture had stood at room temperature for about one hour a spontaneous reaction set in and after three or four hours the mass solidified. The reaction product was then dissolved in benzene and shaken for twenty minutes with an excess of 10% sodium hydroxide. The aqueous layer was separated and acidified. The crude acid which separated was purified by recrystallization from water. It separated from water in the form of a mixture of thick plates and blunt needles melting sharply at 186.5 to 187°.

Anal. Calcd. for $C_8H_9O_4Br$: C, 38.57; H, 3.64; neutral equivalent, 124.5. Found: C, 38.37, 38.65; H, 3.75, 3.65; neutral equivalent, 125.4.

Action of α-Naphthoquinone on Bromoprene. Conversion to β-Bromoanthraqui-none.—To a benzene solution of 15.4 g. (0.12 mole) of bromoprene was added 10 g (0.06) mole of α-naphthoquinone. After standing at room temperature for two days the solution was gently refluxed for one hour. The benzene was then distilled off under reduced pressure. The residual sticky, dark red solid was pressed on a porous tile and then extracted with warm alcohol. The alcohol was decanted from an insoluble tar and, on cooling, 4.9 g. (49%) of unchanged naphthoquinone crystallized out. When the al-cohol mother liquor was diluted with water, 2.6 g. of a nearly black solid separated. After recrystallization from alcohol it was obtained in the form of small, soft, nearly white crystals. When slowly heated on a copper block it began to turn blue at about 115° and slowly deepened in color as the temperature was raised. At 138° it melted sharply; as the temperature was raised further it volatilized completely.

The analyses corresponded with the values calculated for bromo-2-tetrahydro-1,4,4a,8a-anthraquinone-9,10.

Anal. Calcd. for $C_{14}H_{11}O_2Br$: C, 57.74; H, 3.99. Found: C, 57.66, 57.65; H, 3.89, 4.04.

About 0.1 g. of the substance was dissolved in alcohol and a few drops of 10% sodium hydroxide solution added.   The solution was dark red in color.   As air was bubbled through the solution, the red color gave way to green, which in turn disappeared leaving a yellow solid.   After recrystallization from amyl alcohol the oxidation product melted at 205–207°. β-Bromoanthraquinone melts at 207° (2).

Summary

Vinylacetylene reacts with aqueous hydrobromic acid to form bromo-2-butadiene-1,3 (bromoprene) and dibromo-2,4-butene-2.   Bromoprene reacts with maleic anhydride yielding bromo-6-cyclohexene-5-dicarboxylic-2,3 acid, and with naphthoquinone yielding a bromotetrahydroanthraquinone which is readily oxidized to β-bromoanthaquinone.

Bibliography and Remarks

(1) (a) Carothers, Williams, Collins and Kirby, *Journ. Am. Chem. Soc.*, **53**, 4203 (1931); this volume, page 281;   (b) Carothers, Berchet and Collins, *Journ. Am. Chem. Soc.*, **54**, 4066 (1932);   this volume, page 306.

(2) Heller, *Ber.*, **45**, 672 (1912).

V.   The Polymerization of Bromoprene (Third Paper on New Synthetic Rubbers*)†

Chloroprene (I, X = Cl) polymerizes spontaneously to yield a rubber-like product (1), and the speed of this transformation is roughly 700 times greater than the analogous transformation of isoprene.   The present paper deals with the behavior of bromoprene (2) (I, X = Br), and the results may be summarized in the statement that it shows no significant qualitative differences from chloroprene, although its speed of polymerization under most conditions appears to be somewhat greater.

$$CH_2=C-CH=CH_2 \qquad\qquad CH=C-H$$
$$\mid \qquad\qquad\qquad\qquad\quad \mid$$
$$X \qquad\qquad\qquad\qquad\quad X$$
$$I \qquad\qquad\qquad\qquad\quad II$$

In connection with the behavior of these materials the following analogies are of interest.   Vinyl chloride and vinyl bromide (II, X = Cl and Br) polymerize spontaneously yielding products of very high molecular weight (3), but this behavior is not shown by propylene, which polymerizes only in the presence of special catalysts or under drastic conditions and

* For the Second Paper in this sub-series, see this volume, page 384 reference to the reprinted paper by Carothers and Coffman, *Journ. Am. Chem. Soc.*, 54, 4071(1932).

† W. H. Carothers, J. E. Kirby and A. M. Collins, *ibid.*, 55, 789–95(1933);   Contribution No. 107 from the Experimental Station of E. I. du Pont de Nemours and Co.   Received August 11, 1932.   Published February 9, 1933.

then yields products having only moderately high molecular weights. The haloprenes (I) bear the same structural relationship to isoprene that the vinyl halides bear to propylene. Thus the very powerful activating effect of a single halogen atom on ethylene is also manifested in butadiene (when the halogen atom is on the β-carbon). The rate of polymerization is of great importance in studying the behavior of dienes since a high rate not only makes it possible to obtain experimental results in a reasonable length of time, but it permits one to extend the observations over a wide range of conditions. It becomes possible then to recognize the different types of reactions involved in the spontaneous polymerization and to obtain data on the way in which these different types of reactions are affected by changes in the conditions. Data of this type on chloroprene have already been presented, and it will be useful to review them briefly (with some extensions) and to make comparisons with those now available for bromoprene and for other dienes.

The polymerization of chloroprene leads to the four well defined and qualitatively distinct types of polymers shown in the chart.

Volatile (β) polymer ⟵— monoprene —⟶ plastic (α) polymer

granular (ω) polymer   non-plastic (μ) polymer

The influence of various conditions on each of these reactions is indicated in Table I.

TABLE I
INFLUENCE OF CONDITIONS ON THE POLYMERIZATION OF CHLOROPRENE

Condition	Monoprene to β-polymer	Monoprene to α-polyprene	α-Polyprene to μ-polyprene	Monoprene to ω-polyprene
Temperature	+++	+	+	Autocatalytic, ini-
Pressure	+	++	+?	tiated by strong
Light	0	++	0?	ultraviolet light
Oxygen	0	+++	++?	and by metal
Antioxidants	0	− − −	±[a]	surfaces

[a] Certain substances commonly classified as antioxidants (e. g., phenyl-β-naphthylamine) act as inhibitors; others (e. g., benzidine) act as accelerators: + accelerates, 0 no effect, − inhibits.

Of these different types of polymers the most important are the α- and the μ-polyprenes since the former corresponds to unvulcanized rubber and the latter corresponds to vulcanized rubber.

The μ-polyprene is the final product of the spontaneous polymerization of chloroprene; the α-polyprene is an intermediate step in the formation of the μ-product. Isolation of the α-polymer free of μ-polymer is possible only when the reaction is conducted under certain conditions: the temperature must not be too high, since elevated temperature accelerates the transformation of α-polymer to μ-polymer more than it accelerates the formation of α-polymer from monomer; the reaction must not be too slow, since most inhibiting influences have a greater decelerating effect on the formation of the α- than on the μ-product; moreover, very slow reaction frequently leads to the formation of the ω-polymer. Light and pressure both appear to have a greater accelerating effect on the formation of the α-polyprene than on the transformation of this into the μ-polyprene.

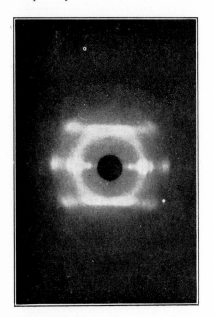

Fig. 1.—x-Ray diffraction pattern of μ-polybromoprene (from latex) stretched 500%.

The β-polymer, a terpene-like material, is an undesirable by-product in the rubber synthesis. In the chloroprene polymerization the production of β-polymer becomes appreciable only at temperatures higher than are necessary to bring about a rapid formation of α-polyprene. Butadiene, isoprene and dimethylbutadiene polymerize very slowly; to get the transformation to proceed at a reasonable rate, elevated temperatures are generally used, and this results in the formation of relatively large amounts of β-polymer.

The ω-polychloroprene is also a useless product; it is made up of discrete rubber-like particles (irregular globules) which are non-plastic and not even swelled by rubber solvents. The formation of this polymer is autocatalytic. When a speck of the ω-polymer appears (or is introduced) in a specimen of incompletely polymerized chloroprene, the entire specimen is soon more or less completely converted into the ω-polymer. The formation of nuclei of the ω-polyprene is favored by strong ultraviolet light and by metal surfaces (e. g., sodium, potassium, mercury, iron, copper and aluminum). The opportunities for the formation of such nuclei are also increased by a long reaction time under any particular set of conditions. Similar polymers, frequently described as cauliflower-like masses, have been obtained from isoprene, butadiene and dimethylbutadiene, and one suspects that they may be the forms in which the polymers of these dienes are most frequently obtained. The very slow rate of the polymerization of these dienes would be especially favorable to the formation of ω-polymer.

The term rubber-like is vaguely used to cover a multitude of the most diverse properties, and the literature of synthetic rubber is exceedingly obscure. Most of the agencies that are available to hasten the very slow polymerization of isoprene and butadiene are such as have been found in the case of chloroprene to affect more strongly the conversion of the α- into the μ-polymer than the formation of the α-polymer. One may expect therefore that the isolation of a true α-polyprene (4) from the isoprene and butadiene products will present especial difficulties. So far as we are aware no clear disclosure has ever been made of an α-polyprene from isoprene or from butadiene. However, when isoprene is subjected to a pressure of 12,000 atmospheres until 30% of the isoprene has polymerized, the polymer is at least 90% soluble in ether (5). If the reaction is allowed to proceed further until 80% of the isoprene has polymerized, the product is completely insoluble (5, 6). Thus the formation of a completely vulcanized rubber-like product without the aid of sulfur is by no means peculiar to chloroprene. In fact the differences between the behavior of chloroprene and the behavior of other dienes appear to be differences of degree rather than differences of kind.

The Spontaneous Polymerization of Bromoprene.—A sample of bromoprene when allowed to stand at the ordinary laboratory conditions in a stoppered flask containing a small amount of air becomes noticeably more viscous after twelve to fifteen hours. As the reaction proceeds, the viscosity increases; after about five days the sample sets to a stiff, elastic jelly containing a considerable amount of unchanged bromoprene. Usually after eight to ten days all of the bromoprene has reacted, but the time required varies considerably in different experiments. The product has a density of about 1.74, and this is 24% greater than the density of the bromoprene. (The increase in density in the formation of μ-polychloroprene is about 28%.)

This product, μ-polybromoprene, corresponds in its properties with the μ-polychloroprene already described. It is tough, resilient and elastic but harder than the analogous product from chloroprene. On standing it gradually undergoes further change: it becomes still harder and less extensible and the resemblance to soft vulcanized rubber pretty largely disappears although it still remains very tough and retains considerable elasticity and resiliency. These changes in the nature of the product are due, at least in part, to a progressive action of air and they can be retarded by the application of antioxidants to the surface of the sample. μ-Polybromoprene is similar to μ-polychloroprene in its behavior toward solvents. It is greatly swelled by chloroform, carbon tetrachloride and aromatic hydrocarbons but remains practically unchanged after prolonged immersion in alcohol, ether, or aliphatic hydrocarbons such as gasoline.

α-Polybromoprene.—The preparation of an α-polybromoprene (plastic polymer) presents no difficulties. A sample of bromoprene was exposed to light from a Cooper–Hewitt lamp at 25°. After twenty-four hours 50% of the material had been converted into polymer. (This rate is about 40% greater than that usually obtained with chloroprene under the same conditions.) The product was an exceedingly viscous, yellow sirup. When it was mixed with a large volume of alcohol the α-polybromoprene was precipitated as a soft, plastic mass. This product showed no tendency to resist permanent deformation and sheeted out very readily on cold rolls. Two per cent. of phenyl-β-naphthylamine was worked into the plastic mass to prevent spontaneous conversion into an elastic polymer (7). The sample was compounded with about 5% of its weight of zinc oxide and heated in a mold at 120 to 125° for twenty minutes. The product was non-plastic, strong, resilient and extensible (500 to 700%). However, compared with a similar product from chloroprene it was somewhat lacking in snap, and its permanent set was rather high. It also showed a greater tendency to "freeze." After about two hours at ordinary temperatures it became very stiff, but the original pliability was restored when it was heated to 80° for a few minutes.

The Polymerization of Bromoprene in Aqueous Emulsion.—Like chloroprene, bromoprene is readily dispersed in water and the resulting smooth emulsion polymerizes with great rapidity to form a stable latex. The preparation and polymerization of such an emulsion is illustrated in the following example.

Twenty-five cubic centimeters of 2% aqueous sodium oleate in a wide-mouthed bottle was surrounded by a bath of ice and water. Two drops of triethanolamine was added to the solution, and then, with vigorous stirring, 25 g. of bromoprene. A smooth, milk-like emulsion resulted. After the mixture had stood in the ice-bath for five hours an aliquot portion was removed and poured into a large volume of alcohol. The weight of the precipitate thus obtained indicated that 78% of the bromoprene had polymerized. Under the same conditions chloroprene is only about 20–30% polymerized. The bromoprene emulsion described above was transferred to a refrigerator. After seventeen hours, more than 95% of the bromoprene had polymerized. Five cubic centimeters of 3% ammonium hydroxide was added to stabilize the emulsion and a small amount of an aqueous dispersion of phenyl-β-naphthylamine (2% on the rubber content) added to function as an antioxidant. The resulting latex was very stable.

As in the case of polychloroprene, the dispersed particles in the synthetic latex derived from bromoprene correspond more closely to the μ- than to the α-polymer. Nevertheless, when the latex is coagulated by the addition of acids, the particles coalesce and cohere very firmly. The coagulum is at first soft and plastic, but it quickly becomes tough, elastic and non-plastic. Homogeneous, coherent films are obtained by allowing the water to evaporate from a thin layer of the fluid latex on a plate of porous porcelain. The films are readily stripped from the plate and the removal of the water can be completed by drying them for a few hours in an oven at 80°. Such films are exceedingly tough and more resistant to tearing than analogous films prepared from chloroprene latices. A typical specimen had a breaking strength of 160 kg./sq. cm. and an elongation at break of 740%. (The elongation of similar polychloroprene films is usually about 800%.) The films exhibited the high permanent set and the tendency to freeze or stiffen already referred to in connection with the vulcanized α-polybromoprene. Like the latter, they were non-plastic and did not dissolve but merely swelled in chloroform and benzene.

β-**Polybromoprene.**—The conversion of bromoprene into a volatile liquid polymer (β-polybromoprene) occurs under conditions similar to those already described for chloroprene (8). A sample of bromoprene containing about 5% of thiodiphenylamine, a substance which powerfully inhibits the conversion of the haloprenes to rubber-like polymers, was heated in a sealed tube at 80° for five days. When the resulting black oil was poured into alcohol a small amount of a black tar separated. From the alcohol there was obtained by distillation a small amount (about 15%) of a yellow oil boiling at 104 to 110° at 11 mm. It had a fragrant, terpene-like odor very similar to that of β-polychloroprene and was a mild lachrymator. It showed no tendency to polymerize further.

ω-**Polybromoprene.**—The formation of ω-polybromoprene, like the formation of ω-polychloroprene, occurs under conditions which result in very slow polymerization. For example, samples of bromoprene containing 0.2% of phenyl-β-naphthylamine or 0.5% of tetramethylthiuram disulfide and 0.3% of sulfur slowly became more viscous and, after two to six weeks, a white deposit having a crystalline appearance began to form. After formation of this substance had started, conversion of the whole mass was complete in a few days. The product turned dark brown in color on standing in air. ω-Polybromoprene is soft, opaque and noncoherent, while ω-polychloroprene is a mass of glistening, hard, rubbery granules. Like ω-polychloroprene, it is not swelled by benzene.

The Structure of Polybromoprene.—Evidence has already been presented for concluding that α-polychloroprene is precisely analogous to natural rubber in its chemical structure. The analogies between polychloroprene and polybromoprene are sufficiently close to justify the assumption of a similar structure (III) for the latter compound. The x-ray evidence is especially interesting. The fact that μ-polychloroprene when stretched furnishes a fiber diffraction pattern has already been disclosed (1). Polybromoprene shows a similar behavior, but it furnishes an even sharper pattern (Fig. 1) (9). So far as we are aware, it has not been possible to obtain fiber diagrams from any other synthetic rubbers, and this fact perhaps justifies the conclusion that polychloroprene and polybromoprene are more regular in their molecular structure than any other known synthetic rubbers.

(III)   ...—CH₂—CH=C—CH₂—CH₂—CH=C—CH₂—CH₂—CH=C—CH₂...
            | | |
            Br   Br   Br

Summary

The polymerization of bromoprene is closely analogous to that of chloroprene, but somewhat more rapid. Spontaneous polymerization yields as the final product μ-polybromoprene, which resembles vulcanized rubber but is more dense than rubber or μ-polychloroprene. A plastic (α) polybromoprene is readily isolated from partially polymerized bromoprene, and it is converted to the μ-product by the action of heat. At elevated temperatures in the presence of inhibitors a volatile liquid (β) polymer is formed. ω-Polybromoprene, a granular, insoluble, rubber-like mass, is produced under conditions that lead to very slow polymerization.

Bibliography and Remarks

(1) Carothers, Williams, Collins and Kirby, *Journ. Am. Chem. Soc.*, **53**, 4203 (1931; this volume, page 281).

(2) Carothers, Collins and Kirby, *Journ. Am. Chem. Soc.*, **55**, 786 (1933); this volume, page 311.

(3) Staudinger, Brunner and Feisst, *Helv. Chim. Acta.*, **13**, 805 (1930).

(4) With the aid of swelling agents, softener and lubricants it is possible to confer a certain amount of plasticity on μ-polychloroprene. It is also possible to obtain from chloroprene plastic polymers that, on being heated, lose their plastic properties very incompletely or not at all. The material that we refer to as α-polychloroprene is an inherently plastic, *polymerizable* polymer; its plastic properties are completely lost and its elastic properties become fully developed when it stands or is heated.

(5) Conant and Tongberg, *Journ. Am. Chem. Soc.*, **52**, 1667 (1930).

(6) According to observations made by Dr. H. W. Starkweather in this laboratory, isoprene polymers prepared in this manner are also completely non-plastic.

(7) Ref. 1, page 4219; this volume, page 298.

(8) Ref. 1, page 4211; this volume, page 290.

(9) The x-ray data will be discussed in more detail in a future paper by Dr. A. W. Kenney. [Such a paper has not apparently been published hitherto. EDS.]

VI. Vinylethinylmagnesium Bromide and Some of Its Reactions*

As might be expected from its structure, vinylacetylene (I) reacts rapidly with ethylmagnesium bromide. The reaction proceeds smoothly and apparently involves only the acetylenic hydrogen; the behavior of the product indicates that it is vinylethinylmagnesium bromide (II). It reacts in the typical manner with a variety of reagents.

Acetone yields vinylethinyldimethylcarbinol (III), a colorless liquid whose structure is established by its hydrogenation to n-butyldimethyl-carbinol. On standing, it polymerizes to a colorless, transparent resin.

The action of carbon dioxide on vinylethinylmagnesium bromide apparently gives vinylpropiolic acid (IV), but it was not found possible to isolate this substance in a state of high purity. Above 110° it polymerizes explosively, and even at lower temperatures it is rapidly converted into a tough, insoluble, rather elastic mass.

The products (V and VI) obtained from α-naphthyl isocyanate and from triphenylchloromethane are stable crystalline solids.

$$CH_2=CH-C\equiv CH \quad CH_2=CH-C\equiv C-MgBr \quad CH_2=CH-C\equiv C-COH(CH_3)_2$$
$$\text{I} \qquad\qquad\qquad \text{II} \qquad\qquad\qquad\qquad \text{III}$$

$$CH_2=CH-C\equiv C-COOH \qquad CH_2=CH-C\equiv C-CO-NH-C_{10}H_{17}$$
$$\text{IV} \qquad\qquad\qquad\qquad \text{V}$$

$$CH_2=CH-C\equiv C-C(C_6H_5)_3$$
$$\text{VI}$$

Experimental Part

Preparation of Vinylethinylmagnesium Bromide (II).—The reaction vessel was provided with a refrigerated return condenser (ice salt) and dropping funnel. The vinylacetylene (10 to 20% excess) dissolved in ether was added in portions with continuous stirring to the ethylmagnesium bromide. The reaction proceeded smoothly with sufficient evolution of heat to keep the ether refluxing gently. The reaction product remained dissolved in the ether.

Vinylethinyldimethylcarbinol (III).—Forty grams of purified acetone was added slowly to a 15% excess of vinylethinylmagnesium bromide. The product of the reaction distilled without residue at 50–59° (15 mm.). On redistillation, 40 g. of a colorless liquid boiling at 59–61° (17 mm.) was collected. The yield in pure vinylethinyldimethylcarbinol was 53%. B. p. 67° (24 mm.); n_D^{20} 1.4778; d_4^{20} 0.8872; M_R calcd., 33.32; found, 35.07. Exaltation, 1.75.

Anal. Calcd. for $C_7H_{10}O$: C, 76.36; H, 9.09; mol. wt., 110.   Found: C, 76.18; H, 8.88; mol. wt. (cryoscopic in benzene), 119.

* W. H. Carothers and G. J. Berchet, *Journ. Am. Chem. Soc.*, **55**, 1094–6(1933); Contribution No. 110 from the Experimental Station of E. I. du Pont de Nemours and Co. Received August 11, 1932. Published March 7, 1933.

The carbinol became increasingly viscous on standing. After two weeks it was a hard, tough, transparent mass insoluble in the common organic solvents. This transformation was accompanied by the absorption of oxygen; the analytical values for carbon and hydrogen became progressively lower. The values for the completely polymerized product were C, 70.7, and H, 8.7. The polymerization was greatly retarded by the presence of hydroquinone.

Hydrogenation of Vinylethinyldimethylcarbinol.—Twenty grams of the carbinol was dissolved in 75 cc. of alcohol. Four-tenths of a gram of platinum oxide was added and the mixture was shaken in a reduction apparatus. It absorbed 0.506 mole of hydrogen in forty-five minutes, or about 93% of the theoretical amount, calculated for three moles of hydrogen absorbed per mole of carbinol. After evaporation of the alcohol the residue distilled at 71–72° at 48 mm. It was a colorless liquid with a pleasant camphor-like odor. Its physical constants agreed closely with those given in the literature for dimethylbutylcarbinol.

	Found		Given in the literature[a]
B. p.	139.5–141° (761 mm.)	B. p.	141–142° (755 mm.)
n_D^{23}	1.4189	n_D	1.41592
d_{20}^{20}	0.817	d	0.8155

[a] Henry and Dewaei, *Bull. Acad. Roy. Belg.*, 957 (1908); *Chem. Z.*, I, 1854 (1909).

Anal. Calcd. for $C_7H_{16}O$: C, 72.41; H, 13.79. Found: C, 72.31, 72.37; H, 13.68, 13.64.

Vinylpropiolic Acid.—One mole of vinylethinylmagnesium bromide was treated with dry carbon dioxide at 0° until a color test showed the absence of any RMgBr. The product was then decomposed with water and the aqueous solution was submitted to continuous extraction with ether for eight hours. The solvent was evaporated *in vacuo*. The residue weighed 50 g. (calcd., 96 g.). Attempts to distil the product at this stage by the usual methods always resulted in explosions. A partially successful distillation was effected at low pressure (about 0.05 mm.) in an all-glass apparatus. This consisted of a flask sealed to a receiver cooled in liquid air. The flask was heated to about 60°. Evaporation occurred at a moderately rapid rate, and the distillate froze to a crystalline solid in the receiver. It became liquid below room temperature. On redistillation in a stream of carbon dioxide most of the volatile product came over between 64 and 71° at 2 mm. It was a colorless, water-soluble liquid which turned yellow on standing. Its molecular weight, determined by titration with $N/10$ sodium hydroxide, was 102, instead of the calculated value 96. The product was evidently not quite pure. It reduced permanganate instantly in acetone solution.

A tube containing a sample of the acid was evacuated with a water-pump and sealed off. The tube was heated for eighty-five minutes at 75°, at the end of which time a rubber-like yellow substance had formed. This was insoluble in water, alcohol, ether, benzene and acetic acid at the boiling points of these solvents. It was partly soluble in hot sodium hydroxide, imparting a yellow color to the solution, from which an amorphous solid separated on neutralization.

α-Naphthylamide of Vinylpropiolic Acid (V).—A solution of 9 g. of α-naphthyl isocyanate in anhydrous ether was added slowly to an excess of vinylethinylmagnesium bromide. The reaction proceeded smoothly. The mixture was refluxed for thirty minutes, then poured onto crushed ice. On extraction of the aqueous solution with ether, 1.5 g. of dinaphthylurea was left undissolved.   On evaporation of the ether solution, a yellowish solid separated.   After two crystallizations from 50% alcohol it was obtained in the form of small yellowish needles melting at 125 to 126° (copper block); yield, 9 g.   It was readily soluble in ether, benzene, methanol and ethanol.   It reduced permanganate in acetone solution very rapidly.   In chloroform solution it absorbed bromine slowly with the evolution of hydrogen bromide.

Anal.   Calcd. for $C_{15}H_{11}ON$:   C, 81.44;   H, 4.97;   mol. wt., 221.   Found: C, 81.50, 81.27;   H, 4.92, 4.85;   mol. wt. (in boiling ethylene chloride), 221, 219.

Vinylethinyltriphenylmethane (VI).—A slight excess of vinylethinylmagnesium bromide was treated with a solution of 10 g. of triphenylchloromethane in anhydrous ether.   After completion of the reaction, the mixture was worked up as usual.   The ether solution left on evaporation 7.5 g. of a yellowish crystalline solid.   After recrystallization from hot alcohol, it melted at 134–135° (copper block).   It reduced permanganate in acetone solution and absorbed bromine, though slowly, in chloroform solution.

Anal.   Calcd. for $C_{23}H_{18}$:   C, 93.87;   H, 6.12;   mol. wt., 294.   Found: C, 94.17, 93.52;   H, 6.14, 6.24;   mol. wt. (in boiling benzene), 320, 315.

Summary

Vinylacetylene reacts with ethylmagnesium bromide yielding vinylethinylmagnesium bromide.   This behaves in the typical manner toward acetone, carbon dioxide, α-naphthyl isocyanate and triphenylchloromethane.   The derivatives thus produced are described.

VII.   Sodium Vinylacetylide and Vinylethinylcarbinols*

Vinylacetylene, like other true acetylenic compounds, reacts with Grignard reagents to form the corresponding organo magnesium halide, and this may be used to introduce the vinylethinyl group into compounds of various types (1).   The present paper is concerned with the formation of sodium vinylacetylide and with its use in a similar manner, especially in the synthesis of vinylethinylcarbinols.

Sodium vinylacetylide is readily obtained by the action of vinylacetylene on metallic sodium.   The metal may be applied directly to the liquid hydrocarbon, or the latter may be diluted with an inert solvent such as ether, toluene or liquid ammonia.   The reaction occurs with great rapidity if the sodium is dissolved in liquid ammonia.   These methods, however, have the disadvantage that the acetylide produced is frequently contaminated with appreciable amounts of polymeric material.   More

* W. H. Carothers and R. A. Jacobson, *Journ. Am. Chem. Soc.*, **55**, 1097–1101 (1933); Contribution No. 111 from the Experimental Station of E. I. du Pont de Nemours and Co.
Received August 11, 1932.   Published March 7, 1933.

uniformly satisfactory results are obtained by the action of powdered sodamide on the hydrocarbon. The latter is preferably dissolved in ether or liquid ammonia.

The sodium vinylacetylide obtained in this manner is a dusty, white powder, and vinylacetylene is regenerated in high yield when it is cautiously treated with water in the presence of a diluent. Its stability is sufficient to permit its storage for two or three days in a stoppered bottle, and with some care it can be handled in the presence of air. However, if the air is moist the acetylide sometimes ignites spontaneously. It attacks many organic reagents with explosive violence, but cooling and dilution permit sufficient control to obtain smooth reaction in most cases. Isolation of the sodium compound is not necessary for its application as a reagent; the intended reactant is preferably added directly to the mixture resulting from the action of sodamide on vinylacetylene.

In dealing with aldehydes and ketones a still simpler and more satisfactory procedure consists in adding powdered sodamide in portions to a mixture of the carbonyl compound with vinylacetylene. In most cases it is advantageous to have present a diluent such as ether. With simple aliphatic and alicyclic ketones this method is very satisfactory. The yields are good and large scale operations are much simpler than with the vinylethinylmagnesium halides. However, sodium vinylacetylide has a more limited range of applicability in the synthesis of carbinols than has vinylethinylmagnesium bromide. Aliphatic aldehydes are partly resinified by the sodium compound, and unsaturated aldehydes and ketones are usually resinified completely. The magnesium compound, however, even with very sensitive aldehydes and ketones, generally yields the expected monomeric carbinols (2).

Vinylethinyldimethylcarbinol has already been described (1) and the other carbinols listed in Table II resemble it in their properties. They react readily with bromine and decolorize permanganate; in the presence of platinum they are smoothly hydrogenated to the corresponding n-butylcarbinols. They can be distilled *in vacuo* without decomposition, but if the temperature of distillation is too high the tertiary carbinols tend to lose water with the production of the corresponding substituted divinylacetylenes. Vinylethinyldi-n-propylcarbinol, for example, thus leads to the compound C_2H_5—CH=$C(C_3H_7)$—C≡C—CH=CH_2. Divinylacetylene itself was obtained by heating vinylethinylmethylcarbinol with p-toluenesulfonic acid.

The tertiary carbinols all polymerize spontaneously on standing (3). The transformation sets in rather quickly and progresses to the stage of a thick sirup during the course of a few days. The mixture then sets to a tough rather elastic mass, but the final product, a hard, transparent glass-like mass, is obtained only after several weeks or months. The transformation is greatly accelerated by certain catalysts, e. g., benzoyl peroxide, especially in the presence of light. The final glass-like products adhere very tenaciously to glass. They are insoluble in the common organic solvents. The polymerization of the carbinols also proceeds more rapidly at elevated temperature, e. g., 100°, but the final product obtained under these conditions is fusible and completely soluble in the common organic solvents. The spontaneous polymerization of the carbinols is strongly inhibited by the presence of a small amount of hydroquinone. The secondary carbinols polymerize very much more slowly than the tertiary carbinols.

Experimental Part

Preparation of Sodium Vinylacetylide.—Powdered sodamide (19.5 g., 0.5 mole) was slowly added to a solution of 75 g. of vinylacetylene in 250 cc. of liquid ammonia. The mixture was stirred for six hours and the ammonia evaporated in a stream of nitrogen, finally at 60°. The residue was a white powder (38 g., calcd. 37 g.) which showed a tendency to ignite spontaneously when exposed to the air. It was covered with toluene, and water was slowly added with constant stirring at 75°. The acetylide finally dissolved without appreciable residue in the aqueous layer. Vinylacetylene was distilled from the mixture and collected in a cold receiver. The yield was 21.3 g. or 82%.

Preparation of the Carbinols.—The general procedure used for the preparation of the tertiary carbinols is illustrated by the following example. The reaction mixture consisted of 555 g. (7.7 moles) of methyl ethyl ketone (Eastman Kodak pract.), 551 g. (10.6 moles) of vinylacetylene, and 500 cc. of dry ether. The solution was contained in a 3-necked flask provided with a mercury-sealed stirrer and a coil condenser, which in turn was connected to a trap. The reaction flask and trap were surrounded with carbon dioxide snow and the coil condenser was kept cold in the same manner. To the cold solution was slowly added 300 g. (7.7 moles) of powdered sodamide and stirring was continued for a total of six hours. The reaction mixture was made acid to litmus by means of 10% sulfuric acid, the ether layer separated and dried with sodium sulfate, and then distilled in a vacuum; 677 g. of pure vinylethinylmethylethylcarbinol was obtained; yield 71%. The carbinol was stabilized with 0.1% hydroquinone in order to prevent spontaneous polymerization.

The same procedure was applied to the preparation of the secondary carbinols but the results were less satisfactory. The preparation of vinylethinylmethylcarbinol is used as an illustration. To a solution of 44 g. (1 mole) of freshly distilled acetaldehyde and 75 g. of vinylacetylene in 75 cc. of dry ether at −10° was slowly added 39 g. of powdered sodamide. After a few grams of sodamide had been added, the mixture became so gummy that additional ether was added. Finally, the mixture formed a cake and stirring was discontinued. After four hours the cake was broken up with a stirring rod, more ether added, and the suspension stirred at room temperature for three hours. The reaction mixture was allowed to stand overnight and then decomposed with water and dilute sulfuric acid. The mixture was extracted several times with ether, and the latter dried with sodium sulfate and distilled. A considerable quantity of ether-insoluble resin remained in the reaction mixture. After removal of the ether and a small amount of low boiling liquid, 25 g. (26%) of vinylethinylmethylcarbinol was collected. It was a colorless liquid with an alcoholic odor slightly resembling that of butyl alcohol. It reacted with dinitrobenzoyl chloride to form the **3,5-dinitrobenzoate of vinylethinylmethylcarbinol**, white needles from dilute alcohol; m. p. 106–106.2°.

Anal. Calcd. for $C_{13}H_{10}N_2O_6$: C, 54.27; H, 3.41. Found: C, 54.34; H, 3.47.

Catalytic Reduction of the Vinylethinylcarbinols.—The carbinols derived from acetone and from methyl ethyl ketone absorbed four atoms of hydrogen very rapidly when dissolved in alcohol and shaken with hydrogen in the presence of Adams' platinum oxide catalyst. The resulting n-butylcarbinols corresponded in their properties with those already reported in the literature, and the yields were almost quantitative. Hydrogenation of the carbinols derived from methyl octyl ketone and from acetophenone yielded the new saturated carbinols described below.

n-**Butylmethyloctylcarbinol.**—Colorless liquid, b. p. (3 mm.) 94°; n_D^{20} 1.4418; d_4^{20} 0.8318; M_R calcd., 68.38; M_R found, 68.03.

Anal. Calcd. for $C_{14}H_{20}O$: C, 78.50; H, 14.02. Found: C, 77.20, 77.30; H, 14.18, 14.25.

n-**Butylmethylphenylcarbinol.**—Colorless liquid, b. p. (6 mm.) 107 to 109°; n_D^{20} 1.5118; d_4^{20} 0.9616; M_R calcd., 55.52; M_R found, 55.52.

Anal. Calcd. for $C_{12}H_{18}O$: C, 80.90; H, 10.11. Found: C, 81.02, 81.16; H, 10.38, 10.24.

n-**Propyl-5-octadiene-1,5-ine-3.**—When the attempt was made to distil vinylethinyldi-n-propylcarbinol *in vacuo* in a flask provided with a long column, dehydration occurred and the non-aqueous distillate was the hydrocarbon n-propyl-5-octadiene-1,5-ine-3. On redistillation it was obtained as a pale yellow liquid having a characteristic odor; b. p. (6 mm.) 57 to 58°; d_4^{20} 0.8047; n_D^{20} 1.4949; M_R calcd., 50.06; M_R found, 53.62. The sample was perhaps not quite pure.

Anal. Calcd. for $C_{11}H_{16}$: C, 89.19; H, 10.81. Found: C, 87.47, 90.27, 87.73; H, 11.11, 9.94, 10.61.

Preparation of Divinylacetylene by the Dehydration of Vinylethinylmethylcarbinol.—To 25 g. of p-toluenesulfonic acid in a 500-cc. flask provided with a stirrer, separatory funnel, and condenser was slowly added 20.8 g. of vinylethinylmethylcarbinol. The flask was warmed on a water-bath to start the reaction, after which it proceeded vigorously. After two hours, the condenser was replaced by a distilling column and the contents of the flask distilled *in vacuo*. Divinylacetylene distilled from the mixture and collected in a trap surrounded by solid carbon dioxide and acetone. The divinylacetylene was not further purified, but was converted into the hexabromide. The melting point of this hexabromide was identical with that of the hexabromide from a known sample of divinylacetylene. The melting points were as follows

Hexabromide from above synthesis   m. p. 105–106°
Hexabromide from known sample of divinylacetylene   104–106°
Mixed m. p.   105–106°

TABLE I

ANALYTICAL DATA FOR VINYLETHINYLCARBINOLS

Structural formula of carbinol	Empirical formula	Calcd.			Found		
		C	H	Mol. wt.	C	H	Mol. wt. in freezing benzene
$CH_3CHOH—C≡C—CH=CH_2$	C_6H_8O	75.00	8.33	96	74.66	8.34	104
$n-C_3H_7CHOH—C≡C—CH=CH_2$	$C_8H_{12}O$	77.42	9.67	124	76.83	9.83	127
$(CH_3)_2C(OH)—C≡C—CH=CH_2$	$C_7H_{10}O$	76.36	9.09	110	76.18	8.88	119
$CH_3(C_2H_5)C(OH)—C≡C—CH=CH_2$	$C_8H_{12}O$	77.42	9.67		77.09	9.87	
$(C_2H_5)_2C(OH)—C≡C—CH=CH_2$	$C_9H_{14}O$	78.26	10.14	138	78.61	10.09	136,141
$(n-C_3H_7)_2C(OH)—C≡C—CH=CH_2$	$C_{11}H_{18}O$	79.52	10.84	166	79.89	11.14	167,171
$CH_3(C_8H_{17})C(OH)—C≡C—CH=CH_2$	$C_{14}H_{24}O$	80.77	11.54		80.17	10.87	
$(CH_2)_4C(OH)—C≡C—CH=CH_2$	$C_9H_{12}O$	79.41	8.82	136	79.36	8.99	145,145
$(CH_2)_5C(OH)—C≡C—CH=CH_2$	$C_{10}H_{14}O$	80.00	9.33	150	79.70	9.29	137,144[a]
$CH_3(C_6H_5)C(OH)—C≡C—CH=CH_2$	$C_{12}H_{12}O$	83.72	6.97	172	83.23	7.08	173

TABLE II

PHYSICAL PROPERTIES OF VINYLETHINYLCARBINOLS

Ketone or aldehyde reactant	Formula of carbinol produced	Physical properties of carbinol						
		B. p., °C.	Mm.	d_4^{20}	n_D^{20}	M_R calcd.	M_R found	Exaltation
Acetaldehyde	$CH_3—CHOH—C≡C—CH=CH_2$	65	22	0.9112	1.4851	28.97	30.20	1.23
Butyraldehyde	$n-C_3H_7—CHOH—C≡C—CH=CH_2$	74–76	10	.8919	1.4775	38.21	39.32	1.11
Acetone	$(CH_3)_2C(OH)—C≡C—CH=CH_2$	68	24	.8872	1.4778	33.32	35.08	1.76
Methyl ethyl ketone	$CH_3(C_2H_5)C(OH)—C≡C—CH=CH_2$	75	20	.8878	1.4802	38.21	39.90	1.69
Diethyl ketone	$(C_2H_5)_2C(OH)—C≡C—CH=CH_2$	62	4	.8875	1.4800	42.82	44.17	1.35
Dipropyl ketone	$(n-C_3H_7)_2C(OH)—C≡C—CH=CH_2$	98–99	22	.8738	1.4745	52.05	53.44	1.39
Methyl octyl ketone	$CH_3(C_8H_{17})C(OH)—C≡C—CH=CH_2$	98–100	5	.8681	1.4734	65.91	67.26	1.35
Cyclopentanone	$(CH_2)_4C(OH)—C≡C—CH=CH_2$	104–105	7	1.0181	1.5228	40.62	(40.79)	(0.17)
Cyclohexanone	$(CH_2)_5C(OH)—C≡C—CH=CH_2$	84–85	2	0.9742	1.5169	45.24	46.57	1.33
Acetophenone	$CH_3(C_6H_5)C(OH)—C≡C—CH=CH_2$	125–126	4	m. p. 40–41[a]				

[a] In boiling benzene.

Polymerization of the Carbinols.—The behavior of vinylethinylmethylethylcarbinol is typical of the tertiary carbinols. On standing in a stoppered bottle its viscosity increased very rapidly during the first few days, and at the end of a week the product was a thick, colorless, transparent sirup. After three weeks it had set to a tough, elastic, rather rubber-like mass which still contained a considerable proportion of unchanged carbinol. After six weeks it had changed to a very hard, translucent mass.

Fifty grams of vinylethinylmethylethylcarbinol containing 0.5 g. of benzoyl peroxide was exposed to a Cooper-Hewitt light (mercury arc in glass). The product obtained after seventy-two hours was a hard, transparent, pale yellow, glass-like resin. It was insoluble in the common organic solvents. When heated it softened somewhat at 125 to 150°, but it did not liquefy completely even at much higher temperatures.

Twenty-five grams of the carbinol containing 0.25 g. of benzoyl peroxide was exposed to a 150-watt Mazda light. In four days a product similar to that described in the preceding example was obtained.

Twenty-five grams of the carbinol containing 0.25 g. of uranyl nitrate was exposed to a Cooper-Hewitt light. In seventy-two hours, a hard, transparent, amber-colored resin was obtained. When no catalyst was present under the same conditions, the transformation to a hard resin required about one week.

A sample of vinylethinylmethylethylcarbinol was heated for several hours at 100° while a slow stream of air was bubbled through it. The product was a brown sirup. At room temperature it solidified to a brittle resin which dissolved readily in the common organic solvents.

Summary

Sodium vinylacetylide obtained by the action of sodium or of sodamide on vinylacetylene is a very reactive white powder which shows a tendency to ignite spontaneously in the air. Under properly controlled conditions it is a convenient reagent for introducing the vinylethinyl group into reactive organic compounds. Vinylethinylcarbinols are readily obtained by treating a mixture of vinylacetylene and a ketone with sodamide. The same method can also be applied to aldehydes but with less favorable results. Nine new carbinols prepared by this method are described.

Bibliography and Remarks

(1) Carothers and Berchet, *Journ. Am. Chem. Soc.*, **55**, 1094 (1933); this volume, page 321.

(2) Unpublished results.

(3) The behavior of the vinylethinylcyclopentanol was exceptional. It had not polymerized after standing for one year at the ordinary conditions.

VIII. α-Alkyl-β-Vinylacetylenes*

Vinylacetylene is a prolific source of new and interesting compounds. The present paper is concerned with homologs of vinylacetylene, which are readily accessible through the mediacy of sodium vinylacetylide (1). Vinylethinylmagnesium bromide reacts with very active alkyl halides such as triphenylchloromethane (2), but not with simple alkyl halides. Sodium vinylacetylide on the other hand reacts almost explosively with simple alkyl halides. The reaction can be moderated, however, by employing low temperatures, and when the halide is cautiously added to the acetylide in liquid ammonia it proceeds smoothly and furnishes good yields of the α-alkyl-β-vinylacetylenes. Alkyl sulfates or sulfonates can be used with similar results. The properties of alkyl vinylacetylenes obtained by these methods are indicated in Table I. The compounds are colorless liquids with characteristic odors. On standing they slowly polymerize, yielding viscous, yellow sirups.

TABLE I

PHYSICAL PROPERTIES OF CH_2=CH—C≡C—R

Nature of R	B. p., °C.	d_4^{20}	n_D^{20}	M_R calcd.	M_R found	Exaltation
CH_3	59.2 at 760 mm.	0.7401	1.4496	22.82	23.94	1.12
C_2H_5	84.5–85.3 at 758 mm.	.7492	1.4522	27.44	28.82	1.38
n-C_4H_9	62–63 at 61 mm.	.7830	1.4592	36.68	37.71	1.03
n-C_7H_{15}	74.5 at 9 mm.	.7962	1.4606	50.53	51.65	1.12

Experimental Part

1-Methyl-2-vinylacetylene.—A one-liter, 3-necked flask was fitted with a mercury-sealed stirrer, a dropping funnel, and an exit tube. The exit tube was connected to a vertical condenser which in turn led to a gas-washing train consisting of an empty bottle, a second bottle containing water, and a third containing 10% sulfuric acid. The exit tube from the latter was connected to a calcium chloride drying tower and this in turn led to a receiver immersed in a Dewar flask maintained at −78°.

To a solution of 104 g. of vinylacetylene in 600 cc. of liquid ammonia was slowly added 58.5 g. (1.5 moles) of powdered sodamide. The mixture was stirred for three hours and then concentrated to approximately 300 cc. by evaporating the ammonia in a current of nitrogen; 189 g. (1.5 moles) of dimethyl sulfate was added slowly through the separatory funnel. The reaction was very vigorous and about four hours were required for the addition. The ammonia was allowed to evaporate and the reaction flask was finally heated on a water-bath. Part of the 1-methyl-2-vinylacetylene collected in the first bottle and part in the second. The portions were combined, dried over calcium

* R. A. Jacobson and W. H. Carothers, *Journ. Am. Chem. Soc.*, **55**, 1622–4(1933); Contribution No. 112 from the Experimental Station of E. I. du Pont de Nemours and Co.

Received September 21, 1932. Published April 6, 1933.

chloride, and distilled. Some low-boiling material came over first and then 37.6 g. (38%) of 1-methyl-2-vinylacetylene was collected. It was a colorless, volatile liquid possessing a powerful hydrocarbon odor somewhat similar to that of vinylacetylene.

Anal. Calcd. for C_5H_6: C, 90.91; H, 9.09. Found: C, 90.97; H, 8.63. Mol. Wt.: calcd., 66; found, 66.1, 66.3 (cryoscopic, benzene).

1-Ethyl-2-vinylacetylene.—A solution of 104 g. (1.5 moles) of vinylacetylene in 500 cc. of liquid ammonia was treated with 58.5 g. (1.5 moles) of powdered sodamide as in the preceding experiment. After three hours, 231 g. of diethyl sulfate was added slowly through the dropping funnel. The mixture was allowed to stand overnight while the ammonia evaporated. Water was added to the reaction flask and the upper layer, weighing 51 g., was separated. After drying with calcium chloride, the liquid was distilled. A small amount of low-boiling liquid came over first, after which 37 g. of 1-ethyl-2-vinylacetylene distilled. The product was a colorless liquid with an odor similar to that of 1-methyl-2-vinylacetylene.

Anal. Calcd. for C_6H_8: C, 90; H, 10. Found: C, 89.47, 89.73; H, 10.20, 9.44. Mol. Wt.: calcd., 80; found, 78.4, 79.5 (cryoscopic, benzene).

1-Ethyl-2-vinylacetylene was also prepared by treating sodium vinylacetylide with ethyl *p*-toluenesulfonate according to the method recently employed by Truchet (3): 58.5 g. (1.5 moles) of sodamide was slowly added to a solution of 104 g. of vinyl-acetylene in 200 cc. of butyl ether at −10° and the mixture was stirred for three hours. A solution of 300 g. (1.5 moles) of ethyl *p*-toluenesulfonate in 200 cc. of butyl ether was then added drop by drop during several hours. The thick mixture was heated in a water-bath at 80° for three hours and allowed to stand overnight. Water was added but such a troublesome emulsion formed that the mixture was set aside for twenty-four hours in a separatory funnel. The ether layer was separated, dried with calcium chloride, and distilled. A considerable quantity of low-boiling material first distilled, and then a fraction weighing 45 g. and boiling at 78–88° was collected. Upon redistillation 28.5 g. (23.7%) of 1-ethyl-2-vinylacetylene boiling at 84–85° was obtained. Of the two methods of preparing this compound, the first was the better.

1-Butyl-2-vinylacetylene.—A solution of 100 g. of vinylacetylene in 400 cc. of liquid ammonia was treated with 39 g. (1 mole) of powdered sodamide. After three hours, 137 g. (1 mole) of butyl bromide was slowly dropped into the solution during about four hours. The mixture was allowed to stand overnight, water was added, and the upper layer separated. The liquid was dried with calcium chloride and distilled. The product was a colorless liquid with a characteristic hydrocarbon-like odor. The liquid polymerized during the course of three months to a yellow viscous sirup.

Anal. Calcd. for C_8H_{12}: C, 88.88; H, 11.12. Found: C, 88.65; H, 10.76. Mol. Wt.: calcd., 108; found, 103, 104 (cryoscopic, benzene).

1-Heptyl-2-vinylacetylene.—A solution of 75 g. of vinylacetylene in 400 cc. of liquid ammonia was treated with 39 g. (1 mole) of powdered sodamide. After three hours, 150 g. (0.84 mole) of heptyl bromide was slowly added during four hours. The mixture was allowed to stand overnight, water was added, and the upper layer (128 g.) separated. After drying with calcium chloride, the liquid was distilled; 101 g. of 1-heptyl-2-vinylacetylene was collected. Based on the heptyl bromide used, the yield was 80% of the theoretical. On standing for two months the liquid polymerized to a yellow viscous sirup.

Anal. Calcd. for $C_{11}H_{18}$: C, 88.00; H, 12.00. Found: C, 87.65, 87.51; H, 11.55, 11.81. Mol. Wt.: calcd., 150; found, 143, 145 (cryoscopic, benzene).

Summary

Sodium vinylacetylide reacts with alkyl halides, sulfates or sulfonates, yielding α-alkyl-β-vinylacetylenes. Compounds of the formula $CH_2{=}$ $CH—C{\equiv}C—R$ are described in which R is methyl, ethyl, *n*-butyl and *n*-heptyl.

Bibliography and Remarks

(1) Carothers and Jacobson, *Journ. Am. Chem. Soc.*, **55**, 1097 (1933); this volume, page 323.
(2) Carothers and Berchet, *Journ. Am. Chem. Soc.*, **55**, 1094 (1933); this volume, page 321.
(3) Truchet, *Compt. rend.*, **191**, 854 (1930).

IX. 1-Alkyl-2-chloro-1,3-butadienes and their Polymers (Fourth Paper on New Synthetic Rubbers)*

Chloroprene (I) polymerizes very rapidly to form a rubber-like product of excellent quality (1).

$$\overset{1}{CH_2}{=}\overset{2}{C}—\overset{3}{CH}{=}\overset{4}{CH_2} \quad (I)$$
$$\underset{Cl}{|}$$

Replacement of the hydrogen at the 3-position by methyl does not appreciably affect the rate of spontaneous polymerization, but the rubber-like product is somewhat deficient in extensibility (2). On the other hand, the introduction of methyl at both the 3- and the 4-positions greatly·diminishes the tendency to polymerize, and the product, although highly extensible, is lacking in resilience (2).

The present paper is concerned with chloroprenes in which a hydrogen in the 1-position has been replaced by alkyl. These compounds are readily obtained by the action of hydrogen chloride on the corresponding α-substituted vinylacetylenes. The latter have already been described (3). Doubtless because of their lesser solubility in water they react more slowly with aqueous hydrochloric acid than does the parent hydrocarbon, which reacts practically completely when shaken for five hours at room temperature with two moles of concentrated hydrochloric acid containing cuprous chloride (4). Under the same conditions α-methylvinylacetylene is less

* R. A. Jacobson and W. H. Carothers, *Journ. Am. Chem. Soc.*, 55, 1624–7 (1933); Contribution No. 113 from the Experimental Station of E. I. du Pont de Nemours and Co. Received September 28, 1932. Published April 6, 1933,

than 40% utilized. Reaction of the higher homologs is still slower, so that elevated temperature was needed for the butyl compound, and the heptyl compound required the addition of alcohol to function as a solvent.

The physical properties of the new homologs of chloroprene are indicated in Table I. They are colorless liquids with characteristic odors. Like chloroprene, they react with α-naphthoquinone to form addition products, which are readily oxidized to α-alkyl-β-chloroanthraquinones (II), and their identity is established by this reaction.

O   (II)

No additions to systems of the type $\text{alkyl}-\overset{(1)}{C}\equiv\overset{(2)}{C}-CH=CH_2$ have been recorded hitherto. It is therefore of interest to observe that the result of adding hydrogen chloride under the conditions described is to place H at (1) and Cl at (2), but in view of the mechanism already established for vinylacetylene (4) it seems probable that the first product is alkyl—CH= C=CH—CH$_2$Cl, which then rearranges to the substituted chloroprene. In any event, current theories, either empirical or electronic, do not appear to account for this result.

TABLE I

PROPERTIES OF CH$_2$=CH—CCl=CH—R

Nature of R	B. p., °C.	Pressure in mm.	n_D^{20}	d_4^{20}	M_R Calcd.	M_R Found	Exaltation
H[1]	59.4	760	1.4583	0.9563	24.61	25.27	0.66
CH$_3$	99.5–101.5	759	1.4785	.9576	29.22	30.32	1.10
C$_2$H$_5$	68.2–69	117	1.4770	.9390	33.84	35.05	1.21
n-C$_4$H$_9$	64–65	18	1.4794	.9366	43.04	43.77	0.73
n-C$_7$H$_{15}$	74–76	1	1.4785	.9141	56.93	57.79	0.86

Polymerization of the Substituted Chloroprenes.—Chloroprene polymerizes practically completely to an elastic, rubber-like mass in forty-eight to eighty hours when directly illuminated by a 150-watt Mazda lamp at 30 to 35°. The substituted chloroprenes listed in Table I all polymerize much more slowly. The methyl compound requires about six or seven weeks, and the higher members of the series require still longer times. The products, with the possible exception of that derived from the heptyl compound, are definitely rubber-like but much inferior in quality to polychloroprene. The product from the methyl compound is the best. Polymerization under direct light from a 150-watt Mazda lamp during one month at the ordinary temperature gave a soft mass containing a considerable proportion of unchanged monomer. The polymer precipitated by the addition of alcohol was a soft, plastic mass resembling milled smoked sheets. It was compounded with 10% of its weight of zinc oxide and then heated at 120° for twenty minutes. The plastic properties were quite largely suppressed by this treatment, but the product appeared to be incompletely vulcanized. It was strong and tough and had a high extensibility, but it recovered from stretch rather slowly, and was deficient in resilience. Vulcanizates obtained from higher members of the series were still softer and more deficient in resilience.

Preparation of 1-Alkyl-2-chloro-1,3-butadienes.—The general procedure was similar to that already described for chloroprene (4). One mole of the hydrocarbon was shaken with approximately 2.2 moles of concentrated aqueous hydrochloric acid containing about 0.25 mole of cuprous chloride and 0.2 mole of ammonium chloride. The nonaqueous layer was separated, stabilized with hydroquinone and distilled; or, in some cases, the reaction mixture was distilled with steam after the addition of hydroquinone. The reaction time varied from five to sixteen hours and the temperature from 23 to

ANALYTICAL DATA FOR THE 1-ALKYL-2-CHLORO-1,3-BUTADIENES

Nature of alkyl	C	Calculated H	Cl	Mol. wt.	Found C	H	Cl	Mol. wt. (cryoscopic in benzene)
CH_3	58.56	6.83	34.61	102.5	58.49	6.92	34.63	102 103
C_2H_5	61.82	7.73	30.45	116.5	61.64	7.97	30.28	116 119
n-C_4H_9	66.45	8.99	24.56	144.5	65.73	8.76	24.57	152 154
n-C_7H_{55}	70.79	10.19	19.02	186.5	70.39	10.04	19.26	189 193

45°. The product in each case appeared to consist entirely of the substituted chloroprene and the unchanged hydrocarbon. Yields were good, but conversions were not complete. No appreciable addition could be obtained with the heptyl compound in aqueous solution, but a fair conversion was obtained when the hydrocarbon was shaken with 3.4 moles of hydrochloric acid in ethyl alcohol with 0.35 mole of cuprous chloride and 0.44 mole of ammonium chloride for five hours at 70 to 80°.

Condensation of Naphthoquinone with the 1-Alkyl-2-chloro-1,3-butadienes.— The substituted chloroprenes were each heated with α-naphthoquinone in the ratio of about 1 g. to 0.5 g. at 100° for about two hours. Alcohol containing sodium hydroxide was added, and air was bubbled through the resulting suspension. The solids were crystallized as indicated below and were thus obtained in the form of yellow crystals (generally needles).

SUBSTITUTED ANTHRAQUINONES OF FORMULA II

R =	Cryst. from	M. p., °C.	Calcd. C	H	Found C	H
CH_3	Acetic acid	181	70.19	3.51	70.16	3.50
C_2H_5	Alcohol	151–152	70.99	4.06	70.93	4.18
n-C_4H_9	Methanol	129–130	72.37	5.03	71.83	5.16
n-C_7H_{15}[a]	Alcohol	112.5–113.5	74.02	6.17	74.12	6.40

[a] In this case the intermediate tetrahydro compound was isolated, probably 1-heptyl-2-chloro-4,4a,9,9a-tetrahydro-9,10-anthraquinone; white crystals from methanol, m. p. 96–98°.

Anal. Calcd. for $C_{21}H_{23}O_2Cl$: C, 73.16; H, 7.26. Found: C, 72.48; H, 7.44.

Polymerization of the 1-Alkyl-2-chloro-1,3-butadienes

1-Methyl-2-chloro-1,3-butadiene.—A sample of 1-methyl-2-chloro-1,3-butadiene was exposed at room temperature to an ordinary incandescent light (150-watt Mazda) for one month. During this period the liquid increased in viscosity—slowly at first, but more rapidly later—until a soft, transparent, elastic, rubber-like solid was obtained. The rubber-like solid was macerated with alcohol to remove monomer and polymers of low molecular weight. The residual polymer was a tough, rubbery, plastic material. Ten per cent. by weight of zinc oxide was incorporated by means of steel rolls and the plastic mass then heated at 120° for twenty minutes. The product was strong, tough and elastic, but recovery from stretch was rather slow.

A sample of 1-methyl-2-chloro-1,3-butadiene was exposed to a 150-watt Mazda light at 30–35° for six and one-half weeks. The liquid progressively increased in viscosity until finally a pale yellow rubbery solid was obtained. This product was more completely polymerized than the product of the preceding experiment. The polymer was highly elastic and resembled cured natural rubber.

1-Ethyl-2-chloro-1,3-butadiene.—A sample of 1-ethyl-2-chloro-1,3-butadiene was exposed to the light of a 150-watt Mazda lamp at 30 to 35° for about four weeks. The product was a pale yellow, transparent, viscous sirup. This was macerated with a large volume of alcohol to remove unchanged monomer. The soft, sticky, coherent mass that remained undissolved by the alcohol was mixed with 10% of zinc oxide and heated in a mold for twenty minutes at 120°. The product was a tough, elastic material resembling the vulcanized product obtained from 1-methyl-2-chloro-1,3-butadiene, but it was softer and less resilient.

1-Butyl-2-chloro-1,3-butadiene.—A sample of 1-butyl-2-chloro-1,3-butadiene, when allowed to stand at the ordinary conditions in a stoppered bottle, after nine and one-half months had changed to a thick, sticky, brown sirup. Precipitation with alcohol then gave a 60% yield of rather soft, rubber-like material. The reaction was accelerated by light. A sample directly exposed to a 150-watt Mazda lamp at 30 to 35° for six weeks had changed to a yellow, viscous, sirup. After five weeks more it was considerably thicker. It was washed with alcohol and the residual sticky solid was mixed with zinc oxide. It vulcanized very incompletely on being heated.

A sample of 1-butyl-2-chloro-1,3-butadiene was subjected to a pressure of 6000 atmospheres at 38°. At the end of ninety-six hours it had polymerized to a transparent soft, sticky solid; 90% of this solid was now insoluble in alcohol. The portion insoluble in alcohol was mixed with 10% of its weight of zinc oxide, 2% of stearic acid, and 1% of benzidine and then heated at 120°. The physical properties of the product indicated that it was very incompletely vulcanized. It was elastic but rather weak and somewhat sticky.

1-Heptyl-2-chloro-1,3-butadiene.—A sample of this diene showed no apparent change in color or viscosity when allowed to stand at the ordinary conditions for nine months. Polymerization occurred slowly when a sample was exposed to light from a Mazda lamp at 30 to 35°. After three and one-half weeks the sample had changed to a colorless, transparent sirup. After six more weeks it had become thick and very viscous. It was finally washed with alcohol and attempts were made to vulcanize the insoluble polymer in the presence of zinc oxide. The product was soft and sticky.

A sample of 1-heptyl-2-chloro-1,3-butadiene was subjected to a pressure of 6000 atmospheres at 38°. At the end of ninety-six hours it had polymerized to a transparent, sticky, elastic mass. Only 4% of the material was soluble in alcohol. The alcohol-insoluble polymer was mixed with 10% of zinc oxide, 2% of stearic acid and 1% of benzidine and heated at 120°. The product was a sticky solid possessing very slight elasticity.

Acknowledgment.—We are indebted to Dr. H. W. Starkweather for the experiments at high pressure.

Summary

Substituted chloroprenes of the formula $CH_2\!=\!CH\!-\!CCl\!=\!CH\!-\!R$ in which R is methyl, ethyl, n-butyl and n-heptyl are described. These compounds all polymerize much more slowly than chloroprene and the polymers, though rubber-like, are inferior in quality to polychloroprene. The methyl compound polymerizes most rapidly and yields the best polymer, but compared with polychloroprene the polymer is lacking in resilience.

Substituted anthraquinones derived from the substituted chloroprenes are described.

Bibliography and Remarks

(1) Carothers, Williams, Collins and Kirby, *Journ. Am. Chem. Soc.*, **53**, 4203 (1931); this volume, page 281.

(2) Carothers and Coffman, *Journ. Am. Chem. Soc.*, **54**, 4071 (1932); this volume, page 384.

(3) Jacobson and Carothers, *Journ. Am. Chem. Soc.*, **55**, 1622 (1933); this volume, page 329.

(4) Carothers, Berchet and Collins, *Journ. Am. Chem. Soc.*, **54**, 4066 (1932); this volume, page 306.

X. The Chlorination of the Hydrochlorides of Vinylacetylene*

The action of hydrogen chloride on vinylacetylene gives rise to the two monohydrochlorides, chloro-4-butadiene-1,2 (I) and chloroprene (II), and the dihydrochloride, dichloro-2,4-butene-2 (III) (1).

$$CH\!\equiv\!C\!-\!CH\!=\!CH_2 \xrightarrow{\text{HCl}} CH_2\!=\!C\!=\!CH\!-\!CH_2Cl \longrightarrow$$
$$\text{(I)}$$
$$CH_2\!=\!CCl\!-\!CH\!=\!CH_2 \xrightarrow{\text{HCl}} CH_3\!-\!CCl\!=\!CH\!-\!CH_2Cl$$
$$\text{(II)} \qquad\qquad\qquad\qquad \text{(III)}$$

All of these compounds react rapidly with chlorine and we now record some observations on the products to which they lead.

* W. H. Carothers and G. J. Berchet, *Journ. Am. Chem. Soc.*, **55**, 1628–31(1933); Contribution No. 144 from the Experimental Station of E. I. du Pont de Nemours and Co.

Received September 28, 1932.   Published April 6, 1933.

Chloro-4-butadiene-1,2 in a series of experiments was chlorinated under various conditions and the combined distillable product was redistilled through an efficient column. Most of the material segregated into two fractions, one boiling at 40 to 41° at 10 mm. and the other at 64 to 65° at 10 mm. Each had the composition $C_4H_5Cl_3$. The lower boiling compound on oxidation with permanganate yielded α,β-dichloropropionic acid as the only recognizable product, and was thus identified as trichloro-1,2,3-butene-3 (IV). The higher boiling compound when similarly oxidized yielded only chloroacetic acid. The compound was therefore trichloro-1,3,4-butene-2 (V). The two compounds evidently arise by the addition of chlorine at the interior and the terminal members of the pair of contiguous double bonds. Other allenes have been observed to behave in a similar manner (2).

$$CH_2{=}C{=}CH{-}CH_2Cl \left\{ \begin{array}{c} CH_2{=}CCl{-}CHCl{-}CH_2Cl \\ (IV) \\ CH_2Cl{-}CCl{=}CH{-}CH_2Cl \\ (V) \end{array} \right\} CH_2Cl{-}CCl_2{-}CHCl{-}CH_2Cl \\ (VII)$$

Further experiments showed that although the two trichlorobutenes were the principal products when one mole of chlorine was added to chloro-4-butadiene-1,2, the ratio in which they were formed varied considerably with the conditions used. At 40 to 50° the 1,3,4-compound predominated, at −60 to −70° the 1,2,3-compound. Saturation of chloro-4-butadiene-1,2 with chlorine led to a compound having the composition $C_4H_5Cl_5$. In view of its origin it may be assigned the formula pentachloro-1,2,3,3,4-butane (VII).

In all of the chlorinations of chloro-4-butadiene-1,2 a considerable fraction (up to about 20% of the total product) consisted of undistillable material. In the chlorination of chloroprene (1 mole : 1 mole) the proportion of undistillable product was still greater (up to about 50%). The distillable product formed either at 40 to 50° or at −60 to −70° was a difficulty separable mixture, but the principal fraction (25 to 30% of the total product) was closely similar in its physical properties to the compound already identified as trichloro-1,3,4-butene-2. This obviously might arise from chloroprene by a process of 1,4 addition.

The chlorination of dichloro-2,4-butene-2 leads to the formation of trichloro-1,2,3-butene-3 (IV), tetrachloro-1,2,3,3-butane (VI) and pentachloro-1,2,3,3,4-butane (VII). This series of products might be accounted for as follows

$$CH_3CCl{=}CH{-}CH_2Cl \xrightarrow{+Cl_2} CH_3{-}CCl_2{-}CHCl{-}CH_2Cl \xrightarrow{-HCl}$$
$$\text{(VI)}$$

$$CH_2{=}CCl{-}CHCl{-}CH_2Cl \xrightarrow{+Cl_2} ClCH_3{-}CCl_2{-}CHCl{-}CH_2Cl$$
$$\text{(IV)} \qquad\qquad\qquad\qquad \text{(VII)}$$

The isolated tetrachlorobutane however is a stable compound, that is, it shows no tendency to lose hydrogen chloride spontaneously. Moreover, a very curious feature of the reaction lies in the fact that at elevated temperature (*e. g.*, 40 to 60°) very little hydrogen chloride is evolved and the predominating product is the tetrachlorobutane; at low temperatures (*e. g.*, −60 to −70°), on the other hand, hydrogen chloride is formed in copious amounts, and the predominating product is the trichlorobutene or the pentachlorobutane, depending upon the amount of chlorine applied. It appears therefore that the trichlorobutene does not originate from the tetrachlorobutane as such, but that both of these compounds arise from a common prior intermediate. Such an intermediate might be VIII, which would be formed by the addition of the chlorine molecule at the deficient carbon in the active form of the double bond (3). Rearrangement of this intermediate would lead directly to tetrachlorobutane; loss of hydrogen chloride followed by rearrangement would lead to trichlorobutene. A sufficient difference in the temperature coefficients of the primary processes would account for the observed facts.

$$
\begin{array}{c}
Cl \\
| \\
CH_3{-}C{-}\overset{-}{C}H{-}CH_2Cl \\
\uparrow \\
Cl{+} \\
| \\
Cl \\
\text{(VIII)}
\end{array}
$$

The above statements in regard to the influence of temperature on the chlorination of dichloro-2,4-butene-2 are illustrated by the following experiments.

One mole (125 g.) of the dichlorobutene in a flask cooled with a slush of solid carbon dioxide and acetone was treated with chlorine gas until 1.33 moles of chlorine had been absorbed. The mixture was allowed to warm up while a slow stream of air was passed through it to remove dissolved gases. During this operation there was a sudden and very copious evolution of hydrogen chloride. The loss in weight corresponded with the evolution of 0.9 mole of hydrogen chloride. The hydrogen chloride collected and titrated was only 0.73 mole, but some was lost owing to the suddenness of the evolution. Distillation of the mixture gave

Trichloro-1,2,3-butene-3	0.440 mole
Tetrachloro-1,2,3,3-butane	0.089 mole
Pentachloro-1,2,3,3,4-butane	0.198 mole

The rest (0.273 mole) was contained in intermediate fractions and residue; the latter comprised 10.3% of the total product. If the losses are distributed proportionately among the three chief fractions, the percentage yields of these are

Trichlorobutene 60.6%   Tetrachlorobutane 12.2%   Pentachlorobutane 27.2%

Since in the formation of the pentachloro compound the trichloro compound is a necessary intermediate, 88% of the dichlorobutene was converted to the trichlorobutene, and only 12.2% to the tetrachlorobutane.

One mole (250 g.) of the dichlorobutene was chlorinated at ordinary temperature, the rate being controlled so that the temperature of the mixture was between 45 and 60°. The increase in weight corresponded with the absorption of 0.61 mole of chlorine, and at the same time 0.36 mole of hydrogen chloride was liberated. Distillation of the mixture gave

Trichloro-1,2,3-butene-3	0.207 mole
Tetrachloro-1,2,3,3-butane	0.343 mole
Pentachloro-1,2,3,3,4-butane	0.100 mole

Chlorination in this case was incomplete and there was considerable loss in residue and intermediate fractions, but the data show that the yield of tetrachlorobutane was greater than the combined yields of the trichloro and the pentachloro compounds. Further experiments showed that by careful adjustment of the amount of chlorine applied at low temperatures the isolated yield of trichloro-1,2,3-butene-3 could be raised to 80%, while at high temperatures the yield did not exceed 25%.

Oxidation of Trichloro-1,2,3-butene-3.—Twenty grams of the compound was stirred with 200 cc. of water while 70 g. of potassium permanganate was added in portions. The alkaline solution was filtered, treated with sulfur dioxide, filtered, acidified and continuously extracted with ether for nine hours. Evaporation of the ethereal solution gave 8.5 g. of acidic oil which distilled at 125° at 25 mm. It was identified as α,β-dichloropropionic acid by its melting point (49–50°) and its neutralization equivalent (calcd., 143; found, 141.1).

Oxidation of Trichloro-1,3,4-butene-2.—Oxidation of this compound under the same conditions as those described above gave chloroacetic acid

TABLE I

CHLORINATION PRODUCTS

Structural formula	Name	B. p., °C.	Mm	d_4^{20}	n_D^{20}	M_R Calcd.	M_R Found
IV	Trichloro-1,2,3-butene-3	40–41	10	1.3430	1.4944	34.78	34.72
V	Trichloro-1,3,4-butene-2	64–65	10	1.3843	1.5175	34.78	34.89
VI	Tetrachloro-1,2,3,3-butane	90	32	1.4204	1.4958	40.14	40.25
		55–57	10				
VII	Pentachloro-1,2,3,3,4-butane	85	10	1.5543	1.5157	45.01	44.77

			Calcd.		Anal.	Found	
	Empirical formula	C	H	Cl	C	H	Cl
IV	$C_4H_5Cl_3$	30.09	3.13	66.77	29.95	3.30	66.34
V	$C_4H_5Cl_3$	30.09	3.13	66.77	29.09	3.01	67.33
VI	$C_4H_6Cl_3$			72.40			71.83
VII	$C_4H_5Cl_5$	20.82	2.16	77.00	21.22	2.36	77.05

as the only product. It was identified by its melting point (63°), mixed melting point and neutralization equivalent (calcd., 94.5; found, 95.1).

Summary

Chlorination of chloro-4-butadiene-1,2 gives mixtures of trichloro-1,2,3-butene-3 and trichloro-1,3,4-butene-2 which react further to produce pentachloro-1,2,3,3,4-butane. The chlorination of chloroprene (chloro-2-butadiene-1,3) gives considerable amounts of trichloro-1,3,4-butene-2. The chlorination of dichloro-2,4-butene-2 at 40 to 60° proceeds with little loss of hydrogen chloride, and the product formed in largest amount is tetrachloro-1,2,3,3-butane. At low temperatures (−60 to −70°) large amounts of hydrogen chloride are liberated during the chlorination, and the principal products are trichloro-1,2,3-butene-3 and pentachloro-1,2,3,3,4-butane.

Bibliography and Remarks

(1) Carothers, Berchet and Collins, *Journ. Am. Chem. Soc.*, **54**, 4066 (1932); this volume, page 306.

(2) Bouis, *Ann. chim.*, [10] **9**, 451 (1928).

(3) Carothers, *Journ. Am. Chem. Soc.*, **46**, 2227 (1924). Evidence that chlorinations involve primarily attack by the chlorine molecule has been presented by Soper and Smith, *J. Chem. Soc.*, 1582 (1926).

XI.   Dichloro-2,3-butadiene-1,3 and Trichloro-1,2,3-butadiene-1,3*

Chloroprene (I) under ordinary conditions polymerizes to a rubber-like product about 700 times as rapidly as isoprene (or butadiene) (1).   Hence in the diene polymerization a chlorine atom at the β-position has a powerful activating influence.   A bromine atom in the same position has an even greater positive effect (2).   On the other hand α-chlorobutadiene polymerizes not much more rapidly than isoprene, and the product, though elastic, has very little strength (3).   The corresponding bromine compound also polymerizes spontaneously but no rubber-like properties have been ascribed to it (4).   Hence the activation produced by the halogen atom is very sensitively related to its position, and multiple substitution does not modify this conclusion, for tetrachloro-1,2,3,4-butadiene-1,3 has been described without any indication that it polymerizes at all (5).   The effect of a single β-halogen atom on diene behavior is in fact unique so far as recorded facts go.   No other type of substitution has yielded a compound that greatly exceeds butadiene in the speed of its spontaneous polymerization and at the same time leads to a rubber-like product.   In the methyl series isoprene polymerizes somewhat more rapidly than butadiene, and β,γ-dimethylbutadiene perhaps yet faster (6); and the product from the latter, though somewhat inferior in snap and extensibility, is still rubber-like.   On the other hand, α-substitution by methyl reduces the tendency to polymerize and unfavorably affects the quality of the product (7).   It appears that both the terminal methylene groups of butadiene must be free: if either of them is substituted even by an activating group the speed of polymerization is diminished and/or the properties of the product are adversely affected (8).

These conclusions stimulated interest in dichloro-2,3-butadiene-1,3 (II) which has at once the two unsubstituted terminal methylene groups and two chlorines properly located to produce a doubly activating effect.   To provide further comparisons trichloro-1,2,3-butadiene-1,3 (III) was also prepared.

Dibromo-2,3-butadiene-1,3 has already been described, but not very fully: "In a sealed tube it remains limpid for several hours, then becomes turbid, and is gradually transformed into a white polymer, but the transformation is complete only at the end of several days." (9).   Otherwise information concerning its behavior is lacking.

* G. J. Berchet and W. H. Carothers, *Journ. Am. Chem. Soc.*, **55**, 2004–8 (1933); Contribution No. 115 from the Experimental Station of E. I. du Pont de Nemours and Co.
Received October 3, 1932.   Published May 6, 1933.

Preparation of Dichloro-2,3-butadiene-1,3 and Trichloro-1,2,3-butadiene-1,3.—Starting materials for the preparation of the two dienes were found in the series of products obtained by chlorinating the hydrogen chloride addition products of vinylacetylene (10). The dichlorobutadiene was obtained from trichloro-1,2,3-butene-3, and the trichlorobutadiene from pentachloro-1,2,3,3,4-butane. The reactions starting from vinylacetylene are

$$CH\!\equiv\!C\!-\!CH\!=\!CH_2 \xrightarrow{\;HCl\;} CH_2\!=\!CCl\!-\!CH\!=\!CH_2 \xrightarrow{\;HCl\;}$$
$$(I)$$

$$CH_3\!-\!CCl\!=\!CH\!-\!CH_2Cl \xrightarrow{\;Cl_2\;} CH_2\!=\!CCl\!-\!CHCl\!-\!CH_2Cl$$

$$CH_2Cl\!-\!CCl_2\!-\!CHCl\!-\!CH_2Cl \xleftarrow{\qquad\;Cl_2\qquad} \;\Big|\;-HCl$$

$$\Big\downarrow\, -HCl$$

$$CH_2\!=\!CCl\!-\!CCl\!=\!CHCl \qquad\qquad CH_2\!=\!CCl\!-\!CCl\!=\!CH_2$$
$$(III) \qquad\qquad\qquad\qquad\qquad (II)$$

The elimination of hydrogen chloride from the trichlorobutene proceeds very rapidly under a variety of conditions. When the trichloro compound is mixed with a slight excess of approximately 6 N methyl alcoholic potassium hydroxide, the theoretical amount of potassium chloride precipitates out within fifteen minutes. Dilution with water then precipitates the dichlorobutadiene as a heavy oil, which, after being stabilized with hydroquinone, is obtained in 86% yield by vacuum distillation. The losses are almost entirely due to polymerization. There is no evidence of the formation of any by-products. Dichloro-2,3-butadiene-1,3 is also obtained by the action of alcoholic potash on butadiene tetrachloride (tetrachloro-1,2,3,4-butane) but the yields are less favorable.

The dichlorobutadiene could not be induced to react with naphthoquinone or with maleic anhydride, and hence no direct and decisive proof of its structure was possible. The structure dichloro-1,3-butadiene-1,3 is not excluded by the methods of synthesis used, but this structure seems very unlikely in view of the rapidity with which the compound polymerizes.

Pentachloro-1,2,3,3,4-butane also reacts rapidly with alcoholic potash. Besides the trichlorobutadiene the product was found to contain some tetrachloro-1,2,2,3-butene-3 whose identity was established by its oxidation to α,α,β-trichloropropionic acid (11). This compound is doubtless an intermediate in the formation of the trichlorobutadiene, and the latter should therefore have the structure (III).

Polymerization of Dichloro- and Trichlorobutadiene.—Under ordinary conditions dichlorobutadiene polymerized completely in about twenty-four hours, at 85 to 90° in about forty minutes. The corresponding times for chloroprene are about ten days, and about twelve hours (estimated). Thus the dichloro compound reacts about ten times as rapidly as chloroprene and about seven thousand times as rapidly as isoprene. The polymerization is inhibited by hydroquinone and accelerated by air or by benzoyl peroxide. The polymer is almost entirely devoid of rubber-like properties. It is a white, opaque, tough, hard mass, non-plastic and lacking in extensibility. It is somewhat (or partly) soluble in chloroform, but very slightly soluble in other common organic solvents including dichlorobutadiene, and under most conditions it separates as an opaque precipitate from the dichlorobutadiene as it is formed. At elevated temperatures (e. g., 85 to 90°), however, the polymer remains dissolved until the polymerization is practically complete. The product is at first a soft, colorless, transparent, sticky, elastic mass, but it becomes opaque, hard, and tough in a very short time. The absence of rubber-like properties in the polymer is consistent with other observations on the influence of substitutents: the spontaneous polymers from $CH_2{=}CCl{-}CMe{=}CH_2$ (12) and from $CH_2{=}CMe{-}CMe{=}CH_2$ are both deficient in extensibility and snap as compared with those from the monosubstituted dienes $CH_2{=}CCl{-}CH{=}CH_2$ and $CH_2{=}CMe{-}CH{=}CH_2$.

The trichlorobutadiene polymerized much more slowly than the dichloro compound. At the ordinary conditions it changed to a jelly-like mass containing about 50% of unchanged diene in ten to twelve days. After one month polymerization was apparently complete. The product was a dark colored, rather soft and friable mass.

Conclusions.—The chlorinated 1,3-butadienes now known may be arranged in the following order so far as the speed of their spontaneous transformation into high polymers is concerned

$$\beta, \gamma \gg \beta \gg \alpha, \beta, \gamma > \alpha \gg \alpha, \beta, \gamma, \delta$$

and only the second member of the series yields a polymer that is definitely rubber-like. The generalizations outlined in the introduction thus receive further confirmation.

Preparation of Dichloro-2,3-butadiene-1,3 (a) from Trichloro-1,2,3-butene-3.—253 g. (15% excess) of potassium hydroxide dissolved in 760 cc. of methanol was placed in a flask provided with a stirrer and an efficient reflux condenser, and 634 g. of trichloro-1,2,3-butene-3 was added with stirring at such a rate that the temperature of the mixture remained between 10 and 15°, the flask being cooled in a bath of ice and water. After all the trichlorobutene had been added the mixture was stirred for two hours, and the potassium chloride was filtered off; yield, 293 g. or 99.4% of the theoretical. The filtrate was poured into a large volume of water and the heavy oil was separated, dried with calcium chloride and distilled in the presence of hydroquinone. The product boiled at 39 to 41° at 80 mm.; yield, 304 g. or 86% of the theoretical. Other properties determined on a purified specimen are: b. p. 41 to 43° at 85 mm., 98° at 760 mm.; n_D^{20} 1.4890; d_4^{20} 1.1829; M_R calcd., 29.47; found, 30.21.

   Anal. Calcd. for $C_4H_4Cl_2$: C, 39.02; H, 3.25; Cl, 57.72. Found: C, 38.76; H, 3.78; Cl, 57.09.

   (b) **From Tetrachloro-1,2,3,4-butane.**—The tetrachlorobutane was prepared by chlorinating butadiene. The sample used was a mixture which contained the solid and liquid isomers in the ratio 1:1.12 (13). In a flask provided with a stirrer and a reflux condenser was placed a solution of 150 g. of potassium hydroxide in 500 cc. of methanol. To this solution 234 g. of the tetrachlorobutane mixed with 100 cc. of methanol was slowly added. The temperature of the mixture was kept between 10 and 18°. Potassium chloride separated immediately. After the addition was complete, the mixture was stirred for two hours at 25° and then filtered. The yield of potassium chloride was 156 g. (88%). The filtrate was poured into a large volume of water and the heavy oil which separated was dried and distilled over hydroquinone. The distillate segregated into two fractions (1) b. p. 39 to 45° at 80 mm., 57 g., and (2) b. p. 45 to 110° at 80 mm., 41 g. The first fraction was β,γ-dichlorobutadiene; on redistillation it boiled 39 to 40° at 80 mm. and it showed the correct refractive index and chlorine content. The second fraction on redistillation boiled chiefly at 84 to 86 at 27 mm. Its chlorine content (found, 57.67, 57.75) agreed with that required for a dichlorobutadiene, and it was perhaps an impure isomeric dichlorobutadiene: d_4^{20} 1.287; n_D^{20} 1.4999.

   Preparation of Trichloro-1,2,3-butadiene-1,3 and Tetrachloro-1,2,2,3-butene-3.—One-half mole (115 g.) of pentachloro-1,2,3,3,4-butane was slowly added with stirring to a solution of one mole of potassium hydroxide in 270 cc. of methanol. The mixture was stirred at room temperature for about two hours. The precipitated potassium chloride was filtered off; yield, 61 g. or 82%. The filtrate was poured into a large volume of water, and the precipitated oil was dried and separated by distillation into two fractions (a) crude trichlorobutadiene boiled at 56 to 65° at 26 mm., 44 g.; and (b) crude tetrachlorobutene boiling at 66 to 75° at 26 mm., 24.5 g. They were further purified by distillation.

   Trichloro-1,2,3-butadiene-1,3.—B. p., 33 to 34° at 7 mm.; n_D^{20} 1.5262; d_4^{20} 1.4060; M_R calcd., 34.34; M_R found, 34.39.

   Anal. Calcd. for $C_4H_3Cl_3$: C, 30.47; H, 1.90; Cl, 67.61. Found: C, 29.50, 29.43; H, 2.33, 2.19; Cl, 68.42, 68.50.

   Tetrachloro-1,2,2,3-butene-3.—B. p. 41 to 42° at 7 mm.; n_D^{20} 1.5133; d_4^{20} 1.4602; M_R calcd. 39.67; M_R found, 39.91.

   Anal. Calcd. for $C_4H_4Cl_4$: C, 24.74; H, 2.06; Cl, 73.19. Found: C, 25.49, 25.16; H, 2.23, 2.24; Cl, 72.66, 72.16.

   Oxidation.—A sample (23 g.) of the tetrachlorobutene was oxidized with excess aqueous potassium permanganate. After filtration and treatment with sulfur dioxide the solution was extracted continuously with ether. Evaporation of the ether gave a liquid residue which distilled at 120 to 125° at 22 mm. It crystallized on cooling and after being washed with petroleum ether melted at 48 to 50°. Neutral equivalent found, 176.4; calcd. for trichloropropionic acid, 177.5.

Summary

Dichloro-2,3-butadiene-1,3 and trichloro-1,2,3-butadiene-1,3 have been prepared and their properties are described. The dichloro compound polymerizes more rapidly than chloroprene, the trichloro compound more slowly than chloroprene. The polymers are not rubber-like in either case. The chlorobutadienes now known may be arranged in the following order so far as their speed of spontaneous polymerization is concerned: $\beta,\gamma \gg \beta \gg \alpha,\beta,\gamma > \alpha \gg \alpha,\beta,\gamma,\delta$; and only the second member of the series (chloroprene) yields a definitely rubber-like polymer.

Bibliography and Remarks

(1) Carothers, Williams, Collins and Kirby, *Journ. Am. Chem. Soc.*, **53**, 4203 (1931); this volume. page 281.

(2) Carothers, Collins and Kirby, *Journ. Am. Chem. Soc.*, **55**, 789 (1933); this volume, page 314.

(3) *Cf. Ind. Eng. Chem.* **26**, 30 (1930).

(4) Willstätter and Bruce, *Ber.*, **40**, 3979 (1907).

(5) Müller and Hüther, *ibid.*, **64**, 589 (1931). *Cf.* also pentachloro and hexachlorobutadiene-1,3, Beilstein, 4th ed., Vol. 1, page 250.

(6) Whitby and Crozier, *Canadian J. Research*, **6**, 203 (1932); Whitby and Katz, *ibid.*, **6**, 398 (1932).

(7) Macallum and Whitby, *Trans. Roy. Soc. Can.*, **22**, 39 (1928); Fisher and Chittenden, *Ind. Eng. Chem.*, **22**, 869 (1930); Whitby and Gallay, *Can. J. Res.*, **6**, 280 (1932).

(8) This statement is also supported by observations on the following compounds in which the speed of polymerization is in the indicated order: $CH_2=CCl-CH=CH_2$, $CH_2=CCl-CMe=CH_2 \gg$ MeCH=CCl—CH=CH_2. CH_2=CCl—CMe=CHMe; Jacobson and Carothers, *Journ. Am. Chem. Soc.*, **55**, 1624 (1933); this volume, page 331; Carothers and Coffman, *Journ. Am. Chem. Soc.*, **54**, 4071 (1932).

(9) Lespieau and Prevost, *Compt. rend.*, **180**, 675 (1925).

(10) Carothers and Berchet, *Journ. Am. Chem. Soc.*, **55**, 1628 (1933); this volume, page 335.

(11) The structure CHCl=CH—CCl_2—CH_2Cl is not absolutely excluded but it seems very unlikely in view of the ease with which hydrogen chloride is lost from the group CH_2Cl—CHCl_2—.

(12) Carothers and Coffman, *Journ. Am. Chem. Soc.*, **54**, 4071 (1932); this volume, page 384.

(13) *Cf.* Muskat and Northrup, *Journ. Am. Chem. Soc.*, **52**, 4054 (1930).

XII.   The   Addition of Thio-p-cresol to Divinylacetylene*

The reaction of acetylene with itself to form an open-chain trimer was described in the first paper of this series (1). This compound, which has the molecular formula C_6H_6, contains no true acetylenic hydrogen; on hydrogenation it yields *n*-hexane; and it differs from the already known dimethyldiacetylene (I). It was therefore assigned the structure divinylacetylene (V) (2). The formulas II, III and IV, which are equally consistent with the above indicated properties, may perhaps be rejected as inherently unlikely; but in connection with a detailed study of the acety-

* W. H. Carothers, *Journ. Am. Chem. Soc.*, **55**, 2008–12 (1933); Communication No. 86 from the Experimental Station of E. I. du Pont de Nemours and Co.
Received September 29, 1932.   Published May 6, 1933.

lene trimer it seemed desirable to obtain direct and decisive experimental proof of the structure represented by formula V.

$$CH_3-C{\equiv}C-C{\equiv}C-CH_3$$
(I)

$$CH_2{=}C{=}C{=}C{=}CH-CH_3 \qquad CH_2{=}C{=}C{=}CH-CH{=}CH_2$$
(II) \qquad\qquad\qquad\qquad (III)

$$CH_2{=}C{=}CH-CH{=}C{=}CH_2 \qquad CH_2{=}CH-C{\equiv}C-CH{=}CH_2$$
(IV) \qquad\qquad\qquad\qquad (V)

Efforts in this direction at first met with difficulties: the compound has a great tendency to combine with itself in the presence of polar reagents, and it does not readily yield well-defined derivatives capable of easy identification, but a solution of the problem was found in the reaction with thio-p-cresol.

It has been shown by Posner (3) that vinyl compounds readily add thiophenols. In the case of styrene the reaction proceeds in accordance with the equation

$$C_6H_5CH{=}CH_2 + RSH \longrightarrow C_6H_5CH_2CH_2-S-R$$

Since the direction of addition alleged by Posner is exclusively the reverse of that required by well-known empirical generalizations and by currently popular electronic theories, the reaction was lately re-examined by Ashworth and Burkhardt with the result that Posner's conclusion was completely verified (4). Thus for the purpose in view the thiophenols as reagents have the advantage that their mode of addition is thoroughly established. Moreover, neither heat nor catalysts are required to induce their reaction with reactive carbon double bonds.

Acetylene trimer (one mole) readily dissolved thio-p-cresol (two moles). When the fluid mixture was allowed to stand at the laboratory temperature during ten days it gradually set to a magma of thin, transparent, leaf-like crystals, and the odor of the thiocresol almost entirely disappeared. The reaction was powerfully accelerated by light, and when the mixture (40 g. of thiocresol and 12.5 g. of acetylene trimer) in a reagent bottle of soda glass was directly illuminated by a mercury arc, reaction was complete in about five hours. The yield of crystalline product was about 80% of the theoretical, and some unidentified oily material was formed.

After crystallization from alcohol and from acetic acid the reaction product melted at 74.5–75.5°. Its composition agreed with that required for di-(p-tolylthio)-1,6-hexine-3 (VI). The verification of this structure through reactions described below decisively establishes the structure of the acetylene trimer as divinylacetylene (V). In its reaction with thio-p-

cresol the double bonds of divinylacetylene function independently of the triple bond. As will be shown in future papers, however, this behavior is not typical: other reactions indicate conjugation between the ethylenic and acetylenic linkages.

Di-(*p*-tolylthio)-1,6-hexine-3 readily adds two atoms⁻ of bromine to form the dibromide X. The action of potassium permanganate leads to a series of oxidation products. When the di-(*p*-tolylthio)-1,6-hexine-3 is dissolved in chloroform and shaken with cold dilute sulfuric acid to which permanganate is added in portions, the acetylenic disulfone, IX, is obtained. When carbon tetrachloride is used as the solvent in this process oxidation proceeds further and one obtains the diketone, VIII. In acetone solution, alkaline permanganate causes rupture of the carbon chain with the formation of the already known β-*p*-tolylsulfonepropionic acid (VII). The acetylenic disulfone, IX, readily adds bromine to form the dibromide XI, and sulfuric acid converts it into the ketone XII.

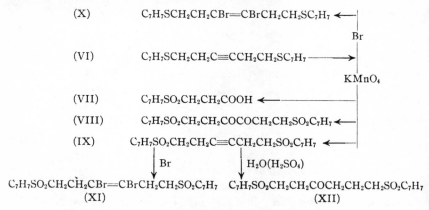

(X) $C_7H_7SCH_2CH_2CBr=CBrCH_2CH_2SC_7H_7$ ←|

                            Br

(VI) $C_7H_7SCH_2CH_2C{\equiv}CCH_2CH_2SC_7H_7$ ——→|

                            $KMnO_4$

(VII) $C_7H_7SO_2CH_2CH_2COOH$ ←————————|

(VIII) $C_7H_7SO_2CH_2CH_2COCOCH_2CH_2SO_2C_7H_7$ ←—|

(IX) $C_7H_7SO_2CH_2CH_2C{\equiv}CCH_2CH_2SO_2C_7H_7$ ←——|

            ↓ Br   ↓ $H_2O(H_2SO_4)$

$C_7H_7SO_2CH_2CH_2CBr=CBrCH_2CH_2SO_2C_7H_7$ $C_7H_7SO_2CH_2CH_2COCH_2CH_2CH_2SO_2C_7H_7$
            (XI)   (XII)

Di-(*p*-tolylthio)-1,6-hexine-3 (VI).—M. p. 74.5–75.5°.—*Anal.* Calcd. for $C_{20}H_{22}S_2$ C, 73.60; H, 6.79; S, 19.65; mol. wt., 326.3. Found: C, 73.50; H, 7.18; S, 20.1 mol. wt. (in freezing benzene), 291, 299, 302, 308.

Oxidation of Di-(*p*-tolylthio)-1,6-hexine-3 (VI) to *p*-Tolylsulfonepropionic Acid (VII).—Ten grams of di-(*p*-tolylthio)-1,6-hexine-3 suspended in 100 cc. of pure acetone in a bottle was constantly stirred and maintained below 32° while 41 g. of powdered potassium permanganate was added during two and a half hours. The permanganate was rapidly reduced. The manganese dioxide was removed by filtration and washed with acetone and water; the filtrates were evaporated, dissolved in water, treated with decolorizing carbon, filtered and acidified. The semi-crystalline precipitate was dissolved in a mixture of ether and chloroform, and the filtered solution was extracted with aqueous sodium bicarbonate solution. The aqueous solution was acidified. The precipitated solid (4 g.) melted at 102–113°. After crystallization from alcohol and then from water it was obtained in the form of needles melting at 110–113° (5).

Anal. Calcd. for $C_{10}H_{12}O_4S$: neutral equivalent, 228. Found: 234.

Partial Oxidation of Di-(p-tolylthio)-1,6-hexine-3 (VI). Formation of Di-(p-tolylsulfone)-1,6-hexandione-3,4 (VIII).—To 3.2 g. of di-(p-tolylthio)-1,6-hexine-3 in 30 cc. of carbon tetrachloride, 100 cc. of 3 N sulfuric acid was added and then ice and powdered potassium permanganate in small portions with constant shaking. About 6.5 g. of permanganate was consumed. The mixture was decolorized with aqueous sodium bisulfite. A white solid, which was suspended in the mixture, was filtered off, dissolved in chloroform, and precipitated with petroleum ether. After crystallization from ethylene chloride, glacial acetic acid, and butyl acetate, it was obtained in the form of fine, yellowish needles which softened at 197–200° and melted at 200–201°.

Anal. Calcd. for $C_{20}H_{22}O_6S_2$: C, 56.85; H, 5.22. Found: C, 56.37, 56.74; H, 5.23, 5.37.

This material was insoluble in ether, petroleum ether, ligroin, benzene, and carbon tetrachloride; readily soluble in warm chloroform and ethylene chloride. It reacted with phenylhydrazine to form a crystalline derivative melting above 215°.

Partial Oxidation of Di-(p-tolylthio)-1,6-hexine-3 (VI). Formation of Di-(p-tolylsulfone)-1,6-hexine-3 (IX).—Three grams of di-(p-tolylthio)-1,6-hexine-3 in 40 cc. of chloroform together with 100 cc. of 3 N sulfuric acid was vigorously shaken in a stoppered bottle while ice and powdered potassium permanganate were added in small portions until a purple color persisted in the mixture. A total of 6.7 g. of potassium permanganate was applied. The mixture was treated with sulfur dioxide to dissolve the precipitated manganese dioxide. The aqueous layer was discarded and the chloroform layer was washed with dilute alkali and water, dried, filtered and evaporated. Crystallization of the solid residue from dilute acetic acid gave 2.4 g. of white crystals melting at 150–158°; recrystallized from butyl acetate; needles, m. p. 157–158°; insoluble in boiling carbon tetrachloride.

Anal. Calcd. for $C_{20}H_{22}O_4S_2$: C, 61.50; H, 5.68; S, 16.43. Found: C, 61.60 61.48; H, 5.85, 6.17; S, 16.54, 16.68.

Action of Bromine on Di-(p-tolylsulfone)-1,6-hexine-3 (IX). Formation of Di-(p-tolylsulfone)-1,6-dibromo-3,4-hexene-3 (XI).—In 10 cc. of 0.13 M bromine in chloroform, 0.38 g. of di-(p-tolylsulfone)-1,6-hexine-3 was dissolved. The mixture was illuminated by a 40-watt Mazda lamp for fifteen minutes. About 40 cc. of petroleum ether was added and the crystalline precipitate was recrystallized from butyl acetate; m. p. 172.5–173.5°.

Anal. Calcd. for $C_{20}H_{22}O_4S_2Br_2$: Br, 29.06. Found: 28.87, 28.92.

Action of Sulfuric Acid on Di-(p-tolylsulfone)-1,6-hexine-3 (IX). Formation of Di-(p-tolylsulfone)-1,6-hexanone-3 (XII).—One gram of di-(p-tolylsulfone)-1,6-hexine-3 was dissolved in 10 cc. of cold concd. sulfuric acid. The colorless solution was allowed to stand for fifteen minutes and was then poured into 50 cc. of water. The resulting white precipitate was crystallized twice from alcohol; m. p. 134–135°.

Anal. Calcd. for $C_{20}H_{22}O_5S_2$: S, 15.77. Found: S, 16.41.

Action of Bromine on Di-(p-tolylthio)-1,6-hexine-3 (VI). Formation of Di-(p-tolylthio)-1,6-dibromo-3,4-hexene-3 (X).—Di-(p-tolylthio)-1,6-hexine-3 in dilute chloroform solution was allowed to stand for a few minutes with an excess of standard bromine, and the excess bromine was then titrated with standard thiosulfate. Approximately 1.05 moles of bromine was consumed by one mole of di-(p-tolylthio)-1,6-hexine-3.

To 1.6 g. of di-(*p*-tolylthio)-1,6-hexine-3 in 15 cc. of chloroform, 20 cc. of *N* bromine in chloroform was added. The solution was allowed to stand for five minutes. It was then shaken with 2 *N* thiosulfate solution, washed with water, dried with sodium sulfate, filtered and evaporated. From the residual oil, colorless crystals gradually separated. These were isolated and recrystallized from a mixture of alcohol and ether as transparent columns, m. p. 46–47.50°.

Anal. Calcd. for $C_{20}H_{22}S_2Br_2$: Br, 32.85. Found: Br, 32.98, 33.07.

Summary

The divinylacetylene described in a previous paper reacts with thio-*p*-cresol to form a crystalline derivative whose structure as di-(*p*-tolylthio)-1,6-hexine-3 is demonstrated by its oxidation to the known β-*p*-tolylsulfonepropionic acid. The following transformation products of the new derivative are described: di-(*p*-tolylthio)-1,6-dibromo-3,4-hexene-3, di-(*p*-tolylsulfone)-1,6-hexandione-3,4, di-(*p*-tolylsulfone)-1,6-hexine-3, di-(*p*-tolylsulfone)-1,6-dibromo-3,4-hexene-3, di-(*p*-tolyl-sulfone)-1,6-hexanone-3.

Bibliography and Remarks

(1) Nieuwland, Calcott, Downing and Carter, *Journ. Am. Chem. Soc.*, **53**, 4197 (1931).

(2) This compound has perhaps been obtained in small amounts, though not completely characterized, by Farmer, Laroia, Switz and Thorpe, *J. Chem. Soc.*, 2948 (1927). See also Mignonac and de Saint-Aunay, *Compt. rend.*, **188**, 959 (1929).

Lespieau and Guillemonat in a recent publication [*Compt. rend.*, **195**, 245 (1932)] have described divinylacetylene under the title "A New Isomer of Benzene." Apparently they have entirely overlooked the paper of Nieuwland, Calcott, Downing and Carter referred to above. They also state that they have obtained about 12 cc. of (impure) vinylacetylene, of which hitherto only 1.4 g. has been prepared (referring to Willstätter and Wirth). It may, therefore, be of interest to state that in the laboratories and works of the du Pont Company many hundreds of kilograms of vinylacetylene and divinylacetylene has been prepared by the process of Nieuwland, Calcott, Downing and Carter.

(3) Posner, *Ber.*, **38**, 646 (1905).

(4) Ashworth and Burkhardt, *J. Chem. Soc.*, 1791 (1928).

(5) Kohler and Reimer [*Am. Chem. J.*, **31**, 175 (1904)] describe β-*p*-tolylsulfonepropionic acid as needles melting at 110–113°. It is partially decomposed by repeated crystallization from boiling water.

XIII.   The Action of Chlorine on Divinylacetylene*

Scarcely any information has been recorded concerning the behavior of multiply conjugated enyne systems in reactions of addition. A system of this kind is found in divinylacetylene, which has been made available through discoveries described in the first paper of this series (1). In its reaction with thio-*p*-cresol only the ethylenic bonds of divinylacetylene are involved (2).

* D. D. Coffman and W. H. Carothers, *Journ. Am. Chem. Soc.*, **55**, 2040–7 (1933); Contribution No. 116 from the Experimental Station of E. I. du Pont de Nemours and Co.

Received October 22, 1932. Published May 6, 1933.

Chlorine behaves in a different manner. Reaction proceeds very rapidly, and a point of apparent saturation is reached when six atoms of chlorine have been absorbed. The product then consists of a crystalline, volatile hexachloride ($C_6H_6Cl_6$), and a pale yellow, very viscous sirup which also has the composition $C_6H_6Cl_6$. The sirup is not volatile and it has a higher molecular weight than that required by the simple formula. The crystalline hexachloride resists chlorination, ozonization and oxidation by hot nitric acid; and the action of alkaline permanganate leads to total destruction. Nevertheless, there can be no doubt that its structure is correctly represented by the formula hexachloro-1,2,3,4,5,6-hexene-3 (IV), and a study of the di- and tetrachlorides throws some light on the mechanism by which it is formed.

The di- and the tetrachlorides are both liquids, and they are not easily obtained in good yields since the application of as little as one mole of chlorine converts part of the reacting divinylacetylene to the hexachlorides. It appears on the other hand that only one dichloride and one tetrachloride are produced: the same tetrachloride is obtained by the chlorination of either divinylacetylene or its dichloride; and chlorination of the tetrachloride yields the hexachloride (IV) already referred to.

The dichloride still contains an open straight chain of six carbon atoms, since it can be hydrogenated to *n*-hexane. Oxidation with permanganate yields as the only identifiable product, chloroacetic acid; hence one of the chlorines is contained in the grouping $ClCH_2C=$ and there is no terminal CH_3 group. The other chlorine is attached to a doubly bonded carbon, since the action of boiling aqueous sodium carbonate liberates only one chloride ion per molecule of the compound. The only reasonable structure for the dichloride consistent with these facts is dichloro-1,4-hexatriene-2,3,5 (II).

I.	$CH_2=CH-C\equiv C-CH=CH_2$
II.	$ClCH_2-CH=C=CCl-CH=CH_2$
III.	$ClCH_2-CH=CCl-CCl=CH-CH_2Cl$
IV.	$ClCH_2-CHCl-CCl=CCl-CHCl-CH_2Cl$
IIa.	$ClCH_2-CHCl-C\equiv C-CH=CH_2$
IIb.	$ClCH_2CH=C=C=CH-CH_2Cl$
IIIa.	$ClCH_2-CH=C=CCl-CHCl-CH_2Cl$
IIIb.	$ClCH_2-CH=CCl-CCl_2-CH=CH_2$
IVa.	$ClCH_2-CHCl-CCl_2-CCl=CH-CH_2Cl$
V.	$CH_2=CH-CCl=CCl-CH=CH_2$
VI.	$CH_2=CH-CCl=C=C=CH_2$
VII.	$ClCH_2-CH=CH-CCl_2-CH=CH_2$
VIII.	$CH_2=C=CCl-CCl=CH-CH_2Cl$
IX.	$CH_2=C=CCl-CCl=C=CH_2$

The tetrachloride of divinylacetylene when oxidized with potassium permanganate also yields as the only identifiable product chloroacetic acid, and hydrolysis with aqueous sodium carbonate shows that two of the chlorine atoms are reactive and the other two inactive. This behavior indicates that it has the structure tetrachloro-1,3,4,6-hexadiene-2,4 (III).

Formally, the relation between the three chlorides and the parent hydrocarbon is that each member of the series is derived from the preceding one by a process of 1,4 addition. It is impossible to demonstrate conclusively that they actually originate by this mechanism. Addition either 1,2 or 1,6 followed by an α,γ shift would lead to the same result. The dichloride (II) might arise thus from IIa or IIb, the tetrachloride from IIIa or IIIb and the hexachloride from IVa.

However, this dual mechanism appears highly improbable since it provides no visible reason for the fact that the observed products are without exception compounds that would result from their precursors by a process of 1,4 addition. There are moreover other independent facts to indicate that 1,4 addition may be a favorite mode of reaction for enyne compounds. Thus the action of hydrogen chloride on vinylacetylene yields chloro-4-butadiene-1,2, $CH_2=C=CH-CH_2Cl$ (3), and this must be a primary product since in the rearranged halide, $CH_2=CCl-CH=CH_2$, the chlorine is attached to a doubly bonded carbon where its mobility is lost. It is perhaps significant in this connection also that the dichloride (II) of divinylacetylene shows no tendency to rearrange into the completely conjugated triene (V) under experimental conditions that might be expected to favor especially such a transformation.

When the dichloride (II) is treated with alcoholic potash it rapidly loses one molecule of hydrogen chloride. The terminal chlorine and its adjacent hydrogen are involved in this reaction, and the product has the structure chloro-3-hexatetraene-1,3,4,5 (VI). When hydrogenated it is converted into n-hexane, and oxidation yields oxalic acid.

In the presence of cuprous chloride the dichloride (II) absorbs one molecule of hydrogen chloride from aqueous hydrochloric acid. In the resulting trichloro compound all three of the chlorines are reactive toward aqueous sodium carbonate. It is therefore the central double bond bearing the inactive chlorine atom of the dichloride which disappears, and the trichloro compound must have the structure trichloro-1,4,4-hexadiene-2,5 (VII). When oxidized it yields chloroacetic acid.

The tetrachloride (III) of divinylacetylene also loses hydrogen chloride when treated with alcoholic potash and yields a trichloro and a dichloro compound. In this case only two positions are available for the loss of hydrogen chloride, namely, the 1,2 and 5,6. The trichloro compound must therefore be trichloro-1,3,4-hexatriene-2,4,5 (VIII) and the dichloro compound must be dichloro-3,4-hexatetraene-1,2,4,5 (IX).

The chloro compounds described above furnish several novel and unusual examples of triad systems potentially capable of allylic rearrangement. One rather striking anomaly that appears in this connection has already been referred to. In the dichloride, II, the terminal chlorine atom shows no tendency to undergo a shift to the γ position, in spite of the fact that such a shift would result in a completely conjugated triene. It is true that the γ carbon is at the center of a pair of twinned double bonds, but this in itself cannot be responsible for the absence of a tendency to rearrange since precisely the same configuration is found in chloro-4-butadiene-1,2, $CH_2\!=\!C\!=\!CH\!-\!CH_2Cl$, which undergoes the α,γ transposition with great facility. In the trichloro hexadiene, VII, also, a triad shift of one of the central chlorines would bring the double bonds into the conjugated configuration. No special attempts have been made to bring about rearrangement in this case, but it has not been observed to occur spontaneously. The absence of spontaneous rearrangements in the compounds III and VIII is not surprising, since a shift of the mobile chlorine atom in these compounds would destroy the conjugation of the double bonds.

Four of the chloro compounds described above (II, VI, VIII and IX) exhibit a structural feature that has, so far as we are aware, not been exemplified in any compounds described hitherto. They contain a pair of conjugated double bonds and at least one of the pair is the first member of a series of two or more contiguous double bonds, thus, $-C\!=\!C\!=\!C\!-\!C\!=\!C\!-$ The question arises, can the carbon atom bearing the twinned double bonds function as one of the ends of the conjugated system? The behavior of the dichloride II toward chlorine provides an affirmative answer to this question. The chlorine here almost certainly adds 1,4 to produce the tetrachloride, III. On the other hand, the addition of hydrogen chloride to the dichloride apparently involves only the 3 and 4 positions. The trichloro compound obtained (VII) is the compound that would be produced by 3,4 addition, and it is not likely that it arises by 1,4 addition followed by an allylic transposition, because the product, $ClCH_2\!-\!CH\!=\!CH\!-\!CCl\!=\!CH\!-\!CH_2Cl$, which would be formed by 1,4 addition, is precisely analogous to dichloro-1,3-butene-2, $CH_3\!-\!CCl\!=\!$

CH—CH$_2$Cl, and deliberate attempts to rearrange this compound have given negative results (4).

With two exceptions (IV and VII) all of the above described chloro compounds contain at least one pair of conjugated double bonds. Nevertheless, none of them reacts either with naphthoquinone or with maleic anhydride at 100°. This failure cannot be ascribed to the fact that in several cases the conjugated system terminates in a series of contiguous double bonds, since, as has already been pointed out above, this arrangement does not preclude 1,4 addition; moreover, this arrangement is not present in the tetrachloride III which also fails to react. Similar failures have been reported before. Thus, X, XI and XII all react very

$$
\begin{array}{ccc}
\text{RCH}=\text{C}-\text{CH}=\text{CH}_2 & \text{CH}_2=\text{C}-\text{C}=\text{CH}_2 & \text{CH}_2=\text{C}-\text{C}=\text{CH}-\text{CH}_3 \\
\quad\ \ | & \quad\ |\ \ \ | & \quad\ |\ \ \ | \\
\quad\ \ \text{Cl} & \quad\ \text{Cl}\ \text{CH}_3 & \quad\ \text{Cl}\ \text{CH}_3 \\
(\text{R}=\text{H, CH}_3,\text{ C}_2\text{H}_5,\text{ C}_4\text{H}_9,\text{ or C}_7\text{H}_{15}) & (\textbf{XI}) & (\textbf{XII}) \\
(\textbf{X})
\end{array}
$$

smoothly with naphthoquinone (5) but XIII and XIV do not (6). It

$$
\begin{array}{cc}
\text{ClCH}=\text{CH}-\text{CH}=\text{CH}_2 & \text{CH}_2=\text{C}-\text{C}=\text{CH}_2 \\
 & \qquad\ |\ \ \ | \\
 & \qquad\ \text{Cl}\ \text{Cl} \\
(\textbf{XIII}) & (\textbf{XIV})
\end{array}
$$

is evident that the diene reaction can be regarded as diagnostic only if it leads to positive results; comparatively trivial substitutions sometimes cause it to fail.

Substitution similarly has a profound influence on the tendency of dienes to polymerize. Of the above described chloro compounds only the dichlorotetraene (IX) shows any great tendency to polymerize spontaneously. In the course of twenty-four hours at the ordinary conditions it was converted into a dark brown, hard, brittle resin. The dichloride II polymerized very slowly on standing, and after three months it was a viscous sirup. The polymerization was greatly accelerated by increased pressure. At 6000 atmospheres and 25° it was changed in twenty-three hours to a yellow, elastic, plastic mass. The chloro-3-hexatetraene-1,3,4,5 at 6000 atmospheres and 25° was changed in twenty hours to a hard coke-like mass. Pressure was not applied to the other compounds, but none of them showed any signs of polymerizing when allowed to stand for several weeks. We are indebted to Dr. H. W. Starkweather for the experiments at high pressure.

Experimental Part

Preparation and Proof of Structure of Dichloro-1,4-hexatriene-2,3,5 (II)

Preparation of Dichloro-1,4-hexatriene-2,3,5 by Chlorination of Divinylacetylene.— Chlorine was passed into a solution of 400 g. (5 moles) of divinylacetylene in 300 g. of dry carbon tetrachloride at −50°. During five hours, 436 g. (6.1 moles) of chlorine was absorbed. Fractionation of the reaction product gave 191 g. (1.28 moles) of dichloro-1,4-hexatriene-2,3,5 boiling at 45–50° (3 mm.) (25% of the theoretical amount). Continued distillation of the residue yielded 57 g. of higher boiling material (b. p. 50–115° (3 mm.)) which was a mixture of the tetrachloro and hexachloro derivatives. The remainder consisted of undistillable material.

A chlorination similar to that described above was carried out by allowing only 332 g. (4.67 moles) of chlorine to be absorbed during five hours at −50°. There was obtained 145 g. (0.97 mole) of the dichloro derivative (19% of the theoretical amount) and 61 g. of tetrachloro-1,3,4,6-hexadiene-2,4. Chlorination of divinylacetylene at 0° (mole for mole) in carbon tetrachloride gave the dichloride in 20% yield.

The properties of dichloro-1,4-hexatriene-2,3,5 are: colorless mobile liquid with a sharp characteristic odor; b. p. 38° at 1 mm., 45–46° at 3 mm.; d_4^{20} 1.1807; n_D^{20} 1.5195; M_R calcd. 38.24; M_R found, 38.34. On standing it very slowly polymerized, and after three months it had changed to a viscous sirup.

The same compound was obtained in very small yield by the action of aqueous hypochlorous acid on divinylacetylene.

Anal. Calcd. for $C_6H_6Cl_2$: C, 48.35; H, 4.03; Cl, 47.62; mol. wt., 149. Found: C, 47.88; H, 4.00; Cl, 47.59; mol. wt. 155.

Reduction of Dichloro-1,4-hexatriene-2,3,5- to *n*-Hexane.—The dichloro compound (25 g., 0.168 mole) in 50 cc. of ethyl acetate (with 0.16 g. PtO₂) absorbed 0.484 mole of hydrogen during three hours (calcd. 0.672 mole). A large amount of hydrogen chloride was formed during the reduction. The filtered ethyl acetate solution was fractionated, and the fraction boiling at 50–75° was collected and allowed to stand over aqueous alkali until saponification of the ester was complete. The water insoluble layer was then separated and further dried over solid alkali. There was obtained 8 g. of *n*-hexane, b. p. 69–70°; d_4^{20} 0.677; n_D^{20} 1.3812. There was also obtained 15 g. of higher boiling material (b. p. range 30–80° at 21 mm.) from which no constant boiling fraction was received.

The Reactivity of the Halogens in Dichloro-1,4-hexatriene-2,3,5. Hydrolysis by Sodium Carbonate.—The dichloro compound (50 g., 0.333 mole) was refluxed with agitation during eight hours with 300 cc. of water containing 72 g. (0.67 mole) of sodium carbonate. Analysis of the aqueous solution showed that 0.281 mole of sodium chloride was formed. Hence only one active halogen atom is present in $C_6H_6Cl_2$. The hydrolysis product was a soft, sticky resin.

Permanganate Oxidation of Dichloro-1,4-hexatriene-2,3,5 to Chloroacetic Acid.— The dichloro compound 50 g. (0.33 mole) completely reduced 300 g. of potassium permanganate added with agitation in small portions to the aqueous solution (200 cc.) during three hours at 35–40°. Sulfur dioxide was passed into the reaction mixture; the manganese dioxide was filtered, and repeatedly washed. Continuous ether extraction of the strongly acidified aqueous solution gave 15 g. of acidic material, which was identified as chloroacetic acid, b. p. 61 to 63° at 2 mm.; m. p. 58–59°.

To complete the identification the chloroacetic acid was converted, through its chloride, into phenylglycocoll anilide, which showed the correct melting point and mixed melting point.

Chlorination of Dichloro-1,4-hexatriene-2,3,5 to Tetrachloro-1,3,4,6-hexadiene-2,4.—Chlorine was passed into 100 g. (0.67 mole) of $C_6H_6Cl_2$ in 54 g. of carbon tetrachloride at 5 to 10° until 42 g. (1.18 moles) of chlorine was absorbed. Fractionation of the product gave 10 g. of tetrachloro-1,3,4,6-hexadiene-2,4; b. p. 85 to 92° at 3 mm.; d_4^{20} 1.4902; n_D^{20} 1.5458. Part of the original dichloro compound (21 g.) was recovered. The remainder of the product consisted of higher boiling residue. The tetrachloro derivative is further described below.

Preparation and Proof of Structure of Chloro-3-hexatetraene-1,3,4,5 (VI)

Chloro-3-hexatetraene-1,3,4,5 Obtained by the Action of Alcoholic Alkali on Dichloro-1,4-hexatriene-2,3,5.—The dichloro compound (105 g., 0.67 mole) freshly distilled was added during one and one-half hours to a solution of 43 g. of potassium hydroxide (15% excess) in 200 cc. of absolute methanol with vigorous agitation at 10–15°. Stirring was continued at 15° during two hours. The insoluble potassium chloride was filtered off, washed with methanol, and dried. The yield of potassium chloride was 47 g. (94% of the theoretical amount). The methanol filtrate was poured into 500 cc. of water, and the water-insoluble material separated and dried. The yield of crude material was 74 g.

The pure chloro-3-hexatetraene-1,3,4,5 was obtained as a colorless liquid; b. p. 127° at 760 mm. (with decomposition), 82° at 163 mm., 55° at 54 mm.; d_4^{20} 0.9997; n_D^{20} 1.5280; M_R calcd., 32.91; M_R found, 34.64.

The same compound was obtained by the action of sodium methylate (in absolute methanol) on dichloro-1,4-hexatriene-2,3,5.

Anal. Calcd. for C_6H_5Cl: C, 64.02; H, 4.45; Cl, 31.53; mol. wt., 112.5. Found: C, 63.99; H, 4.61; Cl, 31.61; mol. wt. (cryoscopic in benzene), 110.

Reduction of Chloro-3-hexatetraene-1,3,4,5 to n-Hexane.—The chloro compound (13 g.) absorbed 87% (0.403 mole) of the theoretical amount of hydrogen (catalyst 0.15 g. of PtO_2) in 25 cc. of ethyl acetate during three hours. A large amount of hydrogen chloride was formed. The ethyl acetate solution was distilled and the distillate up to 80° was collected and allowed to stand over aqueous alkali during four hours. The unsaponifiable material was separated and allowed to stand over solid potassium hydroxide during fifteen hours. There was obtained 2 g. of n-hexane, b. p. 64–70°; d_4^{20} 0.691; n_D^{20} 1.3766. A small amount of high boiling residue was obtained but not identified.

Permanganate Oxidation of Chloro-3-hexatetraene-1,3,4,5 to Oxalic Acid.—The oxidation was made by adding in small portions 224 g. of potassium permanganate to a vigorously agitated, aqueous solution (200 cc.)of 80 g. of potassium carbonate and 21 g. of chloro-3-hexatetraene-1,3,4,5 at 35–45°. After ten hours the solution was decolorized with sulfur dioxide and the manganese dioxide filtered and repeatedly washed. The combined filtrates were strongly acidified with sulfuric acid, while the reaction mixture was cooled in an ice-bath. Continuous ether extraction of the acidified aqueous solution during fifteen hours gave 15 g. of oxalic acid dihydrate (calcd. 25 g.). The acid melted at 101° (copper block).

Neutral equivalent. Subs., 0.2916 g. Required 41.10 cc. of 0.1117 N NaOH Calcd. for $H_2C_2O_4\cdot2H_2O$; neutral equivalent, 63.0. Found: 63.5.

Preparation and Proof of Structure of Trichloro-1,4,4-hexadiene-2,5 (VII)

Addition of Hydrogen Chloride to Dichloro-1,4-hexatriene-2,3,5.—Dichloro-1,4-hexatriene-2,3,5 (75 g., 0.5 mole) was shaken during twelve hours at 27° with 30 g. of cuprous chloride and 75 cc. of hydrochloric acid (sp. gr. 1.18). The water insoluble layer was separated, washed and dried. Fractionation gave 20 g. of the original dichloro compound and 28 g. of trichloro-1,4,4-hexadiene-2,5, which boiled at 100–103° at 4 mm.; d_4^{20} 1.3036; n_D^{20} 1.5585; M_R calcd. 43.58; M_R found, 45.88.

Anal. Calcd. for $C_6H_7Cl_3$: C, 38.83; H, 3.78; Cl, 57.39; mol. wt., 185.5. Found: C, 38.87; H, 3.83; Cl, 57.38; mol. wt. (cryoscopic in benzene), 185.

Permanganate Oxidation of Trichloro-1,4,4-hexadiene-2,5 to Chloroacetic Acid.— The trichloro compound (18 g.) reduced 84 g. of potassium permanganate (added in small portions with vigorous agitation) in alkaline solution during four hours at 30–40°. The filtrates obtained after separating and washing the manganese dioxide were acidified and subjected to continuous ether extraction during fifteen hours. From the ether extract there was obtained 10 g. of chloroacetic acid, which boiled at 65–68° at 4 mm. and melted at 58–59°. It was further identified by conversion through its acid chloride into chloroacetanilide, which showed the correct melting point, 134–135°.

The Reactivity of the Halogens in Trichloro-1,4,4-hexadiene-2,5. Hydrolysis by Sodium Carbonate.—The trichloro compound (5.81 g., 0.0313 mole) was refluxed during seven hours with agitation in 110 cc. of water containing 8.6 g. of sodium carbonate. Analysis of the aqueous solution showed that 0.0763 mole of sodium chloride was formed. Therefore three active halogen atoms were present.

Preparation and Proof of Structure of Tetrachloro-1,3,4,6-hexadiene-2,4 (III)

Chlorination of Divinylacetylene to Obtain Tetrachloro-1,3,4,6-hexadiene-2,4.— Chlorine was passed into divinylacetylene (234 g., 3 moles) at −40 to −50° with vigorous agitation. During five and one-half hours 340 g. (4.8 moles) of chlorine was absorbed, corresponding to 80% chlorination to the tetrachloro derivative. Considerable loss of hydrogen chloride occurred. Distillation gave 119 g. of crude dichloro-1,4-hexatriene-2,3,5 and 96 g. of very crude tetrachloro derivative. Fractionation of 160 g. of the crude tetrachloro derivative (b. p. 50–120° at 3 mm.) gave 50 g. of tetrachloro-1,3,4,6-hexadiene-2,4 boiling at 84–89° at 2 mm.; d_4^{20} 1.4013; n_D^{20} 1.5465; M_R calcd., 48.43; M_R found, 49.71.

Anal. Calcd. for $C_6H_6Cl_4$: C, 32.76; H, 2.73; Cl, 64.51; mol. wt., 220. Found: C, 32.80; H, 2.49; Cl, 63.76; mol. wt. (cryoscopic in benzene), 222.

Permanaganate Oxidation of Tetrachloro-1,3,4,6-hexadiene-2,4 to Chloroacetic Acid.—The tetrachloroderivative (58 g.) completely reduced 220 g. of potassium permanganate (added in small portions with vigorous agitation) during five hours at 35–40°. The filtrate obtained after separating and washing the manganese dioxide was strongly acidified and subjected to continuous ether extraction during fifteen hours. The ether extract gave 20 g. of chloroacetic acid which boiled at 64–66° at 3 mm. and melted at 58–59° after recrystallization from petroleum ether.

The Reactivity of the Halogens in Tetrachloro-1,3,4,6-hexadiene-2,4. Hydrolysis by Sodium Carbonate.—The tetrachloro compound (5 g., 0.0228 mole) was refluxed during eight hours with agitation in 100 cc. of water containing 7 g. (0.066 mole) of sodium carbonate. Analysis of the aqueous solution showed that 0.0414 mole of sodium chloride was formed. Therefore two active halogen atoms are present in the tetrachloride.

The Chlorination of Tetrachloro-1,3,4,6-hexadiene-2,4 to Hexachloro-1,2,3,4,5,6-hexene-3 (IV)

The Chlorination of Tetrachloro-1,3,4,6-hexadiene-2,4 to Hexachloro-1,2,3,4,5,6-hexene-3 (IV).—Chlorine was passed into 27 g. (0.12 mole) of tetrachloro-1,3,4,6-hexadiene-2,4, during eight hours at 60–70°. The product was distilled and from the portion boiling at 95–115° at 2 mm. was obtained 8 g. of pure hexachloro-1,2,3,4,5,6-hexene-3 which melted at 57 to 58° after two crystallizations from petroleum ether; yield, 23%. The remainder of the product was a viscous liquid not further investigated. The hexachloride is described in more detail below.

The Behavior of Tetrachloro-1,3,4,6-hexadiene-2,4 with Alcoholic Alkali. Trichloro-1,3,4-hexatriene-2,4,5 (VIII) and Dichloro-3,4-hexatetraene-1,2,4,5 (IX)

The Behavior of Tetrachloro-1,3,4,6-hexadiene-2,4 with Alcoholic Alkali. Trichloro-1,3,4-hexatriene-2,4,5 (VIII) and Dichloro-3,4-hexatetraene-1,2,4,5 (IX)

The tetrachloro compound (75 g., 0.34 mole) was added during two hours to a solution of 44 g. of potassium hydroxide (15% excess) in 200 cc. of absolute methanol with vigorous agitation at 10–15°. The reaction was allowed to proceed for one hour after which the potassium chloride was filtered off (KCl, 36 g. or 48%). The methanol filtrate was poured into water, and the water-insoluble layer was separated, dried and distilled. From the crude material (50 g.) two fractions were obtained; one was trichloro-1,3,4-hexatriene-2,4,5 (25 g.) which boiled at 50° at 1 mm.; d_4^{20} 1.3132; n_D^{20} 1.5517; M_R calcd. 43.11; M_R found, 44.61. The other was dichloro-3,4-hexatetraene-1,2,4,5 (5 g.) which boiled at 38–40° at 8 mm.; d_4^{20} 1.1819; n_D^{20} 1.5456; M_R calcd. 37.77; M_R found, 39.41.

Trichloro-1,3,4-hexatriene-2,4,5.—*Anal.* Calcd. for $C_6H_5Cl_3$: C, 39.26; H, 2.73; Cl, 58.01; mol. wt., 183.4. Found: C, 39.70; H, 2.75; Cl, 57.52; mol. wt. (cryoscopic in benzene), 190.

Dichloro-3,4-hexatetraene-1,2,4,5.—*Anal.* Calcd. for $C_6H_4Cl_2$: Cl, 48.27. Found. Cl, 48.60, 48.32 (7).

The Chlorination of Divinylacetylene at 60–70° to Obtain Hexachloro-1,2,3,4,5,6-hexene-3 (IV)

The Chlorination of Divinylacetylene at 60–70° to Obtain Hexachloro-1,2,3,4,5,6-hexene-3 (IV).—Divinylacetylene (100 g., 1.28 moles) in 160 g. of carbon tetrachloride absorbed 197 g. (2.8 moles) of chlorine during twelve hours. Distillation of the product gave 30 g. (10% of the theoretical amount) of the hexachloride, which boiled at 110 to 112° at 2 mm. After recrystallization from petroleum ether the white crystals melted at 58 to 59°. The major part (150 g.) of the product from this reaction was an almost colorless, viscous sirup. This is described in more detail below.

Hexachloro-1,2,3,4,5,6-hexene-3 is not attacked by ozone or by hot nitric acid, and the action of alkaline permanganate leads to total destruction. It fails to chlorinate further even at elevated temperatures in the presence of light.

Anal. Calcd. for $C_6H_6Cl_6$: C, 24.76; H, 2.06; Cl, 73.16. Found: C, 25.14; H 2.18; Cl, 73.37.

The viscous sirup that formed the major part of the product of the above-described reaction was obtained as a residue which remained after the removal of the hexachloro-1,2,3,4,5,6-hexene-3 by distillation. This material could not be distilled even at 185° at a pressure of 2 mm. although it darkened rapidly and showed a tendency to liberate hydrogen chloride under these conditions. Its chlorine content was generally 1–3% less than that of the pure hexachloride, and like the latter it showed no tendency to absorb more chlorine even at elevated temperature. This sirup probably results from the coupling together of two or more of the six-carbon atom chains at some stage of the chlorination.

Molecular weight determinations were made on two specimens of the sirup both of which contained a considerable proportion of the dissolved hexachloride. The values obtained were (a) Cl, 68.90%; mol. wt. (cryoscopic in benzene), 360; (b) Cl, 72.90%; mol. wt., 370.

Summary

Divinylacetylene reacts with chlorine to form a liquid dichloride and tetrachloride, a crystalline hexachloride, and a sirupy product having approximately the composition of the hexachloride but a higher molecular weight. The three monomeric products are each formed from their precursors by 1,4 addition and they have the formulas dichloro-1,4-hexatriene-2,3,5; tetrachloro-1,3,4,6-hexadiene-2,4; and hexachloro-1,2,3,4,-5,6-hexene-3. The following transformation products of these compounds are described: chloro-3-hexatetraene-1,3,4,5; trichloro-1,4,4-hexadiene-2,5; trichloro-1,3,4-hexatriene-2,4,5; and dichloro-3,4-hexatetraene-1,2,4,5.

Bibliography and Remarks

(1) Nieuwland, Calcott, Downing and Carter, *Journ. Am. Chem. Soc.*, **53**, 4197 (1931).
(2) Carothers, *ibid.*, **55**, 2008 (1933); this volume, page 344.
(3) Carothers, Berchet, and Collins, *Journ. Am. Chem. Soc.*, **54**, 4066 (1932); this volume, page 306.
(4) Unpublished results.
(5) Carothers and Coffman, *Journ. Am. Chem. Soc.*, **54**, 4071 (1932); this volume, page 384; Jacobson and Carothers, *Journ. Am. Chem. Soc.*, **54**, 1624 (1933); this volume, page 331.
(6) Carothers and Berchet, *Journ. Am. Chem. Soc.*, **55**, 2004 (1933); this volume, page 340.
(7) The analyst found great difficulty in the proper combustion of this compound. The carbon percentage was usually lower and the hydrogen percentage higher than the theoretical amounts.

XIV.   The Dihydrochloride of Divinylacetylene*

The addition of thio-p-cresol (1) to divinylacetylene (2) involves only the terminal ethylenic linkage. Chlorine on the other hand reacts by 1,4 addition to yield first a dichloride and then successively a tetra- and a hexachloride (3). Study of the action of hydrogen chloride on divinylacetylene has furnished further information concerning the behavior of this multiply conjugated enyne system.

Divinylacetylene reacts fairly rapidly when shaken with aqueous hydrochloric acid at room temperature. As in the case of vinylacetylene (4), the reaction is considerably accelerated by cuprous chloride. On the other hand, the same product is obtained whether cuprous chloride is present or not. Under ordinary conditions a point of apparent saturation is reached when two molecules of hydrogen chloride have been absorbed.

* D. D. Coffman, J. A. Nieuwland and W. H. Carothers, *Journ. Am. Chem. Soc.*, 55, 2048–51 (1933); Contribution No. 117 from the Experimental Station of E. I du Pont de Nemours and Co.
Received October 22, 1932.   Published May 6, 1933

The first step in the reaction undoubtedly involves the formation of a monohydrochloride, but apparently this reacts more readily than the parent hydrocarbon. Consequently the chief product is dihydrochloride even when a deficiency of hydrochloric acid is used. The monohydrochloride is produced in poor yields, and it is so difficult to separate from the unchanged hydrocarbon that it has not yet been obtained in a state of purity.

Purification of the dihydrochloride to constant composition requires rather sharp fractionation, and the boiling range (80 to 82° at 17 mm.) is wide enough to suggest the presence of geometrical isomers. Only one chlorine atom of the dihydrochloride is reactive. When heated with naphthoquinone or maleic anhydride the only evidence of reaction is the formation of a small amount of dark gummy material. However, as has already been pointed out (3), negative results in the Diels–Alder reaction are of no value in the demonstration of structure, since many 1,3-dienes fail to react. The compound is stable. It shows no tendency to polymerize spontaneously, but a sample that had been submitted to a pressure of 6000 atmospheres for ninety-three hours at 49° was changed to a dark, somewhat elastic and only slightly plastic mass. When heated with sodium acetate in acetic acid it yields a monoacetate, and the second chlorine atom remains unaffected. Similarly the action of methyl alcoholic potash results in a monomethyl ether. When oxidized with permanganate the dihydrochloride yields acetic acid and chloroacetic acid.

These facts furnish a basis for a discussion of its structure. We assume that the hydrogen atoms of the hydrocarbon retain their original positions during reaction, and the results of oxidation then indicate that the dihydrochloride contains the residues $CH_3—CH=\overset{|}{C}—$ and $ClCH_2—CH_2=\overset{|}{C}—$. Hence the chain has the formula $CH_3—CH=\overset{|}{C}—\overset{|}{C}=CH—CH_2Cl$. Only a hydrogen atom and a chlorine atom remain to be accounted for, and one of these must be attached to the third carbon atom and the other to the fourth carbon atom. No direct experimental method is available for a decision between these two alternatives, but a satisfactory conclusion can be reached by a consideration of the probable mechanism of the reaction. In the following chart the two alternative formulas, dichloro-1,3-hexadiene-2,4 and dichloro-1,4-hexadiene-2,4 are designated as A and B, respectively; the positions of the hydrocarbon chain are marked with the numbers 1 to 6; and the H and Cl of the addendum are called a and b, respectively. Addition at the first stage may be 1,2,3,4, 1,4 or 1,6 and it must bring the chlorine atom to position 1 or position 3 (or 4). The formulas I to IV therefore include all the reasonable possibilities for the monohydrochloride. For further reaction the possibilities are

ADDITION OF HYDROGEN CHLORIDE TO DIVINYLACETYLENE

No.	Mode of addition	Monohydrochloride produced	Mode of addition	Dihydrochloride produced	
I	1a, 4b	CH_2—CH=C=CCl—CH=CH$_2$	3a, 6b	CH_2—CH=CH—CCl=CH—CH$_2$Cl	A
II	4a, 1b	CH_2Cl—CH=C=CH—CH—CH$_2$	6a, 3b	ClCH$_2$—CH=CCl—CH=CH—CH$_2$	A
III	3a, 4b	CH_2=CH—CH=CCl—CH=CH$_2$	1a, 6b	CH_2—CH=CH—CCl=CH—CH$_2$Cl	A
			6a, 1b	ClCH$_2$—CH=CH—CCl=CH—CH$_2$	B
IV	1a, 6b	CH_2—CH=C=C=CH—CH$_2$Cl	3a, 4b	CH_2—CH=CH—CCl=CH—CH$_2$Cl	A
			4a, 3b	CH_2—CH=CCl—CH=CH—CH$_2$Cl	B

I by 1,4 addition (3a, 6b) gives A   III by 1,6 addition (6a, 1b) gives B
II by 1,4 addition (6a, 3b) gives A   IV by 1,2 addition (3a, 4b) gives A
III by 1,6 addition (1a, 6b) gives A   IV by 1,2 addition (4a, 3b) gives B

Thus of the six pairs of reactions that might lead to A or B, four lead to A and only two to B, and probability is two to one in favor of A as the formula of the dihydrochloride. Further than this, however, there are good reasons for rejecting both III and IV as possibilities. Evidence of 1,6 addition in the reactions of divinylacetylene has never been observed, nor of 1,2 addition at the acetylenic linkage of either vinylacetylene or divinylacetylene. Moreover, 1,2 addition followed by 1,6 addition and 1,6 addition followed by 1,2 addition both appear inherently improbable. The addition of chlorine to divinylacetylene proceeds 1,4: CH_2=CH— C≡C—CH=CH$_2$ —→ CH_2Cl—CH=C=CCl—CH=CH$_2$ (3); and the primary step in the action of hydrogen chloride on vinylacetylene is 1,4 addition: CH≡C—CH=CH$_2$ —→ CH_2=C=CH—CH$_2$Cl (4). It seems certain therefore that the dihydrochloride of divinylacetylene is dichloro-1,3-hexadiene-2,4 (A) and the mechanism by which it is formed is most probably represented by II.

Experimental Part

The Addition of Hydrogen Chloride to Divinylacetylene in the Presence of Cuprous Chloride.—Divinylacetylene (80 g.) was shaken at either 0° or room temperature during one hour with 1.5 liters of 12 N hydrochloric acid containing 300 g. of cuprous chloride. The reaction mixture was then subjected to steam distillation. By this process 80 g. of crude dihydrochloride was obtained (53% of the theoretical amount). Fractionation of 241 g. of material (b. p. 70–80° at 11 mm.) through an efficient column gave 170 g. of analytically pure dichloro-1,3-hexadiene-2,4 which boiled at 80–82° at 17 mm.; d_4^{20} 1.1456; n_D^{20} 1.5271; M_R calcd. 38.70; M_R found, 40.42.

Anal. (Carius). Subs., 0.1201 g.; AgCl, 0.2305 g. Calcd. for $C_6H_8Cl_2$: Cl, 46.99. Found: Cl, 47.47.

The Addition of Hydrogen Chloride to Divinylacetylene in the Presence of Calcium Chloride.—Six pressure bottles each containing 150 cc. of hydrochloric acid (sp. gr. 1.187), 30 g. of anhydrous calcium chloride and 80 g. of divinylacetylene were shaken at

25° during one hundred and ten hours. The water-insoluble layer was separated, washed with aqueous sodium carbonate and dried. Distillation gave 242 g. of material boiling above 50° at 70 mm.

Fractionation through an efficient column gave 94 g. of material boiling at 50–60° at 52 mm., and 60 g. of dichloro-1,3-hexadiene-2,4 which boiled at 80–82° at 17 mm. The residue weighed 60 g. The yield of dihydrochloride was 6.8% of the theoretical amount.

Repeated fractionation of the low boiling material (b. p. 50–60° at 52 mm.) failed to give a product having the composition of the monohydrochloride of divinylacetylene (C_6H_7Cl). The chlorine analysis of the samples collected was always less than the theoretical amount for the monohydrochloride, indicating that hydrocarbon material was present.

The Permanganate Oxidation of Dichloro-1,3-hexadiene-2,4 to Obtain Acetic and Chloroacetic Acids.—An analytically pure sample of the dihydrochloride (100 g.) was introduced into an aqueous solution (400 cc.) containing 46 g. of potassium carbonate. Potassium permanganate (486 g.) was added in small amounts during five hours with continuous agitation. The solution was decolorized with sulfur dioxide and the manganese dioxide filtered and washed. The combined filtrates were acidified with 100 cc. of concentrated sulfuric acid and the solution subjected to continuous ether extraction during fifteen hours. The ethereal extract was dried and the ether removed by evaporation. The acidic residue gave by fractionation 15 g. of acid boiling at 105–120° (Fract. C) and 10 g. of acid boiling at 62.5° at 3 mm. (Fract. A).

The determination of the Duclaux values of Fract. C indicated that acetic acid was the material under examination. The Duclaux values observed are 7.3, 6.7, 7.4, compared to 6.8, 7.1, and 7.4 for acetic acid, 3.95, 4.40, 4.55, for formic acid, and 11.9, 11.7, 11.3, for propionic acid. The identification of Fract. C was completed by the preparation of p-acet-toluidide, which showed the correct melting point and mixed melting point (149 to 150°). Fraction A was similarly identified as chloroacetic acid by conversion to chloroacetanilide, which showed the correct melting point and mixed melting point (134 to 135°).

The Action of Alcoholic Potash on Dichloro-1,3-hexadiene-2,4. Preparation of Methoxy-1-chloro-3-hexadiene-2,4.—Dichloro-1,3-hexadiene-2,4 (65 g.) in 200 cc. of absolute methanol containing 38 g. of potassium hydroxide was refluxed with vigorous agitation. Filtration of the reaction mixture gave 30 g. of dry potassium chloride (calcd. 34 g.). Aqueous dilution of the alcohol solution was followed by separation of the water-insoluble layer which was dried and fractionated. There was obtained 20 g. of low boiling material and 21 g. of the methyl ether which boiled at 88–92° at 30 mm.; n_D^{20} 1.4928; d_4^{20} 1.0239; M_R calcd. 40.10; M_R found, 41.57.

Anal. Calcd. for $C_7H_{11}ClO$: C, 57.35; H, 7.51. Found: C, 56.91; H, 7.74.

Action of Sodium Acetate on Dichloro-1,3-hexadiene-2,4. Preparation of Acetoxy-1-chloro-3-hexadiene-2,4(5).—One hundred grams of the dichloro compound, 100 g. of fused sodium acetate, and 300 cc. of glacial acetic acid were refluxed together for four hours. The acetic acid was neutralized with 20% sodium hydroxide and the mixture was extracted with ether. The ether extract was dried with calcium chloride, and then distilled. Three fractionations gave 55 g. of colorless liquid boiling at 84 to 85° at 3 mm.; d_4^{20} 1.0915; n_D^{20} 1.4890; M_R calcd., 44.61; M_R found, 46.14.

Anal. Calcd. for $C_8H_{11}O_2Cl$: Cl, 20.31. Found: 20.58, 20.78.

Summary

The action of aqueous hydrochloric acid on divinylacetylene yields a dihydrochloride. The compound is oxidized by permanganate with the formation of acetic acid and chloroacetic acid, and this fact together with a consideration of the probable mechanism of its formation, indicates that it has the structure dichloro-1,3-hexadiene-2,4 and that it results from two successive acts of 1,4 addition. When treated with sodium acetate its reactive (terminal) chlorine is replaced by acetoxy, and the action of methyl alcoholic potash similarly leads to the formation of a methyl ether.

Bibliography and Remarks

(1) Carothers. *Journ. Am. Chem. Soc.*, **55**, 2008 (1933); this volume, page 344.
(2) Nieuwland, Calcott, Downing and Carter, *Journ. Am. Chem. Soc.*, **53**, 4197 (1931).
(3) Coffman and Carothers, *Journ. Am. Chem. Soc.*, **55**, 2040 (1933); this volume, page 348.
(4) Carothers, Berchet and Collins, *Journ. Am. Chem. Soc.*, **54**, 4066 (1932); this volume, page 306.
(5) We are indebted to Dr. W. F. Talbot for this experiment.

XV.   Halogen-4-butadienes-1,2.   The Mechanism of 1,4-Addition and of α,γ-Rearrangement*

The reactions of vinylacetylene (I) and some of its derivatives exhibit peculiar features which provide a unique opportunity for testing certain assumptions concerning the mechanism of 1,4-addition and of α,γ-rearrangement. We have already shown (1) that the primary product of adding hydrogen chloride to (I) is chloro-4-butadiene-1,2 (II) which is readily rearranged to chloroprene (III) (2).

$$CH{\equiv}C{-}CH{=}CH_2 \qquad CH_2{=}C{=}CHCH_2X \qquad CH_2{=}CX{-}CH{=}CH_2$$
$$\text{(I)} \qquad\qquad\qquad \text{(II)} \qquad\qquad\qquad \text{(III)}$$

We now present further analogous facts as a basis for discussion.

The bromide II is obtained by the action of liquid hydrogen bromide on I at low temperature and by the action of sodium bromide on the chloride II at room temperature.   The second method has also been applied to the preparation of the iodide II, and in both cases the product is free from the isomeric halide III.

The chloride and the bromide II react readily with hot water (preferably in the presence of sodium carbonate) and yield the corresponding carbinol, a strongly lachrymatory liquid, which can then be converted back to the

* W. H. Carothers and G. J. Berchet, *Journ. Am. Chem. Soc.*, **55**, 2807–13 (1933);
Contribution No. 120 from the Experimental Station of E. I. du Pont de Nemours and Co.
Received December 20, 1932.   Published July 6, 1933.

chloride or the bromide II by the action of phosphorus trihalide in the presence of pyridine. The carbinol II is also converted to the chloride II by boiling dilute hydrogen chloride (18%). The action of sodium acetate on the chloride or bromide in boiling acetic acid solution yields the acetate II. The latter is also obtained from the carbinol by the action of acetic anhydride plus sulfuric acid. These reactions all proceed normally, $i.$ $e.$, none of the isomeric compounds III has been detected in the products. In this respect they differ from those involving Grignard reagents described in the next paper (3). Phenylmagnesium bromide acts on the chloride II yielding a mixture of phenyl-4-butadiene-1,2 (normal) and phenyl-2-butadiene-1,3 (abnormal). Methyl- and heptylmagnesium halides gave only abnormal products, while benzylmagensium chloride gave only the normal product. The isomeric chloride III does not react with Grignard reagents.

The bromide II, like the chloride (4), is rapidly converted to the isomeric compound III by dilute HX containing CuX. The iodide isomerizes still more readily: when heated alone to about 130° it suddenly evolves heat and the lower-boiling iodide III rapidly distils. It may be inferred that this transformation also occurs spontaneously at the ordinary temperature since, within one or two days, the iodide II is completely converted to a granular polymer almost certainly derived from III. Deliberate attempts to rearrange the acetate and the carbinol II have been unsuccessful.

In résumé the facts are:

Normal Metathetical Reactions of II: RCl $\longrightarrow$ RBr (I); RCl(Br) $\longrightarrow$ ROH(OAc); ROH $\longrightarrow$ RCl(Br, OAc).

Rearrangements: RCl(Br, I) II $\longrightarrow$ III.

Abnormal Reactions: RCl (II) with Grignard reagents gives both normal and abnormal products.

The halides of series III polymerize rapidly: the speeds for chloroprene and bromoprene (5) are roughly 700 and 1100 times that of isoprene, and iodoprene polymerizes so quickly as to interfere with the determination of its physical properties. None of the compounds of series II shows any tendency to polymerize spontaneously. (The apparent polymerization of the iodide II is accounted for by prior rearrangement.)

Theories (6) concerning the mechanism of 1,4-addition and of α,γ-rearrangements are too numerous to review but, with some concession for differences in terminology, the following propositions (1–4) will be recognized as pertinent to various suggestions that have from time to time been published.

1.   That all apparent examples of 1,4-addition really involve (completed) 1,2-addition followed by α,γ-shift.   This once attractive hypothesis appears to have been generally abandoned; the facts now show that it cannot possibly be true.   The rearrangement of the halides II $\longrightarrow$ III is irreversible, hence II, the 1,4-product, must be a primary product.

2.   That addition at conjugated systems is a two stage process: the cation of the addendum first attacks one end of the system yielding isomeric ions (or intermediate fragments) corresponding to the two isomeric products.   The ions arising from attack of (I) by hydrogen ion would be CH_2= C^+—CH=CH_2 (III) and CH_2=C=$CHCH_2{}^+$ (II).   Thus in the addition of HX to (I), the hydrogen ion attacks the acetylenic (positive?) end of the molecule; the resulting ions are those involved in the isomerizations discussed under 4 below.

3.   That the probable nature of the predominating hypothetical intermediate or of the predominating product can be inferred from conclusions based on fact or on speculation as to which is the more stable.

The facts show that this is not possible, since in the addition of hydrogen chloride or hydrogen bromide to (I) the unstable isomer (II) is a primary product, and is in all probability the only primary product.

4.   (a) That in triad systems it is the ion R^+ not the molecule RX which rearranges.   (b) That R^+ is a necessary intermediate in metathetical reactions of RX involving the formation of X^-.   (c) That the ion R^+, whether formed directly by dissociation of RX or as an intermediate in metathetical reactions of RX, will immediately assume the forms corresponding to the equilibrium products.

The practical implication of (c) is that metathetical reactions of triad systems (involving X^-) must yield an equilibrium mixture of the isomers. This has been taken so much for granted that it forms the basis of a supposed demonstration (7) of the intimate mechanism in the hydrolysis of carboxylic esters.   It is now obviously directly opposed to the facts, since a whole series of metathetical transformations in compounds of type II has been carried out without any rearrangement to the corresponding isomers III.   Not only does no isomerization occur under these conditions where, according to (b), ionization must be assumed to occur, but the iodide II rearranges under conditions that appear to be especially unfavorable to ionization.   This throws considerable doubt on assumption (4a).

Abnormal reactions of triad systems do, nevertheless, exist.   The action of RMgX on the chloride II furnishes an unambiguous demonstration of this fact.   The isomeric chloride III is (experimentally) incapable of reacting with RMgX; hence completed rearrangement cannot precede reaction. The isomeric hydrocarbons II and III cannot rearrange under the conditions used. The isomerization is therefore an integral part of the metathesis. Three explanatory assumptions appear to be possible:

(a) The abnormal reaction consists in addition of RMgX at the double bond followed by elimination of MgX_2. This has the disadvantage of being *ad hoc* since addition of RMgX at simple ethylenic linkages has never been realized.

(b) The initiating step results in the formation of a cation (or some other fragment) which adjusts itself before entrance of the anion of RMgX. This is the currently popular assumption (4a and b above). It presents this difficulty as shown in the comment under 4: the facts now require that these intermediate fragments (if they exist at all) must be capable (contrary to 4c) of resisting or escaping rearrangement under some conditions and not under others. In either case the conditions cannot be specified in advance and the assumption of intermediate ions contributes nothing to the explanation of the facts, but, at best, serves merely as a pictorial method of rationalizing the facts after they are known.

(c) The initiating step is the formation of a complex (coördination compound). This assumption also, in the present state of knowledge concerning complexes, is too vague to furnish a basis for detailed predictions. It is, however, unquestionably closer to reality than the assumption of *free* ions or radicals as intermediates. The closest approach to a simple free alkyl anion is probably found in the alkali alkyls. These materials are extraordinarily reactive; the ethyl anion, for example, is capable of reducing the sodium ion to sodium hydride at temperatures below $100°$ (8). Experimentally, simple alkyl cations are completely unknown; it is reasonable to suppose that they would be still less stable than alkyl anions. Metathetical reactions of organic compounds that can be formulated as proceeding through the intervention of ions generally involve media or catalysts capable of giving rise to coördination compounds (9).

Johnson (10) has shown that coördination and chelation are probably involved in the mechanism of many types of organic reactions including abnormal reactions and α,γ-rearrangements. Our application of his ideas to the present case is illustrated below.

In a triad system the usually accepted valence angles are capable of placing the unshared electrons of X fairly close to the γ-carbon atom, $R—\overset{\gamma}{C}H=\overset{\beta}{C}H—\overset{\alpha}{C}H_2—X$. Polarization at $\beta - \gamma$ favored by the proximity of these unshared electrons permits still closer approach of X toward γ and consequent loosening at α; these tendencies finally bring the two forms into equilibrium. This mechanism is in accordance with the observed order I > Br > Cl ≫ OAc, where the effective diameters of the atoms progressively diminish and the constraints on the electrons increase, while in OAc the Ac group may besides act as a steric obstacle. This may be supposed to apply to the rearrangement of the halides II themselves at elevated temperatures. In fact, for the chloride and the bromide II rearrangement at ordinary temperature appears to require the presence of salts having great coördinating power—conditions merely favoring ionization, e. g., water plus hydrogen chloride, do not suffice.

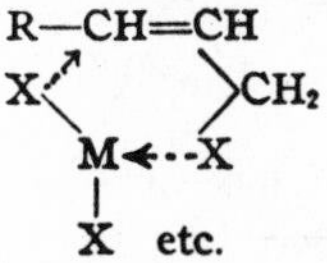

R—CH=CH
X⤹   ⟍CH₂
    M◄--X
    |
    X etc.

On the other hand, water plus hydrogen chloride plus cuprous chloride, or dry ferric chloride alone, induces very rapid rearrangement. An easily conceivable function of the salt in this case is symbolized in the figure, where the steric factors are analogous to those involved in chelation while the metal salt acts as a carrier of the entering group. In reactions of metathesis the chloride II yields abnormal products only with RMgX. Reaction with Grignard reagents generally undoubtedly requires entrance of the reactant into the complex, RMgX(OEt)₂. Coupling of a halide probably involves some intermediate step such as (A). Obviously, in view of the facts, such a purely "dative" electron shell as that which surrounds the magnesium is unusually vague and mobile. This mobility would provide the opportunity for a sufficient approach of R and R′ in forms that are essentially cation and anion without ever requiring the intermediacy of *free* alkyl ions. If R′ is a substituted allyl group the steric factors referred to above will permit the coupling to occur at the γ as well as the α carbon. Reaction of the chloride II with sodium iodide to give the corresponding iodide might appear to require intervention of the cation II indicated in 2 above, but we reject this idea also, and prefer to assume that some kind of coördination precedes reaction and that the cation is never liberated as a *free* entity. On the other hand, the coördinating power of the iodide ion is certainly relatively feeble, and there is nothing in its structure or known behavior to indicate that it could be very effective in the kind of coördination that is here suggested to account for rearrangement or abnormal reaction. The observed absence of abnormality in other reactions of compounds II can be similarly explained.

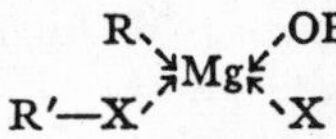

R⟍   ⟋OEt₂
   ⟩Mg⟨
R′—X⟋   ⟍X
      A

Experimental Part

Bromo-4-butadiene-1,2 (II).—Vinylacetylene (one mole) was passed into 3 moles of liquid hydrogen bromide during five to seven hours. The product, washed and distilled, gave two fractions: crude bromo-4-butadiene-1,2, 53.5% of calcd., and dibromo-2,4-butene-2 (11), 36%. Careful redistillation yielded no other products. Under other conditions, bromoprene (11) was found in the reaction product. For example, liquid hydrogen bromide (2.18 moles) added to vinylacetylene (4 moles) at *ca.* −50° after three hours gave the following products: bromoprene, 10%; bromo-4-butadiene-1,2, 19%; dibromo-2,4-butene-2, 12%. The bromide II was also obtained from chloro-4-butadiene-1,2 and sodium bromide in acetone plus water. Conversion was far from complete, repeated distillation was required to obtain a pure product, and the isolated yield was poor (25%); but there was no indication of any bromoprene in the product. Better yields of the bromide II (69%) were obtained from the carbinol II plus phosphorus tribromide in the presence of a little pyridine at 10–20° (*ca.* one hour); a colorless, lachrymatory liquid; b. p. 64–66° (181 mm.), 109–111° (760 mm.); d_4^{20} 1.4255; n_D^{20} 1.5248.

Anal. Calcd. for C_4H_5Br: C, 36.09; H, 3.76; Br, 60.15. Found: C, 36.61; H, 3.91; Br, 60.13.

Iodo-4-butadiene-1,2´ (II).—Chloro-4-butadiene-1,2 with one mole of sodium iodide was allowed to stand in 80% alcohol or in acetone at room temperature for three hours. The heavy yellow oil precipitated by dilution with water was distilled; yield, 46%; b. p. 43–45° (38 mm.); estimated b. p. at 760 mm., 130°; d_4^{20} 1.7129; n_D^{20} 1.5709.

Anal. Calcd. for C_4H_5I: C, 26.66; H, 2.77; I, 70.55; mol. wt., 180. Found: C, 27.00; H, 2.97; I, 70.40; mol. wt. (in freezing benzene), 184.

It reacted instantly with aqueous silver nitrate. When it was allowed to stand at ordinary temperature solid particles began to separate within twenty-four hours; within forty to fifty hours the transformation was usually complete and the product was a granular mass of amorphous, insoluble particles similar to the granular polymers obtained from chloroprene and bromoprene (5). The polymerization is doubtless preceded by isomerization.

Anal. Calcd. for $(C_4H_5I)_n$: I, 70.55. Found: I, 69.49, 69.44.

Iodoprene (III).—When the iodo compound (II) was heated at 125–130° a short but lively reaction took place; the product then distilled at 111–113° (760 mm.), while a large amount of viscous residue remained in the flask. The change in physical properties indicated that the distillate was the isomeric compound, iodo-2-butadiene-1,3; n_D^{20} 1.561. It polymerized completely within forty-eight hours.

Hydroxy-4-butadiene-1,2 (II).—Chloro-4-butadiene-1,2 (6 moles) was stirred at 60–90° with 6 moles of sodium carbonate in 1500 cc. of water for fifteen hours. Ether extraction and distillation gave the carbinol in 50% yield (losses were due to solubility in water and formation of higher-boiling products); colorless liquid miscible with water and most organic solvents; sharp pungent odor, lachrymatory, strongly vesicant; b. p. 68–70° (53 mm.), 126–128° (756 mm.); d_4^{20} 0.9164; n_D^{20} 1.4759. The carbinol was also obtained in 50% yield by similarly hydrolyzing the bromide II.

Anal. Calcd. for C_4H_6O: C, 68.57; H, 8.57. Found: C, 68.65; H, 8.68.

Hydrogenation of the carbinol gave *n*-butyl alcohol identified through its 3-nitrophthalic ester (mixed m. p. 145°).

The carbinol was recovered unchanged after being refluxed with sodium ethylate in ethanol, 25% aqueous sulfuric acid, or 2% aqueous hydrogen chloride.

When the carbinol (0.5 mole) was refluxed with 100 cc. of 18% hydrogen chloride for one hour, a 9% yield of chloro-4-butadiene-1,2 was obtained; the rest was unchanged carbinol.   By the action of phosphorus trichloride on the carbinol in the presence of a little pyridine a 62% yield of chloro-4-butadiene-1,2 was obtained.   No chloroprene was found in the product.

Acetate of Hydroxy-4-butadiene-1,2.—To hydroxy-4-butadiene-1,2′ with excess acetic anhydride was added a drop of sulfuric acid.   The lively reaction was moderated by cooling and the mixture was finally refluxed for one-half hour.   Dilution with water, extraction and distillation gave a 75% yield of the acetate; b. p. 85–86° (125 mm.), 140–140.5° (780 mm.); d_4^{20} 0.9641; n_D^{20} 1.4504.   The same compound was obtained by refluxing for seven hours one mole of chloro-4-butadiene-1,2 with 2 moles of sodium acetate dissolved in 200 cc. of glacial acetic acid; yield 59%.   Similarly from bromo-4-butadiene-1,2 a 73% yield of pure acetate was obtained.   There was no indication in either case of the presence of any isomeric compound.

Anal.   Calcd. for $C_6H_8O_2$: C, 64.28; H, 7.14.   Found: C, 64.30; H, 7.16.

Hydrogenation of the acetate gave pure *n*-butyl acetate.   Saponification gave pure hydroxy-4-butadiene-1,2.

Rearrangement of Chloro-4-butadiene-1,2 (II).—To the observations recorded previously (1) the following may be added.   The chloride II (30 g.) with 50 cc. of 18% hydrogen chloride after two hours at 70–80° gave 2 g. of *crude* III.   The rest was unchanged II.   The chloride II (50 g.) with 150 cc. of 18% hydrogen chloride and 10 g. of cuprous chloride shaken at 20° for sixteen hours gave a 70% yield of III.   The rest was polymer; no II was recovered.   When 3% of dry ferric chloride was added to the chloride II heat was evolved and distillation set in at once.   The distillate was a mixture of II and III.   We are indebted to Dr. D. D. Coffman for the last two of these experiments.

Summary

Compounds of the formula $CH_2{=}C{=}CHCH_2X$ in which X is Cl, Br, I, OH and OAc undergo a series of metathetical reactions without yielding abnormal (rearranged) products.   The chloride and the bromide are formed by the 1,4-addition of HX to vinylacetylene.   They are easily and irreversibly rearranged to $CH_2{=}CX{-}CH{=}CH_2$.   The iodide rearranges spontaneously.   The direct bearing of these facts on theories concerning the mechanism of 1,4-addition and of α,γ-rearrangement is discussed.

Bibliography and Remarks

(1) Carothers, Berchet and Collins, *Journ. Am. Chem. Soc.*, **54**, 4066 (1932); this volume, page 306.

(2) Carothers, Williams, Collins and Kirby, *Journ. Am. Chem. Soc.*, **53**, 4203 (1931); this volume, page 281.

(3) Carothers and Berchet, *Journ. Am. Chem. Soc.*, **55**, 2813 (1933); this volume page 368.

(4) Carothers, Berchet and Collins, *Journ. Am. Chem. Soc.*, **54**, 4066 (1932); this volume, page 306.

(5) Carothers, Collins and Kirby, *Journ. Am. Chem. Soc.*, **55**, 789 (1933); this volume, page 314.

(6) See for example, Gillet, *Bull. soc. chim. Belg.*, **31**, 366 (1922); Prévost, *Bull. soc. chim.*, **43**, 996 (1928); Burton, *J. Chem. Soc.*, 1651 (1928); Burton and Ingold, *ibid.*, 904 (1928); Whitmore, *Journ. Am. Chem. Soc.*, **54**, 3274 (1932).

(7) Ingold and Ingold, *J. Chem. Soc.*, 756 (1932).

(8) Carothers and Coffman, *Journ. Am. Chem. Soc.*, **51**, 588 (1929); **52**, 1254 (1930).

(9) *Cf.* Meerwein, *Ann.*, **455**, 227 (1927).

(10) Johnson, *Journ. Am. Chem. Soc.*, **55**, 3029 (1933).

(11) Carothers, Collins and Kirby, *ibid.*, **55**, 789 (1933); this volume, page 314.

XVI. The Preparation of Orthoprenes by the Action of Grignard Reagents on Chloro-4-butadiene-1,2*

The term orthoprene is here presented as a designation for derivatives of butadiene-1,3 having a single substituent and that in the 2-position (III). Isoprene is the historically important member of this class and (except for a single reference (1) to ethylbutadiene) it was the only one known until the discovery of chloroprene (2) and bromoprene (3). The extraordinarily superior properties of these compounds from the standpoint of rubber synthesis prompted the preparation and examination of other dienes (4). The results (5) suggested that similarly desirable properties are not likely to be found among any other types of dienes than the orthoprenes as such, and it became important to obtain further members of this class. The lack of any satisfactory general method for this purpose led to the development of the method described here, which is based on the observation that chloro-4-butadiene-1,2 (I) like other substituted allyl halides (6) reacts with Grignard reagents to produce abnormal (III) as well as normal (II) products. The theoretical implications of this fact have been discussed in the preceding paper (7).

$$CH_2{=}C{=}CHCH_2Cl \ (I) \quad CH_2{=}C{=}CHCH_2R \ (II) \quad CH_2{=}CR{-}CH{=}CH_2 \ (III)$$

For the purpose in view the new method leaves much to be desired. Yields are rather low, and separation of the desired product from by-products is rather laborious. No doubt further study would lead to considerable improvement. In its present state, however, the method has sufficed for the isolation of two orthoprenes especially wanted: n-heptoprene and phenoprene. As precursors of rubber neither of these compounds approaches chloroprene; they are in fact probably inferior to isoprene. Heptoprene polymerizes rather more rapidly than isoprene but the product obtained under most conditions appears to be softer and weaker. Phenoprene polymerizes ten to one hundred times as rapidly as isoprene. Under most conditions the predominating product is the dimer, a crystalline solid which has, of course, no rubber-like properties. The high polymer formed, for example, at very high pressure appears to have a relatively low molecular weight and, although slightly rubber-like, it is soft and deficient in strength and elasticity. The experiments here reported dealt with reagents in which R was methyl, n-butyl, n-heptyl, phenyl and benzyl.

* W. H. Carothers and G. J. Berchet, *Journ. Am. Chem. Soc.*, **55**, 2813–7 (1933); Contribution No. 121 from the Experimental Station of E. I. du Pont de Nemours and Co.
Received December 20, 1932. Published July 6, 1933.

From methylmagnesium chloride or iodide or from n-heptylmagnesium bromide only the abnormal products (III) were isolated in a state of purity. The product from n-butylmagnesium bromide contained a considerable amount of n-octane from which the butyl-2-butadiene-1,3 could not be completely separated. The presence of the latter compound was, however, demonstrated by the Diels–Alder reaction. Phenylmagnesium bromide gave both the normal and the abnormal products which were separated and isolated in a state of purity. From benzylmagnesium chloride only the normal product was isolated. The structures of the orthoprenes were established by their reaction with naphthoquinone to form the crystalline addition products (IV), which were readily oxidized to the corresponding anthraquinones (V). The phenyl-4-butadiene-1,2 was identified by hydrogenation to n-butylbenzene. Benzyl-4-butadiene-1,2 was identified by its conversion to phenylpropionaldehyde by ozonization.

IV   V

Experimental Part

Preparation of Isoprene.—A Grignard reagent from 312 g. (2.2 moles) of methyl iodide and 53 g. of magnesium (2.2 moles) in n-butyl ether was treated slowly with 177 g. of chloro-4-butadiene-1,2 (2 moles). The mixture was refluxed for one-half hour, acidified, and the material boiling below 120° (74 g.) removed from the butyl ether by distillation. In a similar manner methylmagnesium chloride from 40 g. (1.65 moles) of magnesium in butyl ether with 132 g. of chloro-4-butadiene-1,2 (1.5 moles) yielded 35 g. of liquid boiling below 110°. The products from the two experiments were combined and distilled. Except for a considerable dark residue having the odor of dibutyl ether, only a single fraction was obtained. This was isoprene (47 g.) boiling at 34.5 to 35°.

In alcohol solution it reacted readily with naphthoquinone yielding methyl-2-tetrahydro-1,4,4a,9a-anthraquinone-9,10 (IV, R = CH₃) which crystallized from alcohol in white needles melting at 86° (copper block) (8). When suspended in alcoholic potash it was readily oxidized by air to β-methylanthraquinone, m. p. 177° (9).

n-Butyl-2-butadiene-1,3.—Six moles of butylmagnesium bromide in ethyl ether was treated with 5 moles of chloro-4-butadiene-1,2. After acidification, distillation of the ethereal layer yielded a series of fractions boiling between 33–45° at 49 mm. and a residue composed of a viscous, somewhat elastic mass. The largest fraction (126.5 g.) boiled at 44–45° (29 mm.) (121–123° (760 mm.)). This is very close to the boiling point of n-octane (125°) and analysis (C, 84.8; H, 13.5) showed that its composition lay between that of octane and butylbutadiene. Bromine titration indicated the presence of about 57% of the latter compound, and this was demonstrated to be butyl-2-buta-diene-1,3 by the fact that the mixture when heated for two hours with an equal weight of napthoquinone yielded **butyl-2-tetrahydro-1,4,4a,9a-anthraquinone-9,10,** (IV, R = n-C_4H_9), white microscopic crystals from 80% alcohol, m. p. 63–64° (copper block).

Anal. Calcd. for $C_{18}H_{20}O_2$: C, 80.59; H, 7.46. Found: C, 79.40, 80.31; H, 7.21, 7.53.

Oxidation with air in dilute alcoholic potassium hydroxide gave β-n-**butylanthra-quinone** (V, R = n-C_4H_9); yellow crystals from alcohol, m. p. 89° (copper block).

Anal. Calcd. for $C_{18}H_{14}O_2$: C, 81.81; H, 6.06. Found: C, 81.08, 80.83; H, 6.43, 5.69.

n-Heptyl-2-butadiene-1,3 (Heptoprene).—One mole of n-heptylmagnesium bromide in ethyl ether was treated with one mole of chloro-4-butadiene-1,2. After acidification, distillation of the ethereal solution yielded (a) 13 g. boiling at 47–48.5° (5 mm.), (b) 32 g. at 52–54° (5 mm.), and (c) 42 g. boiling chiefly at 99–101° (3 mm.). Fraction (c) crystallized on being cooled, and it was apparently tetradecane (calcd.: C, 84.84; H, 15.15. Found: C, 84.05; H, 15.19); m. p. 5–7°. Analysis of fraction (a) showed that it contained considerable amounts of material other than hydrocarbon. Fraction (b) was n-heptyl-2-butadiene-1,3; n_D^{20} 1.4511; d_4^{20} 0.7796; M_R calcd., 52.05; M_R found, 52.52.

Anal. Calcd. for $C_{11}H_{20}$: C, 86.84; H, 13.15. Found: C, 85.43, 85.44; H, 12.96, 13.40.

When heated with naphthoquinone at 90–100° for two hours it gave **n-heptyl-2-tetrahydro-1,4,4a,9a-anthraquinone-9,10** (IV, R = n-C_7H_{15}); white needles from ace-tone; m. p. 81°.

Anal. Calcd. for $C_{21}H_{26}O_2$: C, 81.29; H, 8.38. Found: C, 81.02; H, 8.64.

Oxidation with air in the presence of alcoholic potash gave β-n-heptylanthraquin-one; pale yellow crystals from alcohol; m. p. 87° (copper block).

Anal. Calcd. for $C_{21}H_{22}O_2$: C, 82.35; H, 7.18. Found: C, 81.77; H, 6.96.

Action of Phenylmagnesium Bromide on Chloro-4-butadiene-1,2.—This reaction was complicated by the fact that considerable amounts of phenol were always formed even when attempts were made to exclude air by passing a stream of nitrogen into the re-action flask. The following experiment is typical. Seven moles of phenylmagnesium bromide in ethyl ether was treated with 6 moles of chloro-4-butadiene-1,2. The mix-ture was washed first with dilute acid and then with dilute alkali to remove the phenol, dried and distilled. A certain amount of benzene due to the excess of the Grignard re-agent distilled first, and then the following fractions were collected: (a) 52–60° (17 mm.), 23.5 g.; (b) 60–61° (17 mm.), 72 g.; (c) 61–72° (17 mm.), 8.5 g.; (d) 72–73° (17 mm.), 31 g.; (e) residue, 209 g.

The fractions (b), (d) and (e) were further purified as described below and the following compounds obtained: phenyl-4-butadiene-1,2 (4–7.2%), phenyl-2-butadiene-1,3 (8.4–9.2%), dimer of phenyl-2-butadiene-1,3 (25.3–26.7%). The yields are based on the chloro-4-butadiene-1,2 applied, and the two sets of figures result from two separate experiments. By a slight modification of the conditions the yield of phenyl-2-butadiene-1,3 was greatly increased. The reaction product was decomposed very rapidly with ice and dilute acid, the ethereal solution was kept at low temperature until it could be dis-tilled, the ether was evaporated *in vacuo*, and the distillation was carried out at a lower pressure (2.5 mm.) than was used in previous experiments. The yield of pure phenyl-2-butadiene-1,3 was 24%.

Fraction (b) was redistilled and then showed n_D^{20} 1.5489; d_4^{20} 0.9226; M_R calcd., 43.85; M_R found, 44.93. It was identified as **phenyl-2-butadiene-1,3 (phenoprene)**.

Anal. Calcd. for $C_{10}H_{10}$: C, 92.31; H, 7.69. Found: C, 91.60; H, 7.69.

When heated with an equal weight of naphthoquinone at 90–100° it gave **phenyl-2-tetrahydro-1,4,4a,9a-anthraquinone-9,10** (IV, R = C_6H_5); crystallized from acetone, m. p. 146–147° (copper block).

Anal. Calcd. for $C_{20}H_{16}O_2$: C, 83.33; H, 5.55. Found: C, 83.00; H, 6.00.

Oxidation with air in the presence of alcoholic potash gave β-phenylanthraquinone, identified by mixed melting point (163–164°) (10).

Anal. Calcd. for $C_{20}H_{12}O_2$: C, 84.50; H, 4.22. Found: C, 84.14; H, 4.43.

Fraction (d).—After redistillation this showed n_D^{20} 1.5460; d_4^{20} 0.9220; M_R calcd., 43.85; M_R found, 44.64. It was identified as **phenyl-4-butadiene-1,2** by its analysis and by hydrogenation to *n*-butylbenzene. It failed to react with naphthoquinone.

Anal. Calcd. for $C_{10}H_{10}$: C, 92.31; H, 7.69. Found: C, 92.44; H, 7.77.

Hydrogenation in alcohol with PtO$_2$ catalyst was rapid and complete. The product had b. p. 178–179°; d_{20}^{20} 0.863; n_D^{23} 1.4895. *n*-Butylbenzene has b. p. 180°; d^{15} 0.864; $n_D^{13.5}$ 1.494 (11).

Fraction (e).—Distillation of fraction (e) gave first some diphenyl, and then the bulk of the material distilled at 220–225° (10 mm.) with only a very small residue. The distillate solidified when cooled, and after crystallization from ethanol gave white needles melting sharply at 62°. The same product was slowly formed from phenyl-2-butadiene-1,3 on long standing or more rapidly under the action of heat, but not from phenyl-4-butadiene-1,2. Analysis shows that it is a **dimer of phenyl-2-butadiene-1,3**.

Anal. Calcd. for $C_{20}H_{20}$: C, 92.31; H, 7.69; mol. wt. 260. Found: C, 92.92; H, 7.71; mol. wt. (in freezing benzene), 232, 232.

Benzyl-4-butadiene-1,2.—One and one-half moles of benzylmagnesium chloride in ethyl ether was treated with 1.13 moles of chloro-4-butadiene-1,2. The reaction had a tendency to proceed by spurts. Distillation of the reaction product through an efficient column gave three fractions: (a) 30.5 g. 72–73° (7 mm.); (b) 73 g. 76–77° (7 mm.); and (c) 30 g. of residue. Fraction (c) was probably mostly dibenzyl. Neither (a) nor (b) reacted with naphthoquinone. Fraction (b) was identified as benzyl-4-butadiene-1,2 and (a) was apparently a less pure specimen of the same material. Fraction (b) showed n_D^{20} 1.5400; d_4^{20} 0.9169; M_R calcd., 48.45, M_R found, 49.28.

Anal. Calcd. for $C_{11}H_{12}$: C, 91.66; H, 8.33. Found: C, 91.12; H, 8.87.

When oxidized with potassium permanganate it yielded benzoic acid. Ozonization in chloroform solution followed by hydrolysis gave an oil having the odor of **phenylpropionaldehyde**. Its **oxime** melted at 95–97°.

Anal. Calcd. for $C_9H_{11}ON$: C, 72.48; H, 7.38; N, 9.39. Found: C, 71.68; H, 7.32; N, 8.83.

Summary

Diene hydrocarbons of the formulas $CH_2{=}CR{-}CH{=}CH_2$ and/or $CH_2{=}C{=}CHCH_2R$ are obtained by the action on chloro-4-butadiene-1,2 of RMgX where R is methyl, n-butyl, n-heptyl, phenyl and benzyl. Some polymers and derivatives are described.

Bibliography and Remarks

(1) Ipatiew, *J. prakt. Chem.*, [2] **59**, 534 (1899).

(2) Carothers, Williams, Collins and Kirby, *Journ. Am. Chem. Soc.*, **53**, 4203 (1931); this volume, page 281.

(3) Carothers, Collins and Kirby, *Journ. Am. Chem. Soc.*, **55**, 789 (1933); this volume, page 314.

(4) Carothers and Coffman, *Journ. Am. Chem. Soc.*, **54**, 4071 (1932); this volume, page 384; Jacobson and Carothers, *Journ. Am. Chem. Soc.*, **55**, 1624 (1933); this volume, page 331.

(5) See also Whitby and Gallay, *Can. J. Research*, **6**, 280 (1932).

(6) Prévost and Daujat, *Bull. soc. chim.*, [4] **47**, 588 (1930).

(7) Carothers and Berchet, *Journ. Am. Chem. Soc.*, **55**, 2807 (1933); this volume, page 361.

(8) Diels and Alder [*Ber.*, **62**, 2357 (1929)] report 81°

(9) Diels and Alder report 175°.

(10) Scholl and Neovius [*Ber.*, **44**, 1075 (1911)] give 160 to 161°. The melting point recorded above is observed in a capillary tube on slow heating. On a copper block the substance first melts at about 145° with the evolution of some gas; it then solidifies and melts again at 161 to 165°. If the substance is first heated *in vacuo* at 125°, only a single melting point of 163–164° is observed. β-Phenylanthraquinone from another (commercial) source showed a similar behavior.

(11) Beilstein, IV ed., Vol. V, page 413.

XVII.   Mercury Derivatives of Vinylacetylene*

As a means of identifying true acetylenic compounds the derivatives formed by the action of K_2HgI_4 are useful since they are generally crystalline and have definite melting points (1). When this reagent is applied to vinylacetylene (I) it furnishes di-vinylethynyl-mercury (II), which separates from alcohol in the form of white leaflets melting at 144 to 145°. The compound is readily soluble in chloroform, but on standing in the air for twenty-four to forty-eight hours it becomes yellow in color and insoluble in chloroform. Analysis indicates that considerable amounts of oxygen are absorbed during this transformation. The oxidized product does not melt, but sometimes explodes on being heated or subjected to mechanical shock.

Di-vinylethynyl-mercury undergoes the following transformations. Cold dilute hydrochloric acid regenerates the vinylacetylene; chlorine and bromine yield the α-chloro- and bromo-vinylacetylenes (III); and metallic sodium in dry benzene produces sodium vinylacetylide.

Di-vinylethynyl-mercury is also produced by the action of mercuric acetate in acetic acid on vinylacetylene at ordinary temperatures, but if the

* W. H. Carothers, R. A. Jacobson and G. J. Berchet, *Journ. Am. Chem. Soc.*, **55**, 4665–7 (1933); Contribution No. 125 from the Experimental Station of E. I. du Pont de Nemours and Co.

Received July 21, 1933. Published November 7, 1933.

temperature is raised to 60 or 70° reaction proceeds further with the formation of a compound whose composition and chemical behavior agree with that required for 1,1-di-acetoxymercuri-2-acetoxymercurioxy-1,3-butadiene (IV). The same product is obtained by treating di-vinylethynyl-mercury with mercuric acetate in acetic acid at 60 to 70° (2).

$$CH_2=CH-C\equiv CH \qquad (CH_2=CH-C\equiv C)_2Hg \qquad CH_2=CH-C\equiv CX$$
$$\text{(I)} \qquad\qquad\qquad \text{(II)} \qquad\qquad\qquad \text{(III)}$$

$$CH_2=CH-(CH_3COOHgO)C=C(HgOOCCH_3)_2 \qquad CH_2=CH-CO-CH_3$$
$$\text{(IV)} \qquad\qquad\qquad\qquad\qquad \text{(V)}$$

$$CH_2=CH-CO-CBr_3 \qquad CH_2=CH-(OHgX)C=C(HgX)_2$$
$$\text{(VI)} \qquad\qquad\qquad \text{(VII)}$$

This compound is a white crystalline solid somewhat soluble in water and more soluble in dilute acetic acid. It is infusible. By the action of hydrochloric acid it is decomposed with the formation of methyl vinyl ketone (V). Similarly by the action of bromine it is converted into tribromomethyl vinyl ketone (VI). The action of potassium iodide, bromide or chloride on IV causes replacement of the acetyl groups by halogen and gives insoluble products corresponding in composition with the general formula VII.

Di-vinylethynyl-mercury.—The addition of an alcoholic solution of vinylacetylene to an excess of the alkaline mercuric iodide reagent (1) yielded a copious precipitate. This was filtered off and crystallized from boiling absolute alcohol. It separated in the form of white leaflets melting at 144 to 145°.

Anal. Calcd. for C_8H_6Hg: Hg, 66.25. Found: Hg, 66.46, 66.35.

The same compound was obtained by adding vinylacetylene (30 g.) to a cold solution of 5 g. of mercuric oxide in 250 cc. of acetic acid.

Anal. Calcd. for C_8H_6Hg: C, 31.72; H, 1.99. Found: C, 32.00; H, 2.46.

Upon standing for forty-eight hours the di-vinylethynyl-mercury became yellow in color and insoluble in chloroform. It had also acquired the ability to explode under the action of heat or mechanical shock. Analysis of this explosive product showed the presence of only 27.70% carbon and 2.23% hydrogen.

Freshly prepared di-vinylethynyl-mercury reacted with bromine or iodine to give the corresponding bromo- and iodo-vinylacetylenes. In one experiment 23.5 g. of the mercury compound in 177 cc. of chloroform was treated slowly with a 10% solution of bromine in chloroform; 22.64 g. of bromine was absorbed before decolorization ceased. The chloroform was removed, and distillation of the residue (11 g.) then gave 3 g. of 1-bromo-2-vinylacetylene, b. p. 50 to 52° at 210 mm.

1,1-Di-acetoxymercuri-2-acetoxymercurioxy-1,3-butadiene (IV).—A solution of 5.2 g. of vinylacetylene in 100 cc. of acetic acid was added to a solution of 86.6 g. of mercuric oxide in 700 cc. of acetic acid surrounded by a water-bath at 45°. After one-half hour the temperature of the bath was increased to 60° and maintained between 60–70° for four hours. During this period a white crystalline solid separated. The mixture was filtered and the solid (79 g.) crystallized from dilute acetic acid; yield 93.4%. The product was somewhat soluble in water, more so in dilute acetic acid, but insoluble in the common organic solvents.

Anal. Calcd. for $C_{10}H_{12}O_7Hg_3$: C, 14.18; H, 1.43; Hg, 71.15. Found: C, 14.14; H, 1.95; Hg, 70.72.

1,1-Di-iodomercuri-2-iodomercurioxy-1,3-butadiene.—To a hot solution of 4 g. of 1,1-diacetoxymercuri-2-acetoxymercurioxy-1,3-butadiene in 100 cc. of 50% acetic acid was added slowly with stirring 2.8 g. of potassium iodide in 20 cc. of water. The yellow precipitate was filtered, washed several times with hot 50% acetic acid, then with water, and finally with acetone. The pale yellow solid was insoluble in water and in the common organic solvents.

Anal. Calcd. for $C_4H_3OHg_3I_3$: Hg, 57.34; I, 36.28. Found: Hg, 55.22, 55.47; I, 36.27, 36.45.

1,1-Di-bromomercuri-2-bromomercurioxy-1,3-butadiene was obtained in a similar manner from potassium bromide as a white solid insoluble in water and in the common organic solvents.

Anal. Calcd. for $C_4H_3OHg_3Br_3$: Hg, 66.23; Br, 26.37. Found: Hg, 67.82, 68.14; Br, 25.18, 25.29.

1,1-Di-chloromercuri-2-chloromercurioxy-1,3-butadiene was obtained in a similar manner from potassium chloride as a white solid insoluble in water and in the common organic solvents.

Anal. Calcd. for $C_4H_3OHg_3Cl_3$: Cl, 13.72. Found: Cl, 14.38.

Hydrolysis of 1,1-Di-acetoxymercuri-2-acetoxymercurioxy-1,3-butadiene.—To 423 g. of the mercury compound (0.5 mole) in 200 cc. of water was added 300 cc. of hydrochloric acid (37%). After three hours, a small amount of hydroquinone was added, and the solution distilled until the distillate amounted to 300 cc. From the latter, pure methyl vinyl ketone was isolated by ether extraction and distillation. With phenylhydrazine it gave the known derivative phenyl-1-methyl-3-pyrazoline melting at 76° (3).

Action of Bromine on 1,1-Di-acetoxymercuri-2-acetoxymercurioxy-1,3-butadiene.—Bromine (239 g.) was slowly added to a suspension of 285 g. (0.337 mole) of the mercury compound in 700 cc. chloroform until decolorization was complete. Cooling was required to maintain the temperature below 60°. After standing, the mixture was filtered, washed with 10% hydrochloric acid and with water and distilled. At 0.5 mm. 44 g. of a yellow viscous liquid boiling at 128–130° was obtained. On standing for forty-eight hours it solidified. Three crystallizations from petroleum ether gave white rectangular plates melting at 73–75°. Although additional crystallizations did not alter the melting point, the product was not analytically pure. However, the ease with which bromoform was liberated when the crystals were warmed with dilute alkali indicates that the product was mainly tribromomethyl vinyl ketone contaminated perhaps with dibromomethyl vinyl ketone.

Anal. Calcd. for $C_4H_3OBr_3$: C, 15.64; H, 0.98; Br, 78.15. Found: C, 16.42, 16.85; H, 1.89, 1.75; Br. 72.18, 71.89.

Summary

Vinylacetylene when treated with potassium mercuri-iodide or with mercuric acetate at the ordinary temperature yields di-vinylethynyl-mercury, a crystalline solid melting at 144 to 145°. The action of mercuric acetate on vinylacetylene at 60 to 70° yields 1,1-di-acetoxymercuri-2-acetoxymercuri-oxy-1,3-butadiene. Some reactions of these compounds are described.

Bibliography and Remarks

(1) Johnson and McEwen, *Journ. Am. Chem. Soc.*, **48**, 469 (1926).

(2) Myddleton, Barrett and Seager, *ibid.*, **52**, 4405 (1930), have presented evidence favoring the general structure —C(OHgOAc)=C(HgOAc)$_2$ for the products obtained by the action of mercuric acetate on monosubstituted acetylenes.

(3) Maire, *Bull. Soc. Chim.*, (4) **3**, 272 (1908).

XVIII. 1-Halogen-2-vinylacetylenes*

By the action of alkaline hypohalites, true acetylenic hydrogens are generally replaced by halogen (1). This reaction has now been applied to vinylacetylene, and the 1-halogen-2-vinylacetylenes whose properties are listed in Table I have been prepared. In a general way they resemble other halogen acetylenes. They are liquids with highly characteristic repulsive sickening odors. Under diminished pressure in an atmosphere of nitrogen they can be distilled, but dangerous explosions occur if air is present, or if heating of the residue is carried too far. A sample of the chloro compound in one instance inflamed spontaneously when a specimen was being removed for analysis.

The compounds when freshly distilled are colorless but they darken on standing and are finally transformed into black, brittle solids. These solids are sensitive to heat and percussion and they explode with considerable violence. The product from the iodo compound is the most sensitive and violent; that from the chloro compound the least.

PHYSICAL PROPERTIES OF CH_2=CH—C≡C—X

Nature of X	B. p., °C.	n_D^{20}	d_4^{20}	MRD calcd.	MRD found	Exaltation
Cl	55 to 57 at 760 mm.	1.4663	1.0032	22.94	23.89	0.95
Br	52 to 53 at 217 mm.	1.5182	1.4804	25.81	26.80	.99
I	78 at 125 mm.	1.5948	1.8968	31.07	31.88	.81

The bromo compound was formed rather rapidly when vinylacetylene was treated with potassium hypobromite; hypochlorite acted very much more slowly and the yields of the chloro compound were rather low. In

* R. A. Jacobson and W. H. Carothers, *Journ. Am. Chem. Soc.*, 55, 4667–9 (1933); Contribution No. 126 from the Experimental Station of E. I. du Pont de Nemours and Co.

Received July 21, 1933. Published November 7, 1933.

preparing the iodo compound a solution of iodine in potassium iodide was used. The iodo and bromo compounds have also been obtained (2) by the action of iodine and bromine on di-vinylethynyl-mercury. The iodo compound was also formed when vinylethynylmagnesium bromide was treated with iodine. Since a deficiency of iodine was used, it appears that the tendency of the iodo compound to react with the Grignard reagent is very slight.

In alcoholic solution the iodo compound adds one molecule of hydrogen chloride. This reaction was carried out in the expectation that the product would be the substituted chloroprene, $CH_2{=}CH{-}CCl{=}CHI$. The product did indeed polymerize spontaneously, but it yielded only a sticky black tar and no attempt was made to confirm its structure.

Experimental Part

Preparation of 1-Bromo-2-vinylacetylene.—Bromine (80 g.) was added at 0° to 180 g. of potassium hydroxide in 800 g. of water. Then 30 g. of vinylacetylene was added during one-half hour with stirring under nitrogen. After two hours a heavy oily layer separated. This was dried with calcium chloride and distilled under reduced pressure of nitrogen. Some vinylacetylene was recovered, and then 36.4 g. (55%) of 1-bromo-2-vinylacetylene was collected between 52 and 53° at 217 mm. A small amount of liquid remaining in the distilling flask exploded when further distillation was attempted. The bromovinylacetylene though colorless at first, quickly became yellow and then progressively darker upon standing. Its odor was nauseating and exposure to its vapors caused headaches. A specimen stabilized with hydroquinone did not polymerize within a month. When examined several months later it was a highly explosive black solid.

Anal. Calcd. for C_4H_3Br: C, 36.66; H, 2.27, mol. wt., 130.9. Found: C, 36.72; H, 2.46; mol. wt., 131, 136 (cryoscopic, benzene).

Preparation of 1-Iodo-2-vinylacetylene.—To a solution of 84 g. (1.5 mole) of potassium hydroxide in 1000 g. water at 0°, 65 g. of vinylacetylene was added and then, with vigorous stirring during two hours, a solution of 140 g. of potassium iodide and 127 g. of iodine in 110 cc. of water. After standing overnight, the 1-iodo-2-vinylacetylene (95 g.) which had separated to the bottom was removed, dried with calcium chloride, and distilled under reduced pressure of nitrogen; yield, 49 g. or 27.5%. The compound was at first colorless, but on standing it became reddish-brown. After a month at 10° it had polymerized to a jelly, and after several months to a black solid similar in appearance to charcoal. This polymer was extremely explosive.

Anal. Calcd. for C_4H_3I: C, 26.97; H, 1.69; mol. wt., 177.95. Found: C, 27.30; H, 1.75; mol. wt., 181 (cryoscopic, benzene).

The iodo compound was also obtained by the action of iodine on vinylethynylmagnesium bromide. To an ethereal solution containing one mole of the reagent, 127 g. (one gram atom) of iodine was slowly added. A smooth reaction occurred and the iodine instantly dissolved with decolorization. A small test sample was removed and found to take up considerably more iodine. However, the main portion was distilled in vacuum and a liquid boiling at 82 to 83° at 150 mm. was collected. This agreed in odor and physical constants with the 1-iodo-2-vinylacetylene described above.

Preparation of 1-Chloro-2-vinylacetylene.—Some difficulty was at first experienced in obtaining this compound, but with the following procedure it was isolated in yields of about 10%. To a solution of 500 g. of potassium hydrioxde in 1800 cc. of water at 0° were added 225 g. of chlorine and then 300 g. of vinylacetylene. The mixture was stirred for eight hours. After standing overnight the upper layer (47 g.) was separated, dried with calcium chloride, and distilled under nitrogen. Two distillations gave 23 g. of 1-chloro-2-vinylacetylene boiling at 55 to 57°. It had a nauseating odor and, while colorless at first, it darkened on standing and ultimately polymerized to a black, brittle resinous solid.

Anal. Calcd. for C_4H_3Cl: C, 55.49; H, 3.49; mol. wt. 86.5. Found: C, 55.28; H, 4.06; mol. wt., 87, 89 (cryoscopic, benzene).

Addition of Hydrogen Chloride to 1-Iodo-2-vinylacetylene.—A solution of hydrogen chloride (38 g.) in 95% alcohol was mixed in a pressure bottle with 49 g. of 1-iodo-2-vinylacetylene, 10 g. of ammonium chloride, and 15 g. of cuprous chloride. The bottle was shaken for twenty-four hours at 25° and the oily layer was distilled first with steam and then under nitrogen. The distillate was red in color and boiled at 73.5–74.5° at 35 mm.; yield, 26 g. (44%); d^{22}_2, 1.9161; n^{22}_D 1.6073.

Anal. Calcd. for C_4H_4ICl: C, 22.38; H, 1.88; total silver halide, 0.1704 g.; mol. wt., 214.4. Found: C, 22.34; H, 2.07; total silver halide, 0.1609 g.; mol. wt., 225, 228 (cryoscopic, benzene).

Upon standing for several months the compound polymerized to a soft black tar.

The addition of hydrogen chloride to 1-bromo-2-vinylacetylene under similar conditions also gave a volatile product which polymerized on standing.

Summary

The acetylenic hydrogen of vinylacetylene has been replaced by bromine, iodine and chlorine and the corresponding 1-halogen-2-vinylacetylenes obtained. These compounds are unstable liquids which polymerize upon standing to black solid polymers. The latter are explosive when heated or submitted to mechanical shock. Addition of hydrogen chloride to the iodo compound yielded an addition product which also polymerized spontaneously.

Bibliography and Remarks

(1) Straus, Kollek and Heyn, *Ber.*, **63**, 1868 (1930).

(2) Carothers, Jacobson and Berchet, *Journ. Am. Chem. Soc.*, **55**, 4665 (1933); this volume, page 372; Vaughn and Nieuwland, *Journ. Am. Chem. Soc.*, **55**, 2150 (1933), report that iodovinylacetylene is obtained from iodine and vinylacetylene in liquid ammonia.

XIX. The Structure of Divinylacetylene Polymers*

Divinylacetylene, when allowed to stand in contact with a little air, is transformed to a soft, transparent, oxygen-containing jelly which is dangerously explosive (1). The action of heat in the absence of air yields a quite different type of polymer, a yellow oil which dries to hard, chemically resistant films (1, 2).

We now record some observations concerning the nature of this oily polymer. The reaction involved in its formation is a typically *thermal* polymerization; the rate is but slightly affected by oxidants or antioxidants. In a typical case about 8% of a sample of divinylacetylene was polymerized in three hours at 80°. If the reaction is carried too far (somewhere between 20 and 50%) the mixture sets to a gel. Before this stage is reached, the polymer is easily isolated by evaporation in a vacuum of the unchanged monomer. The properties of the residual oil vary considerably depending upon how far the reaction has progressed. In one experiment a sample taken when 13.4% of the monomer was polymerized (ten hours at 80°) had an apparent molecular weight of 230 (3 × C_6H_6 = 216).

The oil is a mixture partly soluble, and partly insoluble, in alcohol. Attempts to distil it completely in high vacuum lead, in the end, to sudden explosive decompositions, but by careful operation a considerable volatile fraction can be isolated and redistilled. This material has the composition (approximately) and molecular weight $C_{12}H_{12}$. It is thus a dimer of divinylacetylene which is, in turn, a trimer of acetylene. A fairly pure specimen, when spread out in a layer, dried rapidly to an exceedingly hard, insoluble film with the absorption of considerable oxygen (e. g., 14.3% after two weeks). Bromination of the dimer gave crystalline octa- and deca-bromides. When hydrogenated, the dimer absorbed 12 atoms of hydrogen, and by oxidation it was converted into *trans*-1,2-cyclobutane-dicarboxylic acid. Its structure must, therefore, be represented as divinyl-ethynyl-1,2-cyclobutane (I)

(The absolute homogeneity of the material is, however, not completely established.) Similar dimerizations of substituted ethylenes are well known (e. g., the truxillic acids), but the above structure was unexpected since most addition reactions of divinylacetylene appear to proceed 1,4 (3).

Attempts similarly to isolate a trimer failed on account of the thermal

* M. E. Cupery and W. H. Carothers, *Journ. Am. Chem. Soc.*, **56**, 1167–9 (1934); Contribution No. 139 from the Experimental Station of the E. I. du Pont de Nemours and Co.
Received January 25, 1934.

instability of higher fractions. To increase its stability, the mixed polymer was hydrogenated. Its behavior was peculiar since, with PtO_2 (Adams) and various other catalysts, reaction ceased after 1.5 to 2.9 moles of hydrogen had been absorbed (per C_6). The catalyst was then colloidally dispersed and could not be removed by filtration; fresh catalyst caused no further hydrogenation. The material could, however, be distilled in vacuum without decomposition, and the distillate was easily hydrogenated to saturation with fresh catalyst. From the product a liquid $C_{18}H_{34}$ was isolated. In view of the facts mentioned above the trimer from which it was derived may, with reason, be assigned formula II.

The diversity and the tremendously complex potentialities of polymerization processes are again emphasized by the compound II, which results from two successive steps of self-combination starting with acetylene, and which, in air, is spontaneously transformed into much larger and more complicated molecules.

Experimental

(1) Freshly distilled divinylacetylene was heated at 80° under nitrogen:

Time, hrs.	0	1.5	3	6	9
% non-volatile	0	4.9	8.1	11.6	18.1
n_D^{20} (of mixture)	1.504	1.5074	1.5092	1.5115	1.5173

(2) Polymer from heating of divinylacetylene for ten hours at 80° was isolated by evaporating monomer in vacuum.

	d_4^{20}	n_D^{20}	Mol. wt.
Fresh monomer	0.785	1.504	72 (calcd.)
Isolated polymer	.968	1.581	227, 234 (in freezing benzene)

(3) **Bromide of Polymer.**—A polymer (14.6 g.) similar to that of (2) with 90.5 g. of bromine in cold carbon tetrachloride gave a heavy viscous oil; purified by solution in hot alcohol and precipitation by cooling.

Anal. Calcd. for $C_{12}H_{12}Br_6$: Br, 75.5; mol. wt., 636. Found: Br, 76.65; mol. wt., 591,608 (in freezing benzene).

(4) **Dimer of Dinvylacetylene.**—From 940 g. of divinylacetylene, with 2.5 g. of pyrogallol, heated at 81–82° for five hours, by evaporation of monomer and distillation

under nitrogen at 0.1 mm., 10 g. of colorless distillate was isolated.   On redistillation it boiled at 53–55° at ca. 1 mm.; d_4^{20} 0.9248; n_D^{20} 1.5495; MR_D calcd. (for I) 50.48; MR_D found, 53.73.

$Anal.$ Calcd. for $C_{12}H_{12}$:   C, 92.25; H, 7.75.   Found: C, 90.27; H, 7.77.

(5) **Bromination of Dimer.**—Freshly distilled dimer (22 g.) with 95 g. of bromine (8.1 atoms per mole) in carbon tetrachloride was allowed to stand for sixteen hours without light and the excess bromine and solvent were removed by evaporation.   The residual oil at 0° yielded crystals (27 g.) which after repeated recrystallization from absolute ethyl acetate melted at 211°.

$Anal.$ Calcd. for $C_{12}H_{12}Br_{10}$:   C, 15.07; H, 1.27; Br, 83.56.   Found: C, 16.05; H, 1.94; Br. 83.86.

Residues from the ethyl acetate mother liquors were recrystallized from alcohol and finally melted at 137°.

$Anal.$ Calcd. for $C_{12}H_{12}Br_8$:   C, 18.10; H, 1.52; Br, 80.37; mol. wt., 795.4. Found: C, 18.88; H, 1.95; Br, 80.71; mol. wt. (in freezing benzene), 803.

(6) **Oxidation of Dimer.**—Ozonization in carbon tetrachloride gave much insoluble material from the water-soluble fraction, after oxidation with permanganate, succinic acid was isolated.

Oxidation with warm (50–60°) alkaline permanganate gave oxalic acid, succinic acid, $trans$-1,2-butanedicarboxylic acid and an oily acid.

Oxidation with cold permanganate: the dimer (9.6 g.) in acetone was slowly added to potassium permanganate (116 g.) in dilute aqueous sodium hydroxide at 5–10°. The mixture was acidified with sulfuric acid and further potassium permanganate (29 g.) added to permanent color.   After solution of manganese dioxide by sulfur dioxide, continuous ether extraction gave 7.44 g. of oil from which 3 g. of crystals (m. p. 124– 127°) was isolated by filtration.   After several crystallizations from benzene the m. p. was 129–130°.   A mixed melting point with a sample of $trans$-1,2-butanedicarboxylic acid kindly furnished by Dr. R. C. Fuson gave the same value.

$Anal.$ Calcd. for $C_6H_8O_4$:   C, 49.98; H, 5.60; neutral equivalent, 72.   Found: C, 49.18; H, 5.65; neutral equivalent, 72.

The oil (above) completely freed of crystals was perhaps a hydroxycyclobutane-carboxylic acid.

$Anal.$ Calcd. for $C_6H_8O_3$:   C, 51.72; H, 6.95; neutral equivalent, 116.   Found: C, 50.48; H, 6.95; neutral equivalent, 116.8.

The oil was converted into its dry sodium salt and heated with p-bromophenacyl bromide.   The product, crystallized from 95% alcohol, melted at 145°.   Its composition agreed with that calculated for a bromophenacyl ester of a hydroxycyclobutane-carboxylic acid.

$Anal.$ Calcd. for $C_{12}H_{13}O_4Br$:   C, 49.84; H, 4.15.   Found: C, 49.45, 49.53; H, 3.85, 3.95.

(7) **Hydrogenation of Alcohol-Soluble Polymers.**—Crude polymer in absolute alcohol was hydrogenated (using PtO_2), distilled, and rehydrogenated until no further absorption occurred.

A fraction corresponding to hydrogenated dimer was washed with sulfuric acid, dried over sodium and separated into fractions by distillation through a good column.

Physical properties and composition were determined for the first (A, 38 g.) and last (B, 25 g.) fractions as shown below.

(A) B. p. 36–38° at *ca.* 0.1 mm.; d_4^{20} 0.7858; n_D^{20} 1.4342.

(B) B. p. 38–40° at *ca.* 0.1 mm.; d_4^{20} 0.8045; n_D^{20} 1.4432.

Anal. Calcd. for $C_{12}H_{24}$: C, 85.62; H, 14.38; mol. wt., 168.2. Found: (A) C, 85.69, 85.44; H, 14.63, 14.52; mol. wt. (freezing benzene), 170.6, 171. (B): C, 85.80, 85.96; H, 14.18, 14.51; mol. wt. (freezing benzene), 172, 171.

The difference in physical properties between (A) and (B) is sufficient to suggest the presence of stereoisomers in the original dimer.

Further distillation of hydrogenated polymer gave higher boiling fractions, and a fairly sharp cut (7.5 g.) separated at 111–113° under 1–1.5 mm. had d_4^{20} 0.8537; n_D^{20} 1.4682. Analysis showed that it was hydrogenated trimer.

Anal. Calcd. for $C_{18}H_{24}$: C, 86.31; H, 13.48; mol. wt., 250.3. Found: C, 86.23, 85.75; H, 13.48, 13.52; mol. wt. (freezing benzene), 255, 251.

The hydrogenated dimer and trimer both absorbed bromine rapidly with the liberation of hydrogen bromide, and were oxidized slowly by hot alkaline permanganate.

Summary

The thermal polymerization of divinylacetylene yields an oily polymeric mixture, from which the dimer has been isolated and identified as *trans*-1,2-divinylethynyl-cyclobutane. The trimer is probably similarly a *bis*-vinylethynylcyclobutylacetylene. The isolated hydrogenated (saturated) derivatives of the dimer and trimer are described.

Bibliography and Remarks

(1) Nieuwland, Calcott, Downing and Carter, *Journ. Am. Chem. Soc.*, **53**, 4197 (1931).

(2) Collins, U. S. Patents 1,812,849 and 1,812,850.

(3) Coffman, Nieuwland and Carothers, *Journ. Am. Chem. Soc.*, **55**, 2048 (1933); this volume, page 357.

XX. The Addition of Alcohols to Vinylacetylene, etc.*

Both acetylenic and ethylenic linkages are activated by conjugation with certain polar groups (*e. g.*, carbonyl) in such a manner that they react readily directly with alcohols. Consideration of the formula of vinyl-acetylene (III) suggested that the acetylenic linkage might here be similarly activated by the vinyl group or conversely the ethylenic linkage by the ethynyl group. Vinylacetylene was accordingly heated at about 105° with methanol and a little sodium methylate. Reaction occurred smoothly

* R. A. Jacobson, H. B. Dykstra and W. H. Carothers, *Journ. Am. Chem. Soc.*, **56**, 1169–70 (1934); Contribution No. 140 from the Experimental Station of E. I. du Pont de Nemours and Co.

Received January 25, 1934.

and a product having the composition $C_4H_4 \cdot CH_3OH$ was obtained. In view of its origin this material might be expected to have the formula I or II.

$$CH_2\!=\!C(OCH_3)CH\!=\!CH_2 \qquad CH\!\equiv\!C\!-\!CH(OCH_3)CH_3$$
$$\text{(I)} \qquad\qquad\qquad \text{(II)}$$

Examination of its reactions showed, however, that it was V. Hydrogenation converted it to methyl n-butyl ether and oxidation gave a mixture of acetic and methoxyacetic acids.

$$CH\!\equiv\!C\!-\!CH\!=\!CH_2 \longrightarrow [CH_2\!=\!C\!=\!CHCH_2OCH_3] \longrightarrow CH_3C\!\equiv\!CCH_2OCH_3$$
$$\text{(III)} \qquad\qquad\qquad \text{(IV)} \qquad\qquad\qquad \text{(V)}$$

The course of the reaction must therefore be interpreted as follows. The alcohol adds 1,4 to the conjugated system, giving rise to the intermediate IV, which is then rearranged by the sodium alcoholate to the acetylenic ether V. It may be recalled that hydrogen chloride similarly adds to vinylacetylene at the ends of the conjugated system, giving rise to a product analogous to IV, but this is capable of being isolated, and subsequent rearrangement follows an entirely different course involving an α,γ-shift (1). As a matter of observation α,γ-shifts in compounds of type IV occur only if the terminal group (instead of OCH_3) is halogen (2). The present case may be compared with observations recorded by Favorski (3): monosubstituted allenes and acetylenes are rearranged to disubstituted acetylenes by heating with sodium alcoholates.

In the present reaction yields based on unrecovered vinylacetylene are good. Side reactions are not extensive; the major one consists in conversion of some vinylacetylene to resinous polymers. In some experiments a very small lower-boiling fraction of the primary product gave positive tests for acetylenic hydrogen, indicating that traces of an isomeric ether were present. There was also obtained a very small amount of product resulting from the addition of two moles of alcohol to one of vinylacetylene.

The addition of alcohols to vinylacetylene appears to be a quite general reaction. Compounds obtained in this manner are listed in Table I. The primary alcohols for the most part reacted at a good rate and gave good results. i-Propyl alcohol reacted quite slowly (4% conversion in six hours at 105°) while t-butyl alcohol was still slower. In these cases the polymerization of the vinylacetylene becomes an important competing reaction affecting the yield. With the exception of the first one all of the compounds of Table I are new. They are colorless liquids having highly characteristic odors.

TABLE I

PROPERTIES OF ALKOXY-4-BUTYNES-2

Alkoxy group	B. p., °C.	$d^{20}{}_4$	n^{20}D	Calcd. M_R	Found
CH_3O-	99.5–100	0.8496	1.4262	24.52	25.36
C_2H_5O-	119–120	.8363	1.4290	29.12	30.23
i-C_3H_7O-	132–134	.8334	1.4244	34.17	34.34
n-C_4H_9O-	161–162	.8366	1.4362	38.32	39.43
t-C_4H_9O-	125–135	.8474	1.4347	38.79	38.81
cyclo-$C_6H_{11}O-$	64 at 2 mm.	.9254	1.4745	45.82	46.24
$C_6H_5CH_2O-$	94–96 at 3 mm.	.9943	1.5271	49.04	49.51
$HOCH_2CH_2O-$	71–73 at 4 mm.	1.0152	1.4802	31.19	31.93
$CH_3OCH_2CH_2O-$	84–87 at 30 mm.	0.9294	1.4462	35.81	36.77

TABLE II

ANALYSES OF ALKOXY-4-BUTYNES-2

Alkoxy group	Empirical formula	Calcd., % C	H	Found, % C	H
CH_3O-	C_5H_8O	71.43	9.52	71.08	9.60
C_2H_5O-	$C_6H_{10}O$	73.57	10.20	73.80	10.38
i-C_3H_7O-	$C_7H_{12}O$	74.94	10.79	73.77	10.43
n-C_4H_9O-	$C_8H_{14}O$	76.12	11.19	75.64	11.15
t-C_4H_9O-	$C_8H_{14}O$	76.12	11.19	75.12	10.63
cyclo-$C_6H_{11}O-$	$C_{10}H_{16}O$	78.88	10.52	78.79	10.85
$C_6H_5CH_2O-$	$C_{11}H_{12}O$	82.46	7.55	82.26	7.24
$HOCH_2CH_2O-$	$C_6H_{10}O_2$	63.11	8.84	61.52	8.95
$CH_3OCH_2CH_2O-$	$C_7H_{12}O_2$	65.58	9.44	65.14	9.77

Experimental Part

Action of Methanol on Vinylacetylene.—The reaction as carried out in steel bombs involved 268 g. (5.2 moles) of vinylacetylene, 132 g. (4 moles) of methanol and 56 g. (1 mole) of sodium methylate heated for seven hours at 105°. Distillation then gave 42 g. (0.8 mole) of vinylacetylene, 33 g. (1 mole) of methanol, 227 g. of product A boiling at 99.5–100° and 2 g. of a fraction B boiling at 137–140°. The residue (127 g.) was water soluble (mostly sodium methylate) except for 58 g. of resinous polymer. The yield of fraction A (methoxy-4-butyne-2) was 61% based on unrecovered vinylacetylene and 90% on uncovered methanol.

Fraction B apparently resulted from the addition of two moles of methanol to one of vinylacetylene: b. p. 137–140°; d^{20}_4 0.9159; n^{20}_D 1.4392.

Anal. Calcd. for $C_6H_{12}O_2$: C, 62.01; H, 10.42. Found: C, 64.23; H, 9.94.

Proof of Structure of Methoxy-4-butyne-2.—Hydrogenation of the ether in acetic acid using PtO_2 gave a quantitative yield of methyl n-butyl ether, b. p. 70.5–71°; d^{20}_4 0.7455; n^{20}_D 1.3728. These constants are in good agreement with those accepted by "International Critical Tables" for methyl n-butyl ether but quite different from those reported for methyl s-butyl ether.

The ether (21 g.) when oxidized with alkaline permanganate at 35–40° gave 7 g. of acetic acid and 3 g. of methoxyacetic acid. The former was identified by its boiling point and its p-toluidide (mixed m. p.), the latter by its boiling point (190–197°).

Methoxy-4-butyne-2 has already been described and the properties recorded (4) are in good agreement with those indicated in Table I.

Hydrogenation of Ethoxy-4-butyne-2.—This gave ethyl n-butyl ether of b. p. (760 mm.) 92.5–93°; d_4^{20} 0.7505; n_D^{20} 1.3820.

Summary

In the presence of sodium alcoholates alcohols add smoothly to vinyl-acetylene at about 100° giving ethers of the general formula $CH_3C\equiv CCH_2OR$. Nine such ethers are described.

Bibliography and Remarks

(1) Carothers, Berchet and Collins, *Journ. Am. Chem. Soc.*, **54**, 4066 (1932); this volume, page 306.

(2) Carothers and Berchet, *Journ. Am. Chem. Soc.*, **55**, 2808 (1933); this volume, page 361.

(3) Favorski, *J. Russ. Phys.-Chem. Soc.*, **19**, 1, 414, 553 (1887); *J. prakt. Chem.*, [2] **37**, 531 (1888); *ibid.*, **44**, 208 (1891); *Chem. Zentr.*, 1540 (1887); 242 (1888); 1201 (1888); II, 615 (1891).

(4) Yvon, *Compt. rend.*, **180**, 748 (1925); Bourguel, *Ann. chim.*, [10] **3**, 325 (1925).

XXI. Homologs of Chloroprene and Their Polymers (Second Paper on New Synthetic Rubbers)*

Chloroprene (chloro-2-butadiene-1,3, I) is obtained by the addition of hydrogen chloride to vinylacetylene (1).

$$CH_2=CH-C\equiv CH + HCl \longrightarrow CH_2=CH-\underset{\underset{Cl}{|}}{C}=CH_2 \qquad (I)$$

In the rate of its spontaneous transformation into a rubber-like polymer it greatly exceeds all previously described dienes (2). The present paper is concerned with homologs of chloroprene obtained by the addition of hydrogen chloride to homologs of vinylacetylene. As Merling has shown (3), compounds (III) of the latter class can be obtained by the action of sodium acetylide on aldehydes or ketones, followed by dehydration of the resulting carbinols (II).

$$RCH_2CO + CH\equiv CH \longrightarrow RCH_2\underset{\underset{R'}{|}}{\overset{\overset{OH}{|}}{C}}-C\equiv CH \longrightarrow RCH=\underset{\underset{R'}{|}}{C}-C\equiv CH$$

$$\underset{\displaystyle R}{|} \qquad\qquad\qquad (II) \qquad\qquad\qquad (III)$$

These reactions were in fact proposed as steps in a process for the synthesis of rubber, since in the case where $R = H$ and $R' = CH_3$, the product II

* W. H. Carothers and D. D. Coffman, *Journ. Am. Chem. Soc.*, **54**, 4071–6 (1932); Contribution No. 98 from the Experimental Station of E. I. du Pont de Nemours and Co. Received June 9, 1932. Published October 5, 1932.

can be reduced to the vinylcarbinol and then dehydrated to produce isoprene. The elegancy of this method has been frequently commended, but from our own experience it appears more elegant than useful, since the yields in the first step were rather low. Nevertheless, the isolation of small amounts of the pure carbinols presents no particular difficulties, and under properly selected conditions the dehydration to the substituted vinyl-acetylene proceeds fairly smoothly.

In the present study the carbinols used were those represented in formulas IV–VI. These and the corresponding vinylacetylenes (VII–IX) have already been described by Merling (3). The substituted vinylacety-lenes were converted into the corresponding substituted chloroprenes (X–XII) by shaking them at room temperature with concentrated hydrochloric acid containing cuprous chloride and ammonium chloride. The reactions proceeded somewhat more slowly than the formation of chloroprene itself by the same process. The yields obtained were rather low but this was due chiefly to incomplete conversion. The substituted chloroprenes reacted smoothly with α-naphthoquinone to form crystalline addition products (XIII–XV), which were readily oxidized to the corresponding anthraquinones (XVI–XVIII).

The amounts of the substituted chloroprenes available did not suffice for a very detailed study of their polymerization. The results obtained, however, indicated quite definitely that, of the three dienes, only chloro-2-methyl-3-butadiene (X) is likely to deserve serious consideration as a precursor of rubber. It polymerizes at approximately the same rate as chloroprene; the polymer obtained is definitely rubber-like; a plastic form of the rubber-like product is readily isolated by distilling the unchanged diene from the viscous sirup or the soft jelly obtained by incomplete polymerization; this plastic material is vulcanized by the action of heat alone without the addition of sulfur. Samples thus obtained were strong, very tough and quite elastic, but their extensibility was rather low. The ultimate product of the spontaneous polymerization of the diene in a sealed tube containing a very little air was rather similar in its properties to the vulcanizate described above; it was a black, lustrous solid very strong and tough, but it had a low extensibility.

The dimethyl compound (XI) polymerized very much more slowly than chloroprene—apparently not much more rapidly than isoprene. The product was elastic, but soft and sticky, and attempts to vulcanize it resulted in only partial loss of the plastic properties. The vulcanizate was coherent and rather strong; its extensibility was fairly high (about 500%) but recovery from stretch was slow.

The tetramethylene compound (XII) also polymerized very slowly, and the product obtained was a very soft and plastic mass. The attempt to vulcanize it was almost entirely unsuccessful; the plastic properties were

$$
\begin{array}{ccc}
\overset{\text{OH}}{\underset{\text{CH}_3}{\text{CH}_3\text{—C—C}\equiv\text{CH}}} & \overset{\text{OH}}{\underset{\text{CH}_3}{\text{CH}_3\text{CH}_2\text{—C—C}\equiv\text{CH}}} & \\
(\text{IV})^a & (\text{V})^a & (\text{VI})^a
\end{array}
$$

$$
\begin{array}{ccc}
\underset{\text{CH}_3}{\text{CH}_2\text{=C—C}\equiv\text{CH}} & \underset{\text{CH}_3}{\text{CH}_3\text{—CH=C—C}\equiv\text{CH}} & \\
(\text{VII})^b & (\text{VIII})^b & (\text{IX})^b
\end{array}
$$

$$
\begin{array}{ccc}
\underset{\text{CH}_3\ \text{Cl}}{\text{CH}_2\text{=C—C=CH}_2} & \underset{\text{CH}_3\ \text{Cl}}{\text{CH}_3\text{—CH=C—C=CH}_2} & \\
(\text{X}) & (\text{XI}) & (\text{XII})
\end{array}
$$

$$
\begin{array}{ccc}
(\text{XIII}) & (\text{XIV}) & (\text{XV})
\end{array}
$$

$$
\begin{array}{ccc}
(\text{XVI}) & (\text{XVII}) & (\text{XVIII})
\end{array}
$$

[a] See Friedr. Farbenfab. von Bayer & Co., German Patents 280,226, 284,764, 286,920, 289,800.
[b] German Patent 290,558.

not appreciably affected, but after standing for several months the compounded sample had become quite brittle although it contained an antioxidant.

These observations together with others already available permit some conclusions concerning the effect of the position and the nature of substituting groups on the polymerization of butadiene. Since butadiene, isoprene, and β,γ-dimethylbutadiene do not very greatly differ in the rate of their spontaneous polymerization, it is evident that methyl is not an activating group. The fact that chloroprene polymerizes about seven hundred times as fast as isoprene illustrates the powerful activating effect of a chlorine atom at the β-position. The introduction of a methyl group at the other interior carbon does not greatly modify this effect, although the polymer obtained is somewhat less extensible; but the introduction of a second methyl group at one of the terminal carbons almost completely checks the activating effect of the chlorine atom.

Experimental Part

Acetylenic Carbinols.—The general method used for the preparation of the acetylenic carbinols has already been described in the literature (4). The ketone (2 moles) was slowly introduced into an ethereal suspension (1 l. abs. ether) of sodamide (2 moles) at $-10°$ with vigorous agitation. After five hours, when the evolution of ammonia had become very slow, acetylene was passed during eight hours into the reaction mixture at $-10°$, under 10–15 pounds pressure with constant shaking. The reaction mixture was then poured onto crushed ice, acidified with dilute sulfuric acid, subjected to ether extraction, the extract dried and distilled. The yields were: ethinyldimethylcarbinol (IV), b. p. 104–108°, 36%; ethinylmethylethylcarbinol (V), b. p. 119–123°, 33%; ethinyl-1-cyclohexanol-1 (VI), b. p. 174° at 760 mm., 53–55° at 2 mm., 50%.

In the preparation of ethinyl-1-cyclohexanol-1 two by-products were isolated and identified: di-(hydroxy-1-cyclohexyl-1)-acetylene (10 g. from 2 moles of the ketone); crystals from carbon tetrachloride or benzene–petroleum ether, m. p. 106–107° (copper block). The literature records its melting point as 102° (5).

Anal. Calcd. for $C_{14}H_{22}O_2$: C, 75.65; H, 9.90. Found: C, 74.74; H, 10.41.

Cyclohexylidine-2-cyclohexanone-1 (35 g. from 4 moles of the ketone), colorless liquid (b. p. 143–145° at 16 mm.; n_D^{20} 1.5049; d_4^{20} 1.001) which readily formed an oxime, m. p. 146° (6).

Ethinylmethylphenylcarbinol.—The condensation of acetylene with acetophenone gave in 2% yield ethinylmethylphenylcarbinol which boiled at 69° under 1 mm. The carbinol after three crystallizations from petroleum ether (b. p. 40–60°) melted at 52–53°.

Anal. Calcd. for $C_{10}H_{10}O$: C, 82.19; H, 6.85. Found: C, 81.71; H, 6.88.

Dehydration of the Acetylenic Carbinols.—The ethinyldimethylcarbinol was heated at 90° (bath) in a distilling flask with an equal weight of p-toluenesulfonic acid for three hours. The methyl-2-butene-1-ine-3 (VII) distilled into the receiver as it was formed, b. p. 34°; yield, 53%.

The ethinylmethylethylcarbinol (60 g.) was slowly added during thirty minutes to 10 g. of p-toluenesulfonic acid contained in a distilling flask surrounded by a water-bath at 80°. The operation was carried out at slightly diminished pressure and the methyl-3-pentene-2-ine-4 (VIII) distilled into the receiver as it was formed, b. p. 68 to 71° at 760 mm.; yield, 25%.

Attempts to dehydrate ethinyl-1-cyclohexanol-1 by heating it with iodine, p-toluene-sulfonic acid, or anhydrous oxalic acid were unsuccessful, but excellent results were obtained by passing the carbinol in a stream of nitrogen over basic aluminum sulfate (from alum) at 240 to 260°. The yield of ethinyl-1-cyclohexene-1 (IX) boiling at 40 to 43° at 12 mm. was about 35% per passage and the remainder was chiefly unchanged carbinol.

Chloro-2-methyl-3-butadiene-1,3 (X).—Methyl-2-butene-1-ine-3 (40 g.) was shaken in a pressure bottle during four and a half hours at 20° with hydrochloric acid (105 cc., sp. gr. 1.19) containing cuprous chloride (15 g.) and ammonium chloride (6 g.). The reaction mixture was subjected to steam distillation, and the products were dried and distilled. The yield of the chlorobutadiene was 25 g. or 40%; b. p. 93° (760 mm.) with polymerization, 41° (113 mm.), 37° (105 mm.); n_D^{20} 1.4689, d_4^{20} 0.9593, M_R (obs.) 29.75, M_R (calcd.), 29.22.

Anal. Calcd. for C_5H_7Cl: C, 58.54; H, 6.83; Cl, 34.63; mol. wt. 103. Found: C, 58.55; H, 6.72; Cl, 34.39; mol. wt. (in freezing benzene), 126.

Chloro-2-methyl-3-tetrahydro-1,4,4a,9a-anthraquinone-9,10 (XIII).—α-Naphthoquinone (0.5 g.) was heated at 100° for half an hour with chloro-2-methyl-3-butadiene-1,3 (1g.). The reaction mixture was cooled and the crystals were washed with absolute methanol. After crystallization from aqueous acetone, the white needles melted at 165–166° (uncorr.).

Anal. Calcd. for $C_{15}H_{13}O_2Cl$: C, 69.09; H, 4.99. Found: C, 68.72; H, 4.86.

Chloro-2-methyl-3-anthraquinone (XVI).—The tetrahydro compound (XIII) was suspended in dilute alcoholic sodium hydroxide. Air was bubbled through the blue solution until only a yellow color remained. The suspension was diluted with water, the yellow crystals were filtered and recrystallized from glacial acetic acid. The material melted at 214–215° (uncorr.). The melting point of chloro-2-methyl-3-anthraquinone is recorded in the literature as 215° and 219° corrected (7).

Chloro-2-dimethyl-3,4-butadiene-1,3 (XI).—Methyl-3-pentene-2-ine-4 (25 g.) was shaken in a pressure bottle during five and a half hours at 20° with hydrochloric acid (58 cc., sp. gr. 1.19), containing cuprous chloride (8.5 g.) and ammonium chloride (3.5 g.). The reaction mixture was subjected to steam distillation and the product dried and distilled. The yield of the chlorobutadiene was 9 g. or 22%. A considerable proportion of unreacted hydrocarbon was recovered; b. p. 57–60° (96 mm.), n_D^{20} 1.4671; d_4^{20} 0.9437, M_R (obs.) 34.26, M_R (calcd.) 33.84.

Anal. Calcd. for C_6H_9Cl: C, 61.80; H, 7.72; Cl, 30.44; mol. wt., 116.5. Found: C, 61.40; H, 7.55; Cl, 29.24; mol. wt., 116.

Chloro-2-dimethyl-3,4-tetrahydro-1,4,4a,9a-anthraquinone-9,10 (XIV).—α-Naphthoquinone (0.5 g.) was heated at 100° during one hour with chloro-2-dimethyl-3,4-butadiene-1,3 (1 g.). The reaction mixture was cooled, and the crystals were washed with absolute methanol. After crystallization from aqueous acetone, the white needles melted at 107° (copper block).

Anal. Calcd. for $C_{16}H_{15}O_2Cl$: C, 69.95; H, 5.47. Found: C, 69.41; H, 5.53.

Chloro-2-dimethyl-3,4-anthraquinone (XVII).—The tetrahydro compound (XIV) was suspended in dilute alcoholic sodium hydroxide. Air was bubbled through the purple solution until only a pale yellow color remained. The ethanol was diluted with water, the yellow crystals filtered and recrystallized from glacial acetic acid. The anthraquinone melted at 171.5° (copper block).

Anal. Calcd. for $C_{16}H_{11}O_2Cl$: C, 70.98; H, 4.07. Found: C, 70.22; H, 4.14.

Chloro-2-tetramethylene-3,4-butadiene-1,3 (XII).—Ethinyl-1-cyclohexene-1 (33 g.) was shaken in a pressure bottle during four and a half hours at 20° with hydrochloric acid (70 cc., sp. gr. 1.19) containing cuprous chloride (10 g.) and ammonium chloride (4 g.). The reaction mixture was subjected to vacuum steam distillation, and the product dried and fractionated. The yield of the chlorobutadiene was 14 g. or 32% of the theoretical, and a considerable amount of unreacted hydrocarbon was recovered; b. p. 55–57° (1 mm.); n_D^{20} 1.5240; d_4^{20} 1.0422; M_R (obs.), 41.84; M_R (calcd.), 40.88.

Anal. Calcd. for $C_8H_{11}Cl$: C, 67.37; H, 7.72; mol. wt., 142.5. Found: C, 67.50; H, 7.90; mol. wt. (in freezing benzene), 143.

Chloro-2-tetramethylene-3,4-tetrahydro-1,4,4a,9a-anthraquinone-9,10 (XV).—α-Napthoquinone (2 g.) was heated at 100° during twenty minutes with chloro-2-tetramethylene-3,4-butadiene-1,3 (4 g.). On cooling crystals formed which were washed with absolute methanol. After recrystallization from absolute ethanol, the white needles melted at 191–192° (copper block).

Anal. Calcd. for $C_{18}H_{17}ClO_2$: C, 71.88; H, 5.66. Found: C, 71.42; H, 5.86.

Chloro-2-tetramethylene-3,4-anthraquinone (XVIII).—The tetrahydro compound (XV) was suspended in dilute alcoholic sodium hydroxide. Air was bubbled through the purple solution until only a yellow color remained. The ethanol was diluted with water, the crystals filtered and recrystallized from glacial acetic acid. The yellow needles melted at 155–156° (copper block).

Anal. Calcd. for $C_{18}H_{13}ClO_2$: C, 72.85; H, 4.38. Found: C, 72.59; H, 4.53.

Polymerization of Chloro-2-methyl-3-butadiene-1,3 (X).—When a sample of the diene was allowed to stand at the laboratory conditions in a sealed tube containing a trace of air it set up to a stiff jelly in about five days. Later the specimen became dark in color and ten months later when the tube was opened the product was a black, lustrous solid, very strong and tough but having only a slight extensibility. A sample of the diene exposed to the light of a Cooper-Hewitt lamp (mercury arc in glass) at ordinary temperature contained 30% of polymer after sixty-five hours. (Under the same conditions chloroprene polymerizes at a greater rate than this—about 30% in forty hours.) The sample was then a soft jelly. The polymer was precipitated, washed with alcohol, and compounded with 1% of phenyl-β-naphthylamine, 5% of zinc oxide, 2% of stearic acid, and heated in a mold at 140 to 145° for fifteen minutes. The resulting sheet was coherent, strong, tough and rather elastic, but it was deficient in resiliency and extensibility. It appears that the polymer from chloro-2-methyl-3-butadiene-1,3 more closely resembles the products from dimethylbutadiene (methyl rubber) than those obtained either from isoprene or from chloroprene.

Polymerization of Chloro-2-dimethyl-3,4-butadiene-1,3 (XI).—A specimen placed in a sealed glass tube under air and exposed to the light of a 100-watt Mazda lamp for two months at the ordinary temperature was converted to a very soft, sticky, elastic mass which still contained a considerable proportion of volatile material—apparently unchanged monomer. After standing for eight months more in the absence of direct light its properties had not undergone any further change.

A sample of the diene was submitted to a pressure of 8000 atmospheres for 106 hours at 40°. The product was a soft, plastic, elastic mass containing about 70% of polymer. It was compounded with 1% of phenyl-β-naphthylamine, 10% of zinc oxide, 2% of stearic acid, 1% of benzidine and 1% of tetramethylthiuramdisulfide and was then heated in a mold at 120 to 125° for seventy minutes. The product obtained in this way was rather soft and lacking in resiliency and nerve. The extensibility was fairly high (400 to 500%).

Polymerization of Chloro-2-tetramethylene-3,4-butadiene-1,3 (XII).—A specimen in a glass tube under air was exposed to the light of a 100-watt Mazda light for forty-eight days. The product was a thick, dark mass. Removal of the unchanged monomer by washing with alcohol yielded about 70% of polymer. This was very soft, plastic and sticky. It was compounded in the same manner as the polymer described in the preceding paragraph, but after being heated it still remained soft and plastic. After standing for ten months it had become brittle. A specimen of the diene was submitted to a pressure of 6000 atmospheres at 38° during ninety-six hours. The product was quite soft and plastic and when compounded as in the preceding example and heated for seventy minutes at 120° it showed no appreciable signs of vulcanization.

We are indebted to Dr. H. W. Starkweather for the experiments at high pressures.

Summary

Three substituted vinylacetylenes were treated with hydrogen chloride and thus converted to the corresponding chlorobutadienes. Chloro-2-methyl-3-butadiene-1,3 polymerized very rapidly and yielded a rubber-like polymer, which after vulcanization was less extensible than the corresponding product obtained from chloroprene (chloro-2-butadiene-1,3). Chloro-2-dimethyl-3,4-butadiene-1,3 polymerized very slowly and the product, even after vulcanization, was soft and lacking in nerve. Chloro-2-tetramethylene-3,4-butadiene-1,3 also polymerized very slowly and the product was very soft, plastic and sticky.

The structures of the three new chlorobutadienes were established through their reaction with α-naphthoquinone to form crystalline addition products, which were oxidized to the corresponding anthraquinones.

Bibliography and Remarks

(1) Carothers, Berchet and Collins, Journ. Am. Chem. Soc., 54, 4066 (1932); this volume, page 306.

(2) Carothers, Williams, Collins and Kirby, Journ. Am. Chem. Soc., 53, 4203 (1931); this volume, page 281.

(3) Merling, Friedr. Farbenfab. von Bayer & Co., German Patents 280,226, 286,920, 285,770, 288,271; Scheibler and Fischer, Ber., [2] 55, 2903 (1922); Sung Wouseng, Ann. chim., [10] 1, 343–416 (1924).

(4) Sung Wouseng, Ann. chim., [10] I, 343–416 (1924).

(5) Iotsitch, J. soc. phys.-chim. r., 38, 656 (1906), G. Dupont, Ann. chim., [8] 30, 498 (1913).

(6) Wallach, Ber., 29, 2965 (1896); Mannich, ibid., 40, 157 (1907).

(7) Keimatsu and Hirans, J. Pharm. Soc. Japan, 49, 140-7 (1929).

XXII.   The Synthetic Rubber Problem* (1)

This paper is an attempt to indicate the nature and current status of the synthetic rubber problem from the standpoint of organic chemistry. It includes an outline of unsolved problems and some new data bearing on the relation between the structure of dienes and their suitability as starting materials for the synthesis of rubber.

Two objectives in attempts to synthesize rubber are (1) to discover or demonstrate completely the structure of rubber and explain its properties in terms of this structure, and (2) to produce artificially a commercially acceptable substitute.   The second of these objectives is now an accomplished fact, but the first is far from having been achieved.

The difficulties in this connection can be illustrated by first viewing the facts in the light of the assumption that rubber hydrocarbon is a chemical individual in the usual sense—*i. e.*, that it is made up of identically similar molecules capable of being represented by a single definite formula.   If this were true it should be possible to infer the structure by a study of chemical behavior and then to make a rational synthesis—that is, from known starting materials to build up by known and deliberately controlled steps the supposed structure.   If the synthetic product was then exactly identical in all its properties with the natural product, the structure of the latter would be proved.

What is sometimes referred to as the synthesis of rubber consists essentially in this: Isoprene on standing passes slowly into an elastic solid having the chemical composition and many of the chemical reactions of rubber.   But although this material is elastic, it is not physically identical with rubber; few experts in the field would mistake it for rubber.   The product synthesized, then, is probably not rubber; and, even if it were, the synthesis is not rational.   It is a spontaneous or accidental transformation of unknown mechanism from which little can be inferred concerning the structure of the product.

The question then arises as to how one can determine whether a given sample of material is rubber.   The determination of identity is complicated by the fact that rubber is lacking in easily measured and sharply characteristic physical properties.   Moreover, those properties that can be measured—*e. g.*, plasticity—are not necessarily the same for different samples or even for the same sample at different times.   The result is

* W. H. Carothers, *Ind. Eng. Chem.*, **26**, 30–33 (1934).   Contribution No. 138 from the Experimental Station of E. I. du Pont de Nemours and Co.
Received November 23, 1933.

that there must be considerable latitude in the specifications as to what constitutes rubber, and it is almost impossible to set any definite numerical limit for a given property. This lack of definition unfortunately makes it possible to designate as rubber-like almost any material having any appreciable degree of resilience and elastic extensibility; partially polymerized styrene is said to be rubber-like, and so are some aqueous dispersions of starch, gelatin and sodium silicate. It is in this sense that many of the so-called synthetic rubbers are physically rubber-like. Chemically those derived from isoprene resemble rubber very closely, but so also do chicle, balata and guttapercha which also have resilience and elastic extensibility but are not called "rubber" because they do not possess these properties in sufficient degree.

In spite of the looseness with which the term "rubber-like" is used, rubber is a unique material. When vulcanized it possesses an extraordinary degree of elastic extensibility combined with great strength. No other type of material (with the exception of those noted below) remotely approaches it in the magnitude of these combined properties. Rubber is also unique in the nature of the patterns that it furnishes when examined by x-rays. Unstretched samples yield a diffuse pattern characteristic of amorphous materials; stretched samples furnish a point diagram characteristic of fibrous crystals. The fiber diagram disappears instantly when the sample is released from stress. The unique properties of rubber are: great strength combined with an elastic extensibility of about 900 per cent., and instantaneously reversible fiber orientation.

It is now generally recognized that the physical variability of rubber is inherent in (or at least reconcilable with) its chemical structure. Rubber molecules are long chains or threadlike structures built up by the regular 1,4-combination of units having the formula $—CH_2—C(CH_3)=CH—CH_2—$. Chemical properties are conditioned by the presence of this unit, but the physical properties are determined by the average length of the chains and the way in which the individual lengths are distributed above the average. Geometrical isomerism due to the presence of the double bonds may also come into play. When isoprene polymerizes, its molecules apparently unite to form chains similar to those indicated above. But if the product is to approach rubber in its properties, the unions must occur regularly 1,4- (without inversions) and the configurations about the double bonds must be the same as those in natural rubber, as must also the average length of the chains and the distribution about the average.

The complete description of rubber in terms of molecular structure (distribution of lengths, geometrical state, etc.) has not yet been accomplished; the mechanism of the polymerization of isoprene is unknown. Practical approach to the synthetic rubber problem must therefore be highly empirical. Starting with the historically important observation that isoprene on standing is transformed to an elastic solid, the attempt is made to modify favorably the properties of the product by controlling the conditions under which the transformation occurs. The enormously extensive experiments in this direction with isoprene, and with the related compounds butadiene and dimethylbutadiene, have no doubt led to improved products, but, so far as any published information goes, they have never led to anything closely approaching rubber.

The possibility was early recognized that some dienes might be found whose polymerization would yield products much superior to those obtained from isoprene, but the exploration of this possibility was hampered by the dearth of suitable methods for synthesizing dienes.

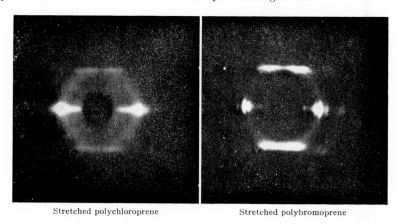

Stretched polychloroprene   Stretched polybromoprene

Fig. 1.—X-ray diffraction patterns.

Revolutionary progress in this direction recently became possible with the discovery (9) of a simple process for preparing vinylacetylene. The latter is an especially suitable starting material for the synthesis of new types of dienes. Among the new dienes obtained from it are chloroprene and bromoprene (6, 7):

$$CH\equiv C-CH=CH_2 + HCl \longrightarrow CH_2=C-CH=CH_2$$
$$\underset{\text{Vinylacetylene}}{} \qquad\qquad \underset{\text{Chloroprene}}{\overset{|}{\underset{Cl}{}}}$$

These compounds polymerize several hundred times as rapidly as does isoprene, and they lead directly to products which are equal to rubber in strength and elastic extensibility. Moreover the products exhibit instantaneously reversible fiber orientation (Figure 1). Polychloroprene and polybromoprene are therefore the first synthetic products that equal rubber in those qualities which make rubber unique, and in this important sense they are the only true synthetic rubbers yet known.

The field of synthetic rubber still presents many unsolved or incompletely solved problems. Among these may be mentioned the following:

Development of Satisfactory Methods for Physically Characterizing Rubber in Significant Numerical Units.—If there were, for example, two properties, x and y, simply measurable on small samples and such that together they furnished a numerical indication of quality, cumulative progress in the study of rubbers would not be so difficult. Obviously important practical indications of quality are extensibility and breaking strength, but these properties must be measured on the rubber after it is vulcanized, and the values obtained will depend partly upon a very complicated set of factors which constitute the conditions of vulcanization. The difficulties here are to a large extent inherent in the nature of rubber and are presented also by other macromolecular materials. The problem of physically characterizing such materials in significant numerical units is of the utmost importance to the whole field of resins, plastics and fibers, and it should receive more attention jointly from physicists and chemists. Meanwhile, in future studies of synthetic rubber, quantitative data must be obtained whenever possible, since the accumulation of systematic information is impossible without quantitative data.

Complete Determination of the Molecular Structure of Rubber.—This will probably have to await the development of more information concerning macromolecular compounds generally.

Relation between Physical Behavior and Molecular Structure.—It is quite certain that high strength requires the presence of very long molecules while elastic extensibility implies low internal viscosity, but these conditions are certainly not sufficient. Solution of this problem will obviously require more knowledge concerning the structure of rubber, and the study of synthetic materials of more or less known structure may be expected ultimately to throw considerable light on it.

Influence of Structure on Diene Polymerization.—Dienes vary greatly in their ease of polymerization and in the nature of the product. The fact that chloroprene and bromoprene are so much superior to isoprene emphasizes the importance of completely exploring the relation between structure and polymerization of dienes. Some data bearing on this point are presented in Table I. If the inferences from these data can be relied upon, it appears that the best dienes will be of the type $CH_2=CX-CH=CH_2$ in which X is an activating group other than alkyl or aryl.

Control of Diene Polymerization.—The product obtained spontaneously and accidentally from isoprene is so much like natural rubber in some ways that it is difficult to believe that it will always be impossible to control the reaction in such a way as to obtain a product fully equal to natural rubber. In the absence of simple objective measures of physical quality, progress in this direction must of necessity be slow. Another complication arises from the fact that dienes are enormously susceptible to catalytic effects not only in the speed of their polymerization, but also in the physical properties of the products. Exact reproducibility is therefore possible only under the most elaborately controlled conditions, and one of the conditions that must be controlled is the amount of exposure of the diene to air and light. In spite of the enormous amount of work implied by the voluminous patent literature, the factors indicated above have been generally ignored. Exact indications concerning the effect of conditions on the nature of products obtained from diene polymerizations are exceedingly meager. The possibility still remains of so controlling such reactions as to obtain improved products.

Mechanism of Diene Polymerization.—If the mechanism of diene polymerizations were sufficiently understood, a theoretical attack on the control of such reactions would become possible.

Synthesis of Rubber-Like Materials by Other Reactions than Diene Polymerization.—One method of attacking the synthetic rubber problem would be to synthesize giant molecules of known structure, study the relation between physical behavior and structure and from inferences thus established proceed to the synthesis of materials having the required structure. The deliberate and rational synthesis of sufficiently large molecules having a completely known structure is at present impossible, but an approach to this ideal is found in reactions of condensation polymerization, which proceed by a definitely known mechanism and lead to products whose general structural plan can be certainly inferred (2). Some of the complications and obscurity inherent in reactions of addition polymerization are thus immediately dispensed with and a clearer theoretical approach is made possible. It may be expected that this method of approach will ultimately throw considerable light on the relation between structure and rubber-like properties.

Influence of Structure on Diene Polymerization.—Table I contains data concerning the influence of structural variations on the relative speeds of polymerization of various dienes and on the nature of the products.

Very little quantitative significance can be attached to the numbers presented because they are derived by calculations sometimes involving extrapolations from data of uncertain reproducibility. The numbers are, however, useful for indicating relative degrees of magnitude.

TABLE I.   ESTIMATED RELATIVE SPEEDS OF POLYMERIZATION OF VARIOUS DIENES AT 25° C. COMPARED WITH ISOPRENE

Compound	Position and Nature of Substituent C=C—C=C				Estd. Speed[a]	Character of Polymer
	1	2	3	4		
1	....	Cl	Cl	....	2000	Hard, not extensible
2	....	I	..	....	1500	Rubber-like under certain conditions
3	....	Br	..	....	1000	Good rubber
4	....	Cl	..	....	700	Excellent rubber
5	....	Cl	CH3	....	500	Fair rubber but low extensibility
6	Cl	Cl	Cl	....	120	Soft, elastic
7	....	C6H5	..	....	90	Soft
8	CH3	Cl	..	....	30	Soft
9	C2H5	Cl	..	....	30	Soft
10	C4H9	Cl	..	....	10	Soft
11	C7H15	Cl	..	....	10	Soft
12	....	C7H15	..	....	9	Soft
13	Cl	...	..	....	7	Soft, sticky
14	....	CH3	CH3	....	3	Fair rubber but low extensibility
15	CH3	CH3	Cl	....	1.5	Soft
16	....	CH3	..	....	1.0	Fair rubber
17	....	...	..	....	0.8	Fair rubber
18	CH3	...	..	....	0.3	....
19	CH3	CH3	..	....	Probably < 1	....
20	(CH3)2	...	..	....		....
21	CH3	...	CH3	....		....
22	CH3	...	..	CH3		....
23	(CH3)2	...	CH2	....		....
24	(CH3)2	...	..	CH3		....
25	CH3	CH3	CH3	CH3		....
26	(CH3)2	...	..	(CH3)2		....

[a] The estimated speeds are based on calculated unimolecular reaction velocity constants. The data from which the constants are derived suffer from a very large factor of uncertainty owing to the fact that, for dienes, the rate of polymerization varies considerably with the history of the sample and with conditions (amount of exposure to light and air) which are not specified or controlled in all of the experiments. These uncertainties are, however, thought to be insufficient to affect the order of magnitude of the indicated numbers. The constant taken for isoprene (1a) was 0.0000048 (in hours), and was derived (by extrapolation) from data presented by Whitby and Crozier (10). The value for compound 14 is also derived from their data. For compound 18, data of

Lebedev and Merzhkovski quoted by Whitby and Gallay (11) were used. Compounds 19 to 26 which are presented in decreasing order of rate without any attempt to estimate numerical values are also taken from the last named paper. The rest of the data were obtained in the writer's laboratory; many of them are derived from extensive unpublished experiments on polymerization at very high pressures made by H. W. Starkweather. Publications on these compounds are as follows: 1, 6, Berchet and Carothers (1a); 2, Carothers and Berchet (3); 3, Carothers, Collins and Kirby (6); 4, Carothers, Williams, Collins and Kirby (7); 5, 15, Carothers and Coffman (5); 7, 12, Carothers and Berchet (4); 8–11, Jacobson and Carothers (8); and 13, unpublished. Whitby and Gallay (11) reach conclusions similar to those stated below as to the effect of substitution on the rate of diene polymerization.

The three types of substituent groups present are halogen, phenyl and alkyl. Comparison of the β-monosubstituted derivatives shows that all of these groups have an accelerating effect; methyl is very feeble, heptyl is appreciably stronger, phenyl is much stronger, and the halogens are very much stronger in the increasing order chlorine, bromine, iodine. The full activating effect is manifested only if the group is on the β- or γ-carbon atom. Alkyl on the terminal carbon inhibits, and it depresses the activating effect of a group on the β-carbon. It appears that to obtain a high rate of polymerization the terminal carbons must be free of any substituents. A substituent at the γ-carbon atom generally reënforces the effect of one already present at the β-carbon, but these disubstituted dienes (Cl, Cl; CH_3, Cl; and CH_3, CH_3) all yield products that are deficient in extensibility. Another specific effect is that due to phenyl. β-Phenylbutadiene polymerizes quite rapidly, but the product is mostly the crystalline dimer. The small amount of higher polymer formed is soft and probably has a relatively low molecular weight. (This effect of phenyl is further illustrated by observations on other aryl butadienes made by Whitby and Gallay, 11.) The formation of dimers is always a competing reaction in the synthesis of rubber from dienes, and it rapidly becomes more serious the higher the temperature used. At ordinary temperatures the rate of dimer formation from isoprene and chloroprene is roughly the same, but the temperatures required to obtain 50 per cent. polymerization of the two dienes in 10 days are respectively about 90° and 25° C., and the percentages of dimer in the products at these temperatures are about 40 and <1. This fact gives additional emphasis to the importance of a high rate of polymerization.

Bibliography and Remarks

(1) Because of the comprehensive historical article on "Synthetic Rubber" published by Whitby and Katz [Ind. Eng. Chem., 25, 2105, 1338 (1933)] since this paper was presented in Chicago, it has been considerably revised with the elimination of historical matter.

(1a) Berchet and Carothers, Journ. Am. Chem. Soc., 55, 2004 (1933); this volume, page 340.

(2) Carothers, *Chem. Rev.*, **8**, 354 (1931).

(3) Carothers and Berchet, *Journ. Am. Chem. Soc.*, **55**, 2807 (1933); this volume, page 361.

(4) *Journ. Am. Chem. Soc.*, **55**, 2813 (1933).

(5) Carothers and Coffman, *ibid.*, **54**, 4071 (1932); this volume, page 384.

(6) Carothers, Collins and Kirby, *Journ. Am. Chem. Soc.*, **55**, 786 (1933); this volume, page 311.

(7) Carothers, Williams, Collins and Kirby, *Journ. Am. Chem. Soc.*, **53**, 4203 (1931); this volume, page 281.

(8) Jacobson and Carothers, *Journ. Am. Chem. Soc.*, **55**, 1622 (1933); this volume, page 329.

(9) Nieuwland, Calcott, Downing and Carter, *Journ. Am. Chem. Soc.*, **53**, 4197 (1931).

(10) Whitby and Crozier, *Can. J. Research*, **6**, 203 (1932).

(11) Whitby and Gallay, *ibid.*, **6**, 280 (1932).

PART THREE

MISCELLANEOUS PAPERS

PART THREE

MISCELLANEOUS PAPERS

I. Association Polymerization and the Properties of Adipic Anhydride*

This paper contributes to the question whether polymers are held together by an unknown type of association forces or by normal chemical main valencies. It favors the latter point of view and emphasizes that adipic anhydride and its polymer are in full agreement with the ideas of the main valence chain theory, although the relationship between monomer and polymer is of a very high degree of mobility.†

Faith in the existence of the once widely accepted hypothetical phenomenon, association polymerization, appears to have been revived (or strengthened) in the minds of some of its proponents by the discovery (1) of a spontaneously reversible relationship between a biosan (?) and a polysaccharide. No certain examples of this phenomenon have ever been adduced among materials of known structure, although its supposedly diagnostic features are clearly presented by certain six-membered cyclic esters (2).

Adipic anhydride, recently studied by Dr. Julian W. Hill in this laboratory, has already been described (3) as a solid melting at 97°, but the published evidence concerning its molecular weight is equivocal. It has now been found that adipic anhydride as prepared by the usual methods is polymeric. Its melting point varies considerably with accidental details of its preparation. It cannot be distilled as such, but on being heated *in vacuo* it is partially depolymerized, and the resulting (7-ring) monomer can be distilled. The latter is a colorless liquid that freezes at about 20°. It reverts spontaneously to the polymeric form. The reversion is catalyzed by traces of water: when it is poured into a not especially dried glass vessel, a scum of the polymer is formed at the walls within a few minutes.

The monomer and the polymer are sharply differentiated by their chemical behaviors. Both react practically instantaneously with aniline at room temperature; but the former yields only adipic acid monoanilide, whereas the latter yields a mixture of adipic acid, adipic acid monoanilide

* W. H. Carothers, *Journ. Am. Chem. Soc.*, **52**, 3470–71 (1930).
Received July 2, 1930. Published August 5, 1930.
† The more detailed description of adipic anhydride and its properties is given in the paper on page 63.

and adipic acid dianilide. The formation of dianilide (in 25% of the theoretical amount) constitutes a direct and decisive demonstration of the presence in the polymer of a series of adipyl residues united in a linear fashion by anhydride linkages

CO—(CH₂)₄—CO—O—CO—(CH₂)₄—CO—O—CO(CH₂)₄—CO—O—etc.

Thus the existence of a very high degree of mobility in the relationship between a monomer and its polymer does not preclude the intervention of real primary valence forces in the process or the presence of a definite macro-molecular chemical structure in the polymer, even though the monomer may not be unsaturated in the usual sense.

A more detailed report of the study of adipic anhydrides will be submitted at an early date.

Bibliography and Remarks

(1) Reilly and Donovan, *Sci. Proc. Roy. Dublin Soc.*, **19**, 409 (1930); Schlubach and Elsner, *Ber.*, **63**, 362 (1930); Vogel, *ibid.*, **62**, 2980 (1929); Pringsheim, Reilly and Donovan, *ibid.*, **62**, 2379 (1929). It now appears, however, that these observations may be capable of quite a different interpretation. See Berner, *ibid.*, **63**, 1356 (1930).

(2) Carothers and van Natta, *Journ. Am. Chem. Soc.*, **52**, 318 (1929); Carothers, Dorough and Arvin, *ibid.*, **52**, 3292 (1930).

(3) Voermann, *Rec. trav. chim.*, [2] **23**, 265 (1904); Farmer and Kracovski, *J. Chem. Soc.*, **1927**, 680.

II. Ueber die angeblichen Isomerien bei cyclischen Oxalsaeure-estern*

It is explained that the different forms of ethylene oxalate, which have been described in the literature can be understood by the easy polymerization of the monomeric substance. Under normal conditions one gets a mixture of polymers, which is not identical with any isomer of the monomeric form. Similar conditions prevail with trimethylene oxalates; no isomers can be obtained.

Aethylenoxalat (I) vom Schmp. 143° wurde zuerst von Bischoff und Walden (1) durch Destillation des Reaktions-Produktes von Aethylenglykol auf Oxalsaeure-monoaethylester dargestellt.   Spaeter erhielt Bischoff (2) durch

I. CO—O—CH₂   II. CO.O.CH₃
    CO—O—CH₂ |
                              CO.O.CH₂.CH₂.OH

* Wallace H. Carothers und Frank J. van Natta, *Ber.* **64**, 1755(1931); 53. Mitteil. aus der Experimental Station of the E. I. du Pont de Nemours and Company.   (Eingegangen am 11. April, 1931.)

Erhitzen von Glykol mit Oxalsaeure-diaethylester ein weniger loesliches Aethylenoxalat vom Schmp. 171–172° und ein anderes, das bei 149–150° schmolz. Bei der Destillation gingen diese in die Form vom Schmp. 143° ueber. Ausserdem beobachtete Bischoff, dass der Schmp. der 143°-Form sich beim Aufbewahren veraenderte, und er vermutete, dass diese Veraenderung von einer Polymerisation herruehre, doch gibt er nichts ueber vergleichende Mol.-Gew.-Bestimmungen an.

Adams und Weeks (3) stellten Aethylenoxalat durch Einwirkung von Oxalylchlorid auf Aethylenglykol her. Ihr Produkt schmolz bei 153°, und sie erklaerten, dass es zweifelsohne dieselbe Verbindung waere, die Bischoff erhielt, ohne jedoch zu erwaehnen, dass Bischoff fuer das Aethylenoxalat mehrere Schmelzpunkte angegeben hatte, von denen keiner sehr nahe bei 153° liegt. Tilitschejew stellte dann ein Aethylenoxalat durch Erhitzen von Aethylenglykol mit Oxalsaeure-dimethylester her (4). Sein umkrystallisiertes Produkt schmolz bei 160–162°. Beim Destillieren ging es in die Form vom Schmp. 143° ueber. Er hielt sein Produkt fuer identisch mit dem von Bischoff gewonnenen. In einer spaeteren Arbeit macht Tschitschibabin (5) darauf aufmerksam, dass dem Aethylenoxalat mehrere Schmelzpunkte zugeschrieben worden sind, und er fasst diese Tatsache als weiteren Beweis fuer seine Theorie der Oxalsaeure-Isomerie auf.

Die Beziehungen der verschiedenen Formen des Aethylenoxalats zueinander wurden in unserem Laboratorium zum erstenmal genau untersucht (6). Im folgenden sind einige der festgestellten Tatsachen angegeben. Monomeres Aethylenoxalat schmilzt scharf bei 143–144°. Es haelt sich nur kurze Zeit. Selbst in einem dicht verschlossenen Gefaess veraendert es sich bei gewoehnlicher Temperatur in einigen Tagen. Bei hoeherer Temperatur verlaeuft die Umwandlung sehr schnell. Das Umwandlungs-Produkt ist ein Gemisch, dessen Schmp. irgendwo zwischen 110° und 172° liegen kann. Je nach der Vollstaendigkeit der Umwandlung enthaelt es groessere oder geringere Mengen von unveraendertem Monomeren mit einer (ununterbrochenen?) Reihe von Polymeren. Durch sorgfaeltige Extraktion mit kalten Loesungsmitteln kann man aus einem solchen Gemisch definierte polymere Fraktionen isolieren, die nach ihrem Verhalten beim Loesen homogen zu sein scheinen, z. B. eine Fraktion, die bei 159° schmilzt und anscheinend ein Mol.-Gew. von ungefaehr 2400 hat. Beim Aufbewahren jedoch veraendern sich alle diese Fraktionen und gehen in kompliziertere Polymeren-Gemische ueber.

Die monomere Form ist ausgesprochen makro-krystallin und viel loeslicher als die polymeren Formen. Die letzteren werden als Pulver erhalten, die unter dem Mikroskop aus sehr kleinen, schlecht entwickelten Krystallen zu bestehen scheinen. Wenn Aethylenoxalat durch Einwirkung von Aethylenglykol auf einen Ester der Oxalsaeure hergestellt wird, so ist das primaere Produkt ein polymeres Gemisch. In Uebereinstimmung mit den Untersuchungen frueherer Forscher wurde beobachtet, dass das Monomere vom Schmp. 143° bis 144° nur erhalten wird, wenn diese primaeren Produkte destilliert werden. Je nach den Versuchs-Bedingungen koennen die primaeren Produkte Schmpp. zwischen 100° bis 172° zeigen. So erhielt Bischoff, wie schon erwaehnt, Produkte, die bei 150° und bei 172° schmolzen, und Tilitschejew gewann einen Stoff, der bei 162° schmolz. Carothers, Arvin und Dorough erhielten Produkte, die sowohl die genannten Schmelzpunkte, wie eine grosse Menge anderer zeigten. Sie stellten fest dass alle diese Stoffe Polymere waren.

Die verschiedenen weiteren Formen des Aethylenoxalats, die von Zeit zu Zeit in der Literatur beschrieben worden sind, finden so eine hinlaengliche Erklaerung in der Leichtigkeit, mit der das Monomere sich polymerisiert, und in der Tatsache, dass die stabile Form unter gewoehnlichen Bedingungen aus einem Polymeren-Gemisch besteht (7). In einer neueren Arbeit bringen nun E. Bergmann und Wolff (8) neues Material ueber die angeblichen Isomerien des Aethylenoxalats. Sie versuchen, noch einmal die Existenz von Tilitschejews Verbindung vom Schmp. 162° zu erklaeren. Warum sie gerade diese Verbindung als einer Erklaerung beduerftig auswaehlen und die anderen von frueheren Forschern erwaehnten unbeachtet lassen, ist nicht klar. Im Zusammenhang mit der Arbeit von Bischoff fuehren sie nur die Verbindung vom Schmp. 143° an. Adams und Weeks erwaehnen sie ueberhaupt nicht. Was die Arbeit von Carothers, Arvin und Dorough betrifft, so sagen sie: "Wir setzen . . . . . voraus, dass Tilitschejew ueberhaupt ein krystallisiertes Produkt in Haenden gehabt hat und nicht etwa eine der polymeren Modifikationen des Oxalsaeure-aethylenesters, ueber die Carothers, Arvin und Dorough kuerzlich berichtet haben." Es scheint darum noetig, noch einmal mit Nachdruck darauf hinzuweisen, dass die polymeren Aethylenoxalate krystallinisch sind (s. die Mikrophotographien, 1. c.). Es mag noch hinzugefuegt werden, dass die Eigenschaften von Tilitschejews Verbindung, soweit er sie anfuehrt, genau die eines polymeren Aethylenoxalats sind, ueberdies hat sie sich unter Bedingungen gebildet, die nach unseren Erfahrungen sicher zu polymeren Produkten fuehren.

Dessenungeachtet ist nach Ansicht von Bergmann und Wolff Tilitschejews Verbindung der Oxalsaeure-methyl-(β-oxy-aethyl)-ester (II). Sie stuetzen ihre Ansicht durch Synthese dieser Verbindung "auf eindeutigem Wege.....naemlich durch Umsetzung von Oxalsaeure-methyl-esterchlorid mit Aethylenglykol." Das so erhaltene Produkt schmolz in reinem Zustand bei 166° und wurde durch Destillation im Vakuum (unter Verlust von Methylalkohol) in Aethylenoxalat vom Schmp. 143° ueberfuehrt. Die Tatsachen sind aber fuer diesen Beweis nicht guenstig, denn es scheint, dass es Bergmann und Wolff niemals gelungen ist, eine Verbindung der Formel II ueberhaupt zu erhalten. Da der entsprechende Aethylester bereits als Fluessigkeit beschrieben worden (6) ist, war es von vornherein unwahrscheinlich, dass Oxalsaeure-methyl-(β-oxy-aethyl)-ester einen so hohen Schmp., naemlich 166°, haben sollte. Wir haben deshalb die Synthese von II durch Einwirkung von Aethylenglykol auf Oxalsaeure-dimethylester ausgefuehrt und die Verbindung sicher identifiziert (s. Versuchs-Teil). Sie geht unter 0.6 mm Druck bei 103–105° ueber und krystallisiert in durchscheinenden Saeulen oder dicken Platten, die bei 32–33° schmelzen. Die von Bergmann und Wolff als Oxalsaeure-methyl-(β-oxy-aethyl)-ester beschriebene Verbindung ist unserer Meinung nach, ebenso wie Tilitschejews Verbindung vom Schmp. 162°, ein polymeres Aethylenoxalat. Die zu ihrer Darstellung benutzte Methode ist durchaus nicht eindeutig genug, um diese Moeglichkeit auszuschliessen, besonders im Hinblick auf die Schwierigkeit, mit der sich Esterchloride frei von den entsprechenden Dichloriden herstellen lassen.

Bergmann und Wolff geben ferner an, dass sie bei ihren Versuchen niemals ein polymeres Aethylenoxalat als primaeres Produkt, sondern immer das Monomere direkt erhalten haben. Ihre Versuche stehen in dieser Beziehung ohne Analogie da, denn keiner der frueheren Forscher, die dieses Gebiet bearbeiteten, hat ueber ein Aethylenoxalat vom Schmp. 143° als primaeres (nicht destilliertes) Produkt seiner Versuche, diese Verbindung herzustellen, berichtet. Besonders schwer erklaerlich erschien die Behauptung von Bergmann und Wolff aber auch aus dem Grunde, weil Carothers, Arvin und Dorough beobachtet haben, dass das Monomere unter den Temperatur-Bedingungen, unter denen die Genannten ihren ersten Versuch ausfuehrten, nicht haltbar ist. Im Hinblick auf diese Diskrepanz haben wir den betr. Versuch unter moeglichst genauer Befolgung ihrer Angaben wiederholt; wir sind hierbei aber zu ganz anderen Ergebnissen gekommen. Das Reaktionsprodukt schmolz nach dem Auswaschen mit Oxalsaeure-diaethylester nicht bei 142°, sondern bei 100–110°. Nach nochmaligem Umloesen stieg der Schmp. auf 125–130°. Ein Vergleich der Krystallform des Praeparates mit authentischen Proben des Monomeren und der Polymeren stellte schliesslich absolut sicher, dass es sich um ein Polymeres handelte.

Wir muessen deshalb schliessen, dass die auffaelligen Resultate von Bergmann und Wolff ihren Grund in irgendeiner Eigentuemlichkeit der Methode oder Technik haben muessen, die aus der Beschreibung ihrer Versuche nicht ersichtlich ist. Jedenfalls ist es Bergmann und Wolff nicht gelungen, zu beweisen, dass irgendeine der vielen Formen des Aethylenoxalats einer anderen Erklaerung fuer ihre Existenz bedarf, als der von Carothers, Arvin und Dorough vorgeschlagenen und experimentell bewiesenen.

Im Hinblick auf Bergmann und Wolffs Anspielung auf die mutmassliche Isomerie des Trimethylenoxalats (9) moechten wir erwaehnen, dass auch dieser Fall von Carothers, Arvin und Dorough (6) erklaert worden ist. Das primaere Produkt (Schmp. ca. 85°) der Einwirkung von Trimethylenglykol auf Oxalsaeure-diaethylester ist ein linearer Polyester, der das Mol.-Gew. von ungefaehr 2000 hat. Die Verbindung vom Schmp. 187°, die daraus durch Waerme-Zersetzung und Destillation entsteht, ist ein cyclisches Dimeres (ein 14-gliedriger Ring). Letzteres ist bestaendig und zeigt keine Tendenz, spontan in eine hoeherpolymere Form ueberzugehen. Ein monomeres Trimethylenoxalat ist nicht bekannt. Aehnliche Verhaeltnisse finden sich bei anderen Poly-estern (10).

Beschreibung der Versuche

Oxalsaeure-methyl-(β-oxy-aethyl)-ester (II): Ein Gemisch von 37.2 g Aethylenglykol und 70.8 g Oxalsaeure-dimethylester wurde in einen Claisen-Kolben gefuellt, der mit einem 20 cm langen und mit zerkleinertem Carborundum gefuellten Aufsatz versehen war. Der Kolben war mit einem Kuehler verbunden und von einem auf 160–185° erhitzten Metallbade umgeben. Nachdem 24 ccm Methylalkohol in die Vorlage ueberdestilliert waren, wurde der fluessige Rueckstand in einen kleineren Claisen-Kolben mit kurzem Aufsatz uebergefuehrt und destilliert. Es hinterblieb ein betraechtlicher Rueckstand von polymerem Aethylenoxalat. Das unter 2 mm Druck bei 90–140° uebergehende Destillat belief sich auf 29.5 g. Bei nochmaligem Destillieren wurde es in zwei Fraktionen getrennt: (a) Aethylenglykol, Sdp.$_{0,6}$ 60–63°; (b) Oxalsaeure-methyl-(β-oxy-aethyl)-ester, Sdp.$_{0,6}$ 103–105°. Ausbeute 12.7 g. Sich selbst ueberlassen, krystallisierte der Ester in durchscheinenden Saeulen vom Schmp. 32–33°.

Folgende Eigenschaften wurden an einer unterkuehlten Probe festgestellt: $n_D^{20} =$ 1.4430; $d_{20}^{20} = 1.2830$; MR fuer II ber. 30.37, gef. 30.58.

2.801 mg Sbst.: 4.176 mg CO_2, 1.425 mg H_2O.—2.674 mg Sbst.: 4.240 mg AgJ (Zeisel).

$C_5H_8O_5$.   Ber. C 40.54, H 5.45, OCH_3 20.96
            Gef. C 40.66, H 5.65, OCH_3 20.95

Der Oxalsaeure-methyl-(β-oxy-aethyl)-ester ist sehr leicht loeslich in Wasser, Alkohol und Aceton, wenig loeslich in Benzol und Aether, unloeslich in Petrolaether. Er ist hygroskopisch. Beim Erhitzen verliert er allmaehlich Methylalkohol und geht in das polymere Aethylenoxalat ueber. So ergaben 4.8 g des Oxalsaeure-methyl-(β-oxy-aethyl)-esters beim Erhitzen mit einer Spur Kaliumcarbonat auf 200–240° 0.6 ccm

Methylalkohol (bei 0.8 ccm). Der Rueckstand schmolz bei 135–140°. Nach wiederholtem Umkrystallisieren stieg der Schmelzpunkt auf 153–159°.

Bibliography and Remarks

(1) Bischoff u. Walden, *Ber.* **27,** 2939 (1894).

(2) Bischoff, *Ber.* **40,** 2803 (1907).

(3) Adams u. Weeks, *Journ. Am. Chem. Soc.,* **38,** 2518 (1916).

(4) Tilitschejew, *Ber.* **56,** 2218 (1923).

(5) Tschitschibabin, *Journ. prakt. Chem.,* (2) 120, 214 (1929).

(6) Carothers, Arvin u. Dorough, *Journ. Am. Chem. Soc.,* **52,** 3292 (1930).

(7) Beilaeufig mag noch erwaehnt werden, dass die Eigenschaft, sich reversibel zu polymerisieren, ganz allgemein bei 6-gliedrigen cyclischen Estern vorkommt (vergl. Glykolid, δ-Valerolacton usw.). Aethylenoxalat unterscheidet sich von den anderen Gliedern dieser Klasse nur durch die Schnelligkeit, mit der die spontane Umwandlung verlaeuft, sowie durch die Tatsache, dass sowohl das Monomere, als auch das Polymere krystalline Niederschlaege sind; vergl. Carothers und van Natta, *Journ. Am. Chem. Soc.,* **52,** 314 (1930); Carothers, *Chem. Reviews,* Juni, 1931. Eine eingehendere Untersuchung ueber reversible Polymerisation von 6-gliedrigen cyclischen Estern wird in naechster Zeit veroeffentlicht werden. W. H. Carothers, G. L. Dorough und F. J. van Natta; *Journ. Am. Chem. Soc.,* **54,** 761 (1932); this volume, page 141.

(8) E. Bergmann u. Wolff, *Journ. prakt. Chem.,* (2) 128, 229 (1930).

(9) Tilitschejew, *Journ. Russ. phys.-chem. Ges,* **58,** 447 (1926).

(10) Carothers u. Dorough, *Journ. Am. Chem. Soc.,* **52,** 718 (1930); Carothers u. van Natta, *ibid.,* 314.

III.   ε-Caprolactone*

*It is briefly outlined, that the results obtained by Stoll and Rouvé† and the authors being at variance can be explained by different experimental conditions.***

Stoll and Rouvé [*Helv. Chim. Acta,* **18,** 1087 (1935)] have recently reported the isolation of pure ε-hydroxycaproic acid and its conversion to the corresponding lactone by application of the high dilution technique. The same lactone was obtained by us previously [van Natta, Hill and Carothers, *Journ. Am. Chem. Soc.,* **56,** 455 (1934)] from a sample of the acid admitted to be impure. Under the conditions described we concluded that the lactone is the principal primary product of the self-esterification of ε-hydroxycaproic acid. Stoll and Rouvé conclude that heating of the pure acid yields chiefly polyesters and very little if any of the monomeric lactone. We do not doubt the correctness of their conclusions, but we maintain also that the results of our own experiments need not be doubted either. Stoll and Rouvé state (footnote, p. 1091) that since we obtained the lactone by an impossible method its identity may be doubted in spite of the correct physical constants, especially since it was not identified by means of known

* F. J. van Natta, J. W. Hill, W. H. Carothers, *Journ. Am. Chem. Soc.,* **58,** 183 (1936). Compare this volume 263.

Received December 6, 1935.

† *Helv. Chim. Acta,* **18,** 1087 (1935).

** Compare paper number XVIII on page 265.

derivatives. As to the impossibility of the method used, our description is an exact record of an actual experiment and it is incomplete in only one point of detail that seems of any likely significance. Our acid was obtained after ether-extraction mixed with water and acetic acid. To remove these impurities under the mildest possible conditions the mixture was allowed to stand for four days (time not given in the text of our paper) at room temperature while connected directly to an evacuated receiver kept at $-80°$. It is quite likely that a large portion of the observed lactonization occurred under these conditions (titration indicated 20% lactone assuming that *all* the acetic acid had been removed). In any event it is evident that our conditions of temperature, catalysis and possible dilution were such that they might easily yield a result different from that reported by Stoll and Rouvé. We have already (*loc. cit.*) pointed out that the ε-hydroxy acid is a transition case where the choice between intra- and inter-molecular reaction may be expected to be especially sensitive to experimental conditions.

As to the identity of our lactone, we *did* prepare and describe a derivative. The same crystalline hydrazide was obtained from: (1) the crude acid, (2) the monomeric lactone, (3) the dimeric lactone, (4) the polyester and (5) the (crude) ethyl ester of the hydroxy acid made by an independent method. Mixed melting points showed no depressions.

IV. Polymers and Polyfunctionality*

First the definitions as used in the series on polymerization and ring formation† are given.

Then the great technical and biological importance of high polymers is pointed out, especially their outstanding mechanical qualities as regards strength, elasticity, toughness, pliability, and hardness; also their great structural complexity and their production through a repetitive reaction are of importance.

Bi- and polyfunctional reactants are explained and examples of their modes of reacting are given, attention being especially drawn to cross linking and cross wetting.

Finally, the molecular weight and the molecular weight distribution is

* W. H. Carothers, *Trans. Farad. Soc.*, **32**, 39–49 (1936).
Received July 12, 1935. Published January, 1936.
† Compare paper I on page 4.

*discussed by the aid of formulas developed and later published by J. P. Flory.**

The importance of polymerizations is indicated by the title of the present program, and it is a curious fact that little agreement exists concerning the accepted meaning of this term. Text-books, dictionaries and even recent publications by original investigators (1), generally state that a monomer and its polymer have identical compositions, and a corollary is that polymerisation consists in pure self-addition, and is peculiar to unsaturated compounds. But it appears that not one of these conditions is necessarily satisfied by reactions that are universally recognized to be polymerizations. Moreover there is little relation between actual usage and text-book definitions.

An accepted polymerization is the transformation of formaldehyde into polyoxymethylene. The process under some conditions perhaps is

$$x\, CH_2O \longrightarrow (CH_2O)_x,$$

and under others (2)

$$x\, CH_2{=}O + H_2O \longrightarrow HO{-}(CH_2{-}O)_x{-}H.$$

In the latter case for moderately small values of x the composition of the polymer will be very different from that of formaldehyde: at large values of x the difference may be questionably detectable, but the question, of course, is one of fact not definition.

Turning to the mechanism of the process, there are various conceivable possibilities, such as:

1. The polymerization of perfectly pure and dry formaldehyde might involve opening of the carbonyl bond giving free radicals $-CH_2-O-$ whose mutual combination would result in a long chain.

2. In the presence of traces of water, we might have first

$$HOH + CH_2{=}O \longrightarrow HO{-}CH_2{-}OH,$$

a manifestation of formaldehyde's very strong tendency to add ROH. The product here is also ROH, and reaction therefore proceeds

$$HO{-}CH_2{-}OH + CH_2{=}O \longrightarrow HO{-}CH_2{-}O{-}CH_2{-}OH,$$

and further similar steps finally lead to a very long molecule (3).

3. In aqueous solutions formaldehyde is largely present as hydrates

$$HOCH_2OH,\ HOCH_2OCH_2OH,\ \text{etc.}$$

* J. P. Flory, *Journ. Am. Chem. Soc.*, **58**, 1877 (1936).

Polymer is formed by adding strong acid to such solutions. The reaction might be

$$\text{HOCH}_2\text{O}\boxed{\text{H} + \text{HO}}\text{CH}_2\text{O}\boxed{\text{H} + \text{HO}}\text{CH}_2\text{OH} \longrightarrow \text{HOCH}_2\text{OCH}_2\text{OCH}_2\text{O}\text{—}$$

i. e., an intermolecular condensation or dehydration.

Further peculiarities are illustrated by polyesters where all of the following transformations can be realised in one case or another (4).

In many cases the acid can be converted into a polyester under conditions where the monomeric lactone C is known to be stable. Moreover, it is then often possible by titration to show that a terminal carboxyl group is present in the ester product in the expected amount. The reaction involved is clearly one of condensation (not self-addition of an unsaturated or cyclic intermediate). Nevertheless, it seems scarcely reasonable or practical to argue that the product is not a polymer. For one thing, such polyesters can generally be transformed under appropriate conditions to the corresponding cyclic monomers (lactones), and the latter can be reconverted to products practically indistinguishable from B. In this case the reaction must consist essentially in self-addition. We can hardly say that a compound of the type B is a polymer if formed by one method, but not if formed by another. Moreover, there are some cases (*e. g.*, δ-lactones and lactide) where transformation between B and C occurs so readily that it is difficult or impossible to know which one is the product first formed from the acid. Similar confusion occurs with many reactions involving formaldehyde: it is often impossible to know whether products arise by direct intermolecular dehydration of a methylol compound or by self-addition of an intermediate methylene compound.

Further illustrations might be offered, but these perhaps are sufficient to show that: the composition of high polymers is not necessarily identical with that of the supposed parent monomers; polymerizations that appear superficially to involve only self-addition may involve preliminary hetero additions, and then actually proceed as condensations (or the reverse may be true); polymerizations are in any event not peculiar to unsaturated compounds (keeping in mind, for example, cyclic anhydrides, esters, acetals, and certain ethers and imines).

It is obvious that definitions need to be revised. It will not suffice to insist merely that usage is frequently wrong. The unfortunate effect of existing discrepancies becomes especially apparent when one reads that a resinification reaction (between an aldehyde and a phenol) doubtless proceeds through an unsaturated monomeric intermediate, because polymerizations are peculiar to unsaturated compounds.

Polymerizations are a special class of reactions, but just how are they distinguished from other intermolecular reactions? Conventionally, they involve the mutual combination of a number of similar molecules, but this is not sufficient: the formation of diethyl ether is not polymerization, and besides we already find references to mixed or hetero-polymerizations where the participating molecules are not all alike.

In the writer's opinion, the essential peculiarity of polymerizations is realised in the statement that they are intermolecular combinations (conventionally, self-combinations) that are functionally capable of proceeding indefinitely (or leading to molecules of infinite size).   This may, in fact, be taken as a definition.   By way of illustration, referring to the formaldehyde reactions outlined above, it is obvious that, regardless of which of the suggested mechanisms if any may be correct, the functional possibilities are such that any given number of formaldehyde molecules might be combined into a single molecule.   The same possibility exists generally with

(a) unsaturated compounds,
(b) cyclic compounds and
(c) polyfunctional compounds generally as, for example, x-R-y where x and y are
      capable of mutual reaction.

The compounds formally capable of polymerization then are all polyfunctional compounds.   Practically the functions must be such as to permit mutual combination, and polymerization will then fail only in those relatively rare cases where reaction is exclusively intramolecular.   A double bond or a reactive ring will count as a double function.

We may note then that polymerizations do not involve a single unique type of reactivity: they are for the most part merely ordinary reactions made manifold by polyfunctionality, and thus made capable of indefinite continuation in one, two, or three dimensions.   But the functions and the mode of their action are generally the same as those already familiar in simple uni-functional compounds (though addition polymerizations of unsaturated compounds certainly present some special peculiarities).

The Peculiar Significance of Polymers; Granular Polymers and Polymerizations in Living Organisms

The most important peculiarity of high polymers is that they alone among organic materials manifest to a significant degree such mechanical properties as strength, elasticity, toughness, pliability and hardness (5). Weight for weight cellulose and silk are stronger than steel; rubber exhibits a combined strength and elastic extensibility that is not even remotely approached by anything in the inorganic world while diamond is harder than any other material. The practical uses of high polymers depend almost entirely on these mechanical properties: our clothing and furniture and much of our shelter are made of such materials. The names cellulose, wool, rubber and silk suggest at once the great importance of the non-chemical uses of natural high polymers.

Probably the bulk of the organic matter in living beings is made up of high polymers. The necessity for this lies in the fact that living organisms must have physical form and coherence, and polymers are the only organic materials capable of supplying these properties. The variability of living matter also requires a high degree of structural complexity, and the possibilities of high polymers in this connection are indicated by Fischer's well-known calculation that 20 different amino acids may form 2.3×10^{18} different polypeptides of 20 units. Another pertinent fact is that the physical properties of high polymers are profoundly affected by their physical history: the melting-points of certain polyesters can be reduced several degrees by the mere application of stress and their strength in the direction of stress is at the same time increased many fold. Finally, reactions of polymerization also appear to be uniquely adapted to the chemistry of vital growth because they are the only reactions that are capable of indefinite structural propagation in space.

Curious analogies with vital growth are found in granular polymerizations which have as yet received very little published attention, although a few observations on chloroprene in this connection have already been described (6).

If we place a few grams of liquid chloroprene in the bottom of a long tube together with a little catechol to inhibit polymerization, chill the tube, pump it out thoroughly and seal the top at the lamp, the tube may be allowed to stand upright for weeks without the appearance of any change. But if we concentrate a strong beam of light on a small spot at the top of the tube, a minute speck of white solid will appear within a short time. The light may then be removed: the speck will grow to a cauliflower-like mass at the expense of the vapors and thence of the liquid monomer until the latter is exhausted. The polymer on superficial inspection seems to be a mass of globules or cellular crystals, but X-ray examination reveals no crystalline pattern. The growth of the mass apparently occurs at different rates in different directions. Sometimes lateral growth is more vigorous than vertical, and the mass will then burst the walls of a very heavy tube, although the total volume of polymer is only a fraction of the available space. Any fragment of the granular mass when placed in fresh chloroprene liquid or vapor will act as seed around which further growth occurs. The viability of the mass as seed will usually persist on standing in laboratory air for several days, but finally it is lost. Similar observations can be made with butadiene and other materials. The analogies of this process with vital growth are obvious. The process may be labelled heterogeneous autocatalysis, but the mechanism of the catalytic effect is obscure. Reactive centers in the sense of free radicals are scarcely admissible, since the viability persists in air, and for various reasons neither adsorption nor solution seems to offer an adequate explanation.

Many different types of synthetic polymers can be made, but no naturally occurring polymerization has yet been exactly simulated. Why should we not be able to synthesize cellulose, or proteins or rubber? We can make innumerable members of each of these types: polyacetals, polyamides and polyprenes. We can even make polyprenes that equal natural rubber in strength and elastic extensibility and are superior to it in many other respects, but the method (*i. e.*, the polymerization of chloroprene) is as yet subject only to empirical methods of control and not to rational methods based on completely elucidated theoretical principles. Besides, this goal has not yet been approached starting from isoprene, and it is not at all certain that nature builds up rubber directly from isoprene: she might, for example, start with methyl-*n*-propylketone and carry out a selective condensation polymerization completely evading the diene intermediate.

$$-C=\boxed{O + H_2}\, CHCH_2CH_2C\boxed{O + H_2}\, CHCH_2CH_2C\boxed{O +}\; \text{etc.}$$
$$\underset{\displaystyle CH_3}{|} \qquad\qquad \underset{\displaystyle CH_3}{|} \qquad\qquad \underset{\displaystyle CH_3}{|}$$

The synthesis of proteins raises a different set of questions. α-Amino acids (or their esters) can be polymerized directly *in vitro*, but the product is usually the cyclic dimer (diketopiperazine). But in the organism, cyclization apparently does not occur: reaction is exclusively intermolecular and a linear polyamide results. Generally speaking, cyclization and chain formation represent two paths, the choice between which is determined almost completely by the nature of the initial reactant (especially its unit length) (7).

The conditions *in vitro* presumably are the normal ones of chance. If both reactions follow the same mechanism, we can say that in a compound of the type $NH_2CH_2CONHCH_2COOH$, intramolecular approach of the terminal groups is more frequent than intermolecular (which means cyclization *in vitro*), but in the organism the probabilities are reversed and chain formation occurs. How can this be? Temperature and moderate dilution have small control over such matters, and perhaps then in the wrong direction. But if reaction is preceded by adsorption at an interface, as it might be biologically, the molecule is no longer free to assume its spatially probable configuration. Its head, tail and middle are fastened to a surface and the only terminal approaches then possible may be intermolecular. This picture is not here proposed as a solution of the mechanism of protein synthesis: it is introduced rather as an interestingly conceivable possibility, but especially for the purpose of emphasising the following points: ring formation and chain formation are the two alternatively possible results of every bifunctional reaction; complete control over these alternatives is possible only by bringing the ends of the molecules together or separating them at will; the only apparent prospect of achieving this result lies in the use of surface forces; reactions *in vivo* probably occur largely at surfaces; and in any event the effect of surfaces on bifunctional reactions presents an almost completely unexplored field (except for the interesting preliminary work of Freundlich and of Salomon) (8).

Polyfunctionality

Polymerizations generally may be divided into those that are bifunctional and those of higher orders. We may take an hydroxy acid as an example of the bifunctional type:

$$HORCOOH + HORCOOH \longrightarrow HORCOORCOOH + H_2O.$$

The two reacting molecules are monomers; the first product is a dimer, since it contains two structural units. At this point, half of the initial functional groups have disappeared; similarly, it is evident that the formation of two ester linkages (trimer) will involve 67 per cent. reaction, a tetramer will correspond with 75 per cent. reaction, etc. In general, if p is the degree (fraction) of reaction and x is the average degree of polymerization,

(1) $$p = 1 - \frac{1}{x}.$$

The following values are further illustrative:—

p	0	0.5	0.8	0.9	0.95	0.99	0.999
x	1	2	5	10	20	100	1000

The average molecular weight rises very steeply with increasing degree of reaction beyond 0.95, and hence it is not impossible (as some authors maintain) to obtain very large molecules from condensation polymerizations. If p should reach one the molecular weight would become infinite.

As a hypothetical example of a more highly polyfunctional reaction, we may take an acid $R(COOH)_4$ and consider the result of intermolecular anhydride formation. We assume that the structure and conditions are such that no intramolecular reaction occurs at any stage. Representing the acid by A^4 the anhydride would be

$$\ldots -A^2-A^2-A^2-A^2-A^2-A^2- \ldots,$$

etc., where the superscripts indicate that each unit bears two unreacted carboxyls. Hence when all of the molecules have been combined into one (and no further intermolecular reaction therefore can occur) only 50 per cent. of the initially present functional groups have disappeared, $i. e.$, $p = 0.5$. The formation of branching chains of course does not affect this conclusion.

A general equation relating degree of reaction, polymerizatic and functionality can be developed.

Let f = degree of functionality ($i. e.$, number of functional groups per monomer molecule).

N_0 = number of monomer molecules initially present.

Then $N_0.f$ = number of functions initially present.

N = number of molecules after reaction has occurred.

$2(N_0 - N)$ = number of functions lost.

$\dfrac{2(N_0 - N)}{N_0.f}$ = fraction of functions lost = p = extent of reaction.

Obviously, $\dfrac{N_0}{N}$ = average degree of polymerization = x.

Hence

(2) $$\frac{2}{f} - \frac{2}{x.f} = p = \text{degree of reaction.}$$

This equation has interesting applications. If we heat together a dibasic acid and a glycol, a linear polyester is formed. As the reaction measured by the disappearance of acid progresses, the average molecular weight rises, presumably in accordance with equation (2). Reaction becomes exceedingly slow after it is 99 per cent. complete, and the calculated molecular weight approaches 15,000 to 20,000. But no matter how far the reaction is carried under normal conditions, the product is both fusible and soluble.

If in a similar manner a dibasic acid is heated with glycerol, one observes at first that the viscosity of the mixture changes only slowly as reaction proceeds, and then it rises to infinity while much of the acid remains still unreacted. The product is completely infusible and insoluble.

Obviously, bifunctional reactions can yield only linear polymers; and there is evidence among such polymers that solubility and fusibility are not lost even at very high molecular weights. But reactions of higher orders always present the possibility of spreading out in three dimensions.

Returning to the anhydride symbolized above as

$$\ldots - A^2 - A^2 - A^2 - A^2 - A^2 - A^2 - \ldots$$

let us suppose that the chain is 100 units long, and bears 200 carboxyl groups. Such a molecule could easily be soluble and fusible. If further intermolecular reaction occurs, the chain must become cross-linked. Obviously, when 2 carboxyls have been lost from each chain, all the chains will be locked into a single molecule. This involves the loss of 1 per cent. of the remaining carboxyls: and it will certainly be accompanied by the disappearance of fusibility and solubility: a gram of matter cannot exhibit the kinetic behaviour of a single molecule.

Referring again to formula (2) if x is very large the second term disappears, and we have $p = 2/f$ which tells at what degree of reaction the molecular weight will become infinite, or where, in polyfunctional reactions, gelation will occur and intermolecular reaction cease.

For a bifunctional reaction $p = \dfrac{2}{f} = 1$, and since this value never can actually be reached, gelation will not occur. For a trifunctional reaction, the limit will lie at $p = {}^2/_3$, for a tetrafunctional reaction at $^1/_2$. We may note in passing that for this reaction at $x = 100$, $p = 49.5$ per cent.; thus the average molecular weight will suddenly change from a moderate to a colossal value with very little change in the extent of reaction: and so far as the utility of the formula is concerned, it is not important whether the transition in properties occurs at a molecular weight of 10^5 or 10^{20}.

In attempting to apply formula (2) the chemistry of the situation must, of course, be taken into account. A double bond will count as a double function only if reaction is exclusively intermolecular at every stage. Multiple function compounds often do not exercise all their functions together. In the formation of polyprenes from dienes, only the 1,4-positions of the latter are at first called into play. The remaining double bond of each unit functions under slightly different conditions to cause cross-linking. Acetylene would be a tetra-functional compound and probably behaves as such in the formation of cuprene. In the formation of divinyl acetylene (9), CH_2=CH—C≡C—CH=CH_2, only half of its unsaturation is involved. This material again in the early stages of its thermal polymerization behaves like a bifunctional compound yielding, for example (10),

$$CH_2=CH-C\equiv C-CH-CH_2$$
$$CH_2-CH-C\equiv C-CH=CH_2$$

but gelation usually occurs long before all of the divinyl acetylene has reacted.

Perhaps a majority of the reactions to which equation (2) would be applied are of the A—B type involving two reactants of complementary function. It is evident that if each reactant is bifunctional, A^2B^2, the reaction as a whole will be in effect bifunctional: A^3B^3 is trifunctional, etc. But if A and B have a different number of equivalents per molecule, the situation is more complicated. We can distinguish two different possibilities:

(a) Suppose that on the average every coupled molecule of A involves also the coupling of an equivalent number of molecules of B; then the degree of functionality is the average number of functions per molecule of the two reactants when they are taken in equivalent amount. Thus in the reaction of glycerol and phthalic anhydride (A^3B^2) we have to take 2 moles of glycerol and 3 of the acid, or 5 altogether, containing 12 equivalents and $f = \dfrac{12}{5} = 2.4$. Then at $x = \infty$, $p = \dfrac{2}{2.4}$ and the limit of the reaction will be $5/6$ (83.3 per cent.). This, in fact, represents the *maximum* amount of reaction that can occur before gelation under any distribution of combinations, provided only, of course, that the reaction is all intermolecular (11).

(b) Another extreme possibility is the following: Suppose the glycerol behaves at first as though it were bifunctional yielding a chain

$$- A' - B - A' - B - A' - B - A' - B -$$

(' indicates unreacted hydroxyl). Then all of the molecules of glycerol could be combined into one with the loss of only $2/3$ of the functional groups (of course $1/3$ of the phthalic anhydride remains entirely unreacted). Here $f = 3$ and 66.7 per cent. is the minimum extent of reaction compatible with gelation. Experimental values found by various investigators for the extent of reaction at gelation generally lie between 75 and 80 per cent. (12).

Reactions of polymerization involving degrees of functionality running into the hundreds or thousands are undoubtedly of great importance. The vulcanization of rubber is an example. The preponderance of evidence lies in favour of the view that vulcanization is the result of cross-linking through reaction at the double bonds. A conservative estimate of the number of double bonds in the average rubber molecule is 5000. Suppose the mechanism of vulcanization is as follows: At some double bond :C=C: + S ⟶ :C—C:. Sulfides of this structure are known to

$$:C \overset{\diagdown \diagup}{\underset{S}{}} C:$$

be unstable, and further reaction might occur with a similar group in a neighbouring molecule,

$$
\begin{array}{c}
:C - C: \\
\diagdown \diagup \\
S
\end{array}
\quad + \quad
\begin{array}{c}
:C - C: \\
\diagdown \diagup \\
S
\end{array}
\quad \longrightarrow \quad
\begin{array}{c}
:C - C: \\
\diagup \qquad \diagdown \\
S \qquad\qquad S \\
\diagdown \qquad \diagup \\
:C - C:
\end{array}
$$

At a minimum then all the rubber molecules could be locked together when only 0.04 per cent. of the double bonds had disappeared, or about 0.02 per cent. by weight of sulfur had reacted. A good estimate for a probable maximum is difficult to make. Experimentally, the minimum amount of sulfur required for the beginning of vulcanization (13) is about 0.15 per cent. Staudinger and Heuer have shown (14) that as little as 0.01 per cent. of divinyl benzene in styrene will lead to the formation of an insoluble polymer.

Molecular Weights and Molecular Weight Distributions

The peculiarities of high polymers are due to the fact that their molecules are very large. Estimates of molecular weights are therefore of the utmost importance, but they are very difficult to obtain. Direct osmotic methods present great practical difficulties. Staudinger has proposed to infer molecular weights from the viscosities of polymer solutions. There appears to be no doubt that, other things being equal, the viscosity of such solutions will increase with increasing molecular weight, and viscosity methods are unquestionably of great value as a means of providing rough estimates concerning the relative order of magnitude of molecular weights in a given polymeric series.   But the absolute values inferred from viscosities are subject to a very large factor of uncertainty.   An initial difficulty lies in the fact that no generally valid relation between viscosity and concentration in solutions of linear polymers has yet been established. Presumably some simple and general relation will be found to exist in solutions that are sufficiently dilute but possibly only at dilutions requiring a higher degree of experimental precision than is now generally available. (In theory, of course, extrapolation to infinite dilution is always possible, but practically such extrapolations may also involve large uncertainties.)

Aside from this point, there is one theoretical complication that has as yet received relatively little attention.   High polymers are generally mixtures covering a wide range of molecular species.   The properties of a polymeric mixture will depend not only upon the average molecular weight, but on the manner in which the different molecular species are distributed about the average.   Moreover, as Kraemer and Lansing (15) have recently shown, it is possible to define various types of averages: specifically, for example, there are the number average $M_n = 1/\Sigma \dfrac{f_i}{M_i}$ and the weight average $M_w = \Sigma f_i M_i$, where f_i is the fractional weight of the constituent of molecular weight M_i in the mixture, and the summation is applied to all the constituents.   The number average is the conventional one: it is this that is inferred from osmotic methods or chemical measurements of end groups.   But all the proposed viscosity relations would give M_w.

If a material is homogeneous, M_n and M_w will be identical: but if we are dealing with a mixture they will generally be different.   If we have 10 molecules of weight 100 and 5 of 1000, M_n is 400 but M_w is 851.   Thus a correlating factor for molecular weight *vs.* viscosity arrived at by observations on a homogeneous material is almost certain to give erroneous values when applied to a polymer.   And unless the type (distribution) of heterogeneity in all polymers is nearly the same, there cannot possibly be any exact generally applicable correlation between viscosity and molecular weight.

As Kraemer and Lansing have pointed out, the Svedberg ultracentrifuge provides the only means yet available for determining experimentally both the average molecular weight and the distribution in polymeric mixtures.   But this method is not simple, and the apparatus is very costly, and hence experimental data are as yet extremely meagre.

It is therefore a matter of considerable interest to make calculations as to the theoretically probable distribution of molecular species in polymerization reactions. Such calculations have been made by Dr. P. J. Flory (16) of this laboratory, and it may be worth while to give a brief indication of some of the results.

The simplest case is the formation of a linear condensation polymer. Here we have a series of stepwise reactions

$$A + A \longrightarrow A—A$$
$$2A—A \longrightarrow A—A—A—A$$
$$A + A—A \longrightarrow A—A—A, \text{ etc.}$$

always involving the same functional groups. Whatever may be the general effect of viscosity on reaction rate, the inherent relative reactivity

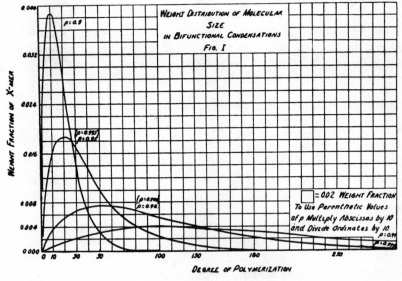

Fig. 1.

of a functional group will presumably be but little affected by the length of the molecule to which it is attached. If this assumption is correct, it is possible to show that

$$\Pi_x = x p^{x-1} (1-p)^2,$$

where p is the extent of reaction and Π_x is the fraction of units present in x-mers (which also equals very nearly, except for low values of p, the weight fraction of x-mer).

In Fig. 1, Π_x is plotted against x for various values of p. It is evident that we are dealing with a wide distribution of species. Certain relations are most briefly shown by means of an example.

If we assume that the weight of the mer or unit is 100, and reaction has been carried to 98 per cent. of completion ($p = 0.98$), then M_n the number average molecular weight is 5000, and the maximum in the distribution curve also occurs at this point. But the nature of the curve is such that only 26 per cent. by weight of the material has a molecular weight below 5000, while 74 per cent. has a weight at or above 5000. Moreover, 40 per cent. of the material has a molecular weight above 10,000. Finally, the weight average molecular weight is 9900 or nearly twice the number average.

Mechanical properties, such as toughness and tensile strength, certainly require the presence of very large molecules. But it is not at all certain that these properties will be improved by the elimination from a material of all fractions having low or moderately high molecular weights. In rubber and cellulose plastics the deliberate addition of small foreign molecules (plasticizers, lubricants, etc.) often has a very favorable effect on properties. It is probable that average molecular weights *per se* will furnish an entirely inadequate basis for the interpretation of those properties which are chiefly of interest in dealing with high polymers. The study of molecular weight distributions and their relation to properties thus presents a field which should ultimately be of great importance to the subject of polymerization.

Bibliography and Remarks

(1) *E. g.*, Staudinger, *Die hochmolekularen organischen Verbindungen,* Julius Springer, Berlin, 1932, page 10.

(2) *Cf.* Staudinger, *loc. cit.*, page 255.

(3) *Cf.* Staudinger, *loc. cit.* page 10.

(4) Carothers, Dorough and van Natta, *Journ. Am. Chem. Soc.*, **54**, 761, (1932); Carothers and Hill, *ibid.*, 1559; Hill and Carothers, *ibid.*, **55**, 5031, 5043, (1933); Spanagel and Carothers, *ibid.*, **57**, 929, (1935).

(5) *Cf.* Meyer and Mark, *Der Aufbau der hochpolymeren organischen Naturstoffe*, Akademische Verlags gesellschaft, Leipzig, 1930.

(6) Carothers, Williams, Collins and Kirby, *Journ. Am. Chem. Soc.*, **53**, 4214, (1931).

(7) Carothers, *Journ. Am. Chem. Soc.*, 1929, **51**, 2548; Hill and Carothers, *ibid.*, **55**, 5023, (1933).

(8) *Helv. Chim. Acta*, **17**, 88, (1934).

(9) Nieuwland, Calcott, Downing and Carter, *Journ. Am. Chem. Soc.*, **53**, 4197, (1931).

(10) Cupery and Carothers, *Journ. Am. Chem. Soc.*, **56**, 1167, (1934).

(11) A similar calculation for the glyptal reaction has already been made by Bozza, *Giorn. chim. ind. applicata*, **14**, 400, (1932).

(12) Bozza, *loc. cit.* (11); Kienle and Hovey, *Journ. Am. Chem. Soc.*, **51**, 509, (1929).

(13) Bruni, *Rev. gen. Caoutchouc*, **8**, No. 75, 19, (1931); Stevens and Stevens, *J. Soc. Chem. Ind.*, **51**, 44T, (1932).

(14) *Ber.*, **67**, 1164, (1934). See also *ibid.*, **68**, 1618, (1935).

(15) *J. Physic. Chem.*, **39**, 165, (1935); *Journ. Am. Chem. Soc.*, **57**, 1369, (1935). See also Kern, *Ber.*, **68**, 1439, (1935), and Staudinger, *Helv. Chim. Acta*, **12**, 941, (1929).

(16) Unpublished results. Remark: These results are published by J. P. Flory in *Journ. Am. Chem. Soc.* **58**, 1877 (1936).

BIBLIOGRAPHY

Serial Number	Title	Authors	Reference	Page of this Vol.
Catalytic Hydrogenation				
	Platinum oxide as a catalyst in the reduction of organic compounds, II. Reduction of aldehydes. Activation of the catalyst by the salts of certain metals	Roger Adams W. H. Carothers	*J. Am. Chem. Soc.,* **45,** 1071–86 (1923)	——
	The preparation of primary alcohols by the catalytic hydrogenation of aldehydes	Roger Adams W. H. Carothers	*J. Am. Chem. Soc.,* **46,** 1675–83 (1924)	——
	A study of the effects of numerous substances on the platinum catalysis of the reduction of benzaldehyde.	Roger Adams W. H. Carothers	*J. Am. Chem. Soc.,* **47,** 1047–63 (1925)	——
	The preparation of some primary amines by the catalytic reduction of nitriles	W. H. Carothers G. A. Jones	*J. Am. Chem. Soc.,* **47,** 3051–57 (1925)	——
Valence				
	The isosterism of phenyl isocyanate and diazobenzene-imide	W. H. Carothers	*J. Am. Chem. Soc.,* **45,** 1734–38 (1923)	——
	The double bond	W. H. Carothers	*J. Am. Chem. Soc.,* **46,** 2226–36 (1924)	——
Reactivity				
	The reactivities of some tertiary bromides	W. H. Carothers	*J. Am. Chem. Soc.,* **48,** 3192–97 (1926)	——
	The preparation and base strengths of some amines	W. H. Carothers C. F. Bickford G. J. Hurwitz	*J. Am. Chem. Soc.,* **49,** 2908–14 (1927)	——
Alkali Alkyls				
	The thermal decompositions of sodium ethyl	W. H. Carothers D. D. Coffman	*J. Am. Chem. Soc.,* **51,** 588–93 (1929)	——
	The thermal decomposition of sodium and potassium methides	W. H. Carothers D. D. Coffman	*J. Am. Chem. Soc.,* **52,** 1254–59 (1930)	——

Serial Number	Title	Authors	Reference	Page of this Vol.
Studies on Polymerization and Ring Formation				
I	An introduction to the general theory of condensation polymers	W. H. Carothers	*J. Am. Chem. Soc.*, **51**, 2548–59 (1929)	4
II	Polyesters	W. H. Carothers J. A. Arvin	*J. Am. Chem. Soc.*, **51**, 2560–70 (1929)	17
III	Glycol esters of carbonic acid	W. H. Carothers F. J. van Natta	*J. Am. Chem. Soc.*, **52**, 314–26 (1930)	29
IV	Ethylene succinates	W. H. Carothers G. L. Dorough	*J. Am. Chem. Soc.*, **52**, 711–21 (1930)	42
V	Glycol esters of oxalic acid	W. H. Carothers J. A. Arvin G. L. Dorough	*J. Am. Chem. Soc.*, **42**, 3292–300 (1930)	54
VI	Adipic anhydride	J. W. Hill	*J. Am. Chem. Soc.*, **52**, 4110–14 (1930)	63
VII	Normal paraffin hydrocarbons of high molecular weight prepared by the action of sodium on decamethylene bromide	W. H. Carothers J. W. Hill J. E. Kirby R. A. Jacobson	*J. Am. Chem. Soc.*, **52**, 5279–88 (1930)	68
VIII	Amides from ε-aminocaproic acid	W. H. Carothers G. J. Berchet	*J. Am. Chem. Soc.*, **52**, 5289–91 (1930)	78
IX	Polymerization	W. H. Carothers	*Chem. Rev.*, **8**, 353–426 (1931)	81
X	The reversible polymerization of six-membered cyclic esters	W. H. Carothers G. L. Dorough F. J. van Natta	*J. Am. Chem. Soc.*, **54**, 761–72 (1932)	141
XI	The use of molecular evaporation as a means for propagating chemical reactions	W. H. Carothers J. W. Hill	*J. Am. Chem. Soc.*, **54**, 1557–59 (1932)	154
XII	Linear superpolyesters	W. H. Carothers J. W. Hill	*J. Am. Chem. Soc.*, **54**, 1559–66 (1932)	156
XIII	Polyamides and mixed polyester-polyamides	W. H. Carothers J. W. Hill	*J. Am. Chem. Soc.*, **54**, 1566–69 (1932)	165
XIV	A linear superpolyanhydride and a cyclic dimeric anhydride from sebacic acid	J. W. Hill W. H. Carothers	*J. Am. Chem. Soc.*, **54**, 1569–79 (1932)	168

Serial Number	Title	Authors	Reference	Page of this Vol.
XV	Artificial fibers from synthetic linear condensation superpolymers	W. H. Carothers J. W. Hill	*J. Am. Chem. Soc.*, **54**, 1579–87 (1932)	179
XVI	A polyalcohol from decamethylene dimagnesium bromide	W. H. Carothers J. E. Kirby	*J. Am. Chem. Soc.*, **54**, 1588–90 (1932)	190
XVII	Friedel-Crafts syntheses with the polyanhydrides of the dibasic acids	J. W. Hill	*J. Am. Chem. Soc.*, **54**, 4105–06 (1932)	192
XVIII	Polyesters from ω-hydroxydecanoic acid	W. H. Carothers F. J. van Natta	*J. Am. Chem. Soc.*, **55**, 4714–19 (1933)	195
XIX	Many - membered cyclic anhydrides	J. W. Hill W. H. Carothers	*J. Am. Chem. Soc.*, **55**, 5023–31 (1933)	202
XX	Many - membered cyclic esters	J. W. Hill W. H. Carothers	*J. Am. Chem. Soc.*, **55**, 5031–39 (1933)	212
XXI	Physical properties of macrocylic esters and anhydrides. New types of synthetic musks	J. W. Hill W. H. Carothers	*J. Am. Chem. Soc.*, **55**, 5039–43 (1933)	221
XXII	Stereochemistry and mechanism in the formation and stability of large rings	W. H. Carothers J. W. Hill	*J. Am. Chem. Soc.*, **55**, 5043–52 (1933)	225
XXIII	ε-Caprolactone and its polymers	F. J. van Natta J. W. Hill W. H. Carothers	*J. Am. Chem. Soc.*, **56**, 455–57 (1934) and *J. Am. Chem. Soc.*, **58**, 183 (1936)	235 407
XXIV	Cyclic and polymeric formals	F. J. van Natta J. W. Hill W. H. Carothers	*J. Am. Chem. Soc.*, **57**, 925–28 (1935)	240
XXV	Macrocyclic esters	E. W. Spanagel W. H. Carothers	*J. Am. Chem. Soc.*, **57**, 929–34 (1935)	248
XXVI	Meta and Para rings	E. W. Spanagel W. H. Carothers	*J. Am. Chem. Soc.*, **57**, 935–36 (1935)	259
XXVII	Polydecamethylene oxide	J. W. Hill	*J. Am. Chem. Soc.*, **57**, 1131–32 (1935)	263
XXVIII	Preparation of macrocyclic lactones by depolymerization	E. W. Spanagel W. H. Carothers	*J. Am. Chem. Soc.*, **58**, 654–56 (1936)	265
XXIX	Polymers and polyfunctionality	W. H. Carothers	*Trans. Faraday Soc.*, **32**, 39–49 (1936)	408

SERIAL NUMBER	TITLE	AUTHORS	REFERENCE	PAGE OF THIS VOL.
Acetylene Polymers and Their Derivatives				
II	A new synthetic rubber: chloroprene and its polymers	W. H. Carothers I. Williams A. M. Collins J. E. Kirby	*J. Am. Chem. Soc.,* **53,** 4203–25 (1931)	281
III	The addition of hydrogen chloride to vinylacetylene	W. H. Carothers G. J. Berchet A. M. Collins	*J. Am. Chem. Soc.,* **54,** 4066–70 (1932)	306
IV	The addition of hydrogen bromide to vinylacetylene, bromoprene and dibromobutene	W. H. Carothers A. M. Collins J. E. Kirby	*J. Am. Chem. Soc.,* **55,** 786–88 (1933)	311
V	The polymerization of bromoprene (Third paper on new synthetic rubbers)	W. H. Carothers J. E. Kirby A. M. Collins	*J. Am. Chem. Soc.,* **55,** 789–95 (1933)	314
VI	Vinylethinylmagnesium bromide and some of its reactions	W. H. Carothers G. J. Berchet	*J. Am. Chem. Soc.,* **55,** 1094–96 (1933)	321
VII	Sodium vinylacetylide and vinylethinylcarbinols	W. H. Carothers R. A. Jacobson	*J. Am. Chem. Soc.,* **55,** 1097–1101 (1933)	323
VIII	Alpha - alkyl - beta - vinylacetylenes	R. A. Jacobson W. H. Carothers	*J. Am. Chem. Soc.,* **55,** 1622–24 (1933)	329
IX	1 -Alkyl - 2 - chloro - 1,3-butadienes and their polymers (Fourth paper on new synthetic rubbers)	R. A. Jacobson W. H. Carothers	*J. Am. Chem. Soc.,* **55,** 1624–27 (1933)	331
X	The chlorination of the hydrochlorides of vinylacetylene	W. H. Carothers G. J. Berchet	*J. Am. Chem. Soc.,* **55,** 1628–31 (1933)	335
XI	Dichloro - 2,3 - butadiene-1,3 and trichloro-1,2,3-butadiene-1,3	G. J. Berchet W. H. Carothers	*J. Am. Chem. Soc.,* **55,** 2004–08 (1933)	340
XII	The addition of thio-*p*-cresol to divinylacetylene	W. H. Carothers	*J. Am. Chem. Soc.,* **55,** 2008–12 (1933)	344
XIII	The action of chlorine on divinylacetylene	D. D. Coffman W. H. Carothers	*J. Am. Chem. Soc.,* **55,** 2040–47 (1933)	348
XIV	The dihydrochloride of divinylacetylene	D. D. Coffman J. A. Nieuwland W. H. Carothers	*J. Am. Chem. Soc.,* **55,** 2048–51 (1933)	357

SERIAL NUMBER	TITLE	AUTHORS	REFERENCE	PAGE OF THIS VOL.
XV	Halogen - 4 - butadienes-1,2. The mechanism of 1,4- addition and of alpha, gamma-rearrangement	W. H. Carothers G. J. Berchet	*J. Am. Chem. Soc.,* **55,** 2807–13 (1933)	361
XVI	The preparation of ortho-prenes by the action of Grignard reagents on chloro-4-butadiene-1,2	W. H. Carothers G. J. Berchet	*J. Am. Chem. Soc.,* **55,** 2813–17 (1933)	368
XVII	Mercury derivatives of vinylacetylene	W. H. Carothers R. A. Jacobson G. J. Berchet	*J. Am. Chem. Soc.,* **55,** 4665–67 (1933)	372
XVIII	1 - Halogen - 2 - vinyl-acetylenes	R. A. Jacobson W. H. Carothers	*J. Am. Chem. Soc.,* **55,** 4667–69 (1933)	375
XIX	The structure of divinyl-acetylene polymers	M. E. Cupery W. H. Carothers	*J. Am. Chem. Soc.,* **56,** 1167–69 (1934)	378
XX	The addition of alcohols to vinylacetylene	R. A. Jacobson H. B. Dykstra W. H. Carothers	*J. Am. Chem. Soc.,* **56,** 1169–70 (1934)	381

Miscellaneous Papers on Polymerization

	Homologs of chloroprene and their polymers (Second paper on new synthetic rubbers)	W. H. Carothers D. D. Coffman	*J. Am. Chem. Soc.,* **54,** 4071–76 (1932)	384
	Association polymerization and the properties of adipic anhydride	W. H. Carothers	*J. Am. Chem. Soc.,* **52,** 3470–71 (1930)	401
	Ueber die angeblichen Iso-merien bei cyclischen Oxalsaeure-estern	W. H. Carothers F. J. van Natta	*Ber.,* **64,** 1755–9 (1931)	402
	The synthetic rubber problem	W. H. Carothers	*Ind. Eng. Chem.,* **26,** 30–33 (1934)	391

B. PATENTS

The main purpose of this collection of papers of W. H. Carothers is to foster scientific research in the field of Polymers and High Polymers. The editors feel, therefore, that a complete reprint of the patents of W. H. Carothers would be beyond the scope of this book. For the sake of completeness, the editors have compiled the following list of patents for reference purpose.

All of the patents mentioned in the following list were assigned to E. I. du Pont de Nemours and Company, Wilmington, Delaware.

PATENT NO.	PATENTEE	TITLE
1934		
US 1,950,431 March 13, 1934	W. H. Carothers A. M. Collins	Addition product from monovinylacetylene and hydrogen halide
US 1,950,432 March 13, 1934	W. H. Carothers A. M. Collins	Polymers such as those of 2-chloro-1,3-butadiene
US 1,950,433 March 13, 1934	W. H. Carothers A. M. Collins	Polymerization of 2-bromo-1,3-butadiene
US 1,950,438 March 13, 1934	W. H. Carothers A. M. Collins J. E. Kirby	Polymerizing 2-halo-1,3-butadiene
US 1,950,439 March 13, 1934	W. H. Carothers J. E. Kirby	Polymerization of 2-chloro-1,3-butadiene
US 1,950,441 March 13, 1934	W. H. Carothers D. D. Coffman	Halobutadienes
US 1,963,074 June 19, 1934	W. H. Carothers G. J. Berchet R. A. Jacobson	Vinylethinylcarbinol polymers
US 1,963,934 June 19, 1934	W. H. Carothers R. A. Jacobson	Vinylethinyl derivatives
US 1,963,935 June 19, 1934	W. H. Carothers G. J. Berchet	Preparation of vinylethinyl derivatives
US 1,965,369 July 3, 1934	W. H. Carothers G. J. Berchet	Di- and tri-chloro-1,3-butadienes and their polymers
US 1,967,860 July 24, 1934	W. H. Carothers A. M. Collins J. E. Kirby	Rubber-like polymerization products of 2-chloro-1,3-butadiene
US 1,967,862 July 24, 1934	W. H. Carothers A. M. Collins	Cyclic compounds prepared from β-substituted α,γ-dienes, etc.
1935		
US 1,995,291 March 26, 1935	W. H. Carothers	Trimethylene carbonates, etc.

429

Patent No.	Patentee	Title
1935 (*Continued*)		
US 1, 998, 442￼ April 23, 1935	W. H. Carothers￼ G. J. Berchet	Dichlorobutadiene
US 2, 008, 003￼ July 16, 1935	W. H. Carothers	Alkylated lead phenolates
US 2, 012, 267￼ August 27, 1935	W. H. Carothers	Esters of dibasic acids
US 2, 013, 725￼ Sept. 10, 1935	W. H. Carothers￼ R. A. Jacobson	Alcohol addition products of unsaturated compounds such as mono- or di-vinylacetylenes
US 2, 019, 118￼ Oct. 29, 1935	W. H. Carothers￼ G. J. Berchet￼ R. A. Jacobson	Laminated glass (Safety glass)
US 2, 020, 298￼ Nov. 12, 1935	W. H. Carothers￼ J. W. Hill	Cyclic esters
1936		
US 2, 029, 410￼ Feb. 4, 1936	W. H. Carothers￼ A. M. Collins￼ J. E. Kirby	Polymerization products suitable for molded articles
US 2, 038, 538￼ April 28, 1936	W. H. Carothers	2-Chloro-1,3-butadiene, etc.
US 2, 061, 018￼ Nov. 17, 1936	W. H. Carothers	Hydrogen Polysulfide addition products of unsaturated aliphatic hydrocarbons (resinous products suitable for use in film forming compositions)
1937		
US 2, 066, 329￼ Jan. 5, 1937	W. H. Carothers￼ A. M. Collins￼ J. E. Kirby	Polymerizing compounds such as 2-chloro-1,3-butadiene
US 2, 066, 330￼ Jan. 5, 1937	W. H. Carothers￼ A. M. Collins￼ J. E. Kirby	Polymerizing 2-chloro-1,3-butadiene in the presence of vinyl compounds to form rubber-like products
US 2, 066, 331￼ Jan. 5, 1937	W. H. Carothers￼ A. M. Collins￼ J. E. Kirby	Polymerizing 2-chloro-1,3-butadienes, etc.
US 2, 067, 172￼ Jan. 12, 1937	W. H. Carothers	Chlorination products of polymerized 2-chloro-1,3-butadiene, etc.
US 2, 071, 250￼ Feb. 16, 1937	W. H. Carothers	Linear condensation "superpolymers" suitable for production of pliable, strong elastic fibers
US 2, 072, 867￼ March 9, 1937	W. H. Carothers	Synthetic rubber and initial materials for its production

Patent No.	Patentee	Title
1937 (*Continued*)		
US 2, 073, 363 March 9, 1937	W. H. Carothers G. J. Berchet	Butadienyl compounds
US 2, 080, 558 May 18, 1937	W. H. Carothers	Dispersing and polymerizing 2-chloro-1,3-buta-diene
US 2, 082, 568 June 1, 1937	W. H. Carothers G. J. Berchet	Vinylacetylene derivatives
US 2, 082, 569 June 1, 1937	W. H. Carothers R. A. Jacobson	Vinylacetylene derivatives
US 2, 102, 611 Dec. 21, 1937	W. H. Carothers A. M. Collins	Dihalogen butenes
1938		
US 2, 104, 789 Jan. 11, 1938	W. H. Carothers	Halogenated butadienes
US 2, 110, 199 March 8, 1938	W. H. Carothers	Tertiary nonaromatic amines
US 2, 110, 499 March 8, 1938	W. H. Carothers	Depolymerization of linear polyacetals
US 2, 124, 686 July 26, 1938	W. H. Carothers H. B. Dykstra	Ketals
US 2, 130, 523 Sept. 20, 1938	W. H. Carothers	Linear polyamides suitable for spinning into strong pliable fibers
US 2, 130, 947 Sept. 20, 1938	W. H. Carothers	Diamine dicarboxylic acid salts (suitable for forming spun fibers, etc.)
US 2, 130, 948 Sept. 20, 1938	W. H. Carothers	Synthetic fibers
US 2, 137, 235 Nov. 22, 1938	W. H. Carothers	Shaped articles from synthetic polymers
1939		
Can. 379, 253 Jan. 31, 1939	W. H. Carothers	Synthetic fibers
US 2, 149, 273 March 7, 1939	W. H. Carothers	Synthetic polyamide resins
US 2, 157, 116 May 9, 1939	W. H. Carothers	Stockings knitted from synthetic polyamide fibers
US 2, 158, 064 May 16, 1939	W. H. Carothers	Polyamides

Patent No.	Patentee	Title
1939 (*Continued*)		
US 2, 163, 584 June 27, 1939	W. H. Carothers G. D. Graves	Polyamides
US 2, 163, 268 June 20, 1939	W. H. Carothers J. W. Hill	Cyclic esters
US 2, 174, 619 Oct. 3, 1939	W. H. Carothers	Polyamides suitable for use in coatings, etc.
US 2, 136, 177 Nov. 8, 1939	W. H. Carothers G. J. Berchet	2,3-Butadienyl amines
US 2, 136, 178 Nov. 8, 1939	W. H. Carothers G. J. Berchet	Reaction products from 4-halo-1,2-butadienes and alkaline earth or alkali metal compounds
US 2, 178, 737 Nov. 7, 1939	W. H. Carothers A. M. Collins	Hydrohalogenation of vinylacetylene
1940		
US 2, 188, 332 Jan. 30, 1940	W. H. Carothers	Flexible coated fabric suitable for containers or wearing apparel

AUTHOR INDEX*

*By Dora Stern, Ph.D.

433

SUBJECT INDEX

* By Dora Stern, Ph.D.

DATE DUE